CW00741079

The BLUE LOTUS

The
BLUE LOTUS
MYTHS AND FOLKTALES OF INDIA

MEENA ARORA NAYAK

ALEPH

ALEPH

ALEPH BOOK COMPANY
An independent publishing firm
promoted by *Rupa Publications India*

First Published in India in 2018 by
Aleph Book Company
7/16 Ansari Road, Daryaganj
New Delhi 110 002

ISBN: 978-93-88292-10-8

1 3 5 7 9 10 8 6 4 2

For Daddyji
whose stories are a part of my life

For Mummyji
whose stories I am just discovering

For Guriya and Jamie
who are writing a brand new story

CONTENTS

PART THREE: THE SEEDED POD

PART FOUR: THE LOTUS

MYTH AND FOLKTALE: DEFINITIONS, DIFFERENCES, AND SIMILARITIES

Myth-making and storytelling in India are traditions of the soil; they have been seeding India's histories and cultures from the very beginning. Even the Indus Valley seals, that are yet to be deciphered, suggest fascinating tales of iconic figures in horned headdresses, unicorn like animals, and homonymic fish and stars.* Other stories, which we do know, originated in the Vedas. For example, when the sky roared and lightning swung wildly across the sky, the myth of the frightening 'tawny' god with 'braided hair' occurred.** When the Saraswati flowed with her seven sisters, her waters swift like a chariot in victory,*** the myth of the glorious goddess was created. And when, in the rainy season, frogs began to croak, sounding like the chant of a Brahmin in ritual sacrifice,**** a fable took shape.

Myths and folktales are both layered narratives that tell of the human experience in all its variety and perfection and imperfection. These experiential tales not only explore the actions of the characters, but they also describe the consequence of the choices they make, and, knowing these tales, people gauge their own behaviours. Sometimes these tales are archetypal, and sometimes they defy categorization. Sometimes they affirm our own human-ness, and, at other times, they make us question the imperatives that drive us. But what is always constant is that they are rooted in the ethos of the culture in which they originate.

It is difficult to define the terms, myth and folktale; however, in order to explain the rationale of this book, a brief explanation of the terms is necessary. Myths can be loosely described as traditional tales about

---

*Edwin Bryant, *Quest for the Origins of Vedic Culture*, New York: Oxford University Press, 2001, p.184.
**Wendy Doniger O'Flaherty (trans.), *The Rig Veda*, London: Penguin Books, 1981, 2.33 & 1.114.1.
***Ralph T. H. Griffith (trans.), *The Hymns of the Rigveda Vol. 1*, New Delhi: D. K. Publishers, 2004, 6.61.10–13.
****Wendy Doniger O'Flaherty (trans.), *The Rig Veda*, London: Penguin Books, 1981, 7.103.1.

cosmology and supernatural beings that are sacred to a whole community. On the other hand, folktales, which are traditional, as well, are more about common people and their daily concerns. They are also more regional and are often conveyed in the language of the people of a specific region. But both myths and folktales are remembered stories and both gain relevance every time they are told.

Another, more significant, distinguishing feature between the two is that myth can be a powerful vehicle of change, especially when it is fluid and open to interpolations, as it was during the composition of the Hindu epics. For example, Vasudeva Krishna's divinity was in its formative stage in the early years of the *Mahabharata*, and, more than likely, it was through the interpolated myths of the epic that he gained acceptance as a full-fledged divine—an avatar of Vishnu. In fact, in the *Mahabharata* and Puranas, there is mention of another Vasudeva—Paundraka, who may have been Krishna's contender for the position.

In addition to facilitating change, myth is also a barometer of societal laws. For example, at the end of the *Mahabharata*, when Yudhishthira holds an Ashvamedha yajna, as was the brahmanical injunction, a half-golden mongoose arrives to denounce the wastefulness of grandiose yajnas and the violence of animal sacrifice. And when myth itself dictates an injustice; it still leaves room for enquiry about the ethics of customary law. For example, in the *Ramayana*, when Rama kills the Shudra, Shambuka, because he aspired to become a Brahmin, varna order is restored in the story; however, questions arise about unjust practices in an immutable caste system.

One of the most significant enquires in Hindu myth, whose reverberations can still be felt in Indian society today is the question that Draupadi poses in the *Mahabharata*'s catalytic dice-game, in which her husband, Yudhishthira, wagers and loses her: did Yudhishthira lose himself before he staked her, and if so, how could he wager her? It is obvious that the issue of women's rights was being discussed in epic society, and its inclusion in the popular narrative not only gave it significance but it also rendered it current for all time. In fact, this question made Draupadi a precursor and poster child of feminism in India.

Folklore, on the other hand, instead of underpinning societal norms, creating standards, or evoking enquiry, is more of a mirror which reflects the lives of people whose lives are affected by those norms.

MYTH AND FOLK: PARALLEL AND INTERTWINING TRADITIONS

Despite these differences, myth and folklore in India are not separate traditions, as has been posited by some western scholars. According to this theory, the pan-Indian, classical Sanskrit literatures of the Shrutis (revealed texts, which comprise the Vedas and Vedanta), and the Smritis (remembered texts, which include the epics, Puranas and Dharmashastras), constitute the Great Tradition, and the regional and dialectal folk literatures make up Little Traditions. These distinctions of Great and Little Traditions may be true in other societies, but, in India, this demarcation is erroneous. In India, not only is there more than one Great Tradition, but also both these tradition types are inclusive of each other. Not only that, they are also continuous and heavily interdependent, with a great amount of intertextuality, and they have been so from the earliest of time.

Even when the Vedas were composed and their mantras and hymns were carefully preserved, because they were considered apaurusheya (not coming from men) and thought to contain secret knowledge about cosmic mysteries, there was a folk element present in them. These folk hymns, too, were composed by high priests in archaic metrical scheme, like the other liturgical hymns of sacrificial rites, gods, and celestial battles, but their themes were more earthy, describing ordinary concerns of life. For example, here is a hymn from the *Rig Veda* about a jealous wife who cannot abide her husband's other wife:

> I dig up this plant, an herb of great power [for a magic spell],
> one that drives out the rival wife and wins the husband entirely for
> oneself.
> Broad-leaved plant sent by the gods to bring happiness and the
> power to triumph
> Blow my rival wife away and make my husband mine alone.*

This hymn is, most likely, dedicated to Indrani, wife of Indra, the king of gods, but the emotions and actions described in it are hardly godlike; they are so human that they resonate with any woman who has ever felt jealous of the other woman. In the same vein of this Rig Vedic hymn, the *Atharva Veda* is almost entirely about dailiness and concerns and formulas

---

*Wendy Doniger O'Flaherty (trans.), *The Rig Veda*, London: Penguin Books, 1981, 10.145.1.

to counter hostile elements in everyday life.

When the era of Shruti literatures passed, their cosmological fixity transformed into the protean logos of the Smritis. These Smriti texts still had a divine cast of characters, and they were still being authored by exalted beings, but now these authors were also connected to people. For example, the *Mahabharata*'s authorship is attributed to Vyasa and its scribing to Ganesha; both are related to the immortal as well as the mortal worlds.* Ganesha is a divine whose main attributes and functions are directly connected to the well-being of mortals, and Vyasa, while being a part of Narayana and corresponding to Brahma, is not only mortal himself but is also related to the mortal characters of the epic. Moreover, in many instances, this people-friendly aspect of divine characters fed back into their myths, making them more folk-like. For example, Ganesha's attributes of benevolence towards human beings inform the myths of *Ganesha* and *Mudgala Puranas*.

Added to this secularity were two other significant factors that erased the line between myth and folklore. Firstly, these narratives were recited, not by Brahmins, as it used to happen with the Shrutis, but by bardic sutas, who were so much of the hoi polloi that often they were even outside the caste system, because they had hybrid bloodlines. And secondly, many of the myths and stories of these literatures were actually adoptions from the folklore of various tribes with which the Vedic Aryans were forming exogamous relationships.**

The mise-en-abyme structure of mythological texts, too, allowed for incorporation of folk elements: the stories that were mirrored within the frame myths were, most likely, popular folktales already in existence. For example, within the story of the Pandavas' exile, as a consequence of Yudhishthira's defeat in the dice-game, is the story of King Nala, who loses his kingdom in a dice-game and abandons his wife, Damayanti. Within the story of Garuda's enmity with his Naga cousins is the fable of the internecine quarrel of the tortoise and elephant. Moreover, sometimes these folktales, embedded in the classical texts of mythology, were themselves metanarratives for the key myth; for example, the snake tales in the snake sacrifice genocidal myth cycle of the *Mahabharata* create a metanarrative

---

*Meena Nayak, *Evil in the Mahabharata*, New Delhi: Oxford University Press, 2018, p. 4.
**Ibid., p. 5.

for the story of the Great War in which one clan plans to exterminate the other.

The *Ramayana*, on the other hand, not only includes folktales, it has also engendered many folk traditions in its own different versions. In the 300 and more recognized Ramayanas, many are considered folk because of their regionalization; among these are the well-known *Kamba Ramayanam* in Tamil and the *Sri Ranganatha Ramayanam* in Telegu. In addition to generating regional versions, this epic is also part of other religious traditions, such as Jain and Buddhist, and in each one, while the frame story remains more or less the same, the structure, characterization, motifs, and side stories vary. For example, in the Buddhist *Dasarata Jataka*, Rama and Sita are siblings, and they marry each other after Rama returns from exile. In the Jain *Ramayana*, Lakshmana is the one who kills Ravana; Rama becomes a Jain monk and achieves moksha, and Sita becomes a nun.

This fluidity in traditions never ceased, not even after the epics were formalized as shastras in about the first century CE. Despite their doctrinal seal, the accrual continued, but after the formalization, most of it was relegated to the realm of folk. The Puranas, on the other hand, which were probably oral narratives alongside the epical literatures, were never codified as scripture. However, scholars believe that the early Puranas went through a formal collection during the Gupta Era in the third to fourth centuries CE, which was, perhaps, a Brahmin effort to rescue the Vedic and Brahmanical traditions from the pervasive influence of Buddhism and Jainism. Hence, the folk elements of the Puranas were given divine authority and their myths were presented as divine diktat. An apt example of this hostility and mutation is the Puranic myth of Vishnu's Buddha Avatar. In this myth, Vishnu assumes the avatar of a false sage, the Great Deluder, Buddha, to trick the asuras into following the 'unrighteous' path of Buddhism and Jainism. Thus, through the myth, the Brahmins not only rationalized their apostasy, but also threatened those who may have been thinking of leaving the fold.

The Puranas are classical, henotheistic texts, each one ascribing supreme divine status to the god to which it is dedicated. Within this framework, they deal with a variety of subjects, from cosmology to religion, from practical advice to ritual; basically, they are a miscellany of folklore and myth. They are primarily in Sanskrit, but some are also regional, such as the *Sthala Puranas*, which give an account of shrines and temples, and many of these are part of the Tamil literary tradition. Others, such as the *Devi-Bhagavata Purana* and the *Ganesha* and *Mudgala Puranas*, pertain to deities that may have been regional and folkloric and probably gained pan-Indian status through the popularity of their Puranic myths.

Aside from its inclusion in scriptural texts, folklore also has a full-fledged tradition of its own, which has evolved simultaneously with the mythological tradition. For instance, the *Jatakas* are didactic fables about the Buddha's previous births. They are dated to about fourth century BCE to fifth century CE, the earliest tales coeval with many of the epical and Puranic myths. They are, most likely, the first set of folktales to be composed in India, and while they are an important contribution to the folklore tradition, as part of the Buddhist canon, they also constitute the mythology of the Buddha. Another example is the *Panchatantra*, the third to fourth century BCE collection of allegorical fables woven within a frame story, attributed to Vishnu Sharma. Many of the *Panchatantra* fables are intertextualized with the *Jatakas*, and a few also share elements with *Mahabharata*'s side stories.

The case of the voluminous epic of folktales and fables, *Brihatkatha*, further invalidates the separation of the traditions. Its purported author, Gunadhya, probably a court poet of King Hala, a Satavahana king around the first century CE, wrote *Brihatkatha*, not in Sanskrit, but in an obscure Prakrit language, Paishachi, which disappeared at some point. However, despite its break from the accepted language of classical texts, *Brihatkatha* is sometimes called India's third epic. Unfortunately, like Paishachi, which literally translates into the 'language of the ghosts', the book, too, is lost. But it was adapted and abridged into other texts, including three Sanskrit works that are considered important in the tradition of Indian folklore: *Brihatkathashlokasangraha* by Budha Swami in the eighth century CE, *Brihatkathamanjari* of Kshmendra, a court poet of King Ananta of Kashmir in the eleventh century CE, and, the most popular of them— *Kathasaritsagara* by Somadeva, a Brahmin from Kashmir, also in the eleventh century CE. All of these, while falling into the realm of folktales, can also be considered part of the supposed, Great Tradition, because of their elite language and dominant pan-Indian scope.

The *Kathasaritsagara* itself spawned more collections of folktales. For example, the *Vetala Panchvimshati*, popularly known as *Baital Pachisi*, drew tales from *Kathasaritsagara* to mould its own collection of twenty-five stories, in which a baital, or vetala, (ghost) tells King Vikramaditya riddle-tales. The *Shukasaptati*, (Seventy Tales of the Parrot) also borrowed stories from the same text to put in the mouth of its narrator parrot, who relates tales to a cheating queen about unfaithfulness. Moreover, the protagonist of the former collection, Raja Vikramaditya of Ujjain, became such a legend that he was intertexualized in a number of other collections, such as the *Simhasana Battisi* (Thirty-Two Tales of the Throne), and he continued to also be the hero of many oral folktales. This movement of stories not only kept the tales alive, but they also created sibling stories. An interesting example is in the medieval Jain story of 'Durgila' from Hemchandra's *Parishishtaparvan* and 'The Anklet' from *Shukasaptati*. The latter is the exact replica of one incident in the former, but what is interesting is the shift in motifs and beliefs. This is a story of a married woman who has a lover but is able to successfully deceive her husband. In the Jain text, she is presented as a sinner and punished for it, but in the Hindu text, she is characterized as clever and is exonerated ('The Anklet' is included in this book).

THE FOLK-MYTH CONNECTIVE

An interesting product of these parallel and intersecting traditions was the emergence of the folk-myth, which has kept the connection between myth and folktale even more reciprocal. This genre takes various forms; sometimes the tale is a spin-off from the classical myth to enhance a character's folk-legend. One such example is the folk-myth of Duryodhana and his vulnerability. This story, (included in this collection), humanizes Duryodhana by showing how the Kaurava prince's mother, Gandhari, tries to make him invincible but is thwarted by Krishna. Another good example is the folk-myth of Karna:

> To show Arjuna how truly ingrained generosity is in Karna, Krishna disguises them both as Brahmins and takes Arjuna to the spot in the battlefield, where Karna is dying. Krishna then asks Karna for gifts, but the dying Karna has nothing to give except his gold tooth, and although he is mortally wounded, he knocks out his tooth with a rock and holds it out to the Brahmins. But they reject it because it is covered in blood. Karna then washes the blood away with his tears so that his offering will be accepted.

Stories such as these are not in any of the authoritative pan-Indian *Mahabharata* editions; however, they are very popular in the oral tradition and for an ordinary Hindu, who may never read the voluminous epic, these folk-myths are just as integral to the *Mahabharata* tradition, as are any of its other formally textualized myths.

Sometimes the folk-myth is used not just to enhance the popular appeal of a character but also to express a prevalent political sentiment. An example is the *Ramayana* story of Nal and Nil, the monkey engineers of the Rama Setu. According to the popular tale, these two were gifted the Shvetadwipa (white island), as a reward for engineering the bridge, and Sita bestowed on Rama's monkeys a boon to be reborn there. According to the folk-myth, which probably originated during the British Raj, this island is England, and the reincarnated monkeys are the British. The tale also says that Queen Victoria was actually Trijata, the rakshasi who showed kindness to Sita in Ravana's Asoka Vatika, and so Sita gave her a boon that in one of her reincarnations, she would be an empress who would, one day, rule over seven regions.*

Another compelling thematic form that the folk-myth assumed creates a sort of bridge from classical myth to folktale. These tales, inspired by the Bhakti tradition, portray ordinary people engaged in their ordinary lives, but the story has an additional motif of man-divine relationships. Bhakti was not a new phenomenon; it was already a driving force in many of the Puranas, but in the genre of folk, it became a tradition of its own. Within this folk-myth form, the gods are not really active participants; most often they participate in the action only as a divine presence evoked by the devotee's devotion. Examples of this form are also included in this book: 'Gopal, My friend', 'Kabuliwalla and Banke Bihari', and 'Greatest Devotee', and an early example from *Kathasaritsagara*, 'A Princess, a Mechanical Garuda and a Counterfeit Vishnu'.

One of the most momentous links between the pan-Indian classical tradition and the folktale tradition is the Hindu Goddess, the Devi, and her counterpart, the village goddess. Devi folk-myths originate as regional stories, but sometimes the apotheosis becomes so popular that the village goddess is indistinguishable from the more formalized mythological

---

*Philip Lutgendorf, *Hanuman's Tale*, Oxford University Press, 2007, p. 334. Lutgendorf's source is the 1930 text *Avadh ki Jhanki* by Sitaram.

Goddess; hence, she assumes pan-Indian status. An example of this transformation is the 'Devi Vratakatha', which is a story associated with a ritual and vow and/or fast, such as Karva Chauth, Ahoi Mata, Santoshi Ma, Mariamma, etc. Similarly, all the Devi temples designated as Shakti Peeths have their own particular folk-myths, but they are coalesced into the fountainhead Puranic myth of Sati's immolation and the dismemberment of her body into fifty-one parts (the most accepted number), that fell on earth and became Devi temple sites. In the same way, the various mythical and folk manifestations of Durga are all connected to the key Shakta myth of *Devi Mahatmaya*.

These are just a few examples of the interconnections between folk and myth; thus, if a line exists between the Greater and Little Traditions in India, it is chimerical. The traditions are too many, too fulsome, and too linked. In addition, this network is not just of Vedic, Hindu, Buddhist and Jain traditions. There are other, equally dynamic traditions that are also integral to it—Parsi, Islamic, Sikh, Jewish, Christian, Tribal, etc.; all these together articulate Indian society. Moreover, not only are each of these reciprocal, but they are also complete in themselves with their own classical and folk linkages. Hence, together these traditions of India represent what the *Mahabharata* calls 'A history of mankind'.

MISCONCEPTIONS

Perhaps it is this very immensity that causes misconceptions. This vastness of over three thousand years of storytelling is difficult to fathom, even for an Indian. Most Indians have an idea of the country's general ethos that derives from the overarching pan-Indian traditions; however, people living in one part of the country have little idea of folkloric traditions in another part. And this is true not just from north to south and east to west, but also for contiguous regions. One can only imagine what the British may have felt when they encountered the colossal cultures of India, a large percentage of which were formulated through orality. Their lack of comprehension, and perhaps lack of effort to understand the vastness, led to many false impressions, which have since defined India in the West.

To name just a few general ones:

From the continued prevalence of ancient mythological traditions, it appears to the westerner that Indian society is static—unchanged—because people still believe in myths and practice rituals of three thousand years ago. The fact is that it only appears unchanged. In Hindu cultures, nothing is discarded; however, it is constantly rearranged to keep the system current. So, in actuality, the cultures are both forward-moving and self-correcting, because practices and beliefs readjust in accordance to evolving societal needs. Even the myths evolve. For example, when the early societies no longer needed the old fearsome warrior gods of the Vedas, such as Indra, for survival, they were degraded to elevate more people-friendly gods, such as Vishnu and Shiva; and when these became too sectarian, and society began to fragment, new integrating avatars, like Rama and Krishna became transcendent. Similarly, when oppression against women heightened, the Devi was resurrected in the avatars of Durga and Kali.

Then there are those who only perceive India as an exotic land of scriptures and metaphysical philosophies that spawn temples in every street corner, a litter of half-naked, ash-smeared sadhus in every holy city, and ideologies concerned only with pursuits of Moksha and Nirvana. While these are certainly common traits in India, it is only a one-dimensional image. There are other dimensions that include practical realities, which are evidenced not only in the daily lives of people but also in the literatures. In Hindu traditions, ideals of life negation run parallel to practices of life affirmation. The goal of most people, as anywhere else in the world, is to be engaged in a productive livelihood and live a happy life. The acquisition of wealth to ensure a prosperous life—artha—is a purusharthic ideal that is actually directed by the scriptural texts. Alongside that, there is also the metaphysical concept of Moksha; however, while most Hindus are familiar with this ultimate goal, their lives are not focused on its pursuit. Also, it is hardly ever explored in myths, and it is seldom a theme in folktales.

Another, more significant misconception in the western mind, which, during the colonial era, also led to the establishment of gross malpractice of traditions in India, is the belief that hierarchy of caste is the fundamental architecture of Hindu society and that Brahmins are society's moral authority. Admittedly, Brahmins figure prominently in the myths, and they shaped much of the mythological traditions, but this is only because most of the classical texts had Brahmin authors, and they, through myth, were aggrandizing their own status in society, especially to counter threats to their position by other caste members and practitioners of heterodoxy.

In actuality, these myths are also replete with narratives about Brahmin oppression and people's resentment against the arrogating behavior of men from this caste. The story of Raja Harishchandra (presented in this anthology as 'The Extreme Suffering of Raja Harishchandra') is a perfect example of this.

However, the British, unequipped to understand the complexity of Indian cultures, and overwhelmed by the immensity of the diverse traditions, desperately sought a unitary system they could comprehend so that they could enforce a smooth running of their economic and administrative machinery. Hence, they tried to fit everything into their own concept of a single, monolithic, uniform society that had a clear system of societal codes and religious commandments which applied to everyone. The Dharmashastra texts, such as *Manusmriti*, which dogmatize the hierarchy of caste and institute an aristocracy of the Brahmins, came closest to a codified system which they understood; therefore, these texts became their guidebooks. Thus it was that a system, which had been descriptive and fluid became normative and restrictive, and the rigid ideologies of these texts, which had been quite nebulous and peripheral in Hindu cultures, came to be seen as the defining socio-religious identity of the Hindus. What is even more tragic is that, catering to British interest, the Hindus themselves began to identify themselves with this distortion and began to live dogmatized lives. Sadly, Hindu cultures still haven't fully recovered from this shrinkage.

FOLKLORE TRENDS—COLONIAL TO CURRENT

While the majority of the British who came to India during the two hundred years of British rule were civil servants employed in administration, there were also a few whose interest in India was more scholarly. This was especially so, because with Sanskrit being considered an Ur language, Indomania had gripped Europe. Also, Europeans writers and thinkers were getting inspired by Hindu myth. Hence, many of the Hindu classics were translated into various European languages, and analyses and commentaries about India and its history were becoming quite the rage. This even evoked new interest among the Indian scholars themselves. However, much of this revival was of the Sanskrit classics. Folktales, for the most part, either remained unexplored, or they received only peripheral attention. There were some adventurous British writers and missionaries who did attempt to delve into this tradition, but the efforts did not have the deep scholarship that infused the study of the classics. Instead, the robust, gritty, sometimes bawdy folktales were made milky and saccharine in translation so as to make them palatable to an English society, or they were adapted as children's stories, with translations that an English child could relate to. For example, one of the best-known adaptations, *Wide-Awake Stories* by F. A. Steel and R. C. Temple, included story titles such as 'Sir Bumble', 'The Lambikin', 'Prince Lionheart and His Three Friends', etc.* In fact, outside of the elite, scholarly studies, even the myths became watered down—their complex, multi-layered narratives presented as simplistic moral tales of good vs evil. Sadly, many of these passed into collections that were made available to Indian readers also, and the Indians themselves began to see these much reduced versions of their folktales and myths as the real thing.

However, there were a few other collections of folktales published in the late nineteenth and early twentieth centuries that are noteworthy; such as the journals *North Indian Notes and Queries (NINQ)*, The *Indian Antiquary*, and *Man in India*, and the collections of Lal Bihari Dey's *Folk-Tales of Bengal*, and R. C. Temple's three volumes of *Legends of Punjab*. Then the nationalist movement in India spurred new interest among Indians. To search for an identity and to counter colonial mutations, people began to explore the richness of their own cultures, and this led to a renewal of folklore traditions, including those of tribal cultures.

After Independence, the treatment of folklore went through another remarkable change; it became scholarly. Indian anthropologists began to research and study regional folktales, both in India and overseas, especially, in the US, where the discipline of Folklore Studies was reaching maturation. Thus, with the work of leading scholars such as, A. K. Ramanujan, Jawaharlal Handoo, Komal Kothari, Birendra Nath Datta, Devendra Satyarthi, Jayalakshmi Seethapura, and many others, folklore of India has not only become formalized, but it is also experiencing a renaissance.

---

*A. K. Ramanujan, Brenda E. F. Beck & Peter J. Claus (eds.), 'Foreword', *Folktales of India*, Chicago: University of Chicago Press, 1987, pp. xiii–xiv.

HOW MYTH AND FOLKTALES HAVE BEEN PRESENTED IN THIS BOOK

One of my key efforts in this book has been to incorporate myths and folktales from as many traditions of India as possible: Hindu, Buddhist, Jain, Islamic, Jewish, Christian, Sikh, Parsi, and tribal. However, the majority of the myths in the anthology are Hindu. A simple explanation for this is that there is an abundance of Hindu myths. Another, more significant justification is that Hindu mythology is quite amorphous in India. Aside from underpinning Hinduism, it is not really 'Hindu' in the restrictive construct of the word. It shapes the Indian ethos and permeates the idiom; in other words, it is part of everyday life in India. Therefore, while Hindu myths are included in almost every thematic category, myths from other traditions are more selective. The folktales, on the other hand, have more parity.

MYTHS

All the myths in this anthology are retellings from original sources and authoritative translations. For the Jewish, Christian, Islamic and Parsi myths, I have remained as true to the original as possible. For the Hindu myths, I have taken a few liberties, and I feel comfortable doing so, because Hindu mythology is my field of expertise. I have reshaped some of these myths, because not only are there many differing versions of the same myth, from text to text, but also the back story is often not included in any given myth. Hence, in many of the myths, I have fused different versions to provide a back story, to explain complexities, and sometimes, even to give it a narrative robustness. To use some examples: the Vedic myth about the battle of Indra and Vrta originates in the Rig Veda, but then it occurs in a number of subsequent texts, including three times in the *Mahabharata*. I have used one key version from the *Mahabharata* but included elements from the other versions to fill in the gaps. Similarly, in the myth about Trishanku, I have added Vishvamitra's back story, which explains why he agrees to help Trishanku reach heaven. Another similar example is the story of Raja Harishchandra. In this myth, I have not only added a backstory and fused two versions, but I have also employed two literary devices—temporal distortion, to reconcile the different versions, and the story-within-a-story technique, to replicate the form. Thus, in this anthology, even when the reader encounters familiar myths, he/she may be reading a 'new' version.

Additionally, myth-retelling is always an interpretation presented from the perspective of the reteller. In my narration, the myths are amoral (which, I believe, is the true nature of myth) and do not represent a good vs evil paradigm. For example, the asuras/danavas/daityas are not evil or immoral forces who constantly battle the 'good' devas and are hostile to gods and Brahmins; and by the same standard, neither are the gods and Brahmins 'good' and 'moral'. Both these forces are simply opposing constructs, and this is how they are presented. However, certain myths, especially in the theme of 'Persecution' suggest an ethical stance.

Furthermore, Hindu myths, in general, have a few recurrent themes; hence, in this book as well, certain themes reoccur, such as the battle between the gods and the asuras and the hostility between Vaishnava and Shaivic elements. Also, many myths begin with the premise of a husband and wife desiring offspring. Each of these are inherent in Hindu myth for a significant reason. For instance, the deva-asura battle may have been a narrative device for oral storytelling, allowing the bard to draw on the familiar to connect to his audience. The hostility between Vaishnavism and Shaivism was a socio-political reality of that era, and the myths, aside from reflecting the conflict, either favoured Vishnu or Shiva, depending on the myth-teller's allegiance. Desire for progeny, or lack thereof, was a prime concern in that period, because furthering a family line was considered utmost dharma; therefore, it was the basis for many important myths.

FOLKTALES

I have tried to include both classical folktales from *Jatakamala*, *Kathasaritsagara*, *Panchatantra*, *Hitopadesha*, *Shukasaptati*, and *Baital Pachisi*, and modern and popular stories. Most often, I have used the common version, but for some stories, I have also selectively combined elements. Additionally, most classical collections, like *Panchatantra*, use a combination of verse and prose in the narrative, with the characters bursting into verse to convey the beauty of nature, emotion, etc., very much like the song and drama of Indian films. In some of these stories, I have retained short pieces of verse that are integral to the plot, but for others, I have either altered the verse into prose or left it out entirely to maintain narrative flow. Also, most of the classical texts use the story-within-a-story technique; they have a frame story and a main narrator, and all the subsequent stories are spun within this framework. Most of the time, I have extracted individual tales, but for some stories, I have also kept this structure. The tale of 'Why the Fish Laughed' from *Shukasaptati* is one such example.

For the more contemporary stories, my effort has been to showcase not only tales from various regions but also a sampling of the various genres of Indian storytelling; hence, I have selected stories that differ in form, structure, and narrative style. For example, qissa is a genre of long romantic tales, featuring a noble hero who faces a number of challenges and, in the process of overcoming these, he experiences many magical adventures. Among the most well-known qissas in India are 'Qissa-i-Sanjan', 'Sheet Basant', 'Chabbili Batiyari', 'Laila Majnu', and 'Tota Maina'. The folktale of 'Hiraman Parrot' in this anthology is excerpted from the 'Tota Maina' qissa. Another variety of stories is the chain tale, in which actions and words repeat to create a simple plot through a cumulative, rhythmic structure. The tradition of the chain tale in India goes back to the *Panchatantra* with the story of the mouse-maiden who meets various bridegrooms, but ultimately chooses the mouse. This story is included in the book, along with the modern tale, 'Death of a Mosquito'.

Witty tales of wisdom attributed to legendary characters, such as of Tenali Raman, Gopal Bhar, Akbar and Birbal, Mullah do-Piyaaza, Nasruddin, and Luqman Hakim is another genre of storytelling in India that is very popular, and I have included a number of these. Even though the characters of Luqman Hakim and Sufi Nasruddin did not originate in India, their stories are very much a part of Indian lore. The same is true for the story of Rustam and Sohrab, from Firdowsi's epic *Shahnameh*. This tale is from Persia, and Rustam belonged to Zabulistan–Zabul province of Afghanistan; hence, both the Parsi and Islamic traditions claim it as their own, and it is included here. Another popular storybook form is the comic series of *Amar Chitra Katha,* which was launched in the sixties to teach Indian children about their culture. A couple of tales in this anthology are adapted from this source, and I have converted the structure from a children's comic to narrative, while retaining the motifs and characterizations. In same way, I have adapted a classical play—Bhasa's *Svapnavasavadatta,* which is based on the folklore of King Udayan of Vatsa and his queen, Vasavadatta.

Another genre in folktales, not just in India, but in most societies that have oral cultures, is origination tales—how something came to be. These tales of origin hold a very important place, because they constitute a community's memory about why things are the way they are. I have included a few origin stories, such as how Kurukshetra became the battlefield for the *Mahabharata*, a Manipuri tale about how man and dog became friends, and a Bengali story about the origin and nature of opium. The Vratakatha is also another genre related to origination. In this 'katha' or story, the reason for a vrata—ritual fast is substantiated. Karva Chauth, Ahoi Ashtami, Santoshi Mata fast, etc. are all examples of Vratakathas; the former two are in this anthology.

Finally, I have included here a few tales that are part of my own memory. These are stories I heard from my parents as I was growing up, and I have passed them to my daughter, who, I hope, will share them with her children. In the course of my research, when I saw versions of these stories in various collections, I felt gratified, because they reaffirmed the connection between my own family's storytelling tradition to the folktale traditions of India.

STYLE

I have tried to retain the original style for each piece—from ornate to sparse—and have remained true to the expressions and figures of speech, as much as possible. Hence, there are many characters whose faces are 'like a lotus' or as 'bright as a moon'. There are also protagonists and antagonists (especially in myth), who are so tall that 'they touch the sky,' or their strength makes 'the three worlds tremble'. However, I have taken some liberties as well, especially in tone. For example, in myths about castes divisions and oppression of women that are presented as dharma practices in the epics and Puranas, I have a maintained a tone of authorial objectivity so as to allow the reader his/her own perspective.

THE TITLE OF THE BOOK: THE BLUE LOTUS

A blue lotus does not exist. There is a blue water-lily, but no blue lotus. Perhaps, once upon a time, along with pink, red, and white, the lotus also bloomed in blue. If this is so, then that lotus is now extinct. Now a blue lotus exists only as a symbol, and in that incarnation, it is the flower par excellence.

Blue is the colour of everything that is and also everything that isn't (such as the sky and the waters). And the lotus in India is everywhere and in everything. It is in religious iconography, architecture of ancient gardens, mosaics of temples and gurudwaras, and friezes of mosques. It is the metaphor of mystical thought, symbol of Moksha and Nirvana, and the mantra—*Aum mani padme Hum*. It is the Lotus Seat, Lotus Feet, Lotus Eyes, Lotus Heart, Lotus Womb, Lotus Wisdom, and Lotus Knowledge. Today, it is even a popular tattoo, representing all of these concepts, or something more personal for each individual who wears it. For example, my daughter has a red lotus tattooed on the inside of her wrist, on her pulse point. For her it means Shakti—a woman's courage to do.

The significance of the lotus in India is possibly pre-Aryan. A Harappan woman figurine wears a headdress of flowers that look like lotuses; perhaps, symbolizing royalty, fertility, sexuality, or perhaps, it is simply an adornment to enhance her beauty. In Vedic literatures, it is closely associated with creation and eternal life. In a key creation myth in the *Rig Veda*, Agni or tapas is the first one to arise from the primordial waters,[*] and he is born by rubbing of the blue lotus—pushkara.[**] Then Agni himself becomes the lotus of the earth, just as Surya is the lotus of the sky.[***] The lotus pond in heaven is also the ultimate eschatological aspiration for people.[****] And now scholars believe that the soma, which the Vedic seers eulogize as the elixir of immortality, may have been an extract from the lotus.[*****]

Aside from these examples of the lotus's significance, there are various other references to the lotus in Vedic literatures, including the defining metaphor of the lotus leaf terra firma on which Prajapati places the earth and begins creation:

> Before the world was created, there was water everywhere. Desiring to create the universe, Prajapati noticed a lotus-leaf. He saw it supported by the lotus stalk; he thought it must be standing in something. Assuming the form of a boar, he plunged into the water

---

[*]Wendy Doniger O'Flaherty (trans.), *The Rig Veda*, London: Penguin Books, 1981, 10.129.3.
[**]Author (trans.), *Rig Veda*, Sacred-texts.com, 6.16.13.
[***]Julius Eggeling (trans.), *Satapatha Brahmana*, Sacred-texts.com, 4.1.5.16.
[****]Ralph T. H. Griffith (trans.), *Atharva Veda*, Sacred-text.com, 4.34.5.
[*****]Andrew McDonald, 'A Botanical Perspective on the Identity of Soma (Nelumbo Nucifera Gaertn.) Based on Scriptural and Iconographic Records', *Economic Botany*, Vol. 58, 2004, pp. 147–173. <www.jstor.org/stable/4256916>.

and found the ocean floor. With his snout, he dug out wet mud, which he spread on the lotus leaf. Because he spread it, it became the earth—Prithvi. Contented, he desired to create the mobile and immobile creatures, and because they came into existence there, the lotus-leaf became bhumi. (*Taittiriya Brahmana* 1.1.3–6*)

In Puranic literature, the sacredness of the lotus is even more pronounced. Most significantly, the pink lotus symbolizes the Hindu Goddess, Sri Lakshmi, who her herself is padmamalini (wearing a lotus garland), and she represents prosperity, happiness, fertility, earth-bound life, and procreative energy and also beauty. She abides in the lotus and has the colour of the lotus.** Hence, when this lotus becomes the padmasana, the lotus seat of all the other Hindu deities, especially the male divines, it connotes a perfect synergism of the masculine and the feminine and also an equation of the Universal Self and Individual Self.

Non-attachment is another key attribute of the lotus, and many sacred texts describe the metaphor. For example, the Guru Granth Sahib says, 'In the pure, immaculate waters, both the lotus and the slimy scum are found./ The lotus flower is with the scum and the water, but it remains untouched by any pollution'. (*Maaroo*, 'First Mehla').*** This same meaning of the lotus also makes it ubiquitous in Buddhism. According to myth, before Queen Maya conceived the Buddha, she dreamed that a white elephant holding a lotus in his trunk entered her womb, and after his birth, wherever the Buddha stepped, pink lotuses bloomed under his feet, representing his indifference to the world. Thus, in Buddhist mythology, the lotus is Prajna Paramita, the Goddess who embodies Perfection of Enlightened Wisdom, and this is why there is a lotus in the hand of Padmapani or Alokiteshvara. Also, in the transience depicted in the mandala, the eight-pettaled design is the cosmic lotus. Consequently, this flower is an integral part of all Buddhist art and architecture. It decorates not just pillars and walls of stupas, but it is also the seat of the Buddha in Sarnath, where he sits in padmasana to deliver his first discourse and set the wheel of

---

*R. L. Kashyap (trans.), *Taittiriya Brahmana,* Vol. 1, Bengaluru: Sakshi Sri Aurobindo Kapali Sastry Institute of Vedic Culture, 2011, 1.1.3–6, Adapted.
**Swami Krishnananda (trans.), *Shri Suktam*, Divyajivan.org, 4.2, Accessed on 9 August 2018.
***Sri Guru Granth Sahib, 'First Mehla', *Maaroo*, Srigurugranth.org, Ang 990–8, Accessed on 9 August 2018.

dharma in motion. Therefore, the lions of Ashoka's pillar are erected on the base of an inverted lotus with curved petals.

In Hinduism and Buddhism, the lotus symbol is supreme and abundant; in every other cultural and religious tradition in India, it is less prolific but equally pre-eminent. It is the inverted golden dome of the Harmandir Sahib in Amritsar, and the base of the Mar Thoma Sliba (St. Thomas Cross). It is in the design of ponds in Mughal lotus gardens, and there are lotus buds on mural fringes of mihrabs. Mithra is shown standing on a lotus, and the embroidery pattern on a Parsi's child jhabla is often a lotus. It is the design of a chudamani that a Badagas tribal woman would wear and also of the earrings in a Santhal woman's ears. In Jainism it is the thousand-petalled siddhachakrayantra—the auspicious mandala of Jain worship, and in Tantric yoga, it is sahasrachakra—the many-coloured, thousand-petalled crown chakra of pure consciousness and awakening.

A MAP OF BOOK

While the title of the book incorporates all the above symbolic connotations of the lotus from which the various Indian traditions draw meaning, the book's arrangement is based more specifically on the metaphor of the lotus flower and the analogy of its life cycle. A creation myth in the *Vishnu Purana* evokes this metaphor: a pink lotus, the Padma of a thousand petals, sprouts from Vishnu's navel, as he sleeps on the primordial ocean on his cosmic serpent, Ananta. Brahma climbs up the stem of this lotus and, finding a seat amidst its thousand petals, scribes the world.

The flower's life cycle lends itself to the thematic structure of the book. The lotus flower grows in shallow, murky water with its roots firmly planted in the soil. It sends out a long rhizome that remains buoyant because of the air spaces in it, and when the leaves emerge, they are wide, and they spread above the water. The flower sprouts above on a sturdy stem, and aside from regulating its own temperature, (just as humans), it also blooms during the day and closes its petals at night. When the flower dies and the petals fall, a conical seed pod remains, in which the seeds become hard and loose. These seeds are impervious to air and water, and they contain within them perfectly formed leaves. After the pod ripens, the stem bends over and the pod tips into the water, releasing the seeds.

The released seeds sink to the water bed—to take root again, or not. Botanists note that lotus seeds can hibernate for over a thousand years and then suddenly germinate.

To connect the metaphor to the schema of the book: it is divided into four parts, and each part is divided into different themes. Part one represents the flower's roots and rhizome, which are firmly planted in cosmic soil. It has two themes—the world's creation and being human. The roots are creation, and the rhizome is the state of becoming human. In Part two, the wide leaves that spread above the water is the earth, and the sturdy stem on which the flower blooms is what prepares us to live our lives. The flower is life itself; its petals the human existence. This part contains eighteen themes representing various human experiences—kinship, desires, greed, conflicts, friendship, treachery, compassion, arrogance, persecution, empowerment, secrecy, romance, suffering, courage, challenges, wisdom, sexuality, and spirituality. I have tried to arrange these themes organically, as they occur in life. For example, 'Kinship' is followed by 'Desires', because very often our desires are connected with the people in our lives. Then the stories of desire are followed by tales of 'Greed', because, desire gone awry become greed. I have also placed the themes in loose juxtaposition to depict the duality of life—the polarities within which our lives our stretched—samsara. For example, 'Friendship' is followed by 'Treachery', which is juxtaposed with 'Compassion', etc. However, the seemingly opposing poles are also a reciprocal yin yang; without one there wouldn't be the other. All together, the thousand experiences of life are the thousands petals of the flower. In Part three of the book, decay sets in and the petals begin to fall, as in the tales of 'Death.' Then the soul, like the impermeable seeds, which encapsulate the perfect replica of life, disperse to experience 'Rebirth'. But then there is the rare seed, like a Realized Being, who is not reborn but achieves 'Enlightenment'. Sometimes, it germinates after a thousand years, like a Buddha or a Jesus, to return to earth to show the others the path of truth. This is Part four—the Lotus—the symbol itself.

Contained within each part of the lotus are myths, folk-myths and folktales from various Indian traditions, connected through the human experience, yet distinct in their culture. Hence, each category is a representative—a microcosm of India. But, as A. K. Ramanujan says, "'representativeness" is a chimerical ideal; …a holograph where every part

is a true representative of a whole which can never be seen as whole'.[*]
Thus, while the thousand-petalled lotus is a totality of the different colours
of India, this book can reflect only the shortest wavelength of blue.

---

*'Foreword', Brenda E. F. Beck et al (eds.), p.xii.

Part One

Roots and Rhizome

1

THE GOLDEN EGG AND THE LOTUS

In the beginning, the universe was uncreated. Brahman, who cannot be perceived, discerned, or described, was everywhere. It was formless but also had form. It had traits but was also without traits. It had no beginning and no end.

In the beginning, there was only water. Then, in the water, there appeared a golden egg, like a floating, gilded bubble, and Brahman, with the purpose of creating, primed the egg. Everything there is in the world was already in it in embryonic form—the devas, the asuras, the sun, the moon, the stars, the planets, the wind, and male and female in union. With ten times the water, the environment of the egg was created. With ten times the energy, water became mobile. With ten times the wind force, energy occurred. The wind force arose from the sky, and it was in five elements of imperceptible gross materiality. These elements became manifest in the great primeval man, Brahma, who gave seed to all creatures.

When Brahma broke open the egg, Om, the cosmic syllable, was born from it. Then arose bhur, bhuvah, swaha: the planes of earth, air, and heaven. Next arose the heat of the sun, and it evaporated the water. Then the embryonal sun, moon, stars, planets, wind, male and female in union hardened into shape. The placenta became Mount Meru, the afterbirth became the mountains, and the waters of the womb became oceans and rivers.

Brahma is the original cause, and since the egg became the golden womb for his seed, from which everything is born, he himself is called Hiranyagarbha—golden womb. He himself is the origin; he himself had no birth and is called Aja. Because he is selfborn, he is called Swayambhu, and because he is the lord—'pati'—of all—'praja'—he is called Prajapati.

For the purpose of creating the universe and delivering the Vedas, he united himself with the quality of impurity and became the four-faced Brahma. Then, to preserve creation, he united with the quality of purity and became Vishnu. At the end of time, he will combine with the quality of darkness to destroy the world as Rudra. Because he is the greatest of all, he is called Mahadeva, because he is the ultimate, he is called Brahma, and because he is superior to all, he is called Parmeshwara. These three, though only one, appear as one, two, or three gods to create, preserve, or destroy.

When Brahma sleeps, his night is pralaya, and when he wakes up and creates, it is his day.

At the end of Brahma's day, everything is destroyed—gods, sages, men—and the three worlds immerse in darkness. Then there is nothing but the vast, desolate sea. And in that desolation sleeps the Supreme person, Narayana, lying on the bed of Sheshanaag. He, who is contemplated by wise men, has a thousand heads, a thousand eyes, a thousand feet and a thousand arms. He dwells in the hearts of yogis.

Once, while he slept, a beautiful, wondrous, pure lotus—the very essence of the three worlds—just naturally arose from his navel. The petals of the lotus spread to a hundred leagues; it was radiant as the soft sun and auspicious; its calyx and stamens were flawless. Brahma was immediately enchanted by him. He approached the being and said sweetly, 'Who are you, lying hidden here by yourself in this dreadful, desolate sea?'

Smiling, Narayana, who is also Vishnu, replied in a deep voice, like the rumbling of a cloud, 'I am Narayana, the origin of the world, lord of Yoga, indestructible, supreme.' And then, even though he knew the identity of Brahma, he asked, 'Who are you?'

Laughing softly, Brahma, the keeper of the Vedas, responded to the Being who was splendid like the lotus. 'I am the Creator, Ordainer, the self-existent Grandfather. Everything is established in me. I am Brahma who faces in all directions.'

Hearing Brahma's answer, Vishnu, whose truth is his power, entered into Brahma's body by the power of Yoga. Inside Brahma's belly, he saw all three worlds, the gods, the demons, and men. Then, exiting from Brahma's mouth, Vishnu said to him, 'Now you must enter my eternal body and see for yourself the wondrous worlds inside. In Vishnu's belly, Brahma observed the three worlds and devas and asuras and men. He also saw the continents, mountains, and seven seas. He saw the whole universe and cosmic order. But he was astonished to see that it was limitless. He also could not see any entry or exit. Then he saw a passage through Vishnu's navel and, ascending through the stalk of the lotus, he found his way to a seat within its petals. Sitting there, shining radiantly, Brahma scribed the world.

Myth from the Puranas

◆

2

THE BATTLE OF AHURA MAZDA AND AHRIMAN

The light was above and the darkness below, and in between the two was void. Zurvan, who is Great Time, offered sacrifices for a thousand years to have offspring and bring the world into existence. Zurvan believed the sacrifice to be good and full of light, and after a thousand years, Ohrmazd was born from his belief. Zurvan also doubted whether the sacrifice was good and full of light, and after a thousand years, Ahriman was born from his doubt. Hence, of the twins born together, Ohrmazd was born from light and Ahriman was born from darkness.

Ohrmazd knew Ahriman existed, and he also knew of his desire to do battle, but Ahriman did not know of Ohrmazd's existence or of light. He wandered below in the desolate darkness, but when he surged up, he saw a point of light. Because the substance of light was so different from himself, he sought to obtain it, and his desire for it grew until it became as great as his desire for the darkness he possessed. When Ahriman came to the brink where light began, Ohrmazd prepared for battle to prevent him from entering, and by virtue of the Truth that was the Word of the Law, he was able to hurl Ahriman back into the darkness. Then, as protection against the Lie that was Ahriman's darkness, Ohrmazd fashioned the Truth of sky, water, earth, plants, cattle, man, and fire—all in quintessential form. With these Truths, Ohrmazd held Ahriman back for three thousand years. But all this time, Ahriman, too, prepared weapons in the darkness.

At the end of three thousand years, Ahriman returned to the line of separation, and threatening Ohrmazd, he said, 'I will strike you. I will strike your creatures. Are you thinking of designing a Creation—you who are the Bounteous Spirit? I will utterly destroy it.'

Ohrmazd answered: 'O Lie, you cannot.'

But Ahriman threatened again, 'I will make it so that all existence will hate you and love me.'

'You cannot,' Ohrmazd answered again. But he saw that Ahriman would not be deterred. He knew that unless Ahriman was girdled, he would return to his own quality of darkness and prepare more weapons, and the conflict would be endless. Ohrmazd realized in his wisdom that unless the conflict was restricted by time, Ahriman would continue to threaten. So he went to Zurvan and begged him for help. Time is good and needful, and it creates order. Thus, with Zurvan's help, Ohrmazd shaped time into three periods of three thousand years each. Ahriman desisted for those periods.

After fixing time, Ohrmazd chanted the Ahunvar[1] to show Ahriman three things: First, that everything righteous is because it is willed by Ohrmazd. This makes it clear that all things that are not righteous are against the will of Ohrmazd, because these are rooted in the Vay,[2] which is heresy, and of a different substance. Second, he who does the will of Ohrmazd is rewarded and recompensed; and he who does not, is punished. This shows that the reward of the virtuous is heaven and the punishment of sinners is hell. Third, Ohrmazd is sovereign and prosperous, and through these qualities, he keeps all suffering away from the poor. This shows that the rich and wealthy must help the needy and poor, and those with knowledge must teach the ignorant.

By this word Ahriman was defeated and he fell back into darkness.

Then Ohrmazd cast Creation onto the temporal world: first, the sky; second, water; third, earth; fourth, plants; fifth, cattle; sixth, man. Then fire permeated all six elements, infusing them for a period of time that lasted no more than a blink of an eye.

At first, the three thousand year Creation was corporeal but immobile. Sun, moon and stars all existed above, but they were frozen. At the end of this period Ohrmazd said, 'What use is this Creation to us if it is motionless?' Hence, with the help of sky and Zurvan, of infinite time, he mobilized creation. But he left the dark creation of Ahriman immobile, to set the two apart—one dark, one light; one beneficent, one harmful.

Zurvan then delivered to Ahriman an implement that was made from the very substance of his darkness, but it was alloyed with Zurvan's own power of Time. He knew that by giving him this tool, the world will have to suffer the Lie, along with Ohrmazd's Truth, but he was certain that, ultimately, Ohrmazd will prevail. Knowing this, he made a deal. He said to Ahriman, 'If at the end of nine thousand years—the period of the treaty—you do not destroy that which you have threatened, you, and everything that is yours, will be devoured by Az,[3] the demon of blinding falsehood'.[4]

Myth from the Selections of Zadspram

◆

3

FROM THE DUST OF THE EARTH

God created the heavens and the earth and all the creatures in six days, and on the seventh day he rested. No plant of the field was yet in the earth, and no herb of the field had yet sprung up, because God had not yet caused it to rain, and he had not yet created man to till the earth. Then a mist arose from the earth and watered the whole ground. God took dust from the wet ground and shaped man from it, and he breathed the breath of life into his nostrils. Thus, man became a living soul.

In the East of Eden, God planted a garden, and there he placed the man he had shaped from dust. Then, from the ground, God raised every tree that is pleasant to look at and is full of fruit. In the midst of this garden, he also planted the Tree of Life and the Tree of Knowledge of Good and Evil. The garden was watered by a river that flowed from Eden and branched into four streams—Pishon, which encompasses the whole land of Havilah, where there is gold and bdellium and onyx stone; Gihon, which flows around the whole land of Cush; and Tigris and Euphrates, which flow east of Assyria.

God placed man in the Garden of Eden so that he could tend to it. He commanded man: 'You may eat freely from any tree in the garden, but you must not eat from the Tree of Knowledge of Good and Evil; for if you do, you will die.'

Man was all alone in Eden, and seeing him so, God thought, it is not good that man is alone. I will make him a helpmate. Then, out of the ground, God formed every beast of the field and every bird of the heavens and brought them to man to see what he would call them, and whatever name man called each creature, that became its name. But, even after all the cattle, beasts of the field, and birds of the heavens were named,

God still had not found a helpmate for man. Then God caused a deep sleep to fall upon Man, and when he slept, God took one of his ribs and closed up the flesh. From this rib, God made woman and brought her to man. Man looked at her and said, 'This is now bone of my bone, and flesh of my flesh. She shall be called Woman, because she was taken out of man'. Therefore, a man shall leave his father and mother, and cleave to his wife, and they shall be one flesh.

In the Garden of Eden, man and his wife were both naked, but they were not ashamed.

Myth from the Old Testament

◆

4

HE WHO HAS MADE EVERYTHING

He has made everything, and whatever He has created is Most Good: He began the creation of man with nothing more than clay and made his progeny from his own quintessence but from the seed of his despised fluid. He also fashioned him proportionately, and breathed into him a part of His own spirit.

Yet, you, the unregenerate, whom He gave the faculties of hearing and sight and feeling, and even understanding, do not give Him thanks.
Al Sajdah, Surah 32:7–9

Your Guardian-Lord is Allah, who created the heavens and the earth in six days. Then He established Himself on the Throne to enforce the laws of creation: He draws the night as a veil over the day, and the day covers the night—each seeking the other in rapid succession. He created the sun, the moon, and the stars—all governed by laws under His Command.

Is it not His to create and to govern? Blessed be Allah, the Cherisher and Sustainer of the Worlds!
Al Araf, Surah 7:54–58

From the Holy Quran

◆

5

ADI SHAKTI CREATES GODS AND HUMANS

Adi Shakti was born from Dharma. After birthing her, Dharma left her and went away to meditate, but, before leaving, he filled two jars—one with honey, that was his spirituality, and one with poison, that was his procreative energy. Soon Adi Shakti gained maturity and with that, sexuality and desire, and, one day, in a moment of heightened desire, she drank the poison from the jar. She conceived three sons—Brahma, Vishnu and Shiva. Because Adi Shakti was in the throes of blind desire when she drank the poison, all three of her sons were born blind.

Adi Shakti told her sons to do penance on the sea of action to gain sight. When they were engaged in penances, she decided to test them. Becoming a decomposing corpse in the water, she began to float towards them. When Brahma sensed a large object covered in white, floating towards him, he knew from the rotting smell what it was. Taking water in the cup of his hand, he sprinkled it on the dead body to purify it and, repeating this ritual two more times, sent it downriver. When Vishnu's nose caught the repulsive smell, he also knew what it was, and he, too, purified it with three palms full of water and sent it down the river. When Shiva smelled the dead body, he was intrigued. 'How can there be death, when there hasn't been birth?' he asked himself and knew that this was an illusion created by Adi Shakti. So, instead of anointing it, as his brothers had done, he reached into the water, grabbed the body, and pulling it out, began dancing with it, calling on the Goddess to show herself.

Pleased with Shiva and his discernment, the Goddess changed into her divine form and touched Shiva on his blind eyes and also on his forehead. 'You were blind in two eyes. I give you sight in both those eyes and also a third eye that will see beyond this visible world,' she said to Shiva, and then told him to ask her for another boon.

'Let my two brothers also have sight,' Shiva requested.

'You yourself have that power,' she said. 'You are the embodiment of knowledge and truth. Your mouth knows nothing but the truth. That is why not just your words but also your spittle is veracious. Give your brothers sight with that truth.' Shiva then touched his spittle to the eyes of his two brothers and, instantly, they could see.

Adi Shakti then took Shiva as her husband. He changed into a linga, and the Goddess took the shape of yoni, and merging together as Linga-Yoni, Shiva Shakti then submerged into the primordial waters. From them all male and female beings of the world are born.

Folk-myth from Bengal

◆

6

SAVED BY THE FISH, MANU CREATES THE HUMAN RACE

Shraddhadeva Manu, the progenitor of the current human race, was once washing himself at the water's edge, when a fish came into his hands. It spoke to him in a human voice, 'Rear me. One day I'll save you.'

'How will you save me?' Manu asked.

'A flood will carry away all the creatures. I'll save you from that flood.'

'How am I to rear you?' Manu wanted to know.

The fish said, 'As long as we are small, we are destroyed: fish devours fish. You must rear me till I am no longer small. At first keep me in a jar, and when I outgrow that, dig a pit in the ground and keep me in it. When I outgrow that, take me down to the sea, for then I shall be beyond destruction.'

Manu reared the fish until it became a ghasha, the largest of all fish, and then he took it down to the sea. Before it swam away, the fish said to Manu, 'In a certain year the flood will come. Follow my advice and build a boat, and when the water has risen, get into the boat, and I will save you from the flood.'

In the same year that the fish had indicated, Manu followed its advice and constructed a boat, and when the flood came and the waters rose, he got into it. The fish then swam up, and taking the vessel's rope, tied it to its own horn. Then it swiftly pulled the boat up to the northern mountain. 'I have saved you,' it said to Manu. 'Fasten the boat to a tree and go to the top of the mountain. When the water subsides, you can descend.'

Just as the fish had said, the flood then swept away all the other creatures, and Manu, sitting on the mountain top, survived. Once the water subsided, he descended. Then, being all alone, he desired offspring. For that purpose, he engaged in many austerities and performed a sacrifice in the water in which he offered clarified butter, sour milk, whey, and curds. After a year had passed, a beautiful young woman rose from the water and walked up to the bank, leaving footprints that were filled with clarified butter. Seeing her, the gods, Mitra and Varuna, immediately desired her, and appearing on the bank, asked her who she was.

'I am Manu's daughter,' she replied.

'Say that you are ours,' they entreated.

'No,' she said, 'I am his daughter who brought about my birth.' Then she passed by the gods and came to Manu.

'Who are you?' Manu asked her.

'I'm your daughter,' she replied.

'Illustrious one, how are you my daughter?' he asked.

'You have begotten me from those offerings of clarified butter, sour milk, whey, and curds that you made in the waters. I am the benediction from them. Make use of me at the sacrifice, and you will become rich in offspring and cattle. Whatever blessing you invoke through me—all that will be granted to you.'

Accordingly, Manu made use of his daughter as the benediction in the middle of the sacrifice—in between the fore-offerings and the after-offerings to Agni. Then, with her, he worshipped some more and performed more austerities, wishing for more offspring. Through her, Manu generated this human race, which is called the Race of Manu; and whatever blessings he invoked through her, all that was granted to him.

Myth from the Brahamanas

◆

7

PILCU HARAN AND PILCU BUDHI

In the beginning, there was water. There was earth, too, but it was below the water. Because there was only water, the creatures that Thakur Jiu made all lived in the water—crabs, alligators, crocodiles, boarfish, prawns, worms, and turtles. Then he asked himself, 'What else can I make?' And he decided to make man. He made two people from wet clay, but even as he gave them life, the sun-horse above trampled on them, and they died. Thakur Jiu was so sad that he decided not to make mud people again. 'Instead, I'll make birds,' he said to himself. Then he rubbed his chest, and from the dirt of his skin, he made a goose and gander and named them Has and Hasil. When he held them in his hands, he saw that they were good, so he breathed the breath of his soul into them. They flew off into the air, but not finding anything to perch on, they returned to Thakur Jiu's hands. Thakur Jiu was in a quandary—without a place to dwell, the creatures would not procreate.

When the sun-horse dipped into the water to quench its thirst, foam dripped from its mouth and floated on the water. 'Go and perch on that foam,' Thakur Jiu told Has and Hasil, and when they did, the foam drifted away like a boat. The two birds were happy, but then they were hungry.

'What should we eat?' they asked Thakur Jiu.

Thakur Jiu called the crocodile.

'Why have you called me?' the crocodile asked.

'Can you bring me some earth?' Thakur Jiu requested.

'Since you have asked me, I'll try,' the crocodile replied and dove into the water, but when it brought up earth on its snout, the mud dissolved in the water.

Thakur Jiu then called the prawn and said, 'Can you bring me some earth,' and the prawn, too, replied, 'Since you have asked, I'll try.' But when the prawn fetched earth held between its pincers, it also dissolved in the water.

Thakur Jiu then asked the crab, the alligator, and the boarfish to bring earth, but as soon as each creature carried it up, the water just liquefied it.

Finally, Thakur Jiu called the worm. 'Why have you called me?' the worm asked.

'Can you bring me some earth?' Thakur Jiu requested.

'Since you have asked me, I'll try,' the worm replied. 'But let the turtle stand on the surface of the water to receive it.'

Thakur Jiu then called the turtle and directed it to stand on the surface of the water so that the earth that the worm brought up could be safely deposited on its back.

When the turtle stood on the surface of the water, Thakur Jiu tied its legs to the four corners, and there it stood, secure and stable, with its shell above the water. Then the worm wriggled its way down to the bottom of the water and, sucking earth into its sheath-like body, wriggled its way back up to the surface and climbed onto the turtle's back. There it excreted the earth from its tail, and the grains settled on the turtle's back like a skin. The worm then went back into the water, repeatedly, and brought back more and more earth to deposit on the turtle's back, till all the earth from the bottom of the water was on the back of the turtle, and there it lay in clumps and clods.

Thakur Jiu then levelled the earth with a clod-crusher, but some clumps stuck to the spikes. These became mountains. When the foam from the water rose and settled on the levelled earth, Thakur Jiu planted sirom grass seed in it. This is how the first grass grew. After that he planted the kedi kadam tree and then the sal and mahua and all the other trees.

When the earth became hard and firm and the thatch grass grew tall, Has and Hasil made their nest in it. Then the goose laid two legs, and, while she sat on the eggs, the gander provided food. Soon the eggs hatched and two human beings—a boy and a girl—were born.

'What should we feed them?' Has and Hasil asked Thakur Jiu, and he planted kaskom. Once the cream flowers withered and cotton balls appeared, he plucked a ball and showed Has and Hasil how to soak it in the juice of whatever they ate and then squeeze the juice into the infants' mouths.

When the boy and girl grew big, the birds asked Thakur Jiu, 'Where should we keep them?'

'Go and find a place,' Thakur Jiu replied, and the birds flew over the land, looking for a suitable place to dwell. They found it in the west—a place like paradise—peaceful and balmy—where trees of sal and mahua and kedi kadam grew. There was also an abundance of bananas, papayas, guavas, and vegetables of all kinds. There were fields of rice and cotton as far as the eye could see; the grain was already husked and the cotton was already picked. It was a place where there was no toil. This was Hihiri Pipiri.

It was to this paradise that Has and Hasil brought their children, whose names were Pilcu Haram and Pilcu Budhi.

Myth from the Santhal tribe

◆

8

BONG AND BOMONG

Sedi, the earth, and Milo, the sky, married. The Wiyus (Spirits), animals, and men, were all happy for them, but whenever the two joined together, everyone else was crushed between them. Aching and exhausted from constantly being squeezed, the Spirits and all the creatures finally held a Kebang to discuss what could be done. They decided that to save themselves they had to somehow separate Sedi and Milo—permanently. Wiyu Sedi-Diyor was the strongest and wisest of the Spirits, and he assured everyone that he would find a way. He beat Milo till the sky fled far above, but before he was forced to flee, Milo had joined with Sedi one last time, and she had conceived. The earth gave birth to two daughters, but she was so heartbroken at being separated from the sky that she could not bear to look at her children or to feed them. Sedi-Diyor had to find a wet nurse for the infant girls.

The girls were full of light, which became brighter as they grew older. But then the nurse died, and Sedi-Diyor buried her in the ground. The two little girls were inconsolable, and they cried so copiously that they, too, died. With them, the light died as well, and the world became dark. The Wiyus and the animals and the men were afraid, and they wondered if the nurse had stolen something from the girls that had made them cry all the time, so they dug up the nurse's body to see if they could find this thing she may have taken. In the grave, they found the nurse's rotting corpse and two shining bright eyes. When they looked closely into the eyes to see what made them shine, they saw their own reflection. They took the eyes and washed them in a stream for five days and five nights, but they could not remove their reflection from them. Then the carpenter was called, and he carefully tore open the eyes. As soon as he extracted the image, it became two radiant girls. They named them Sedi-Irkong-Bomong and Sedi-Irkong-Bong.

Bomong and Bong were kept in a house and not allowed to go out. Then, one day, Bomong dressed in beautiful clothes and jewellery and left the house to go wandering over the hills. Wherever she went, she spread the light of day. In the meantime, Bong waited for her sister to return, and when she didn't, she, too, left the house to look for her, and just like Bomong, she, too, lit up every direction in which she went. But now, with the combined light of the two girls, the world became so bright and fiery that trees began to wither, rocks began to crack, and men began to faint.

The Wiyus, the animals, and the people now called another Kebang, and it was decided that one of the girls must be killed. But who would do it? No one was willing to do the deed. Then Frog reluctantly volunteered. Taking up a bow, he shot two arrows at Bong's two sides and killed her. With her death, the world became less bright, and the trees became green again. But seeing Bong's body lying there, all the creatures felt bad. 'Someone must tell her sister,' they all said. Wiyu Kirte, the rat, then took her body on his back and carried it to the river where Bomong sat. When Bomong saw her sister's dead body, she was so grieved that she hid her head under a large stone. And, instantly, the world became dark again. Now the Wiyus and the animals and the men sent Cock to console Bomong, but she refused to show her face. 'They killed my sister, and they'll kill me too,' she wailed. 'Tell them that I'll only show my face if they bring Bong back to life.'

Once again the carpenter was called. He worked very hard and was able put some of the light back into Bong's body. She became alive again, but with reduced brightness. Seeing her sister restored to life, Bomong came out from under the stone.

Bong became the moon, Bomong became the sun, and everyone was happy.[5]

Myth from the Minyong tribe

◆

9

PURUSHA SUKTAM: SACRIFICE OF THE COSMIC BEING

Purusha has a thousand heads, a thousand eyes, and a thousand feet. He was born from the sovereign, shining primeval Being—Viraj, and when he was born, he ranged in every direction beyond the earth, behind it, and before it.

He pervades the earth on every side and extends ten fingers wide into space. This Purusha is all that has been, all that is, and all that is to be. He is the ruler of immortality when he transcends the gross world through food. His greatness is mighty, yet he is greater even than greatness. His three quarters are ascendant and immortal, and his one quarter is all these creatures on earth. This quarter of him that remains on earth becomes creation again and again, and he spreads in all directions, over sentient and insentient beings.

Purusha was Sacrifice itself. In the sacrifice, spring was the ghee, summer was the fuel, and autumn was the oblation. When the devas sprinkled consecrated water on Purusha, he also became the sacrificial offering.[6] From that sacrifice, the melted fat was collected and from it were formed creatures of the air and land—both domesticated and wild. Horses were born from it and also sheep and goats and all other beasts with two rows of teeth. From that sacrifice, the verses of the *Rig Veda* and the chants of the *Sama Veda* were also born, as were the charms and spells of the *Yajur Veda*.

When they divided Purusha, into how many parts did they apportion him? What did they call his mouth and two arms? What did they call his thighs and feet?

His mouth became Brahmin, his arms Kshatriya. His thighs became Vaishya, and his feet Shudra.[7] From his mind was born the moon, and from his eyes, the sun. Indra and Agni came from his mouth, and Vayu came from his breath. From his navel the middle realm of space arose, and from his head the sky was fashioned. From his feet came the earth, and the quarters from his ears. Thus, the gods arranged the world in order.

The sacrificial altar had seven sticks to contain the fire and three times seven sticks to fuel it. To spread the sacrifice, they bound Purusha as the sacrificial beast.[8] With the sacrifice, the gods sacrificed to the sacrifice. These were the first dharmas by which men lived their lives.

Myth from the Rig Veda

◆

10

BRAHMA'S EXPERIMENTS WITH DISMEMBERMENT

Sitting in the lotus arising out of Vishnu's navel, his mind purified by contemplation of the Divine, Brahma created the ascetics Sana, Sanada, Sanatana and Sanatkumara and tasked them to populate the earth. However, the sons of Brahma, being rigid ascetics, controlled their seminal fluid and directed it upwards towards their mind. 'My sons,' Brahma chided them, 'I created you for the purpose of progeny. Why do you not create beings?' But the sons, their minds set upon Liberation, refused. Brahma became fired up with wrath at his sons' disobedience. He tried to control his anger, but it blazed in the space between his eyebrows, and from this anger a being was born. He was coloured blue and yellow and, as soon as he was born, he began to cry. 'Why do you cry?' Brahma asked him.

'I need a name,' the blue-and-yellow one cried. 'I also need a place to live.'

'Don't cry,' Brahma consoled him. 'I'll give you a name and also a place to live. Because you're crying like a little boy, you'll be known as Rudra, and you'll live in the heart, sense organs, life, sky, air, fire, water, earth, sun, moon, and asceticism. Brahma then assigned him eleven more names: Manyu, Manu, Mahinas, Mahan, Shiva, Ritadhwaja, Ugraretas, Bhava, Kala, Vamdeva, and Dhritvrata. And for each, he also assigned a residence—heart, sense organs, life, sky, air, fire, water, earth, sun, moon, and asceticism. Then Brahma bestowed on each of the forms a wife: Dhi, Dhriti, Rasala, Niyut, Sarpi, Ila, Ambika, Iravati, Swadha, Diksha, Rudrani. 'Accept your names and places of residence, and go along with your wives and create beings,' Brahma advised his son, born blue and yellow from his wrath.

'So be it,' the blue-and-yellow one replied and, according to his temperament, strength, and appearance created countless beings, but they were all ferocious Rudras, who began to swallow the universe. Fearing that they would cause utter destruction, Brahma hurriedly called Rudra back and commanded, 'Stop! There is no need to create any more of these beings with fierce eyes and hungry mouths, who are consuming the cardinal points and also me. Go instead and carry out austerities so that the world can benefit from your rigid practices, and, through you, people can realize in their hearts, Adhokshaja—one who is beyond the senses.' Bowing before him, Rudra went away to the forest to meditate.

Once again Brahma began to muse over Creation. As he contemplated, ten sons[9] were born from his body, who were capable of creating human beings: Marichi from his mind, Atri from his eyes, Angiras from his mouth, Pulastaya from his ears, Bhrigu from his skin, Vasishtha from his life force, Daksha from his thumb, and Narada from his lap. Morality was born from his right nipple, where Narayana himself resides, and unrighteousness, which causes a person to a meet terrible death, sprang from his back. Lust was born from his chest and wrath from the space between his eyebrows; also were born covetousness from his lips and speech from his mouth. The ocean came from his penis and Nirriti, with dark designs of destruction, came out of his anus. From his shadow was born the sage Kardamma. However, although Brahma's energy permeated the world, his sons, the holy sages, still did not multiply. He thought, surely, some great Destiny is working against me. And even as he contemplated Destiny, his body split in two, and from those two halves, two beings—male and female—sprang. The self-sprung male was Swayambhu (self-sprung) Manu and the self-sprung female was Satarupa. From the union of these two, five children were born: two sons, Priyarvata and Uttanapada, who became great rulers of the world, and three daughters, Akuti, Devahuti and Prasuti. Devahuti was married to sage Kardamma, and they had nine daughters and one son, Kapila, who founded the system of Samkhya. Prasuti was married to Daksha, and theirs was the first marriage.

And hence, Brahma who created this universe from his body and mind became its Grandfather.

Myth from the Puranas

◆

11

THE SIXTH CREATION: MANKIND

Gayomard, the first man, was created from mud by Ahura Mazda. When he was about to die, he fell on his left side. Lead flowed from his blood, tin from his head, silver from his marrow, iron from his feet, copper from his bones, glass from his fat, steel from his arms, and gold from his life. Then death flowed into his body from the same side. Thus it is that deathfulness comes to all people who are born—until the time of Frashegird, when the universe will be resurrected and made perfect again.

As he was passing away, Gayomard emitted seed, and this seed was purified by the light of the sun. Two parts of it were entrusted to Neryosand, the god of prayer, and one part of it was assigned to Spandarmad—holy serenity—who is in charge of the earth. Gayomard's seed remained within the earth for forty years, and then, in the body of a rhubarb plant that had one stem with fifteen leaves which grew in fifteen years, the twins Mashye and Mashyane were born. The two beings were joined in such a way, with their hands resting behind each other's shoulders and their waists so close together, that it was difficult to distinguish between them, or to perceive who was male and who was female. In fact, it was hard to even tell in whom was placed the soul given by Ahura Mazda—which one was produced first, and which one was the material body—for the soul is produced first and allotted work, and then it is fit appropriately into a human body.

Ahura Mazda spoke to Mashye and Mashyane, 'You are the seed of man; you are the ancestors of the world; you are created perfect by me through devotion. Now go and perform work and fulfil lawfulness with perfect devotion—practice Humata, Hukhta, Huvarshta—think good thoughts, speak good words, do good deeds, and do not worship the daevas.'[10]

Mashye and Mashyane thought about Ahura Mazda's words and then went and performed their first good deed—they washed themselves thoroughly. Then they returned and spoke their first good words: 'From the immutable righteousness of law, You, Ohrmazd, have manifested the Water, the Earth, the Tree, the Beneficent Animal, the Stars, the Moon, the Sun, and all that is good.' But then, at that moment, Ahriman attacked their thoughts and corrupted their minds, and they suddenly exclaimed, 'The Evil Spirit has given the Water, the Earth, the Tree, and other things'. This was the first false utterance. Compelled by the daevas to utter it, this falsity made the two beings wicked, and their souls were condemned to remain in wickedness throughout life.

At first Mashye and Mashyane put on skin garments. Then they wove cotton cloth in the wilderness and wore that. They also dug a pit in the ground and obtained iron, which they beat out and sharpened with a stone. With that they cut wood and made a shelter from the sun.

At first the daevas filled them with violent and evil thoughts, and bearing malice in their hearts, they attacked each other, tearing at each other's hair and face. Then the daevas shouted out of the darkness, 'You are human; worship the daevas and your malice may subside.' Mashyane then sprang forward, and milking a cow, sprinkled the milk towards the northern quarter to worship the daevas; this made the daevas very powerful.

To prevent Mashye and Mashyane from procreating, the daevas made them so dry-backed that the two had no desire for intercourse. For fifty years they did not beget children. But after fifty years, the power of the daevas lessened, and their desire for each other returned—first Mashye's and then Mashyane's. Mashye said to Mashyane: 'When I see your nakedness, my desire rises.' Mashyane replied, 'Brother Mashye, when I see your desire rising, I tremble with excitement.' After satisfying their desire, they reflected: 'This was our duty from the start. This is what we should have been doing for the past fifty years.'

In nine months, two children were born to them—a male and a female, but Mashye and Mashyane felt such tenderness towards the infants, that the mother devoured the female, and the father the male. Ohrmazd then removed the tenderness of offspring so that parents could take care of the children they would bear. After that, from Mashye and Mashyane were born seven pairs of twins, male and female, all brothers and sisters, who became husbands and wives. Of the seven pairs, one was Siyamak, the man, and Nasak, the woman; and from them a pair was born, whose names were Fravak, the man, and Fravakain, the woman. From them fifteen pairs of twins were born of whom every single pair became a Sardak—a race—who started the generations of the world. After creating fifteen races of mankind and having lived a hundred years, Mashye and Mashyane died.

Myth from the Bundahishn

◆

12

EATING THE FRUIT OF GOOD AND EVIL

The serpent was shrewder than any beast in the field that God had created. Seeing man and woman wander naked and unabashed in the Garden of Eden, he asked the woman, 'Has God told you not to eat of any tree in the garden?'

'No,' the woman replied. 'We can eat fruit from all the trees in the garden, except from the tree that's in the middle. God has said that if we eat from that tree or even touch it, we'll die.'

'Surely you won't die,' the serpent said. 'God knows that the day you eat fruit from that tree, your eyes will open, and you'll be like the gods, because you'll know good and evil.'

The woman then saw that the tree was full of fruit, and it was beautiful to look at. She also believed that if the fruit from that tree made one wise, then one must desire it. So, plucking one of the fruits, she ate it, and then she shared it with her husband, who ate it, as well. Instantly, their eyes opened. Now they both knew that they were naked, and this made them feel ashamed, so they sewed together fig leaves and covered themselves.

That evening, when they heard God walking in the garden, man and his wife quickly hid from him behind the trees.

'Where are you?' God called out to man.

'I heard your voice and became afraid,' man replied. 'I'm naked. That's why I have hidden from you.'

'How do you know you are naked?' God commanded. 'Have you eaten from the tree that I forbade?'

'The woman that you made for me gave me the fruit, and I ate it,' man replied.

'What have you done?' God then asked the woman.

'The serpent beguiled me and made me eat the fruit,' the woman replied.

God cursed the serpent: 'Because you have done this, you will live below the cattle and every other beast of the field. You will crawl on your belly, and, from now on, this is how you will live and eat. I will also make you and the woman enemies forever, and your children and her children will always detest each other. They will trample on your head, and you will bite their heel.'

Then to the woman God said, 'I will multiply your sorrows. You will bear children in pain. You will desire your husband, but he will rule over you.'

And to man God said: 'Because you listened to your wife and ate of the fruit that I commanded you not to eat, the earth you live on will be cursed because of you. From now on, you will eat from it, but you will have to labour to get whatever you eat. It will yield thorns and thistles, and you will have to weed these to get to the grain of the field. All your life, you will eat the bread of your own sweat, till you return to the ground from which you were born. For you were born from dust and to dust you will return.'

God called man Adam, and man gave his wife the name of Eve, because she was the mother of all living beings. Then God gave coats of skin to Adam and Eve so that they could clothe their bodies.

'Behold!' God said to his angels. 'Man has become like one of us, because he knows good and evil.' Fearing that man may also take from the tree of life and live forever, God drove man away from the Garden of Eden to go and till the ground from which he was born. Then, in the east of the Garden, he posted the Cherubim and also installed a rotating sword that threw flames in every direction so that man would not be able to get to the tree of life.

Myth from the Old Testament

◆

13

PRITHVI, THE LAND OF MILK AND HONEY

When King Vena became emperor of the earth, he banned worship of all deities and also forbade sacrifices to them. 'I am the only lord of the sacrifice,' he proclaimed. 'All worship, oblations, and gifts should be offered to me, and only to me.'

The Brahmins of his kingdom were shocked. Warily, they approached him and offered him gentle advice in appeasing tones. 'Gracious king, please hear us out,' they said. 'For the good of the kingdom and your subjects and for your own long life, allow us to worship Hari. Hari is the God of gods and the Lord of the sacrifice. Also, permit us to perform a Dirgasatra, the thousand-year sacrifice, to invoke the benevolence of the gods so that they'll keep the land in your kingdom fertile and your subjects meritorious. And you, as monarch, will also receive your due of one-sixth share of all the yield and all the merit. When Vishnu is propitiated through sacrifice, he'll fulfil all your desires as well. So, for everyone's benefit, permit us, dear, generous king.'

'No one is superior to me,' Vena declared. 'That is why I'll be the sole recipient of everything that you and my people want to offer to the gods. This is my command; see that it's followed. And if I hear of anyone opposing it, he'll be severely punished. I am your Lord, and I must be obeyed.'

'O king, we beg you to reconsider. Your command should be that virtue and piety be preserved. Those are the qualities necessary for prosperity, and they are only sustained through propitiation of the gods; if these are not sustained, the world will end.'

'Ignorant Brahmins!' Vena shouted. 'In the person of king are all the gods—Vishnu, Brahma, Indra, Surya, Chandra, Shiva, Varuna—all of them—even Agni. The essence of the king is everything divine. I am King. Worship me!'

'He'll destroy the kingdom,' the Brahmins whispered amongst themselves, afraid of the impending doom. 'He's not fit to be king. He should be slain,' they cried. So all the rishis fell upon the king and beat him with blades of holy grass, till he was dead.

Soon after Vena died, the rishis saw a great dust cloud rising near the boundary of the kingdom. 'What is this?' they asked the people.

'These are the approaching armies of our neighbouring kingdoms,' the people told them. 'They have found out that we have no monarch and have sent their troops to plunder and usurp the kingdom. A kingdom without a king is easy prey.'

'This can't be,' the rishis exclaimed and conferred once again. Deciding quickly on a plan, they began to rub the thigh of King Vena's corpse, and soon a dwarfish being sprang out of it. He was as black as a crow and had a flat nose, a wide mouth, protruding chin, red eyes, and brown hair. This was Vena's wickedness. 'What should I do?' the being asked the rishis. 'Be outcaste,' they declared, and the being immediately left the kingdom and went to reside in the mountains. Thus, Vena's evilness was expelled.

Now the rishis rubbed the right arm of Vena's corpse, and this time, the being that emerged was lustrous and magnificent, like a manifestation of Agni; they named him Prithu. As soon as Prithu was born, Shiva's bow, Ajagava, a quiver full of celestial arrows, and a full suit of armour fell from heaven for his use. This affirmed the blessedness of Vena's son, and with his birth, Vena himself, who was born from the Hell named Put, was redeemed, and his spirit went to Heaven.

Everyone rejoiced at Prithu's birth and prepared him to be installed as king. To inaugurate Prithu's kingship, the seas and rivers appeared in their corporeal form, bringing gifts of precious jewels and gems and also anointed water to bathe the king. Brahma, accompanied by his host of gods and holy rishis, also came to bless him, and seeing the mark of Vishnu's discus in the lines of Prithu's palm, recognized him as a portion of Vishnu. And so they declared Prithu, Chakravarti—one who will rule over territories that will be as vast as the area that Vishnu's chakra can cover. Brahma then performed the consecration. During the ceremony, the moon-plant was pressed to produce Suta and Magadha—bards that would eulogize Prithu's kingship; and thus the tradition of eulogy was established in the world. But, being the first of their kind, Suta and Magadha didn't know how to extol the king: 'We don't know King Prithu. What will he accomplish? What fame will he achieve? What territories will he conquer? How will he treat his subjects? Will his subjects love him? On what should we base our eulogies?' they asked Brahma.

'Praise him for the merits he will achieve; applaud him for the virtues that he will display. Commend him for the justness he will uphold, and laud him for the love he will bear his subjects. Base your eulogy on what he will do in the future,' Brahma advised.

When Prithu heard the bards celebrate his accomplishments, he realized that he would have to live up to all that he was expected to achieve. So he listened carefully to the sweet voices of the bards and memorized everything they spoke. They said he was always truthful, kept his promises, and was patient, brave, just, compassionate, and kind. Hence, Prithu imbibed these very qualities, and this is how his character was formed. The bards also glorified his sacrifices, and so Prithu performed many sacrifices to protect the earth and to provide for this subjects.

However, no matter how hard Prithu tried, his people still suffered. The anarchy that had occurred between the time that Vena was slain and Prithu was born had let loose a famine that was rampant in the land, because, since then, the earth had withheld all vegetation.

'Help us,' Prithu's people pleaded with him. 'You've been appointed our protector and provider. It's your duty to take care of us.'

Prithu took the bow, Ajagava, and his quiver full of arrows and marched towards Earth to punish her for withholding her bounty that was meant for humans. Frightened, Earth took the form of a cow and fled from region to region, from Brahma's abode to Indra's heaven, with Prithu in hot pursuit. Finally, exhausted, Earth stopped and faced Prithu. 'Don't you know it's a sin to kill a female?' she demanded.

'When the happiness of many can be secured by destroying one harmful being, then the killing of that being is a virtue, not a sin.'

'But if you kill me, how will you provide for your people?' she asked.

'I'll provide for them with the power of my own devotion.'

Earth then realized that King Prithu did, in fact, have the power to make her expendable. Knowing him to be a practical man, she advised: 'All endeavours can be successful with the right means. I'll give you knowledge of how to produce new plants and grow food by using my milk. Bring me a calf so that I can produce milk. Also make everything level, so that when the milk flows, it'll irrigate the whole land.'

Before Prithu's time, there were no cities and towns and villages; in fact, there were no defined boundaries. There were also no pastures and cultivated land, or highways for businessmen. Prithu uprooted mountains and levelled the ground, traversing hundreds of thousands of miles to spread the advancement. Then he called Swayambhu Manu, the divine ancestor of man, and requested him to be Earth's calf. When the calf suckled on Earth's teat, milk began to flow in abundance, spreading in every direction, nourishing the ground, making it fertile, so that all kinds of grains and vegetables could grow.

Earth's milk was so enriched that even the celestials came to earth with their vessels to receive it, and they used it to nurture their own attributes: Brihaspati, the chief priest of the gods, used it to produce soma, Indra used it to gain celestial powers, and the holy Meru Mountain used it to produce herbs and minerals and gems.

Prithu granted Earth her life, and she was as though reborn, and from then on, Earth has been called Prithvi, the daughter of Prithu.

Myth from the Puranas

◆

14

GANGA IS TAMED TO LIBERATE MORTAL SOULS

Sagara was a Suryavanshi king of the Ikshvaku clan of Ayodhya. He was pious and good and always concerned for the happiness of his subjects; however, his own life lacked joy. He had two beautiful and virtuous wives—Kesini and Sumati—but no children. Desperate for offspring, King Sagara decided to appeal to the great Rishi Bhrigu, who was one of the seven mind-born sons of Brahma and was created as a patriarch to perpetuate the human race. Accompanied by his wives, Sagara went to Bhrigu Prasravana, a mount in the Himalayas where Bhrigu resided, and began to meditate on him. The king and his wives meditated for a hundred years without a break, uncaring of their bodies' needs and undeterred by the extreme conditions. Pleased by their dedication, Bhrigu appeared before them and gave the king a boon: 'One of your wives will have a son who will perpetuate your race, and the other will give birth to sixty thousand sons of unequalled fame.' The queens wanted to know which one of them would have which offspring. 'That is for you to decide,' the rishi replied, and so the elder chose the option of one son, who would be heir to the throne, and the younger agreed to have sixty thousand sons of unequalled fame. The royal family then thanked Rishi Bhrigu, circumambulated him in reverence, and returned to Ayodhya.

In due time, the elder queen, Kesini, gave birth to her son, Asamanja, and the younger queen, Sumati, produced a foetus shaped like a bitter gourd. When they split it open, sixty thousand embryos emerged, which they placed in sixty thousand covered jars full of ghee, and soon the embryos developed into infant sons. These sixty thousand brothers grew up to be charming, obedient boys, but Kesini's one son was a terror. He disobeyed his parents, was rude to his teachers, and bullied his younger brothers till they cried. His favourite sport was to push his brothers into the Sarayu river. By the time Asamanja became a young man, Sagara was so fed up with him that he exiled him from the kingdom. However, the prince was married by that time and also had a son, Anshumana, and the boy was the exact opposite of his errant father; he was well-behaved and kind-hearted; so much so that everyone urged the king to make him his heir, instead of Asamanja.

King Sagara, too, had been thinking along the same lines, but he decided that before he declared his successor, he would perform the traditional Ashvamedha yajna to establish his sovereignty over all the territories that fell between the Himalayas and the Vindhya ranges. Commanding that the sacrificial horse be allowed to roam free in that region for a year, he made his young grandson, Anshumana, chief of the warriors who accompanied the horse, even though he was certain that no king in that territory would impede his imperial pursuit by obstructing the horse's path.

All went as planned. The horse roamed unopposed for a whole year, and then Anshumana guided him back to Ayodhya. After the horse's return, King Sagara organized a large communal ceremony for the final sacrifice, to which he invited every citizen of Ayodhya. In public view and amidst much celebration, the queens, Kesini and Sumati bathed the horse and adorned him with auspicious marks and jewellery to prepare him for the sacrifice to Brahma. But even as the horse stood ready to be asphyxiated for the sacrifice, Indra, disguised as a rakshasa, descended at the site and stole the horse. The ceremony ground to a halt. 'This does not bode well for Ayodhya,' the high priest warned King Sagara. 'The prosperity of the kingdom depends on the success of this yajna. The thief must immediately be caught and punished, and the horse must be brought back so that the sacrifice can be concluded.'

Sagara commanded his sixty thousand sons to scour the earth for the thief and bring him and the horse back. 'Divide the earth amongst yourselves into one yojana each and ransack it. Find that evil rakshasa and force him to tell you where he has taken the imperial horse. If they're not on the earth, dig into the earth. Just bring them to me.'

The sixty thousand princes searched for the horse night and day in the whole of Jambudwipa,[11] each one searching his sixty-four kilometre area minutely. But none of them could find a single clue about the horse or the horse-thief. Angry and frustrated, they began digging into the earth, using their bare hands as shovels. They dug relentlessly into the layers of Patala, till they reached five layers below—to the top of the penultimate layer, Rasatala, in which the danavas and rakshasas live. But by now, they had created so much chaos that the gods began to fear that their digging would level all the spheres and destroy the order of creation. 'Stop them,' they implored Brahma. 'To fulfil their father's selfish desire of sovereignty, they are destroying the world and its creatures.'

Brahma pacified them. 'Don't worry,' he said. 'This earth and all its levels belong to Lakshmi, and Vishnu is supporting it in all his various forms. In fact, this theft is part of his grand cosmic scheme, and so is this hunt for the horse by Sagara's sons. Believe me, Vishnu is not only aware of this, he is also ready to execute his next move. Be patient and let the drama unfold, as has been scribed.'

Back on the terrestrial plane, not finding a single trace of the horse, the exhausted sons of Sagara returned to their father. 'We have circumambulated the whole world and dug our way to Rasatala but have found neither the horse nor the thief,' they told him, shame-faced.

'Dig deeper!' Sagara ordered. 'Go back and dig into Rasatala. That is probably where the thief is hiding. Nab him in his lair, and then bring him to me.'

And so the sons returned to the subterranean site with actual spades and ploughs and began to make their way into the sphere of Rasatala. This sixth level of the netherworld was guarded by four world elephants—one on each quarter—that bore the globe, with its mountains and forests and seas and cities, on their heads. The eastern quarter was guarded by Virupaksa, the southern by Mahapadma, the western by Saumanasa, and the northern by the snow-white Bhadra. Reaching these quarters, Sagara's sons circumambulated each of the four guardian elephants and then tunnelled their way into Rasatala. Here, as they proceeded in a north-easterly direction, they came upon a sage who was sitting on a verdant hill, and near him, grazing lazily, was the sacrificial horse. The sixty thousand sons of Sagara rushed at the holy man in anger, brandishing their spades and ploughs and uprooting trees and rocks to use as weapons. 'You evil thief,' they shouted. 'How dare you steal our father's sacrificial horse? Prepare to die.'

The sage just sat there quietly and watched them approach, and when the sons were a few paces from him, he closed his eyes and took a deep breath. As he exhaled, a hum arose from his body, and, within seconds, Sagara's sixty thousand sons became ashes. This sage was none other than Vishnu himself, who had taken the form of Rishi Kapila.

Back in Ayodhya, Sagara grew worried about his sons. 'I fear that something has happened to them,' he said to Anshumana. 'Go, my son, and search for them. Bring your uncles home as well as the sacrificial horse. Go quickly. I wish you speed and success.'

Using the tunnel that his uncles had dug into the subterranean worlds, Anshumana quickly reached Rasatala. Seeing the four guardian elephants at the entrance, he asked them if they had seen his uncles, but the elephants said nothing. 'Have you seen my grandfather's sacrificial horse?' Anshumana then asked. All four elephants nodded and assured him that he would be able to return home with the horse. Bowing to the guardians of the quarters, Anshumana went further into Rasatala and wandered in that beautiful land till he came to a verdant hill on which he saw a pile of ashes; grazing near it, he saw the sacrificial horse. Anshumana knew immediately that the ashes were his uncles' and was stricken with grief. He looked around to see if he could find water to sprinkle on the ashes, but he could not see even a rivulet. Sitting down in despair near the mound of ashes, he wept, wishing he had water to consecrate his uncles' ashes. Then he thought about his maternal uncle, Garuda, the celestial king of birds, who had eyes that could see across the world and would be able to tell him if there was a stream or a lake nearby. Instantly, Garuda appeared before him. 'Don't cry, dear boy,' he consoled Anshumana. 'These events have occurred to save the human race. But I understand your grief. Perhaps you could find a way to liberate your uncles' souls.'

'How can I do that?' Anshumana cried. 'I can't even find water to sprinkle on their ashes. Can you help me find water?'

'Your uncles were reduced to ashes by the fiery vision of Rishi Kapila, and the only way to liberate them is with the divine waters of Ganga. She is the eldest daughter of Himavana, the mountain king. But she lives in heaven, and your uncles' ashes are here in this subterranean level. It seems impossible.' Garuda shook his head at the hopelessness of the situation. 'Disregard my earlier suggestion, my boy. My advice to you is to just grieve for your uncles, as is appropriate, and then move on. Take the sacrificial horse and return to earth so that your grandfather can complete his Ashvamedha.'

Bidding the wise Garuda farewell, Anshumana returned to Ayodhya with the horse and related everything to his grandfather. Sagara wept for his sons and then completed his yajna, which established him as the almighty emperor with dominion over all territories between the Himalaya and Vindhya ranges. But grief for his sixty thousand incinerated sons remained in his heart.

In due time, King Sagara passed away, and his grandson, Anshumana, became king. Anshumana ruled the kingdom for a while, but his heart wasn't really in it; he couldn't forget his uncles' lost souls. Finally, handing over the kingdom to his own son, Dilipa, he went into the forest to devote his time to meditation, hoping that asceticism would reveal to him a way to bring Ganga to the earth. He did tapasya for thirty-two lakh years and built up so much ascetic merit that he went straight to heaven, but he could not bring Ganga to earth. Dilipa, too, inherited his family's grief for the lost souls of King Sagara's sons. All his life, he, too, thought of ways to persuade Ganga to come down to the terrestrial plane, but to no avail. He ruled well for thirty years and was considered a dharma-abiding king, and when he passed away, he, too, went to Indra's heaven.

When Dilipa's son, Bhagiratha, became king, the evil effect of the undelivered souls of Sagara's sons finally caught up with this Suryavanshi family. Bhagiratha and his wife remained childless after years of marriage, and Bhagiratha knew that if he did not liberate the souls of his ancestral uncles, the Ikshvaku clan would become extinct with him. He then decided that the family had grieved enough. It was now time to take serious and deliberate action. So, entrusting the kingdom to a body of loyal and wise ministers, he went to do tapasya on the summit of Gokarna in the Himalayas, ready to undergo such severe penance that Ganga would have no choice but to capitulate. For thousands of years, he kept fires burning in the four quarters, and with the fifth fire of the sun above, he stood meditating with raised arms, his body scorching in the heat. Finally, Brahma, unable to watch Bhagiratha suffer any more, manifested before him. 'Enough!' he said to Bhagiratha. 'What is it that you desire? Ask me for one boon.'

'I want to liberate the souls of my ancestors—Sagara's sixty thousand sons—by immersing their ashes in the holy waters of Ganga, and once they are liberated and their spirits go to heaven, I want to have a son who will carry on the race of Ikshvaku. I know that these sound like two boons, Brahmaji, but really, it's just one boon, because only when my ancestors' souls are delivered will I be freed from the family's grief, which has now become my curse. Only when this curse is lifted will my race be perpetuated.'

'Granted,' Brahma declared. 'I promise you that Ganga will descend to the earth and redeem your ancestors. But the fulfilment of this boon is not as simple as it sounds. Ganga is the mightiest of rivers—so mighty, in fact, that when she falls to earth, her force could sink the earth. Have you thought about that?'

Bhagiratha shook his head. 'What should I do, Brahmaji? Please advise me.'

'Ganga's force is the pure force of the Goddess. The only Being who can withstand her in all her power is Shiva, who is pure consciousness, even when he is combined with matter. He's the only one who can create the necessary balance to sustain individual souls and help them realize liberation. Go and beg Shiva to receive Ganga. Tell him it is for the good of the people on earth. If you succeed, and he agrees, I will send Ganga to the earth.'

Now Bhagiratha began to mediate upon Shiva, practising even more rigorous control; for a whole year, he stood on the tip of just one big toe, with his mind set on pure consciousness. Pleased with his yogic discipline, the Lord of Yoga, Shiva, appeared before him and promised him, 'I'll receive the daughter of Himavana on my head. Go get her.'

Up in heaven, Ganga swelled into a mighty torrent and prepared to descend to the earth. Hearing about this momentous event, all the gods and celestial beings came to watch her as she fell, streaking through the sky like lightning, the creatures living in her waters, thrashing and screeching as they were swept along in the deluge. As she descended, she felt her force increase even more and exulted. She had heard that Shiva planned to curtail her, and she hoped to thwart him. She knew that the propulsion of her fall could plunge her straight down into Patala, and she intended to take the Great God with her. He would not be able to contain her feminine power.

When Ganga landed on Shiva's head in full force, Shiva understood her intention. He smiled to himself with respect for the heavenly lady's chutzpah, and then, controlling his energies, he expanded his jatta—the matted locks on his head—till they became so colossal that Ganga was trapped in the mass. She swirled around on his head, roaring, seeking an opening to escape, but the coils of his locks would not allow an exit. Finally, exhausted, Ganga allowed her feminine force to be merged with Shiva's yogic power.

In the meantime, Bhagiratha, eagerly awaiting Ganga, realized what had happened to her, so he began to appease the mighty god once again with more austerities. Having created the balance that the world needed, Shiva released Ganga and let her fall into Brahma's lake, Bindusara, in the Himalayas. But by now Ganga's force had been so reduced that when she exited Shiva's locks, she split into seven streams. Three of them, Hiladani, Pavani and Nalini flowed towards the east, and three, Suchakshu, Sita and Sindhu became westerly rivers. The seventh stream then began to follow Bhagiratha's chariot, as he led her towards the ashes of Sagara's sixty thousand dead sons.

Everywhere that Ganga's holy waters flowed, rising and falling, meandering between rocks and trees, creatures frolicked in her waves and played in her spray. The mortals, gratified by her cleansing waters, bathed in her and felt absolved of their sins.

Following in the direction that Bhagiratha rode, Ganga's seventh stream swept through large tracts of land, not even paying attention to where she was being led. In one particular field, Rishi Jahnu was performing a long sacrifice to increase his asceticism. Without noticing him Ganga swept through the site that he had specially consecrated for his ritual sacrifice. Enraged at the river's disregard, the rishi scooped up all the waters in his cupped hands and, in one gulp, swallowed Ganga. Bhagiratha, who was riding ahead, leading the river goddess, had no idea that she was no longer following him, but the gods and heavenly creatures who were following behind Ganga saw this and immediately intervened. They begged Jahnu to release Ganga for the good of the human race, and so the rishi, understanding Ganga's purpose, let her flow out of his ears. Since she was born again from his body, she became his daughter—Jahnvi.

Once again, Ganga began following Bhagiratha and reached the spot where Sagara's sons had dug a tunnel into Rasatala. Entering the tunnel, Ganga descended to that subterranean level and followed Bhagiratha to where the ashes of Sagara's sixty thousand sons were still piled in a mound, awaiting deliverance. Stepping aside, Bhagiratha folded his hands before the goddess in gratitude. Instantly, Ganga flooded the area. Her holy waters, the purest of all waters, enriched with the essence of Shiva's pure consciousness, washed over the ashes, taking the sixty thousand souls into her fold like a mother and dissolving all their sins.

Brahma then appeared before Bhagiratha and congratulated him. 'By giving the souls of your ancestors the waters of Ganga, you have released them. They are now liberated and will ascend to heaven. Here on earth, Ganga will continue to liberate mortal souls, and you will be remembered by all humanity for the good deed you have done. One stream of Ganga will still flow in heaven as Divya, but here on earth, she will also be known as your daughter and be called by your name—Bhagirathi.'

Myth from the Ramayana

◆

15

THE TOWER OF HUMAN CONFUSION

There was a time when everyone on earth spoke just one language, and they used the same words to talk to each other. They all travelled to the east and, coming upon a plain in the land of Shinar,[12] settled there. They said to one another, 'Come, let's make bricks by baking them, and let's build ourselves a city and a tower whose top reaches the heavens. Let's give ourselves a name so that we're not scattered over the earth as different people.' And so, using bricks for stone and bitumen for mortar, they made such a city and built such a tower.

Then the Lord came down to see the city and tower that these children of men had built, and he said, 'Here they are, one people with one language, gaining strength from each other, and now that they have begun to build a tower that reaches heaven, nothing will withhold them from pursuing another objective, if they see a reason to do so. Come, let us confound their speech, so that they will not understand one another and will scatter.' And so the Lord made it that everyone began to speak a different language, and no one knew what the other was saying.

With their speech a confused babel, people could not communicate with each other anymore. They stopped building their city and their tower that could reach the heavens and disbanded, all taking off in different directions. That is why it is called Babel; it was here that God confounded the language of the people and scattered them across the earth.

Myth from the Old Testament

◆

16

SOPHET BNENG

From the time of Creation, a tree grew on the hill of Sophet Bneng.[13] It was a world tree whose upper branches reached heaven, and heavenly creatures used it as a ladder to descend to earth. At that time earth was a beautiful place with all manner of trees and flowers and mountains and rivers, and it was uninhabited. Only the heavenly beings came to visit it during the day, and they returned to heaven in the evening.

Adjacent to Sophet Bneng was another tract of land which was unploughed but extremely fertile, so the heaven-dwellers decided to cultivate it. The sixteen heavenly families took care of the field, with each family taking turns to tend to it. Soon it was lush with grain.

Among the heaven-dwellers was one who resented the sovereignty of the Creator and wanted to be ruler. One day, he was down on earth, along with seven of the sixteen families, when he surreptitiously left the others working in the field and, climbing Sophet Bneng, cut off the world tree. The seven families, unable to return to heaven, were left stranded on earth. These became the ancestors. Thus, the human race began from these seven roots—the Ki Hinniew Skun, as the Khasis[14] say.

Folktale from the Khasi tribe

◆

17

KARMA, THE VEHICLE OF LIFE

There was once an old lady named Gautami, who had attained peacefulness by practising patience all her life. She had a young son whom she loved very much, but one day a snake bit the boy and he died. She was inconsolable. Grieving for her son, she wondered why the Creator was making her suffer like this. 'I've never harmed anyone in my life,' she lamented. 'Why would you take away an old woman's only support in life?'

A fowler named Arjunaka caught the snake and brought him to Gautami. 'Here's your son's killer,' he said. 'He should suffer just as you are suffering. Tell me how you want him killed. Should I throw him in the fire, or should I cut him up into pieces? He's a murderer and shouldn't be allowed to live.'

'Set him free,' Gautami told Arjunaka. 'Why would you want to incur sin by killing a creature? Besides, his death will not bring back my son. If the snake has sinned, his own karma will pay him back for it.'

'You're a wise lady for leaving everything in fate's hand. I'm a practical man. If I can alleviate your grief by punishing your son's killer, then let me do it.'

'No. Don't kill him. Whatever happened to my son was his own fate. Let the snake go.'

'I don't agree with you,' Arjunaka said. 'He's a killer and we'll be doing the world much good by destroying him.'

The snake then spoke in a human voice, 'If you think I'm the killer, then you're a fool, Arjunaka. I didn't kill the boy of my own accord. Mrityu—Death—sent me to do his bidding. So, if there's any sin in this, it is Mrityu's.'

Just then Death appeared. 'I was guided by Kala—Time,' he said to the snake. 'It was on Kala's orders that I sent you to kill the boy. So neither you nor I are responsible for his death. Don't blame us,' he said to Arjunaka. 'Blame Kala.'

And then Time also joined the conversation. 'I'm the one who brings cause and effect to fruition, but I'm only a neutral facilitator. I'm not responsible for either the cause or the effect. In fact, not the snake, nor Mrityu, nor I are responsible for what happened to the boy. We're only the immediate causes of what occurred. The actual cause of the boy's death was his own karma. What is more, the boy is not responsible for Gautami's suffering. We each are made happy or made to suffer only because of our own accumulated karma. So the actual cause of Gautami's suffering is her own karma, not her son, or any one of us.'

Arjunaka set the snake free, and each one—the fowler, the snake, Mrityu, and Kala—went on his own way. Gautami, too, went home, feeling consoled.

Myth from the Mahabharata

◆

18

OUR ORDINARY LIVES

Preaching in his masjid one day, an Imam described to his congregation the torments that sinners have to suffer in Jahannam. As his description of hell became more gruesome, his voice rose in excitement, his face became animated, and his henna-red beard trembled with zeal.

Suddenly a member of the congregation burst into tears.

'Ah,' said the Imam in satisfaction. 'I see that my sermon has had an impact. Is the thought of dozakh making you think about your sins, my son?' he asked.

'No, Imam sahib,' the man replied, wiping his tears with the edge of his scarf. 'I was thinking about my goat. He got sick last year and died. I miss him very much. He had a beautiful beard—exactly like yours.'

Folktale from Punjab

◆

PART TWO

A Thousand Petals

19

PASSION AND PROGENY

One spring day, King Vasu, the ruler of Chedi, was hunting deer in a forest to procure meat for a shradha ceremony for his ancestors, when he was struck by the sensual beauty of the wilderness. The champak and punnag were fragrant, the kokila birds were cooing, and the bees, their sacs bursting with pollen, were buzzing. Suddenly, Vasu was overcome by a burning desire for his wife, Girika. Sitting under a tree, he relieved himself, but he didn't want to waste his sperm, because he knew his wife was particularly fertile at the time. Collecting his sperm on a leaf, he called a hawk that was flying overhead and requested it to take it to his wife. The hawk took the leaf in his beak and flew off over the Yamuna, but it was attacked by another hawk in mid-air, and, in the fracas, the leaf fell into the river. There, a fish, who was an apsara suffering a curse, swallowed King Vasu's sperm. Nine months later, a fisherman caught the fish, and when he opened her belly, he discovered two infants—a boy and a girl. He took the babies to King Vasu, who adopted the boy and named him Matsya. He gave away the girl to the chief fisherman, because her body smelled like a fish. For this reason, everyone called her Matsyagandha (fish smell), although she was named Satyavati.

When Satyavati grew up, she helped her father in his trade by plying a boat on the waters of the Yamuna. She was a very beautiful woman, and one day, her beauty caught the eye of Rishi Parashara, who was waiting to cross the river along with a group of pilgrims. 'O beautiful maiden,' he said to her, 'I desire you. Come, lie with me.'

'Holy rishi,' she replied. 'Look at the river banks; they're filled with travellers and holy men. How can I grant your wish in the presence of all these people?'

'That's easily fixed,' Parashara said and created a fog that covered the whole place in darkness. Matsyagandha was distressed. She had used the excuse of lack of privacy to deter the rishi, but it hadn't worked, so she decided to speak the truth: 'I'm a virgin,' she appealed to him. 'Surely you know that if I lie with you, I'll be ruined. How will I return home? How will I face my father? How will I face society?'

'Beautiful maiden, don't worry about that. After you've been with me, I'll restore your virginity. I promise you.'

'I'm under my father's care. If I do this, he'll be very hurt, and I can't bear to hurt him,' Satyavati objected. But the rishi was persistent, enticing her with rewards. 'If you fulfil my desire,' he said, 'I'll also give you a boon. Ask me anything. I'm a very powerful rishi and can grant anything.'

'Can you take away my fishy smell and make my body fragrant?'

'Of course,' Parashara declared.

And so it happened that Matsyagandha became Gandhavati (sweet-scented), and she had no choice but to accept the embraces of Rishi Parashara. From that union, she conceived and gave birth to a son. He was born on an island in the Yamuna that Parashara covered with dense fog, and for that reason he was called Krishna Dvaipayana. Soon after, the boy left his mother to become an ascetic; and later he became known as Rishi Vyasa. Satyavati herself, now emitting a unique, sweet fragrance, returned to her father and continued to ply the boat, rowing travellers across the Yamuna.

One day, King Shantanu, of the illustrious Kuru dynasty of Hastinapur, was walking along the banks of the Yamuna, when a tantalizing scent drifted to his nose. He looked all around but he could not find the source of the unique fragrance. Then he saw a woman of mesmerizing beauty, sitting on the bank near a moored boat, and he realized that the fragrance was coming from her body. 'O sweet-smelling maiden with black eyes, what are you doing here?' he asked her.

'I'm the daughter of the chief of the fishermen,' she replied. 'I've been commanded by my father to row people across the river.'

The perfumed heat coming from her body filled Shantanu with intense desire and he wanted to possess her. 'Lovely maiden,' he said. 'I want to marry you. Tell me where you live so that I can talk to your father.' Shyly, Satyavati led Shantanu to her dwelling.

The chief of the fishermen was delighted to receive Shantanu's proposal. 'I'm honoured,' he stated. 'Even if I look in every corner of the world, I won't be able find a husband like you for my daughter. But I can't marry my daughter to you unless you give me a pledge. Promise me that you will.'

'My good man. How can I make a promise without knowing what it is you ask? If I'm able to grant it, I will. Tell me what you want.'

'Promise me, O king, that the son born of this girl will be your successor to the throne.'

The fisherman's words struck Shantanu like a heavy bolt of fire. He burned with desire for the girl, but the condition her father placed on him made his heart sink. How could he give away the kingdom that he had promised to his son Devavrata, who had been lost to him until only four years ago?

Shantanu had been married before—to Ganga, in her human form, although he hadn't known her identity when he married her. Before co-habiting with him she had imposed a condition that he would never question her, no matter what she did, whether it was agreeable to him or not, and if he interfered, she would leave him that very instant. He consented, and the two of them lived happily for a while, till she gave birth to a son. That very morning, she went to the river and threw the infant into the water. All Shantanu could do was watch his newly-born son drown, because he knew that if he uttered a single word, he would lose his beloved wife. In this way, she drowned seven of their sons, but when she took the eighth son to the river, Shantanu could not hold himself back anymore, and he stopped her. 'Don't kill him,' he pleaded. 'Who are you and why have you been murdering our sons?'

'Since you have stopped me, I won't kill this child,' she replied. 'But now I must leave you. I am Ganga. These sons were eight celestial Vasus who were cursed by Rishi Vasishtha to take human birth as punishment for stealing his boon-granting cow, Nandini. I agreed to take human form to bear them in my womb and also free them from human birth as soon as they were born. I have freed seven of them. This one was the Vasu named Dyonai. He was the main culprit, and it appears that his sin is not yet expiated; he needs to remain on earth for some more time. He will stay with me, and his name will be Gangadutta.' And then Ganga disappeared, taking her son with her, while Shantanu returned to his palace, wife-less and son-less—heartbroken.

Then, one day, many years later, Shantanu was pursuing a deer he had wounded when he noticed that the river Ganga had suddenly become very shallow, and he was amazed to see that her waters were being held back by arrows that a youth was shooting into the water. Even as Shantanu wondered who the child might be, the boy disappeared and Ganga appeared in human form, holding the youth by his hand. 'This is your son,' she said to Shantanu. 'I've carefully reared him. He's an expert with weapons and is a superior bowman. He has also studied the shastras with the great Rishi Vasishtha and is well-versed in all the Vedas and Angas. Take him home. He is yours now.'

With a joyful heart, Shantanu brought his son, Gangadutta, home and gave him another name—Devavrata. He couldn't have asked for a more accomplished, loving, and obedient son, and he loved him more than anything else in the world. Four years later, Shantanu installed him as heir apparent, and all of Hastinapur celebrated.

And now, here he was, his own desire threatening his beloved son's future. Shantanu knew what he had to do; he refused the fisherman and returned home. But he couldn't stop thinking about the girl, and the more he thought about her, the more morose and distant he became from everyone, even from his dear son.

Devavrata watched his father's growing depression, and finally, one day, he asked him what was wrong. 'What is this malady that is slowly destroying you? Tell me please what is the remedy?'

'Dear son, scion of the Bharata race, I am indeed melancholy. I see you always engaged in dangerous sports, and this worries me. Life is so unpredictable. What if something happens to you? Having no other descendants, I'll become sonless. Truly, you are equal to a hundred sons, and I want no other. With all my heart, I wish you prosperity and a long life. But, this is the cause of my worry—that if the worst happens, what will happen to Hastinapur?'

Devavrata heard his father out, but he felt that there was something else that he was not telling him, so he went to his father's chief minister to ask him if he knew the real reason for his father's constant grief. The minister revealed to him all that had happened with the maiden and the condition her father had imposed.

'Is that all? I'll talk to the chief of the fishermen myself,' Devavrata declared and, taking the kingdom's key ministers with him, he went to pay Satyavati's father a visit. 'My father is a good and generous man,' he told the old man. 'He is a great Kshatriya and a powerful king. If you search the whole world, you won't find a better husband for your daughter.'

'It is true. If I were Indra himself, I wouldn't be able to reject such a match,' the fisherman said. 'But if my daughter marries your father, her son will never be king, because you have the first right of inheritance. This is my objection to the marriage.'

'Listen to what I have to say,' Devavrata then said to Satyavati's father. 'With my father's key ministers as witness, I take a vow that your daughter's son will be king.'

'I am grateful for your vow,' the old man replied. 'But I'm the father of a daughter, and I'm not convinced. I don't doubt at all that you'll fulfil this vow, but how can you guarantee that your sons will not violate it? After you, they may claim the throne.'

'In that case, I will not have sons. Here, with these witnesses, I take another vow—that from this day onwards I will become celibate.'

Devavrata's formidable declaration reached the heavens, and the heaven-dwellers were amazed. They gathered at the end of the firmament and showered flowers down on Devavrata, exclaiming, 'This man is Bhishma (the Terrible).'

Satyavati's father fell at Bhishma's feet in awe. Then he handed over his daughter to him without another word, and Bhishma brought her to Hastinapur with all the respect due to a mother. When Shantanu discovered what his selfless son had done, he was overcome with love. 'You are truly Bhishma,' he said, embracing his son. 'With a father's pride and gratitude, I give you a boon: you will die only when you wish to. Death will not come to you till you yourself summon it.'

Myth from the Mahabharata

◆

20

AKANUNDAN

The king and queen of Rajapuri had seven daughters but no son. They doted on their girls, but they longed for a boy who would be able to perpetuate the royal line. The raja was a conscientious ruler who cared for his subjects very much and did everything he could to keep his kingdom prosperous. The queen, too, was a good soul, spending her time in charity and good deeds. The people of Rajapuri were grateful to have such a king and queen, and they offered heartfelt prayers to the gods, hoping that the royal couple's desire for a son would be fulfilled.

One day, a fakir came to the queen's door, begging for food. Normally, the queen's handmaidens took care of beggars, but when the queen heard this fakir's voice, she found something so compelling in it that she went herself to the door. 'What can I give you, baba?' she asked.

'Anything in the name of god,' the fakir replied.

The queen put some gold and precious stones in the fakir's begging bowl, and as he was about to leave, she stopped him. 'Will you give me a blessing, baba?' she asked.

'Of course. What is it you desire?'

'My husband and I really want a son,' she said. 'Can you bless me with a son?'

'I can grant you a son,' the fakir replied. 'But there's one condition: you must return the boy to me when he turns twelve.'

Something about the way he said this rang so true that the queen was convinced she would finally have a son, and she became overwhelmed with such happiness that she barely paid any heed to the condition. 'Yes, yes,' she said to the fakir, pouring more gold and jewels into his begging bowl. Soon after, the queen conceived, and, in due time she gave birth to a healthy, handsome boy. The king was overjoyed, the princesses were excited, and the whole kingdom celebrated. Every street in the kingdom was decorated with flowers and flags, and there was much dancing and singing. The royal couple also gave a grand feast to which all the citizens were invited.

They named the boy Akanundan, which means 'only son'. He was a true miracle of a boy. He had a joyful spirit and a sharp brain, and he was charming to boot. His teachers loved him, his friends admired him, and his parents and sisters doted on him.

Eleven years passed in the blink of an eye. On Akanundan's twelfth birthday, as the kingdom of Rajapuri celebrated, the fakir showed up at the queen's door. 'I've come for the boy,' he said. The king and queen were in anguish. They had deluded themselves into believing that the fakir would have forgotten about that condition. In fact, they had hoped for this so desperately that they had rarely mentioned it, in case someone heard it and reminded the fakir. But, often at night, when sleep eluded

that some years later, the country in which he settled was hit by severe famine. By this time, he had already squandered away all his wealth, and he did not have enough to even feed himself. So the young man went looking for a job and was hired by a landowner to tend to his pigs. But, here, too, he was hardly given any food and was in such a state of starvation that he envied the pigs the husks that they were fed.

Disgusted by his own pathetic condition, the young man began thinking about his father and the number of servants he had and how, in his father's house, they were abundantly provided with food. And here I am, he thought, starving to death. The young man then decided that he would return to his father and beg him to take him back. 'I'll say to my father,' he said to himself, 'I've sinned against heaven and against you; I'm not worthy to be called your son; accept me as a hired servant.' And so the young man set off for his father's house.

The old man was out, tending to his work, when he saw his younger son from a distance. His heart filled with love and compassion. He ran to meet his son and embraced him and kissed him.

The son said to him, 'Father, I've sinned against heaven and against you. I'm not worthy to be called your son. Can you accept me as your hired servant?'

But the father said to his servants, 'Quickly. Bring my best robe and dress my son in it. Put a ring on his finger and shoes on his feet. And bring the fatted calf and kill it. Let us eat and make merry to celebrate this day, for this son of mine was dead and is alive again. He was lost and is found.'

In the meantime, the elder son, who was out in the field, returned home. When he neared the house, he was surprised to hear music and dancing. He asked one of the servants what was going on.

'Your brother has returned,' the servant informed him. 'And your father has killed the fatted calf, because he has him back safe and sound.'

The elder son was so angry at this news that he refused to go in. And when his father came out and entreated him, he replied, 'I have slaved for you all these years, following your every order, never once disobeying you. And you never gave me so much as a kid to have a feast with my friends. But now this son of yours shows up after wasting all your money on prostitutes, and you kill a fatted calf for him.'

'My dear son,' the father said. 'You are always here with me, and everything I have is yours. But this day is special and needs to be celebrated, because your brother who was dead is alive again. He was lost and is now found.'

Parable from the New Testament

◆

24

SISTER IN THE FLUTE

In a village there lived seven brothers and a sister. The brothers were all married, but the sister still took care of all the family's cooking, not allowing the brothers' wives to assist in any part of this important duty. For this reason, the wives resented their sister-in-law. They tried to talk to their husbands, each one presenting a case of her superior culinary skills, but the brothers were loath to deprive their sister of her place in the household. So the wives decided to get help from a bonga[15] of their tribe:[16] 'Can you ensure that our sister-in-law is delayed at the water tank when she goes to fetch water at mid-day?' they asked.

'Yes, I can make it happen. When her pitcher touches the waterline, the water will disappear, but when she removes the pitcher, the water will reappear,' the bonga suggested.

'That's brilliant,' the sisters-in-law said. 'That way, she'll just keep trying to fill her pitcher and won't be able to return in time to cook the evening meal, and we'll have to do it.'

'What will you give me in return?' the bonga asked.

'You may keep the girl,' they replied.

At noon that day, the sister went to the tank as usual, but when she dipped her pitcher into it, the water level suddenly dropped. Wondering what was going on, she drew her pitcher back, and as soon as she did that, the water began to rise again. When it reached her ankles, she tried to dip the pitcher in it again, but the vessel would not submerge in the water, no matter how hard she pushed. By now the girl was frightened, and she began to cry, calling to her brothers:

'O brothers, the water reaches to my ankles,
still, the pitcher will not dip.'

The water continued to rise until it reached her knees, and she tried once again to dip her pitcher, but the vessel would still not go under. Then she cried:

'Oh brothers, the water reaches to my knees,
still, the pitcher will not dip.'

The water rose some more, and when it reached her waist, she tried again to dip her pitcher into it, but the waterline was like a wall, and she wailed:

'Oh brothers, the water reaches to my waist,
still, the pitcher will not dip.'

The water rose even higher, and as it reached her neck, she wailed even more loudly:

'Oh brothers, the water reaches to my neck,
still, the pitcher will not dip.'

Then the water rose so high that it went over her head, and she went under, pitcher and all, and still her wails could be heard:

'Oh brothers, the water is over my head
and the pitcher begins to fill.'

When the pitcher filled to the brim, she drowned. The bonga then changed her into a bonga like himself and carried her off.

Time passed, and the girl who had been turned into a bonga became a bamboo plant, growing on the embankment of the tank in which she had drowned. There was a jogi who used to often pass by that embankment, and when he saw the bamboo that had grown to an immense size, he said to himself, 'This will make a splendid flute.' So the next day he brought an axe to cut it down, but when he was about to begin cutting, the bamboo called out, 'Don't cut at the root; cut higher up.' When he lifted his axe to cut higher up on the stem, the bamboo cried out again, 'Don't cut near the top, cut at the root.' When the jogi again made to strike at the root, the bamboo called, 'Don't cut at the root, cut higher up;' and, once again, when he raised his axe, the bamboo said, 'Don't cut near the top, cut at the root.'

By this time, the jogi was sure that a bonga was trying to mess with him and, becoming angry, he took the axe and struck the bamboo at the root. Then he carried it home and made a flute out of it. The instrument had such a superior sound that all who heard it were entranced. The jogi took this flute with him whenever he went begging, because when people listened to it, they were compelled to give generously. One day, making his rounds in the neighbourhood, the jogi begged at the house of the seven brothers whose sister had drowned in the tank. When the brothers heard his flute, they felt a strange anguish in their hearts and tears began to roll down their cheeks.

'Sell me your flute,' the eldest brother said to the jogi. 'How much is it?'

'It's not for sale,' the jogi replied.

'If you give it to me, I'll take care of all your needs for one whole year.'

It was an attractive offer, but the jogi was not interested.

Then, one day, the jogi went to beg at the village chief's house. When he played his flute, everyone in the chief's house was enchanted, especially his son, who was an amateur musician.

'Sell me the flute,' the village chief ordered the jogi.

'My flute is not for sale,' he replied.

'I'll pay whatever price you name,' the chief said.

'This flute is my livelihood. How can I sell it?'

'I understand,' said the chief. 'I'll not ask you again to sell it. But let me offer you some food.'

The chief's servant brought the jogi a plateful of food and, along with that, a bottle of liquor. Eating just a few mouthfuls, the jogi started on the bottle and kept going till the last drop was gone, and soon he fell on his side, completely drunk. The chief then had his man replace his flute with another one that looked just like it. Much later, when the jogi recovered from his drunkenness, he quickly gathered his belongings and left, not realizing that he was leaving behind his magical flute.

Now the chief's son began to play the jogi's flute every evening, and he sounded so accomplished that everyone was amazed. During the day, the chief and his family worked in the field, so in the morning, before going to work, the chief's son would leave the flute sitting in a corner of his room. For the first few days, the bonga girl in the flute remained in the flute, but, slowly, as the days passed, she began to feel at home, and one morning, when the family left, she came out of the flute and walked around the son's room. The next day, she walked around the house, and the day after that, she found the kitchen. That day she prepared a sumptuous rice meal for the family and, making a plate for the young man, she brought it to his room and hid it under the bed. Then she slipped back into the flute.

When the chief's son returned from work, he smelt the food in his room and found the plate under his bed. Wondering who had placed it there, he took a bite and then quickly ate everything on the plate because it was the most delicious food he had ever eaten. When he stepped out of his room, he heard the women talking excitedly about the delicious rice meal that had been prepared for the whole family.

'There was a plateful in my room as well,' he told them.

'Ah ha!' they exclaimed. 'We were wondering.'

'What do you mean?' he asked.

'It's obvious that one of your girlfriends has done this to impress us.'

The chief's son was very good-looking and had many girls constantly vying for his attention; hence, everyone accepted this explanation, even the young man himself. When food began to appear every day in the kitchen and under his bed, the family decided to find out which of his girlfriends was making it. So, the following morning, the young man did not go to work; instead, he hid behind a pile of wood in his room. Soon, he saw a beautiful girl come out of the bamboo flute. As he watched in astonishment, she went to the mirror and, sitting down before it, piled her long black hair on her head. When she left the room, he followed her and realized that she was headed to the kitchen. There, she washed her hands and began cooking a meal of rice, and after she was done, she filled a plate and carried it back to his room, where she slipped it under his bed.

As the flute girl was about to go back into the flute, the young man caught her in his arms.

'Let me go,' she begged.

'Who are you?'

'I'm a bonga,' she told him.

'I want to marry you,' the young man said.

And so the bonga girl and the chief's son were married and began to live happily.

It so happened that the seven brothers of the sister who had drowned were close friends of the chief, and they often visited his house. When the new bride was introduced to them, she recognized them immediately, but they did not know who she was. She cooked them a meal of rice, and when they were served, she sat with them. Eating the rice dishes, the eyes of the seven brothers filled with tears. When the chief asked them what was wrong, they said, 'This food reminds us of our sister who passed away.'

'I am your sister,' the girl told them and related all that had happened to her, and when she was done with her story, she said, 'You knew how your wives were treating me, but you did nothing, my brothers. You must have known when they set me up to drown, and still you did nothing to save me.'

The brothers looked at their sister, shamefaced.

And that was all the complaint she made.

Folktale from the Ho and Munda tribes

◆

25

SADDA MAMA

Yazdegerd III was the last Sasanian Emperor of Iran. He was defeated by the Arabs in the battle of Nihavand in 642 CE, and he and his soldiers went into hiding. After the collapse of the Persian Empire, the Arabs began persecuting the Zoroastrians, forcing them to change their faith, or die. Many Zoroastrians fled across the Karakum desert in the Marv region near the sea.

One day, suffering from the intense heat of the desert sun, exhausted and wracked with hunger and thirst, the Zoroastrians saw a well in the distance. What they did not know was that hiding behind the well was a troop of Arabs, waiting to ambush them. Sitting on the parapet of the well was a chameleon, watching both the murderous Arabs and the hapless Zoroastrians. He knew that as soon as the unsuspecting Zoroastrians drew near the well, the Arabs would pounce on them, and he wondered how he could save the Zoroastrians from being massacred. Then he hit upon a plan.

He knew that in the desert sun, everything appeared brown and dull, but a flash of colour would stand out. So, he jumped on the shoulder of an Arab soldier and made his body green. Then he jumped on another shoulder and turned himself red, and, in this way, he kept jumping from shoulder to shoulder in different colours. Seeing the sudden flashes of colour, the Zoroastrians knew that something was not right and dispatched a scouting party from a different direction. Sure enough, the scouts saw the concealed Arabs and also a little chameleon hopping from one shoulder to the other, shaking his head from left to right as though to tell the Zoroastrians that there was danger lurking near the well and to stay away from it.

The scouts returned and informed the others about the Arabs waiting in ambush and also about the little chameleon who seemed to be warning them about the danger. Heeding the warning, the Zoroastrians prepared themselves and were able to rout the Arabs. By this time, the chameleon had once again landed on the well's parapet and, from there, he nodded his head up and down in approval, as though to tell them that the chameleon would always be there to guide them, whenever they were in doubt and needed help.

Since then, Zoroastrians have revered the chameleon and never kill it. Children consider the Sadda (chameleon) as their Mama—their mother's brother—and they seek it out whenever they are unsure if an action is right or wrong. If the chameleon shakes its head in warning, they know they need to consider another path, and if it nods its head in approval, they know that Truth is with them.

Parsi folk-myth

◆

26

SONS-IN-LAW

One day, hunting in a forest, Akbar saw a tree that was particularly crooked. He stood looking at it for a while, and then he asked Birbal, 'Why is that tree crooked?'

'That tree, Jahanpanah, is the son-in-law of all the other trees in the forest.'

'How do you know?' Akbar asked.

'Because of the saying: a dog's tail and a son-in-law are always crooked.'

'Does this mean that my son-in-law is also crooked?' Akbar asked.

'Of course,' Birbal replied.

'Then have him executed!' Akbar declared.

A few days later, Birbal requested Akbar to come to the square in which all executions were carried out. When he arrived there, Akbar saw that three crosses had been erected—of gold, silver and iron.

'Who are these for?' Akbar asked, quite perplexed.

'The gold cross is for you, O Refuge of the World; the silver one is for your son-in-law, and the iron one is for me.'

'Why are you and I to be executed along with my son-in-law?' Akbar asked.

'Because, Jahanpanah, you are your father-in-law's son-in-law, and I, too, am a son-in law.'

Akbar's laughed. 'In that case,' he said. 'Let my son-in-law go.'

Akbar-Birbal folktale

◆

27

THE BLUE ALIEN

There was once a jackal named Chandarava who lived in a forest on the outskirts of a village. One day, hungry, searching for food, he went into the village. There, some street dogs saw him and began chasing him. Trying to get away from the barking and snarling mob of vicious dogs, the jackal didn't pay attention to where he was going and ran through an open doorway of a dyer's house where he tumbled right into a large vat of indigo dye.

Climbing out of the vat, when Chandarava looked down at himself, he saw that he was blue. He didn't look like a jackal at all. Bemoaning his luck, he slunk out of the house, praying that he wouldn't have to face the dogs again, but by this time the village dogs had lost interest and had gone their separate ways. The jackal then made his own way back to the forest.

When he entered the forest, he saw many animals wandering around, as they ordinarily did. Trying not to attract any attention, he headed towards his cave, but suddenly someone spotted him and exclaimed, 'Who's that?' And soon a crowd of animals began to gather around him. But, for some strange reason, none of them would come any closer; they all kept their distance—even the lion. Then Chandarava began to hear quivering whispers: 'What kind of creature is this?' 'We've never seen anything like him.' 'Where has he come from?' 'Is he strong?' 'Will he prey on us?' Then he heard an urgent voice say, 'Flee! Save your lives,' and all the other animals began running away from him. The jackal realized that in his blue avatar the animals did not recognize him. In fact, they were afraid of him. That's when a plan began to form in his mind.

'Greetings,' he called loudly in a calm voice. 'Don't be afraid. I won't hurt you. I've been sent by Lord Brahma himself. He said to me, 'The animals in the forest need a king.' Then he anointed me and commanded me to come here and be your ruler. In my kingdom, all will live safely and happily. Come, my subjects, and bow to your king.'

The animals believed him and slowly began gathering around him again, this time moving closer to him. Lions, gazelles, monkeys, leopards, hares, elephants and jackals—they all came and bowed to him in respect. 'Tell us, O Lord, how can we serve you?' they asked.

Chandarava then assigned duties to each one of them: he made the lion his chief minister, the tiger his lord chamberlain, the leopard his bodyguard, the elephant, the gatekeeper of his cave, and the monkey, the bearer of his royal umbrella. But the jackals he could not abide and commanded the other animals to chase them away.

And so it was that Chandarava began to live the life of a king, with the other animals taking care of his every need. While the smaller animals cared for his comforts, the bigger ones brought him all their kill so that he could divide it among his subjects, as he saw fit.

Many days of peace and quiet passed. Then one day, as Chandarava was presiding over his royal assembly, he heard a sweet sound—the howling of a pack of jackals. His own jackal heart leapt at that sound and, without thinking, he let out a loud, shrill howl in return. When the other animals heard that high-pitched jackal howl coming from their king, they were aghast. 'Why, he's just a jackal!' they exclaimed. For an instant they felt embarrassed for having been fooled by a mere jackal, but then they were filled with anger at being duped, and they all fell upon him. The jackal, realizing that the game was up, tried to escape, but the tiger clamped his mighty jaws around his throat and tore him to pieces.

That is why the wise say: one who spurns his own trusted kin makes himself easy prey for others.

Folktale from the Panchatantra

◆

28

WORLDS AND UNWORLDS

Seeking to detach himself from the world, Rishi Vasishtha looked for a place where he could meditate in seclusion—a place without the distractions of the city, forest, sky, ocean, clouds, creatures, gods, or souls. He found a spot in space that was so far away from earth that even the natural elements could not reach it. In that empty place, he imagined a small hermitage and made it inaccessible to the rest of the world. Then he sat down in it in the lotus posture, and quietening his mind, went into samadhi for a hundred years.

On awakening, when he willed his consciousness to return, he heard a sigh. In this place of his imagination, which was so far away in empty space, where not even air could intrude, he wondered where that sound was coming from, and from whom. So he went back into the infinite consciousness of his mind and began searching. In his mind were order and disorder and countless universes in different stages of creation and destruction. None of these universes knew the other existed; they were all dormant realities, resting in one indivisible, infinite consciousness. As he wandered in this infinite space, Vasishtha heard the sound of a lute. Following it, he came upon a radiant, magnificent celestial woman who was singing sweetly. When she saw Vasishtha, she stopped singing and came to him. 'Who are you, and why have you come to me?' Vasishtha asked her.

'Beyond the boundaries of this universe are world and unworld mountains—the Lokalok. In these are many worlds of light and darkness that are inhabited by humans, gods, and demons. On the northeastern slope of one of those mountains, there is a rock. I live in that rock with my husband. We have lived in it for aeons. My husband is a Brahmin and a brahmachari—a celibate—and our marriage has never been consummated. He knows the scriptures and what they say about the necessity of domestic life, so he created me to simply help him fulfil that duty, but he has never been moved by desire for me, even though I'm a most alluring woman. I, on the other hand, had the normal desires of a woman. Ever since I passed puberty, I burnt with desire. Beautiful flowers, cooling snow, soft beds—no matter where I lay, I lay on ashes, because I was burnt dry from desire. And so, married to my husband, my youth was wasted. But now I am tired of it all. Now I have detached myself and have no desires; I only want release. My husband, too, is old. He has lost all sense of attachment and has his mind under control. Our lives have no meaning now, and we see no point in living, so we seek liberation. I have come to plead with you to teach us self-knowledge so that we can be liberated. Have pity on us.'

'How do you live in that rock? What is your world like?' Vasishtha asked.

'It's just like your world. There's a heaven and a hell; there are devas and asuras, sun and moon, the sky, the stars, the hills, the oceans, creatures, particles of dust, air. Why don't you come with me and visit it to see for yourself?'

Vasishtha accompanied her to Lokalok and saw the rock. But all he could see was the rock. 'Where is the world?' he asked the woman. 'I see only hard, solid rock.'

'How can you not see it?' she said. 'I see it reflected in me all the time. It projects all the experiences that I have had. Perhaps, you can't see it because these are my experiences, not yours; that's why it's my world. Or perhaps, you can't see it, because, O sage, you are much evolved and beyond dualities of real and illusory. But if you concentrate, you may be able to experience my world.'

Vasishtha then sat down in samadhi again and invited the universe of the stone into the infinite space of his mind. When the celestial woman entered the rock, he entered it with her. Inside, she went to the creator of that universe, and, sitting down before him, introduced Vasishtha to him. The creator opened his eyes and welcomed Vasishtha and offered him a jewel-seat. Then, celestial music began to play and a sweet voice began to sing.

'Listen to me, O sage,' the creator said, 'I'm just a small vibration of the infinite consciousness that is unborn. So are you. What you see here—you, I, this dialogue between us—is just two waves colliding in the ocean. We are not separate from the infiniteness of the ocean. We are just notions that spontaneously arise in it. I have never been created. You have never been created. This woman here, who claims to be my wife, has never been created. She was just my notion—a thought wave. Just as she is your notion—a thought wave. She got caught in desire and the bonds of samsara, and through the memory of her own karmic experiences, created her own notions of a universe and husband and stone. Today is the day of dissolution of this world. I feel dispassionate, and when I leave this cosmic mind and enter infinite consciousness, all vasanas—desires—will dissolve. Hence, this woman, who is manifested desire, will also perish.'

Then that creator uttered 'Om', and as he withdrew the notion of the universe back into his mind, chaos erupted: numerous natural disasters occurred on that earth, causing floods and fires. Men and women became immoral, and a dust storm arose to cover the sun. War, pestilence, famines spread wide, and people everywhere began to wail and cry. Unrighteousness spread like darkness, and kings began to rule with might. Temples were looted and violence spread. Then the waters broke all bounds and began to flood that earth. Great waves rose, reaching up to the clouds, creating great walls, taking into their fold mountains and caves and cities and animals and people. The earth was consumed in its own natural elements. Then the danavas appeared and overpowered the devas. The stars and heavenly bodies fell out of orbit and collided, creating great explosions, before vanishing into space.

Vasishtha looked at the creator, who was still meditating, even though his world had become blank. Then he saw a sun rising in every direction— right from the bowels, like a subterranean fire. Eleven fires arose, with three more, like the three eyes of Shiva. The entire firmament was quickly ablaze—scorching—and beings began to char and crackle. Soon heaven and earth were also ablaze, and everything, becoming ashes, disappeared without a trace, like ignorance disappears when wisdom burns. Nothing remained.

Then a great wind blew, so violently that even the netherworld seemed to press deeper below, and it created a deep cold, which crackled like the cosmic sound of Brahma's golden egg breaking. Soon rain began to pelt down on the waters of the seven oceans. Twelve suns became like whirlpools in this rain, and ocean creatures streaked across like lightning. Whatever was left was drowned in the rain. The doomsday rain mixed with the doomsday fire, which was still burning, and the ashes of destruction spread everywhere.

There was no space, no directions. There was neither below nor above, neither element nor creation. There was only limitless ocean, completely still.

When Vasishtha looked inside the rock again, he now saw many creations. In whichever corner he looked with concentration, a whole creation came into existence. In some of the creations, Brahma had just begun creating; in another, the danavas were fighting the devas, and in yet another, people were dying of old age, or Ravana was abducting Sita, as also Rama was rescuing Sita. And Vasishtha realized that all these creations were within himself, in his own body, as the tree is in its seed. Each person sees the vision of his own world and that is the world he inhabits. It's like a dream that each one dreams only himself.

Even as he contemplated this, he became an atom, a ray of light, each of the five elements of creation, and he himself became all the universes and also himself.

After all this, Vasishtha returned to his own cottage in the hermitage in space. But he saw that sitting in his seat in lotus position, meditating, was an old sage with a radiant face and a body that radiated light. When Vasishtha had gone with the woman who lived in the rock, he had left his own body behind; he could not see it anywhere. He thought that perhaps this sage, like me, wanted to go into deep samadhi, secluded from the world, and finding this empty hermitage, decided to use it. He may even have waited for its inhabitant to return, but when he didn't return for a long time, he may have assumed that the sage had abandoned his body and reached nirvana, and so he occupied this hut.

Let me return to my own world, Vasishtha thought, and even as he thought this, the hermitage ceased to be. Vasishtha went from space to earth, and the sage, who had been sitting in lotus position in the hut, also began to fall like stone. He landed, still in lotus posture, having controlled his breath, and hence gravity. He didn't even wake up on landing—just kept on meditating. To wake him up, Vasishtha had to become rain and thunder and pour down on him. When the sage awakened, Vasishtha asked him who he was. 'I was tired of this world of senses and desires and wanted to detach myself from my egotism,' the sage replied. 'Seeking extreme solitude, I came upon your hut in space and occupied it thinking you had probably abandoned your body after achieving nirvana.'

'I, too, wanted release from desires and sought seclusion,' Vasishtha told the sage. 'Come. Let us live in that world together and live each in his own environment.' So saying, they both ascended to the sky and bid each other farewell. Then the sage went where he thought fit, and Vasishtha went where he wanted.

Myth from the Yoga Vasishtha

◆

29

IN PURSUIT OF PERFECTION

Once there was a royal couple who longed for children. They tried everything—prayers, fasting, medicines, mantras, spells—but the queen could not conceive. Then one day, an old and vagrant-looking fakir came to the palace and requested an audience with the king.

'If the queen drinks the potion I give her, she will have twin sons,' he told the king. 'But there is one condition. You must give me one of the boys when I ask for him.'

The king had heard many people claim that they had the magic formula that would make the queen conceive, but none had sounded as certain as the fakir, so the king decided to give his potion a try. He conferred with the queen, and they both concurred that although the thought of losing one of their sons was disturbing, the fact that they would have twins and be able to keep the other one was enough incentive for them to accept the fakir's offer.

The fakir gave them the potion, the queen drank it, and, to everyone's delight, she became pregnant. For the whole nine months of her pregnancy, the kingdom rejoiced. Every day there were prayer sessions in the town's temples and celebrations in the town's square. In due time, the queen delivered twin sons who were identical—they were two of the most magnificent infants ever born. Not only were they handsome, but they were also very bright. They learned quickly and excelled in everything—math, literature, public policy, administration, as well as archery and sword-fighting. They had princely demeanours and were also compassionate, charitable, and fair. All in all, both the princes were ideal heirs.

For the first few years, the king and queen were constantly afraid that the fakir would come and claim his due. But when ten years passed and no one came, they thought about him less and less. Occasionally, when the queen brought up the subject, the king responded, 'He's probably dead by now.' And, as more years passed, they became even more convinced that he must be dead.

Then, on the day that the boys turned sixteen, a very old and decrepit man showed up at the palace gates and said to the guards, 'Tell the king I've come for my boy.'

The king and queen were dumbfounded, then the queen began beseeching the king. 'You're king. You make the rules. Just tell him no. Please.'

For a second, the king did consider saying no, but he was a righteous and just king. 'I can't,' he said sadly to his wailing wife. 'You know that I must honour my word.'

'I don't care about your word. How can anyone expect a mother to hand over one of her children? It's inhuman. Why can't you refuse on that ground? Surely it's more important to remain true to compassion than to an inhuman word of honour?'

That made sense to the king, and he began to think how he could make a case to the fakir. But just then another guard came and fearfully delivered a message from the fakir: 'Don't even think about dishonouring your word, King. You have no idea what I can do.'

Hearing this, the queen fell to wailing even louder. There was no doubt now that she would have to lose her son. The only question that remained was which son would she give up?

'I'll go,' said the younger to the older. 'You're Father's heir. The kingdom needs you.'

'No, I'll go,' the older said to the younger. 'You're the favourite of both Father and Mother. They need you.'

Finally, the boys drew sticks to decide who would go. The eldest got the shorter stick, so he was the one that the king and queen had to give up. Before leaving, the elder prince planted a tree in the front yard of the palace. 'This is my life's tree,' he told his family. 'When you see it flourishing, you'll know that I'm well. If it starts to wither, you'll know that all is not well with me, and if it dies, know that I'm no more.'

Then, saying goodbye to his kingdom, his weeping people, his lamenting parents, and his woebegone younger brother, he walked out of town with the old fakir, who was headed towards the forest.

On the road to the forest, they passed a bitch who had a handful of pups playing between her legs. One of the puppies became very excited to see the prince and said to his mother, 'I want to go with that young man who looks like a prince. Please, may I go?' His mother agreed, and the puppy jumped into the arms of the young prince.

A little further down, a hawk was tending her chicks in her nest. One of the chicks grew excited when he saw the prince and asked his mother, 'May I please go with that young man who looks like a prince?' 'Go,' said the hawk, and the chick flew and sat on the prince's arm.

The fakir and the prince and his two companions—the puppy and hawk chick—journeyed for a while and then crossed the forest and, finally, at the end of the forest, they arrived at the fakir's tiny wooden hut.

'You'll live here with me,' said the fakir to the young prince. 'Your main chore every day will be to gather flowers for my worship and bring them to me. Aside from that, you can do whatever you want, go wherever you feel like, eat whatever fruit you desire, drink from whichever brook you find. The only thing you must never do is go towards the north. If you do, evil will befall you.'

The prince didn't mind at all living in the forest with the fakir. In fact, he quite enjoyed the freedom. Every morning he gathered flowers for the fakir, but after that, all day, he ran around with his two companions, hunting and sporting. He ate whatever fruits he wanted from the numerous fruit trees growing in the forest, and he drank from whichever brook he liked whenever he felt thirsty.

Back home, the younger prince and his parents watered the elder prince's tree of life every day and watched it grow tall and green and consoled themselves that at least their beloved was well.

Then, one day, the prince who lived with the fakir saw in the forest a stag with elegant, long legs and proud antlers that spanned many feet. He strung his bow and, aiming an arrow, shot at it. The arrow hit its mark, but the stag did not fall; it continued running, heading north. The excited young prince followed it without even thinking about the direction in which he was going, with his puppy running beside him and his hawk flying above him. The stag led the prince out of the trees into an open area, where there was a lone house, and it ran right into it. Following the stag, the prince entered the house and came upon a young woman who was sitting before a dice board. She was the most beautiful woman he had ever seen.

'Welcome,' said the beauty to the prince in a soft, lilting voice. 'Come and play a game of dice with me.'

'I was actually looking for a stag that I shot,' the young prince replied. 'He ran into your house.'

'Chance has brought you here. You must stay to play this game of chance on the dice board,' she said.

'Okay,' the prince accepted, and sat down across from her.

She set the pieces and also the stakes. 'If you lose, then you must give me your hawk, and if I lose, I'll give you another hawk just like it.'

The prince agreed and threw the first dice. The woman won the game, and the prince handed over his hawk. She took the bird, put it in a hole in the ground, and covered it with a wooden plank. 'How about another game?' the prince asked the woman. Even though he had lost, the game had been very exciting, and also he was smitten by the woman's beauty.

'Okay,' she said. 'This time if you lose, you'll give me your puppy, and if I lose, I'll give you another one just like it.' And she threw the dice. She won again, and the prince handed over his puppy with a sad heart. The woman took the puppy and put it in another hole and covered that up with a plank, as before.

'Can we play again?' the prince asked.

'If you like,' the woman replied. 'But this time you'll have to wager yourself. If you lose, you have to hand yourself over to me, and if you win, I'll give you another young prince exactly like yourself.'

This time, too, the prince lost, and the woman grabbed him and, thrusting him down a hole, covered it securely with a wooden plank. Then the woman changed her form. She was actually a rakshasi who fed on human flesh, and the thought of the young prince's succulent meat made her salivate. But she had just had a big lunch, so she saved him for her next meal.

In the meantime, back in the palace, the younger prince noticed that the leaves of his brother's tree had begun to fall. 'He's in danger,' he told his parents urgently. 'I must go and find him and help him.' The king and queen were loath to let him go, but they reluctantly agreed, and bidding him farewell, begged him to be careful. Before he left, the younger prince, too, planted a tree for his life and gave his parents the same instructions: 'Water it every day. If it is flourishing, know that I am well, if it begins to wither, it means I am unwell, and if it dies, know that I am no more.'

Then the young prince saddled one of his father's horses and raced out of town. Near the forest, on the roadside, he saw puppies playing near their mother, and one of the pups, thinking him to be his brother, called out to him: 'You took my brother with you. Take me too so that I can be with him.' The young prince happily took the puppy with him. A bit further, he saw a nest full of young hawks, and one of them called out to him: 'You took my brother with you. Take me too, so that I can be with him.' The prince happily accepted him, as well. Accompanied by the puppy and the hawk, the prince arrived at the fakir's hut, and pulling out his sword, entered it. The fakir was sitting at an altar, praying. 'What have you done with my brother?' the young prince demanded, advancing towards him, threatening him with his drawn sword. 'If you don't tell me immediately, I'll kill you.'

'I told him not go to the north. A rakshasi lives in the north, and she has captured him. In fact, she has probably eaten him by now.'

Sheathing his sword, the young prince rushed out of the hut and, leaping on his horse, raced north. Suddenly, a beautiful stag shot out in front of him. The prince strung his bow and struck him with an arrow, but the stag kept running, and the prince kept following it, till he arrived at the edge of the forest and saw a house before him. When the stag ran into the house, he followed it but stopped dead in his tracks, because before him was a woman of such exquisite beauty, she took his breath away. But the young prince knew right away that this was the rakshasi that the fakir had mentioned. So he approached her cautiously, not saying a word.

'Welcome,' she said in a dulcet voice. 'Come, play a game of dice with me.'

The young prince nodded and sat down across from her. 'What are the stakes?' he asked.

'If you lose, you'll give me your puppy, and if I lose, I'll give you one just like it.'

'Agreed,' the prince said and threw the dice and won the game. The young woman took off the plank from one hole and handed him the puppy she had put in there earlier. The two puppies excitedly greeted each other, very happy to be united.

'Shall we have another game?' the woman asked.

'Sure. What are the stakes this time?'

'If I win, you'll give me your hawk, but if you win, I'll give you one exactly like it.'

'Agreed,' the prince said and won the game again. The woman opened the second hole and handed over the hawk that she had taken from the older prince. The two hawks, too, were ecstatic to see other.

'One more game?' asked the woman.

'Sure,' said the prince. 'Name the stakes.'

'This time you'll have to wager yourself. If you lose, you'll give yourself to me to do with as I please. But if you win, I'll give you another young man exactly like you.'

'Let's play,' the young prince said evenly, making sure his face did not reveal what he knew.

The young prince won this game, too, and, reluctantly, the woman removed the cover from the third hole and pulled out the elder prince. The two brothers fell into each other's arms, laughing and crying. Then the young prince drew his sword and leapt across the dice board to kill the woman, who had already turned into the rakshasi that she was. But she begged him for mercy. 'If you spare my life, I'll tell you a secret that will save your brother's life.'

The prince put away his sword and asked her what she meant. 'The fakir is not really a fakir. He's a tantric who desires to be perfect. For this purpose he has already sacrificed six young men to goddess Kali. He just needs to sacrifice one more. Seven will make the perfect number, and your brother is the seventh.'

'Don't believe her,' the elder prince cautioned his brother. He remembered the carefree days he had spent with the fakir, and the flowers he used to gather for him every morning for his worship; they didn't seem to be related to any tantric practice.

'If you don't believe me, go to the Kali temple hidden behind the grove of trees. You'll see six skulls there; they're of the young men that the fakir has already sacrificed.'

The two young princes went to the Kali temple to see if the rakshasi was telling the truth. As soon as they entered the dark, cavernous temple, they were greeted with ghastly laughter. Lighting a lamp they held it up but almost dropped it in horror, because staring at them were six laughing skulls placed in six niches in a wall next to an immense stone statue of Kali.

'Why are you laughing?' the elder prince asked the skulls.

'Because soon you'll join us,' the skulls cackled. 'When the fakir completes his final ritual, he'll chop off your head and achieve his objective of perfection.'

'Is there any way I can save myself?' the prince asked. 'Can you help me?'

'Before he severs your head, you must find a way to cut off his head, instead. If you can think of a way, you're saved.'

Thanking the skulls, the princes left the temple, desperately thinking of ways in which they could turn the sword on the fakir. They returned to the hut and told the fakir that they had managed to escape the rakshasi's clutches with great difficulty and asked him if they could both stay with him. The fakir agreed, giving them the same instructions he had given the older prince about the day's routine. So, every morning, the princes gathered flowers for the fakir, and then, for the rest of the day, they were free to do whatever they pleased. They spent the time planning. Then, one morning the fakir asked the elder brother to accompany him, telling the younger one to stay in the hut. 'I just need your brother today,' he said. 'Sure,' the younger prince said. 'Can I just have a word with my brother?' When the fakir nodded and turned away, the younger prince whispered a few words to his brother and handed over his sword to him, which the older prince quickly slipped inside his clothes.

The fakir took the prince northward to the Kali temple hidden in the trees. When they entered, the skulls in the niches did not laugh; today, their gaping eye holes looked at the prince with pity. The fakir led the prince to the statue of Kali and said, 'Bow to the goddess.'

'I don't know how to,' the prince replied. 'I'm a prince. I've never bowed to anyone. Show me how to do it.'

'Watch me,' the fakir said and then folded his hands and bowed his head. As soon as he did, the elder prince drew out the sword and severed his head from his body. The skulls broke out into cacophonous laughter. The goddess was pleased with the sacrifice, and she bestowed perfection on the prince. The skulls were then united with their bodies, which were lying at the base of the temple's wall, and the six young men became alive again.

The two princes returned home to their parents. They not only lived long, happy lives, but the older prince also achieved perfection.

Folktale from Bengal

◆

30

A SUITABLE BOY

The Vedic scholar and brahmarishi, Yajnavalkya, lived in a hermitage on the banks of the Ganga. Every morning he used to go to the river for his bath and morning rituals. One day, after completing his ablutions, as he cupped water in his palm and raised it to his lips to rinse his mouth, a little mouse fell from the beak of a hawk, right into his hand. Yajnavalkya took the little creature who was dying and gently placed it on a peepul leaf. Then he bathed in the holy river again and repeated all the rituals. After he was done, he picked up the mouse and, uttering a mantra, changed the creature into an infant girl.

He brought the girl home and gave her to his wife, who was childless. 'She's a gift from above,' he said. 'The daughter you always wanted.'

Yajnavalkya's wife was delighted. She brought up the little one with care and love, and when the girl passed puberty, she said to her husband, 'It's time for our daughter to be wed. Find her a worthy bridegroom.'

Yajnavalkya replied:

It's true,
the gods shape women.
The Moon gives them purity
of mind and body.
Fire makes them perfect
and the Gandharvas give them pleasant speech.
Women are without blemish.

Before puberty, a girl is pure and brilliant.
After she starts menstruating
her allure blossoms.
Moon performs her rites of marriage,
Fire glows in the passion of her monthly flow.
The Gandharvas make her breasts a shrine.

'Manu has said that, "Girls should be married at a tender age, otherwise they may never find a suitable husband. And a father who doesn't marry his daughter when she is at the right age will be condemned by society."' Looking at his beautiful, virtuous daughter, Yajnavalkya was also reminded of the dharma that when a father goes looking for a suitable boy, he needs to consider seven factors: family and fortune; learning and virtue; good looks, good health and good connections.

Even as he thought this, Yajnavalkya realized who would be the perfect groom for the girl. 'I'll approach Sun and offer him our daughter in marriage,' he said to his wife. He then invoked Sun, and when the Lord of Light appeared, the brahmarishi requested, 'O Sun. This is my daughter. Will you marry her?' Then he turned to his daughter and asked her if she would accept Sun as her husband.

'No,' said the mouse daughter immediately. 'He's blazing with heat. How will I live with him? Please Father, find me someone superior to him.'

'O Lord of Light,' Yajnavalkya asked the Sun. 'Is there someone superior to you?'

'There sure is. Cloud is. When he covers me, I disappear.'

Yajnavalkya then summoned Cloud and showed him to his daughter. 'Will this great bearer of rain suit you, dear daughter?'

'No,' she replied. 'He doesn't please me at all. His complexion is dark and he appears to be so gloomy and heavy-spirited. Find me someone superior to him.'

'Who is superior to you, O Cloud?' Yajnavalkya asked Cloud.

'Wind!' Cloud declared. 'I have no power when he blows.'

Yajnavalkya then called Wind and asked his daughter if she was agreeable to a match with him.

'But he's agitated and unruly, and always on the move. I'll never know where he goes and what he blows. No, Father. I won't marry him.

You'll have to find someone greater than him.'

'Do you know anyone greater than you?' Yajnavalkya asked Wind.

'Of course. That would be Mountain. I'm powerless before him.'

When Mountain was called and presented to the girl, she immediately refused. 'His heart is stony and his demeanour is forbidding. I'll never be happy with him, Father. How could you even think he would be suitable?'

'Who can be greater than you, O Mountain,' Yajnavalkya said apologetically to Mountain. 'But I am a father who must find a groom that my daughter likes. Do you know anyone who surpasses you in greatness?'

'I do,' said Mountain. 'Mouse! He's the only one who can gnaw through my rocky heart.'

When Yajnavalkya summoned Mouse, and that handsome creature stood before his daughter, she was ecstatic. 'Perfect!' she exclaimed. 'He's exactly what I was looking for.'

Yajnavalkya smiled, and, with a mantra, changed his daughter back into a mouse.

The two were ceremoniously married, and Yajnavalkya's mouse daughter and son-in-law went away to live happy lives most suited to them and their kind.

Folktale from the Panchatantra

◆

31

POSTOMONI, THE OPIUM GIRL

There was a rishi who lived alone by the Ganga. His only companion was a mouse that he had found in his palm-tree hut and had befriended. Every evening, after he returned from his meditation and sat down to relax, the mouse would come and sit at his feet, nibbling away on a piece of guava or tal seed or whatever the rishi gave him. The Brahmin became very fond of the mouse and often talked to him, wishing that the animal could respond and communicate with him. So, one day, cupping water in his palm, the holy man uttered a mantra and bestowed a human voice on the mouse. After that, the rishi was never lonely, because he was able to talk with his rodent companion.

One evening, as the rishi settled down to eat his supper of mango and lotus seeds, and the mouse came and sat at his feet, he gave him some seeds and asked him how he was faring. 'Not so well anymore,' the mouse replied. 'Every day, when you leave, a cat comes into the hut, and I have to look for places to hide. If she ever sees me, I know she'll pounce on me and eat me. How I wish I were a big cat, so that I could deal with her on equal ground. You've been very kind to me. Would you do me another kindness and change me into a cat?'

'Of course,' said the rishi, and taking another palmful of mantra water sprinkled it on the mouse, turning him into a large grey cat. The mouse was ecstatic and could hardly wait for the morning when his adversary would come looking for him.

Many days passed, and then one evening, placing a saucer of milk before the mouse-cat, the rishi asked, 'How goes it, dear friend? I hope you're enjoying the life of a cat.'

'It was a wonderful life for a while, but it isn't any more. I live in constant fear. Every day when you leave, a pack of dogs come and bark and sniff around. I know they smell me, and I tremble at the thought of what'll happen to me, if I so much as step outside the hut. You've been so very generous and kind, giving me a human voice and changing me into a cat, but please could you do me just one more favour and change me into a dog? Then I won't be afraid to face my foe.'

The rishi did his water and mantra thing again and the cat became a ferocious dog.

For a while, the rishi and dog lived in happy companionship, but then, one day, the dog complained to the rishi that he was tired of being a dog. 'I'm hungry all the time,' he said. 'There's never enough food for me. I thank you for sharing your food with me, but a bowl of milk and tit-bits of fruits and nuts just don't satisfy me anymore. I see apes out on the trees, who swing from mango tree to guava to bel to banana. They can eat to their heart's content. How I wish I were an ape.'

The rishi was a kind-hearted man and he hated to see his friend's pain, so, once again, he did the necessary with water and mantra, and the dog changed into an ape. Immediately, he swung out of the house and disappeared among the trees. He was happy, because living out in the open gave him a sense of freedom, and having so many fruit-laden trees at his disposal made him feel that he was in food heaven. But soon, summer came. The sun shone down with such intensity that the mouse-ape felt like peeling off his fur. Sitting in the meagre shade of banana leaves, he would see wild boars frolicking in the water on the banks of the Ganga and envy them.

One morning, trying to catch the morning breeze as he climbed up a tree, he saw his rishi friend walking on the bank. 'Are you going for your morning bath, dear friend?' the ape called down.

'Yes,' the rishi said looking up at the black form of his friend in the dawn sun. 'And I can hardly wait to get into the water. It's a hot morning.'

'You're telling me,' the ape said, his voice filled with regret.

'So, is the fruit feast as satisfying as you imagined?'

'Oh yes,' the ape replied. 'But the heat is unbearable. I see the wild boars who come to the Ganga ghat and cavort in the cool water all day. I wish I could join them.'

'I know what you mean,' said the rishi. 'This summer is hotter than I've ever known.'

'Would you...I mean...is it at all possible that you'll consider doing one very last favour, dear friend? I think the life of a wild boar is the coolest. Would you do that for a friend? You've been more than kind, and I hate to ask you again, but, this last time...'

'All right,' the rishi said. 'Come on down, and I'll see what I can do.'

The ape climbed down and sat eagerly before the rishi, who then tipped his water jar and, taking a palmful of water, read a mantra that changed the ape into a wild boar.

All through the summer, the mouse-boar splashed in the water and rolled in the wet sand, grateful to his rishi friend for saving him from the scorching heat. Then, when fall came, he joined a sounder and began moving from forest to forest. One day, the king of the land came into the forest, where the wild boars were, and began hunting them. He was sitting on a majestic royal elephant that had a silk embroidered cover on his back and was fitted with a golden howdah. Two of the boars were killed by the king's arrows that day, and the rest of the sounder scattered, along with the mouse-boar. All day he ran, and in the evening he arrived at his friend's hut again.

'I can't take this,' he begged his friend. 'I'll surely be killed by the king. But, oh, how beautiful was the elephant he rode. So kingly, so majestic, and the only person who ever rides him is the king himself. I have finally realized what I really, really wish to be. I want to be a royal elephant. If you make me an elephant, I'll never ask you for another thing. I promise.'

With water and mantra, the rishi made the boar a regal elephant.

The mouse-elephant thanked the Brahmin and went towards the city with a plan. He remained in the fringe of trees bordering the palace till he saw the king. Then he sauntered out and trumpeted, and let the king's men catch him without any resistance. When the king came to examine him, his heart pounded with excitement, but he stood majestically, showing off his proud trunk, curving tusks, and well-proportioned limbs. The king declared that he should be trained as a royal mount, and the elephant catchers put him in the royal stables. There, he began to live in style, eating expensive foods, bathing in scented water, and wearing covers of soft fabrics with paisley patterns of red, yellow and blue. From then on, whenever the king desired a ride, he called upon his new elephant, and the mouse-elephant felt like he had achieved his life's goal.

One day, the queen expressed a desire to bathe in the river, so the king ordered his favourite royal elephant to be readied. The mouse-elephant was not happy at this turn of events, because he could not bear the thought of a woman riding him. When the queen climbed into the howdah fitted on his back, he gave a loud trumpet and raised his front legs in affront. The queen fell down, and the king came running to her. He picked her up, kissed her and checked her for injuries, and then kissed her again and carried her in his arms into the palace.

Oh to be that queen, the elephant thought. Loved and cossetted by the king, living in the lap of luxury. What a life! That evening he broke his ropes and ran out of the royal stable into the forest. Arriving at the palm tree hut of his rishi friend, he banged on the door with his trunk.

When the rishi opened the door, he recognized the elephant. 'Welcome, my dear friend,' he said. 'You look grand, dressed up as the king's elephant. Have you come to show me your finery?'

'No...actually...' and the elephant told the Brahmin all about the queen and how he felt insulted by her but then realized that no one on earth could be happier than the queen. 'Now, that's a life worth living,' he declared. 'The life of a queen! If you make me a queen, I'll never ask you for anything else.'

The rishi laughed. 'I can change you into anything you like, my friend, but even I can't make you a queen; for that you need a king to marry you. But here's what I can do. I can change you into a beautiful young woman, and then it's up to you to secure your own king. What do you say?'

'Yes,' said the elephant.

The rishi performed the ritual, and the elephant was transformed into the most enchanting, intoxicatingly beautiful woman in the world. The rishi named her Postomoni, the poppy seed girl. She began living with the rishi in his hut, and she was quite happy to be back home, but every day she waited for the king of her dreams to come and make her his queen.

One day a king did come. He had separated from his hunting party and was lost. The mouse-woman was at the window, looking out, when she saw him in the courtyard, and she knew immediately that this handsome man on a regal horse was her king. Going outside, she coyly asked him who he was, and when she found out that he was, indeed, a king, she invited him into the hut.

'Who are you?' the king asked her, hardly able to take his eyes off her loveliness. 'Are you a rishi's daughter?'

'No,' the young woman replied. 'I, too, am a princess by birth. The rishi who adopted me told me what happened to me. You see, my father's kingdom was conquered, and he and my mother had to flee. They hid in the forest, but a tiger ate my father. My mother, who was pregnant with me, died as soon as she gave birth to me. I lay on the ground all by myself, hungry and helpless, but hanging from the tree under which I was born, was a beehive from which honey was dripping, and it fell into my mouth. That's what kept me alive till the rishi found me. He brought me home, and this is where I've been living all my life.'

'I'm in love with you, O beautiful maiden,' the king said. 'And now that I know you are also of royal blood, I want to make you my queen.' Postomoni readily agreed, and she and the king were married that very day with the rishi's blessings. After that the two left for the king's capital.

Back in his palace, the king deposed his first queen and installed his beautiful new bride as the chief queen. The two of them lived happily for a while, and all went well for Postomoni, but then one day, as she stood by a well, she suddenly felt dizzy and fell in and died. The king was heartbroken. He ordered his men to bring out the body of his beloved queen so that she could be cremated with full royal honours. But just then, the rishi appeared. 'Leave Postomoni in the well,' he advised the king.

'How can you say that,' said the shocked king. 'She was not only of royal blood but also my queen, and she deserves last rites that are suitable for her status.'

'She was not of royal blood or your queen. She was a mouse that I changed into a cat, a dog, an ape, a wild boar, an elephant, and finally a beautiful maiden. Let her be. Instal your own queen as chief queen again, and let the mouse remain in the well.'

'Whoever she was, I loved her,' the king replied, 'And I want to memorialize her.'

'Then have the well filled with soil,' the rishi instructed. 'From her flesh and bones a plant will grow out of the well; it'll be a poppy with beautiful red flowers that will bear her name—Posto. People will use the seeds of that plant to create a powerful opiate. Whoever uses it will have the qualities of all the forms that Postomoni desired in her life. He will be restless like a mouse, sly like a cat, suspicious like a dog, mischievous like a monkey, filthy like a boar, powerful like an elephant, and oblivious like a queen.

And that is the story of opium.

Folktale from Bengal

◆

32

THE NEPHEW

A long time ago, in the Dambo Rongjeng area of upper Garo Hills in Meghalaya, there used to be an old Achik village. Most of the people who lived in it worked in jhum fields, and during the cropping season, they would leave the village to live in temporary huts near the fields. Hence, during the time they were gone, the village would be deserted.

One time, all the villagers left the village except for one man, his wife and infant son. The man was very sick, and his condition was worsening day by day. His wife was taking care of him, but there wasn't much she could do. One morning, seeing her husband in excruciating pain, she decided to get him some medicine from the apothecary who was on the other side of the village, past a small wood. Strapping her baby on her back and her dao—the sword she always carried for protection—to her side, she left the house. On the way, as she was crossing the wood, she began to think about her husband. If he is not going to recover, then maybe it is better for him that he die, she thought. I can't bear to see him in so much pain. 'Either take away his pain, or take him,' she whispered. Then, she scolded herself for thinking these thoughts and hurried on.

On the way back from the apothecary, she was waylaid by a man. 'How is uncle today?' he asked her. Looking at him, the woman felt a strange fear course through her body, although there was really nothing fearful about him. He was big-boned and had a dark face, but he was dressed in the ordinary clothes of a poor farmer. His voice was a bit gruff, but his speech was cordial. His eyes were sharp, perhaps too sharp, but that could have been a play of sunlight.

'Who are you?' she asked him, her hand reaching for the dao strapped to her side.

'I am your husband's nephew,' the man replied, warily eyeing her dao. 'I heard uncle is sick, and I've come to meet him.'

The wife knew all her husband's nephews, and she couldn't recall ever seeing this man.

'Can I come this evening?' he asked in a persuasive voice.

Surely there can't be any harm in that, the woman thought. It may even do her husband some good to receive a visitor, especially now when there was no one in the village to visit him.

'Fine,' she said to the man. 'Come in the evening.'

'Thank you. I will be there, but would you please do me a favour? Would you remove all metal objects from the house like knives and swords?'

What a strange request, the wife thought, but what was even stranger was that, despite herself, she found herself promising him that she would do as he requested. And, as soon as she arrived home, she gathered all knives and swords and other sharp metal objects and took them behind the house.

That evening, when the knock sounded on the door, and the woman went to let in the visitor, a wave of fear passed through her again, and she quickly drew back. The nephew stepped through the door and, as he took his first step into the hut, the sick man drew his last breath. The wife did not know of this; she thought her husband had quietened down because there was a guest in the house.

'I'll sleep beside my uncle tonight,' the nephew said, and, spreading a sheet near the sick bed, he lay down. The wife took her infant child and sat near the hearth, as far away as possible from the man. She remained awake for a while, keeping her eye on the nephew, but soon the soft heat from the hearth lulled her to sleep.

She was awakened in the middle of the night by the baby's loud wail. Groggy with sleep, her eyes half closed, she began rocking her son back to sleep, when a hazy, phosphorescent light in the middle of the room caught her attention. It was an eerie light that seemed to be emanating from the nephew's body, but he wasn't the man who had come into her hut; he was a large, hairy creature with one feral eye in the centre of his forehead. He was sitting on her husband's bed, crunching on the bones of a human leg; beside him was her husband's half-eaten body.

For a second, the woman sat transfixed with terror. She couldn't move, she couldn't breathe, she couldn't scream. Then her boy's wailing jolted her. She quickly wrapped her arms around him and shot up on legs that were shaking so badly, she could hardly stand, but, somehow, she was able to dash out of the hut. Once outside, she ran as she had never run before, towards the jhum fields, not stopping till she reached the temporary huts to which the villagers had moved. There she crumpled on the ground and fainted. When she regained consciousness, she saw the friendly faces of the villagers looking down at her. 'What happened?' they asked her, and she narrated the events of the evening.

'You invited a Mehmang Gitting to your house,' one of the village elders said. 'A ghoul. We Achik call these bad spirits of the woods that feed on human flesh Tsine Nat. The only things that they are afraid of are sharp metal objects. They won't go into any house that has a sword or knife or even touch anyone who is holding such an object.'

Some brave men decided to investigate and went back to the woman's hut in the village. They found no trace of the Tsine Nat or of the husband. It seemed that the creature had devoured every last bit of the man—bones, flesh skin, hair, blood—so much so that even the sheet on which the sick man had lain was gone.

Folktale from the Garo tribe

◆

33

DEER OF DESIRE

It was a beautiful spring morning in Panchavati. Kanaka, champa, asoka, and mango trees were in full bloom. Sita was outside her hut, plucking flowers to make garlands. Suddenly, she saw a deer grazing nearby that was unlike any that she had seen before. Hundreds of pearly spots sparkled on its coat, which looked like rippling silver; the animal was so dazzling, it seemed like it had a sun shining from inside him.

'Come quickly,' she called to Rama and Lakshmana. 'Come and see this wonderful creature. I've never seen anything like it.'

The brothers came to look. Lakshmana was immediately suspicious. 'This can't be a deer,' he said. 'It's not possible for deer to have spots that look like jewels. I think this is the rakshasa, Maricha, Ravana's uncle. He's a shape-shifter and can take any form at will. He's led many kings and ascetics to their death with his enchanting forms. Be careful,' he warned his elder brother and sister-in-law. 'There must be a reason why he's put on this magic show.'

But Sita was captivated. 'How can you say it's not a deer? There are so many different kinds of deer in this forest. It could be of a variety we've never seen before. I want it,' she said to Rama, pouting her lovely lips. 'Please catch it for me. I want it as a pet, and when our exile is over, I'll take it back with me to Ayodhya. Everyone will be amazed by it. And if you can't catch it alive, I can make a mat of his silver and golden skin. Can you imagine what pleasure it'll give us to sit on it?'

Rama, too, was curious. He had seen many variety of deer in Panchavati forest—Kadali and Priyaki that had the softest skin, and the most wondrous Mriga that also wandered in heaven and had a star named after it. But this deer, with its sapphire-coloured horns, tongue that darted like lightning, and belly shining like a conch shell, was truly unique. It must be caught, he concluded. If it's real then Sita will have her desire, and if it's a deception sent to entrap us or the ascetics of the forest, then we need to put an end to it. 'I'm going to catch it and bring it to make Sita happy,' Rama said to Lakshmana. 'Stay here and protect Sita while I'm gone. I won't be long. One arrow is all it'll take.'

Strapping on his sword and two quivers and picking up his triple-curved bow, Ram approached the deer with stealth. But as he drew near, the deer sprinted off a few paces and stood looking at Rama with jewelled eyes. When Rama moved towards it, the deer took a leap further into the forest, disappearing from sight. Rama followed in the direction it had leapt and saw it again in the distance. It was standing and peering at him again, but when Rama moved, it leapt again. In this way, it disappeared and appeared repeatedly, enticing Rama, till it had led him far away from the hermitage.

Soon Rama began to tire and, deciding to end the chase, he pulled out a missile with a serpent head that never missed its mark, and shot it at the deer. The weapon pierced the creature's heart, and with one last leap that was as high as a palmyra tree, the deer crashed to the ground with a roar. But the bloodied body that fell was not that of a deer; it was of the rakshasa, Maricha. He was breathing with difficulty, and with his last breath, he uttered a distressed cry in a human voice that sounded exactly like Rama's: 'Oh Sita! Oh Lakshmana!'

Rama stood stunned. Lakshmana was right, he thought. This was a trick meant to deceive me. But what of Sita? Had she heard the call? Did she hear me calling her in distress? How would she react? Fear piercing his heart, Rama hefted his bow and, leaving the rakshasa on the ground, he rushed back to the hermitage.

But it was already too late, because Sita had, indeed, heard her husband's troubled voice calling out. She pleaded with Lakshmana to go to his brother's aid, but he refused to leave her alone.

'I know why you won't go. You're an enemy of Rama, disguised as his brother,' Sita said. 'Otherwise how can you stand here unperturbed by his plight.'

Lakshmana knew Sita spoke harsh words only because she was filled with anxiety. 'Your husband is unconquerable,' he reassured her. 'There isn't a single being in this world—naag, asura, gandharva, animal or human— who can hurt Rama. Don't be afraid for him. Besides, I'm certain that wasn't his voice we heard. It was a trick played on us by some rakshasa, like an illusory city in the sky. Once Rama has killed the creature, he'll surely return. I can't go to him. You are a sacred trust placed in my charge by my high-souled brother. I dare not leave you. When we killed the asura, Khara and his forces in this forest, I fear we made many enemies. You're not safe by yourself.'

But Sita was too worried to listen to Lakshmana's reasons. 'It seems to me that the enemy we need to fear is you,' she berated. 'I'm convinced that you have followed us into the forest with ulterior motives. Maybe you have been planted by Bharata, the usurper. Or is it that you have designs on me? Perhaps, this is the moment you've been planning all along—to be alone with me.'

Sita's words struck Lakshmana like red-hot steel arrows piercing his heart. He burned with indignity and hurt, but his loyalty to his brother protected him like a shield. He joined his hands and bowed before his sister-in-law. 'You're like a devi to me. I'll not respond to your accusations. I think it's the nature of women to be fickle and hard-hearted and to create discord. Now, I call upon the sprits of the forest to bear witness to my words. Even though I've spoken the truth and followed my brother's command, you have distrusted me and castigated me with harsh words. So, I'll leave you and go to Rama. May the forest spirits protect you, but the bad omens make me fearful. I hope I'll still see you here when I return with Rama.' And then Lakshmana left, but even as he walked away, he couldn't help looking back at her one more time, a sense of foreboding in his heart.

This was exactly the opportunity that Ravana was seeking. Quickly donning the disguise of a wandering sadhu—wearing ochre-coloured garments and dreadlocks and carrying umbrella, staff and kamandalu—he went towards Rama and Sita's hut. He may have been in disguise, but the forest recognized who he was. As he strode through it, the trees stopped waving, the wind stopped blowing, and the water in River Godavari became still. By the time Ravana reached Sita's hut, the whole forest was suspended in fear. Standing outside the hut, he stole a quick glance inside to see what Sita was doing. Dressed in yellow silk, she was sitting abjectly on the floor with tears flowing down her cheeks. Even in her anguish she was as lovely as the full moon, and Ravana was pierced with darts of desire. Moving to the entrance of the hut, he began chanting Vedic mantras, and when Sita appeared, he asked innocently: 'Who are you, O lady who appears to be a goddess? This forest is the home of asuras and rakshasas. What are you doing here all by yourself? Aren't you afraid?'

Taking him to be a wandering sadhu, Sita invited Ravana into the hut with the respect due to a Brahmin guest. She offered him a seat and brought him food, and then she told him who she was and how she and her husband and brother-in-law were living out their fourteen years of exile in this forest. Then she asked him his name.

Ravana continued sitting in a relaxed pose so as not to startle Sita. 'I am Ravana,' he said conversationally, 'King of Lanka, the celebrated ruler of the asuras. I want to make you my wife. Come with me to Lanka, my capital, that is built on a hill in the midst of the sea. There, you will reign as my queen, and five thousand maid servants, decked in ornaments, will wait on you.'

Sita stood up in shock, her limbs trembling. 'How dare you?' she cried. 'I'm Rama's wife and I have vowed to always follow him. You are a jackal coveting a lioness. You dare covet the beloved consort of Rama? You seek to extract a tooth from the jaws of a hungry and powerful lion. You seek to carry away a blazing fire in a piece of cloth. You desire to cross the sea with a rock tied around your neck. Laying a hand on me is like treading on the sharp tip of an iron pike. Even if you get me, you won't be able to keep me, for I am the consort of the powerful, invincible Rama. Why would I want you? He's an elephant among men, and you are like a puny cat; he's pure like sandalwood and you're dirty like mud. Go away. What you desire will never happen.'

Enraged, Ravana jumped to his feet and expanding his mountainous chest, roared, 'I'm the ten-headed brother of Kubera. On hearing my name, everyone—gods, asuras, human beings—trembles in fear. I can lift the earth with my bare hands, drink up the ocean in one gulp, torment the sun with heat, and kill Death himself.' And even as he spoke, his body transformed into a gigantic form with ten heads and twenty arms. Sita watched in awe, her throat drying, but she did not reveal her fear. 'I don't care who you are,' she said.

Coming back to his normal form, Ravana now tried to cajole Sita with soft words. 'I'm a husband worthy of you, O beautiful lady. I'll treat you well and keep you like a queen. Forget your silly husband, who has been banished from his kingdom and is keeping you in a forest full of wild animals. Set your affection on me and I'll make you happy.'

Without saying another word, Sita pointed him towards the entrance of the hut.

Ravana grabbed Sita and, clutching her hair with his left hand and her thighs with his right, he strode outside. Then, calling his Pushpak

Viman, he threw Sita in it and took off. As they rose into the skies in the golden aerial chariot, Sita cried in an anguished voice, 'O Rama!'

Myth from the Ramayana

◆

34

WEAVERS CAN NEVER GO TO HEAVEN

There was a rich weaver who made a good living by weaving cloth. He also had a farm, and in this, he grew succulent vegetables and the finest grain. He was very proud of this farm, but one day, he discovered that some big beast had stomped across part of the crop and almost destroyed it. Feeling distraught, he went into the village to ask if anyone knew the culprit who had let loose an animal in his farm.

'No idea,' was the response he received from whomever he asked.

The next day, the farm was trampled some more, and the following day, even more. By now the weaver was seething with anger at the miscreant, and he decided that he would catch him in action. So that night he stayed at the farm, waiting. A little after midnight, he saw a very large bird fly into the farm and land in the section where the crop was still standing and begin grazing, uncaring of the vegetables or paddy it crushed under its massive claws. Warily, the weaver approached the bird, and as he drew near it, he realized that it wasn't a bird at all but a huge elephant with wings. It was a magnificent creature with seven trunks and a pure white body. The weaver knew instantly that this was Airavata, Lord Indra's elephant, because he looked exactly as the holy books described him.

When the winged elephant had had his fill, he spread his wings and got ready to take flight, but just then the weaver grabbed his tail. Indra's elephant took off, and the weaver too ascended with him—all the way to Indra's heaven. When he arrived in Indraloka, the weaver let go of the elephant's tail and looked around. He saw beautiful apsaras dancing and singing, gandharvas—the celestial musicians—playing enchanting music, and resplendent gods with golden crowns, sitting on golden thrones, drinking ambrosia. No one paid any heed to the little human who had surreptitiously arrived in heaven, so much so that when food trays were passed around, the weaver helped himself to celestial food and no one cared.

For the remaining night and all of the following day, the weaver enjoyed heaven. At night, when Airavata spread his wings to fly down to his farm again, the weaver grabbed his tail and returned to earth.

The next morning the weaver excitedly gathered his family and friends and told them where he had spent the night and day. Everyone was amazed.

'I've been thinking,' he said. 'Why should we live here on earth when we can live in heaven? Let's all go to heaven.'

So that night when Airavata finished his meal on the weaver's farm and spread his wings to fly, the weaver grabbed on to his tail. His wife grabbed the weaver's legs; their children grabbed their mother's legs; and, one after the other, in a chain, all the weaver's relatives and friends grabbed the legs of the one above them and began to fly to heaven.

On his way up, the weaver began to think: I should have brought my loom with me; that way, I could have set up shop in heaven and sold cloth to the gods. They would surely pay in gold, and I would very soon be as rich as Kubera, the god of wealth. I'm an idiot. I really should have picked up my loom, he thought, and wrung his hands in regret. And, instantly, the whole human chain fell to the earth.

That is why they say a weaver can never go to heaven!

Folktale from Punjab

◆

35

ONE JAR OF OIL

Sheikh Chilli[17] was idling under a tree one day, when an oil merchant passed by. The man was carrying a big earthenware jar of oil on his head that he was taking to the market, and he had become quite exhausted. Seeing Sheikh Chilli doing nothing, he called to him, 'If you carry this jar of oil to the market for me, I'll give you one anna.' Chilli agreed and took the jar on his head.

It was quite a distance to the market, and on the way, Chilli began thinking about what he would do with the one anna that he would earn. I'll buy some eggs, he thought. Those eggs will hatch and I'll have chickens, and the chickens will lay more eggs, which will also hatch, and I'll have more chickens. When I have enough chickens, I'll sell them and buy a goat, and when the goat has kids, I'll sell them and buy a cow. The cow will give milk, and I'll sell that milk and make enough money to buy a pair of buffaloes. Then, I'll become a farmer and plough my fields with the buffaloes. Soon, I'll have lots of wheat to sell, and with the money I make from it, I'll become a rich man. I'll then buy a big house and marry a beautiful woman. We'll have many children, and I'll send my children to school. But I'll need to make sure that they don't grow up to be spendthrifts. When they say to me, 'Baba give me an anna,' I'll shake my head to tell them no. And, imagining how he'd say no, Sheikh Chilli vigorously shook his head. The jar of oil he was carrying on his head fell to the ground and broke into a hundred pieces, the oil flowing in a thick dark stream down the road.

'Now look what you've done, you idiot!' the merchant chided Sheikh Chilli. 'Who'll pay for this loss?'

Sheikh Chilli looked at the merchant indignantly. 'You're worried about one jar of oil. I've just lost my buffaloes, my field, my wife, and my children.'

Sheikh Chilli folktale

◆

36

THE FOOLISH RICH MAN

One day, while Jesus was speaking to a crowd, a man called out to him, 'Can you tell my brother to divide our inheritance?'

Jesus replied, 'Friend, who has assigned me the role of judge or arbitrator?' Then he said to the people, 'Beware of greed! Guard yourself against it, because even when a man has more than he needs, he wants more, and yet his wealth does not give him life.' And he told them a parable:

'There was a rich man who always had a plentiful harvest. He wondered: what should I do? I don't have the space to store all this abundance. Then he said to himself, 'I know what I'll do. I'll pull down the existing storehouses and build bigger ones. Then I'll store all my corn and other goods in them.' Feeling pleased at the thought, he said to himself, 'When I have stored enough to last me many years, I will say to myself, "You have plenty laid by. Now enjoy yourself; eat, drink and take life easy."'

But God said to him, 'You foolish man. Tonight you will die. What use is your money? After you're gone, who will get it?'

This is what happens to the man who hoards wealth; in God's eyes, he is a poor man.

Parable from the New Testament

◆

37

FEATHERS OF GOLD

Once upon a time the Bodhisattva was born as a Brahmin in Banaras. He and his wife had three daughters, Nanda, Nandavati and Sundarinanda.

After he died, he was born again as a goose that had feathers of real, hammered gold. Even though he was in bird form, he retained the consciousness of his earlier life and remembered clearly that he had been a human being and a father of three daughters. Wondering how his family was faring without him, he went looking for them and found them living in the same house, but in abject poverty, wholly dependent on charity. His heart filled with compassion at their condition, and he thought that if he could give them one of his feathers whenever they needed it, it would ease their misery.

One day, he flew to his former house and alighted on a beam supporting the ceiling. His former wife and daughters were amazed to see this beautiful bird inside their house and asked him who he was.

'I'm your father,' he told the girls, 'Reborn as this golden goose. I'm distressed at the hardship you have had to suffer, so I've come to help. I'll give you my golden feathers, one at a time, and you can sell each one for enough money to keep you in comfort.' Then he drew out one feather of pure gold and threw it down. The women promptly picked it up, and wrapping it protectively in a towel, took it to the market, where they sold it for a lot of money.

The goose bid them farewell and flew off, but he returned often to give them another one of his feathers. Soon, his former family was living quite prosperously. Then one day, the mother said to her daughters, 'I don't trust this goose. We are so dependent on him. What if he doesn't return? What will we do then? I have an idea: next time he comes, let's take all his feathers; that way we'll never have to worry about his comings and goings or about money. We'll be set for life.'

'But if we take all his feathers, he'll be in pain,' the daughters cried. 'We can't bear to hurt our father.' They refused to do as their mother asked.

The mother, however, was consumed with greed. She called the golden goose, and when he came into the house, she grabbed him with both hands and began plucking out all his feathers. But each feather she plucked turned into an ordinary goose feather in her hands. What she didn't know was that the golden goose was born with the condition that his feathers would remain golden only if he gave them away voluntarily, but if someone took them by force, they would lose their gold.

Shorn of his feathers, the goose flapped his bare wings and tried to fly away, but he couldn't. The wife pushed him into a cage and locked him up, thinking that maybe when the feathers grew back, they would be golden; for this reason she fed him every day to keep him alive. His feathers did grow back, but they were not golden; they were just plain white, made of ordinary keratin. Feeling cheated and angry, the woman unlocked the cage and shooed the goose out of her house. The Bodhisattva flew away to his own abode and never came back.

Folktale from the Jatakas

◆

38

Thirty Pieces of Silver

When the high priests were searching for Jesus to arrest him, one of Jesus's twelve disciples, Judas Iscariot, went to them and said, 'What will you give me to betray him to you?'

'Thirty pieces of silver,' they replied. And from that moment of greed onwards, Judas began to look for an opportunity to betray Jesus.

On the first day of Passover, Jesus's disciples came to him and asked, 'Where would you like us to prepare for your Passover supper?'

He answered, 'Go into Jerusalem to the house of such a man and tell him, "The Teacher says, my time is near; I will keep Passover at your house with my disciples."' They did as Jesus had bid them and then prepared for Passover. On the evening of the meal, as Jesus sat down to eat with all twelve of his disciples, he said to them, 'I want to tell you that one amongst you will betray me.'

They all looked at him in anguish and asked him one by one, 'Will it be I, Lord?'

He answered, 'It is one of you who has dipped his hand in the bowl. The Son of Man will go the way that the scriptures have determined for him, but that one by whom the Son of Man will be betrayed shall suffer. It would have been better if that man had never been born.'

Then Judas spoke, knowing very well he was that man: 'Rabbi, is it me?'

Jesus replied, 'It is.'

After Passover supper, they went out to the Mount of Olives, and there, Jesus said to his disciples, 'Tonight, on my account, you will all break faith with me; it is written: "the shepherd will be struck down and his flock will be scattered."'

But Peter, one of Jesus's first disciples, said, 'Even if I must die with you, I'll never disown you.'

Jesus replied, 'I tell you, Peter, the cock will not crow this day until you have denied three times that you know me.'

Jesus then went with his disciples to a place called Gethsemane. 'Sit here,' he said to them, 'while I pray,' and taking Peter and two sons of Zebedee with him, he stepped away from the others. Suddenly, he was overcome with sorrow, and he asked the three to stay with him, but then he himself drew away a stone's throw and, kneeling down, began to pray: 'My Father, if it is possible, let this cup pass me by. But what I wish is not of consequence; let your will be done.' Now an angel from heaven appeared and brought him strength, and Jesus prayed more urgently, breaking out in such a sweat that drops from it fell to the ground like clots of blood.

When he rose from prayer and came to the disciples, he found them asleep, worn out by grief. 'Why are you sleeping?' he asked Peter. 'Rise and pray that you may be spared the test. The spirit is willing but the flesh is weak.' Then he went away a second time and prayed, 'Father, if I must drink from this cup, then let your will be done.' This time, too, when he returned to the disciples, they were sleeping, so he went away a third time to pray, and this time when he came back, he awakened the disciples. 'It is time,' he said. 'I have been betrayed to men who are full of sin. Come. Wake up and let us go. The betrayer will be here soon.'

While he was still speaking, Judas appeared. He had brought with him a crowd of men who were carrying swords and canes and had been sent by the High Priest and the elders. Judas said to them, 'Watch me. I'll kiss the man you want, and you'll know who it is. You can then catch him.' And, stepping forward, he called loudly, 'Hail Rabbi!' and kissed Jesus.

'Friend,' Jesus responded. 'Do what you are here to do.'

The men who were with Judas grabbed Jesus while his own followers watched in confusion and distress. One of them pulled out his sword and struck a servant of the High Priest, cutting off the man's ear. But Jesus said to him, 'Put away your sword. All who take up the sword, die by the sword. If I want, I can appeal to my Father and he will send down twelve legions of angels to rescue me, but then how will the scriptures be fulfilled? What is written, must be.' Then he touched the servant's ear and made it whole again. After that, he turned to the crowd and said to the men, 'Am I a criminal that you have come with swords and cudgels to arrest me? I sat with you in the temple, teaching you day after day; you didn't catch me then. Why now? I tell you, this is all happening to fulfil the written words of the prophets. So be it.'

The disciples then all ran away, and the men who had come with Judas arrested Jesus and brought him to the High Priest's house, where the elders and Council members were gathered. Peter followed them at a distance, and when everyone assembled in the courtyard, he too joined them. The Council members tried to charge Jesus with a crime that would bring about a death sentence, but none of their allegations could be proved. Then two men testified that Jesus had once declared he could dismantle God's temple and rebuild it in three days. 'Is that right?' the High Priest demanded of Jesus. 'What do you have to say to that?' But Jesus remained silent. 'Speak!' the High Priest shouted. 'Are you the Messiah?'

'These are your words,' Jesus replied quietly. 'All I will say is that the Son of Man will sit in Heaven on the right hand side of God, for that is his true place.'

'Blasphemy!' the High Priest accused.

Then the people gathered there also began shouting, 'Blasphemy!' Amidst them was a serving maid who saw Peter and recognized him. 'This man was with him too,' she cried. But Peter denied it: 'Woman,' he said, 'I do not know him,' and he quickly headed towards the doorway. But another maidservant saw him there and also knew him. 'You were with Jesus of Nazareth. I saw you with him,' she said. Peter denied it once again and, with an oath, declared that he did not know Jesus. A little later, someone else noticed him and said, 'You also are one of them. You are Galilean. I can tell from your speech.' But Peter cursed and shouted, 'Man, I have no idea what you are talking about.' At that moment, while he was still speaking, the cock crew, and Peter recalled Jesus's words: 'This day, before the cock crows, you will deny me three times.' He quickly left the house, and when he was outside, he broke down and wept bitterly.

When morning came, the chief priests and elders conferred to discuss how they would implement the death sentence. Putting Jesus in chains, they took him away and handed him over to Pilate, the Roman governor.

When Judas found out that Jesus had been condemned and would be put to death, he was consumed with remorse at what he had done. Going to the chief priests and elders, he tried to return the thirty silver pieces. 'He's innocent,' he pleaded. 'I'm a sinner. Because of me, an innocent man will be put to death.'

'That's your problem,' the priests said. 'It's not our concern.'

Judas flung the thirty pieces of silver on the temple floor. Then going outside, he hanged himself.

Myth from the New Testament

◆

39

THE SPEAKING TREE

In a town lived two friends named Paapbudhi and Dharmabudhi. They were quite wealthy, but while Dharmabudhi was content with his life and his material acquisitions, Paapbudhi was always hankering for more. He was also jealous of Dharmabudhi's intelligence and sense of contentment.

One day Paapbudhi said to Dharmabudhi, 'Your talents are wasted here, my friend. Why don't you go to some other town and take advantage of opportunities there. I can come with you, if you like.' Dharmabudhi liked the idea of going to a new town and having new experiences, so he agreed, and both friends set off. They lived in the new town for many years, and there, with Dharmabudhi's astute mind, they not only availed themselves of many opportunities but were also very successful. When they had amassed a lot of wealth, they decided it was time to return home.

As they were nearing their hometown, Paapbudhi said to his friend, 'You know, we are carrying a lot of money. If our relatives find out, they'll all want a share of it. Why don't we hide some of it and return home with only a little bit?'

'That's a great idea,' Dharmabudhi said. 'Where should we hide it?'

They walked around, looking for a suitable place. Near the edge of a forest, Paapbudhi spotted a huge tree that had a cavernous hole in the trunk. 'I think this would be a good place,' he said to Dharmabudhi.

'Here, in the hole of the tree trunk? Are you sure?'

'No, no. Not in the hole, but in the ground near the tree. This will be our landmark so that when we come back to retrieve our money, we'll be able to find it easily.'

'That's a brilliant idea, friend,' Dharmabudhi said, and the two friends dug a deep pit, put most of their money in a large pot, lowered it into the pit, and then packed it with soil. Then they went home, carrying only a small amount.

A few days later, Paapbudhi returned to the spot and dug out the pot. Then he went to Dharmabudhi and said to him, 'I've run out of money and need some more. Come with me so that I can get some from the stash.'

The two friends went to the spot where they had buried their money and began digging. They shovelled all around the tree, but they couldn't find the pot.

'You're a thief,' said Paapbudhi, turning on Dharmabudhi. 'You've stolen all our money.'

'I didn't steal it. I swear.' Dharmabudhi was very distressed at losing the wealth, but more so at his friend's accusations. 'How dare you call me a thief? Perhaps, you took the money.'

'Are you calling *me* a thief?' Paapbudhi shouted and attacked Dharmabudhi. Soon the two former friends were fighting each other, bloodying each other's face with punches. Finally, they decided to take the matter to the king.

In court, Paapbudhi narrated the whole story about how they had buried their wealth near the large tree and how the pot had disappeared. 'Maharaj, if Dharmabudhi didn't steal it, then who did?' he questioned. 'No one else knew about it…' He paused deliberately, and then continued, 'Except for the tree. Maybe the tree knows who took it. Why don't we ask the tree?'

The king looked at Paapbudhi incredulously. 'Ask the tree? How will the tree tell us?'

'It was the only witness, and the wise say that in matters of justice, nature never lies.'

The king thought for a moment and then agreed to test Paapbudhi's theory. Hence, a date was decided when the king, his judge, and the other ministers would question the tree. On the appointed day, Paapbudhi, Dharmabudhi, the king and his men, and many curious townspeople gathered around the tree. Then the judge asked loudly, 'O divine tree. You are the only one who was witness when these two buried their money. You must have also seen who stole it. Can you please tell us who the thief is?'

For a minute there was deep silence. The people around the tree dared not even breathe so as not to miss the answer in case the tree happened to whisper it. All eyes and ears focused on the tree, but no sound came from it.

The judge repeated his enquiry: 'O divine tree, if you saw the thief who stole the wealth that was buried near your roots, please tell us who it was.'

'Dharmabudhi!' This time a booming voice came from the trunk of the tree.

The king, his judge, and his ministers were flabbergasted to hear the tree declare the name of the culprit, and that too in a human voice. They all turned to look at Dharmabudhi, but that man, instead of looking guilty or even apologetic, was busy piling up dry leaves and twigs around the base of the tree. 'What are you doing?' Paapbudhi shouted in a panicked voice. But, without a word, Dharmabudhi lit a torch and set the dry foliage on fire, which soon spread to the trunk of the tree. Suddenly, loud screams came from the tree and Paapbudhi's father jumped out of the hole, his clothes on fire.

'Aha! So the truth comes out!' the king declared and ordered his soldiers to put Paapbudhi in chains and lock him up.

As they say—greed breeds dishonesty.

Folktale from the Panchatantra

◆

40

LORD OF THE FIELD

There was a farmer who laboured in his field season after season, but, somehow, his crop always failed. One summer evening, tired from the day's toil and the oppressive heat, he lay down in the shade of a banyan tree. Feeling quite hopeless and wondering what he was doing wrong, he gazed across his field. In the distance, he saw an anthill, and beside it a cobra nestling in its massive coils. As he watched, the cobra slowly uncoiled and glided into the anthill.

'Ah!' the farmer exclaimed. 'Now I understand why my field doesn't grow. I didn't pay my respects to the lord of this field.' He hurried home and brought a bowl of milk, which he placed near the anthill. Then, he bowed before the anthill and said with folded hands, 'O Naag Devata, overseer of my field, forgive me, but I didn't know that you resided here. Please accept my offering and allow my field to prosper.'

The following morning, he found that the milk was gone, but sitting at the bottom of the bowl, glinting in the sun, was a gold coin. Thanking Naag Devata, the farmer happily pocketed the coin, and before leaving that evening, he once again placed milk at the foot of the anthill. Sure enough, in the morning he found another gold coin in the bowl. From that day on, the farmer's respect for the lord of the field began to yield a gold coin every day. Soon, his field, too, began to flourish.

One day the farmer had to go out of town, so he handed over Naag Devata's responsibility to his son. 'Make sure that every evening you bring him a bowl of milk and ask for his benevolence,' he told his son, but he didn't say anything about the gold coin. That evening, before leaving the field, the son respectfully placed milk near the anthill, as his father had instructed, and when he returned in the morning, he was surprised to see a gold coin in the bowl. 'Obviously the anthill is full of gold,' he said to himself, excitedly. 'If I dig out the anthill, all the gold will be mine. I just have to kill the snake.' So that evening, instead of placing milk at the foot of the anthill, he waited with a heavy cudgel in his hand, and as soon as the snake appeared, he struck a deathly blow. The snake was badly wounded but it did not die. In one swift move, it reared its head and sunk its fangs into the young man's hand. Instead of finding gold, the greedy young man received a painful death from poisoning.

Folktale from the Panchatantra

◆

41

GOLD MANGOES FOR THE AFTERLIFE

When the mother of Krishnadevaraya, the Raja of Vijayanagar,[18] passed away, he summoned the Brahmins of his kingdom to fulfil her last wish. She had wanted to give away mangoes to the poor, but had died before she could do it, and Krishnadeva was worried that her unfulfilled desire would prevent her from finding peace in her afterlife.

The wise Brahmins shook their heads with a 'tsk-tsk' and pronounced, 'The only way you can provide peace to for your mother's soul now is if you give a hundred Brahmins gold mangoes of weight equal to the mangoes she had intended for charity.'

'And this will ensure that my mother reaps the benefit?'

'Oh yes,' the Brahmins assured him. 'We know it is so, because it is tradition.'

Krishnadeva didn't want to question tradition, especially when it came to his mother's peace in the afterlife, so he had his goldsmith make a hundred mangoes of pure gold, each one weighing as much as a real mango, and on a day that the astrologers deemed auspicious, he distributed them among a hundred Brahmins.

Tenali Raman was Raja Krishnadeva's Vikatakavi—known for his sharp intelligence and wit. When he heard about the incident of the gold mangoes, he sent a messenger to summon the very same Brahmins to his house with the message that Tenali Raman, too, sought peace for his own mother's soul. The Brahmins came eagerly, straight from the palace to Tenali's house. When they arrived, Tenali ushered them into a large room that had a flaming brick oven at one end. Closing the door, he nodded at his servant, who stuck two iron rods into the fire.

'When my mother was alive,' Tenali explained to the Brahmins, 'She had very bad rheumatism and was often in tremendous pain. One day she told me that if I singed her skin, it would help alleviate some of the pain. However, she died before I could fulfil her desire. I want to make sure that she's not in pain in her afterlife and that her soul gets peace.' Then he gestured to his servant, who pulled out the red-hot iron rods and approached the Brahmins.

'What are you doing?' the Brahmins shrieked, backing away in alarm.

'Since I couldn't give my mother this relief, I must give it to you, because you're obviously able to fulfil desires on behalf of the departed and transfer the benefits to them.' He then nodded to the servant again, who purposefully advanced towards the Brahmins, pointing the hot irons at them.

'Are you crazy?' the Brahmins shouted. 'Tell your man to stop.'

'But what about my mother's soul? She needs to be at peace, and you can obviously provide that.'

'No. No, we can't,' they screamed. 'How can we? Your mother's dead. Her body has been cremated, and her ashes are in the river. Who knows where her soul is. How can we bring her peace? We have no way of reaching her.'

'But you promised the king that his mother will find peace through you.'

'Lies. All lies. We lied to the king. We admit it. Please call off your man,' they begged.

At Tenali's nod, the servant halted, but he still stood pointing the rods at the Brahmins.

'And the gold mangoes?' Tenali questioned.

'Greed. You can have them,' they said, and, emptying their bags, they ran out of Tenali's house.

The next day Tenali returned the gold mangoes to the king with the advice: 'The Queen Mother was a good woman who performed meritorious acts all her life. Have faith that she will find peace in the afterlife because of her own good deeds.'

Tenali Raman folktale

◆

42

IRON-EATING MICE

Once there was a merchant's son who had to go to another city on business. He owned a valuable iron scale that weighed a thousand palas,[19] and hoping to keep it safe while he was gone, he decided to leave it with a friend who was also a merchant. 'I'll come and get it when I return,' he told his friend.

'Sure. Don't worry. I'll take good care of it,' his friend assured him.

The merchant's son was gone many years, and when he returned, he went straight to his friend's house to pick up his scale.

'Oh that,' his friend said. 'I'm sorry but the mice ate it up.'

The merchant's son was so shocked that, for a second, he was speechless. Then he said with a straight face, 'That's quite possible. Your house must have a lot of mice who like the taste of iron.'

'So sorry, my man,' the friend said, slapping him on the back. 'It happens. These mice, you know.'

'It's okay,' the merchant's son said. 'Anyway, I've just returned, and I really need a bath. I'm going to the river. Can you send your son with me so that he can watch my clothes while I bathe?'

'Of course,' the friend replied generously, and sent his son to the river with him.

The merchant had the boy sit by his clothes while he bathed, and after he was done, he gave the boy some amalaka fruit and took him to another friend's house. Leaving him there he then returned to the house of the friend whose son he had borrowed.

'Where's my son?' the man asked him, seeing him return alone.

'Oh, a bird flew down from the sky and carried him away.'

'What are you saying? How is that possible? How can a bird carry off a full grown boy?'

'So sorry, but that's what happened,' the merchant's son replied.

'You kidnapper,' the man shouted. 'I'll report you to the king.'

When the case was brought up in court, the king questioned the merchant's son who had taken the boy. 'How can a bird carry off a boy? Please explain to the court.'

'When mice can eat a thousand-palas iron measuring scale, a kite can certainly carry off an elephant, let alone a small boy!'

'What's the meaning of this?' the king demanded, and the merchant's son related to him the whole story about his scale and the mice who had supposedly eaten it.

'Ah,' said the king. 'Those greedy mice. Perhaps they will cough up the scale and give it to the bird in exchange for the boy.'

The greedy man returned the scale and took his son home.

Folktale from the Kathasaritsagara

♦

43

THE WHEEL OF GREED

Four best friends lived in a small town. All of them were wretchedly poor and often talked about how they suffered because of their penury.

'Without wealth, it's better to live among ferocious animals in a dense forest than among friends and relatives,' said one.

'No one respects a poor man. Friends and relatives keep their distance,' said another friend. 'Even one's own children and wife turn away.'

'Without wealth,' said the third, 'A man can have neither fame nor happiness.'

And the fourth friend added: 'With wealth, a coward becomes valorous, an ugly man, handsome, and a foolish man, wise.'

Hence, the friends decided that they must seek their fortune, and since they were not having much luck in their hometown, they set off for a foreign land. After travelling for many days, they came to the bank of River Kshipra in the kingdom of Avanti. There, they took a dip in the waters and, after worshipping Mahakala, they continued on their way. They had gone just a short distance when they met a yogi with dreadlocks piled up on his head. 'My name is Bhairavananda,' the yogi told the friends and invited them to his hermitage.

After a meal, as they were sitting and chatting, the yogi asked the young men. 'What is the objective of your travel?'

'Wealth!' all four replied. 'Either we'll return wealthy, or we'll die trying. This is our resolve. In any case, it's better to die than be poor.'

'But becoming wealthy is a matter of fate,' the yogi said. 'It's not in your hands.'

'True,' said the friends. 'Fate is what makes a man wealthy, but a courageous man also knows when to take advantage of opportunity. Human effort can change even fate. A man's manhood sometimes overpowers godly ordinances. Please don't discourage us with this talk of fate. Instead, advise us. Guide us. How should we go about accumulating wealth? Should we dig deep inside the earth, invoke wood and water spirits, or chant mantras in cremation grounds? Or should we begin dealing with human and animal flesh? You're a yogi and must surely have magical powers, and we are men who are ready to do anything to achieve our desire.'

Pleased at their honest response and knowing them to be worthy, the yogi gave each of the four men a magical diya and told them to go to the Himalaya mountains. 'Wherever your diya falls, stop there and dig; that is where you'll surely find the treasure you seek.'

Following Bhairavananda's directions, the four friends began trudging up the mountainside, carrying their diyas. Soon, one of them felt his diya slipping out of his hand. Thrilled, he began digging in the place where it landed and discovered that the soil there was coppery. 'Look,' he called to his friends in excitement. 'Come here. There seems to be a copper mine here. Let's gather as much copper as we can.'

'Fool,' his friends said to him. 'One doesn't become wealthy with copper. Let's go on. There must surely be something of more value ahead.'

'You go on, if you like,' the young man said, 'I'm satisfied with this,' and began gathering the copper. When he had as much as he could carry, he happily returned home.

Soon, another young man's diya hit the ground. He immediately fell on his hands and knees and began digging in that spot. To his delight, he discovered silver and called to his friends. 'Look! Silver! This will surely make us rich. Let's get a lot of it and return home. We don't need to go any further.'

But the two remaining friends were not satisfied. 'Silver is good, but not good enough,' they said. 'There has to be something more valuable than that. We should keep looking.'

'This is good enough for me,' said the one who had found silver, and collecting as much of it as he could take with him, he returned home, while the other two pressed on.

A little further up the mountain, the third friend's diya, too, fell from his hand, and he discovered that he was standing on a gold mine. 'I knew it,' he exclaimed. 'This is it. Let's take this gold and return home and live as rich men. There's nothing more valuable than gold.'

'Oh yes, there is—diamonds and jewels,' said the fourth friend. 'Where there is copper and silver and gold, there must surely be diamonds. Leave the gold and come with me. Why should we be satisfied with gold when we could be filling our pockets with diamonds and jewels?'

'You go on,' said his friend. 'I'm satisfied with gold.'

And so the remaining friend continued arduously up the mountain, which had now become rocky and snow-covered. His feet became torn and frost-bitten, and his shivering body became weak from hunger and thirst, but he pressed on, climbing and climbing, anxiously waiting for his diya to fall. But the diya remained steady in his hand. After a long time, he met a man who was covered in blood. Whirling in his forehead was a wheel with razor sharp blades. 'Who are you?' the young man asked him. 'And why is there a wheel turning in your forehead? Can you also tell me where I can get water? I'm dying of thirst.'

Suddenly the wheel flew from the man's head and lodged itself in the forehead of the fourth friend. 'What's the meaning of this?' he cried out in pain. 'How did this wheel leave your forehead and get attached to mine?'

'It became attached to my forehead in exactly the same way,' the stranger replied. 'Now it'll only release you when some other greedy person like you comes here and asks you a question.'

'When will that be?'

'I've lost all track of time. Tell me, who is the king now?'

'Veena Vatsaraja.'

'I became poor in the time of Raja Rama and came here at that time with the magic diya. Since then I've not seen any other man.'

'But in all this time what did you do about food and water?'

'After this wheel of greed gets attached to a man's head, he forgets all about hunger and thirst, sleep, and family. He can only whirl after riches—like this wheel—till he dies.'

The stranger turned away and quickly descended the mountain, and the young man stood alone with the wheel of greed whirling in his forehead.

Folktale from the Panchatantra

◆

44

MANTHAN

Once, Rishi Durvasa was observing a Shaivic vow of religious frenzy, when, wandering in the cosmic spheres, he saw a vidyadhari, a magical spirit of the air, wearing a garland of flowers that the Devi had given to her. The flowers were so fragrant that all the regions were redolent with their perfume. Feeling intoxicated with the scent, Durvasa demanded that the vidyadhari give him the garland. Everyone knew that the wrathful rishi could easily be provoked even on a good day, and when he was observing a vow, it was best just to acquiesce to his wishes, and so the vidyadhari handed over the garland without a word. Durvasa put it around his neck and continued in his wanderings.

Along the way, Durvasa met Indra, riding on Airavata, his celestial white elephant with seven trunks. The impassioned rishi took off the garland and threw it at Indra, who caught it deftly and placed it on Airavata's head. The garland sat on the elephant's brow like a crown, but it attracted a lot of bees. Irritated by the loud buzzing, Airavata wrenched the garland off with one of his trunks, tossed it to the ground, and trampled it under his massive feet. Seeing his gift treated so irreverently, Durvasa became livid: 'You arrogant fool,' he called to Indra. 'You don't know how to respect gifts. This garland that I gifted you is from Shri herself. The goddess is the embodiment of fortune and kingship, and by insulting her gift, you have scorned her benefaction. You have also insulted me—Durvasa—the highest of rishis. I gave you the garland to enhance your status; instead, you thoughtlessly gave it to your beast. And so it shall be: you and your gods will become the embodiment of bestiality. Having lost the garland, you will all lose Shri, and losing her you will lose everything that the Devi embodies—grace, generosity and beauty, and also wealth, prosperity and kingship. And that's not all. Just like you have disrespected me, so shall you suffer ignominy.'

Indra and his host of twelve gods were woebegone at Durvasa's curse:

they lost their splendour, their beauty, and their wealth of gold and precious jewels. They also lost their vigour and vitality, and along with that, their maya and hence the ability to call upon celestial weapons. As they lost their godly powers, their connection with the mortals was severed. People stopped sacrificing to them, and soon the very existence of gods began to fade from their memories. Without sacrifices, the gods stopped sustaining vegetation, and prosperity vanished from earth; with prosperity went energy; and without energy, the qualities of intelligence, vigour and courage couldn't survive. People became ignorant, which is the greatest of all evils. With people devoid of prosperity and intelligence, the danavas, who are sworn enemies of the gods, gained power and began harassing the diminished gods, challenging them to battles and winning all of them. Finally, terrorized by the danavas, the gods fled to Brahma.

'Go seek Vishnu,' Brahma advised them. 'He is the causeless cause of Creation, Preservation, and Destruction. Go plead with him for help. Since this cosmos is his creation, he will surely help you bring it back to order.'

Now the gods hastened to Vaikuntha, Vishnu's abode, and propitiated him with praise, calling him in humble appeal. When Vishnu appeared, holding his conch, discus and mace, the ungodly gods told him everything that had happened. 'Please, Lord. Tell us what to do,' they begged.

His response was: 'You need amrita. That immortalizing elixir will restore your splendour. But that elixir belongs to the Earth Goddess and is in her womb in the ocean, and she will not yield it easily. You'll have to churn the ocean to get it.'

Vishnu's words filled the gods with fear and doubt. 'How can we churn the mighty ocean? We don't have any strength left,' they lamented.

'Ask the danavas to help,' Vishnu advised.

'Danavas?' the gods exclaimed in shock. 'They're the reason we fled. Besides, why would they help us? We are their enemies.'

'To gain their help, you'll have to make peace with them. If you promise to share the amrita with them, they'll agree.'

The gods were not at all happy to hear this. 'If the danavas get amrita, they too will become immortal, and then we'll never be able to defeat them.'

'I said, promise them a share of the amrita; I didn't say give it to them. Without their help, this task is impossible. You get them to agree, and I'll make sure that they don't get a drop of the amrita.'

Following Vishnu's advice, the gods went to the danavas, assuming a conciliatory attitude. 'We've come to you for help,' they said innocently. 'We want to churn the ocean, but we can't do it alone. We need your superior strength.'

The danavas were pleased at the compliment but were wary of it. 'Why should we help you?' they asked.

'When the ocean is churned, it'll yield amrita, which makes one immortal. We'll share that prize with you.'

The danavas conferred; they were sure that the gods were planning something treacherous, but the idea of obtaining amrita was so enticing that they decided to help the devas and then rely on their own strength to secure the immortalizing elixir.

With the two factions working together as a team, the danavas and devas began preparations to churn the Earth's primordial, oceanic womb. They started by gathering the equipment that they would need.

They would need a churning pole that would be strong enough to thrust into the Earth's belly and long enough to reach her womb. Mount Mandar[20] seemed to be ideal for this purpose, because it extended eleven thousand yojanas[21] upwards and eleven thousand yojanas downwards. Nevertheless, when the danavas and devas tried to uproot the mountain, they couldn't even budge it, despite their combined brawn. So, once again, the gods sought Vishnu's help, and he volunteered his cosmic serpent, Sesha-Ananta Naag. The serpent wound his tail around the mountain and pulled it out of the earth, but as it was being uprooted, frenzied birds flew out of the trees, twittering and screeching, and all the animals of the forests tumbled and fell in confusion. However, the deed was done and the devas and danavas now had a churning pole with which to churn the ocean.

Next, they needed a churning rope that would be long enough to wind around Mandar and sturdy enough to withstand the friction of pumping and twirling the churning pole. Shiva volunteered Naagraja, Vasuki, the king of serpents, who sat like a necklace of three curls around his neck, facilitating the order of time.

Then they looked for a churning base—a foundation on which the churning pole could be planted and held aloft so that Mandar would not sink into the milky, endless waters—a base that would endure the immense grinding and chafing and still remain erect and firm. Once again they petitioned Vishnu, and he took the form of a tortoise—a Kurma—and dove into the ocean, going to the very bottom, so that Mount Mandar could be mounted on his back.

With the churning pole placed firmly on the churning base and the churning rope wound securely around the pole, the danavas and devas were ready to begin the churning, but then a question arose: who would pull the tail end of Vasuki and who would pull his head? The gods, afraid of the venomous black fumes that would surely rise from the mouth of Naagraja, quickly opted for the tail end, and the danavas were left holding his head, but they didn't mind, because the fumes that Vasuki emitted were not toxic; they ascended to the sky to become clouds, which dissolved into nourishing rain and cooled the churners.

However, the sea creatures and land creatures, who suffered the effects of the churning, didn't fare so well. Those who inhabited the waters were immediately caught in the vortex, and when uprooted trees were hurled into the ocean, those who lived in them were also flung into the massive waves. When torn tree branches rubbed against each other, fires sparked and spread through the forests, incinerating all big and small creatures who lived there. Indra tried to put out these fires by pouring down rain, but this was a cosmic fire caused by the Earth Goddess—impossible to quell even for the king of gods. Hardly anyone survived, and those who did escape the waters and the fires, were pulverized by mountains that shattered and came tumbling down, when the Earth, its watery womb violated, shuddered in its own throes.

But slowly, the sap of hundreds of trees began to flow into the ocean, turning the milky water into an ambrosial drink, which both the gods and demons drank to hydrate themselves, as they churned and churned. Finally, the agitated ocean began to foam in the centre, and from this, it began to ooze out its wealth. The first to arise were brilliant rays from which the moon emerged; he was followed by Surabhi, the all-giving cow. Then came the goddess Shura, who is also called Varuni, her eyes sultry with intoxication, because she is the goddess of wine. Then arose the eternal Parijata[22] tree, and the fragrance from its undying blossoms spread through the three worlds. Following the tree was the gem Kaustubha, which Vishnu claimed and placed on his breast. The apsaras, the most beautiful women in the cosmos, then emerged, and Indra laid claim to them. Next was Ucchaishravas, the divine horse, who is as fleet as the mind. Then, with everyone watching in awe, Shri arose from the foaming, swirling water. She was seated on a pink lotus in full bloom and was holding another in her hand. As her golden radiance spread everywhere, the gods and Brahmins sang her praises, the apsaras, led by Ghritachi, danced before her, and Ganga and the other celestial rivers came to pay her homage. The cloud elephants then poured water on her from golden jars, the milky sea herself presented her with a garland of never-fading flowers, and Vishvakarma, the divine architect, adorned her with ornaments. Bathed and attired, she turned towards Vishnu, who drew her into his embrace and claimed her as his own for the rest of time. With Shri's arrival, the gods' splendour was restored, as was the vegetation of the earth, and the hearts of people filled with reverence for the gods again.

But that was not all. Ulimately, the ocean succumbed and relinquished that for which both the devas and danavas were toiling. Dhanvantari, the divine physician, emerged from the water, holding an urn full of amrita. 'It's ours! It's ours,' both the danavas and devas shouted, dashing into the ocean to grab the urn. But following the amrita was something else that neither the devas nor the danavas had expected. The plundered ocean, in outrage, oozed out Halahala, a poison so virulent that even its fumes were noxious, threatening to permeate all of Creation. Coughing and gagging, the devas and danavas rushed out of the waters, staggering, falling over each other. They screamed for help from Brahma, who himself was overcome. 'Only Shiva can save us now,' Brahma croaked, and everyone rushed to Maheshvara, the great god who lives on Kailash and wears venomous serpents like ornaments. Uttering a mantra, Shiva scooped Halahala in his cupped hands and swallowed it. The poison burned in his mouth, but he did not let it descend beyond his throat, and there it was held, its fiery virulence contained. That day Shiva's throat turned blue, and from then on he was called Nilkantha—Blue-Throated.

Freed from the noxious fumes, the devas and danavas began to fight over the amrita. In a swift, strategic move, the danavas were able to grab the urn from Dhanvantari. The devas, in despair, looked to Vishnu for the help he had promised. Vishnu realized that the devas would never win against the powerful danavas in a fair fight, so he resorted to treachery. He assumed the form of Mohini, a woman of mind-boggling beauty. Sauntering over to the danavas with swinging hips and suggestive looks, Mohini asked them to give her the amrita in a voice that invited many liberties, and they, eager to be seduced, placed the cup in her hands. Mohini brought the urn to the devas, who each took a few sips and were immediately rejuvenated to fight the danavas with renewed strength.

When the devas were drinking the amrita, a danava named Rahu, disguised himself as a deva and also took a sip, but before the immortalizing nectar could descend down his throat, Surya and Chandra recognized him and informed Vishnu, who cut off Rahu's head with his discus. The immortalized, severed head of Rahu rose to the sky, yelling and screaming, and then fell to the earth with a thunderous roar. From that day on, the head of Rahu pursues Chandra and Surya and swallows them every chance he gets.

Enraged at Vishnu's treachery, the danavas flew at the devas, and the battle raged again. Vishnu, back in his form, began to cut down the danavas with his discus, felling hundreds, their heads severed from their bodies. As the sun grew red, the cries of the danavas rose high, but with the last of their strength, they uprooted mountains and trees and hurled them at the devas. Unconquerable though they had become, the devas were unable to bear this new onslaught, and they called for reinforcements. At this time, Nara and Narayana, the twins sons of Dharma, entered the field and began decimating the danavas.

Most of the danavas, who were now asuras—a-sura—without sura or amrita—perished that day, and the few that remained fled to Patala. The devas rejoiced. They placed Mandar back in its place, made Nara the guardian of amrita, and returned to heaven with their plunder.

Myth from the Mahabharata

◆

45

AVENGING DINAH

Dinah, the daughter of Leah and Jacob, was once visiting the women of the land when the local prince, Shechem, son of Hamor, the Hivite, saw her. He grabbed her and, forcing himself on her, defiled her. But then he regretted his action and comforting Dinah, promised her that he would be true to her and marry her. Then he went and told his father, Hamor, his intention. 'Get me this girl,' he said. 'I want her as my wife.'

When Jacob got the news that Shechem had violated his daughter, he was troubled. At that time, his sons were out with the herds, but when they returned and found out what had happened, they were livid. What Shechem had done was intolerable for the Israelites.

When Hamor came to discuss a marriage proposal, he appealed to Dinah's brothers: 'My son Shechem is in love with your sister, I beg you to let him have her as his wife. In fact, let this marriage serve as an alliance between our clans. You give us your daughters in marriage and we will give you ours. Our country will be your country. Feel free to move around as you please, acquire land, settle here. We'll welcome you and your people.'

Shechem, too, came to talk with the father and brothers of Dinah, 'Ask whatever bride-price and gifts you wish,' he said. 'Make it as high as you like, and I'll pay it. Just give me the girl in marriage.'

The response that Dinah's brothers gave was a trap for the Hivites, but they didn't suspect it: 'We consider men who are uncircumcised contemptuous,' the brothers said. 'We can't give our sister to such a man. But there's a way that we can agree to this alliance; fulfil just one condition: have every male in your clan circumcised. Then we'll give you our daughters in marriage and take yours as brides. We'll also live among you as one people. But if you refuse, we'll take the girl and leave, and she'll never be yours.'

Both Hamor and his son Shechem agreed to the condition. Then they went back and gathered all the able-bodied males at the city gate and said to them: 'If we let these Israelites move around freely in our country, their herds, their livestock, and all their property and slaves will be ours. We can marry our daughters to them and they can marry ours. Let us make them our friends. There is enough land in our country to comfortably accommodate them.'

When all the citizens approved, Hamor and Shechem told them the condition: 'Every male among us must be circumcised, just as they have been. If we fulfil this one condition, we can make a strong alliance with them.'

The Hivite men agreed to the condition, and every single one of them got himself circumcised. Two days later, while they were still suffering from the circumcision, Dinah's two brothers, Simeon and Levi, went into the city with drawn swords and killed every male. They killed Shechem, and his father, Hamor; they rescued Dinah from Shechem's house and brought her home. Then Jacob's other sons rushed into the city, and, trampling on the dead bodies of the Hivite men, raided it. They took everything they could—flocks, cattle, asses. They also plundered the houses of the Hivites and carried off their women and children.

When Jacob heard about what Simeon and Levi and his other sons had done, he was very distressed. 'You have ruined my name and brought shame on me among the Canaanites and the Perizzites,' he said to them. 'If they decide to join forces against me and attack me, I'll be destroyed.'

Simeon and Levi answered: 'If our sister is treated like a common whore, shouldn't we avenge her?'

Myth from the Old Testament

◆

46

A WIFE, A WAGER, AND A WAR

After Indraprastha was built, Yudhishthira, the eldest Pandava, held a Rajasuya yajna, which was an inauguration sacrifice to consecrate his kingship. The Pandava brothers invited many monarchs and princes and all their friends and relatives to the event. They also invited their cousins, the Kauravas, with whom they had been in conflict over the throne of Hastinapur. To resolve this conflict, Dhritarashtra, the blind king and father of Kauravas, had given his nephews five villages on which they could build their own city—Indraprastha.

At this site, Maya, the asura architect, had constructed a magnificent palace for the Pandavas. With its gold and silk panels, precious stone inlay decorations, and ingenious architecture, it was like an opulent, mystical palace that had been transported from Indraloka to earth. All the guests who had been invited to the yajna and were staying at the palace were amazed by it, including Duryodhana. But this eldest Kaurava was also burning with jealousy. He was already upset at the lavishness of the yajna sacrifice and the expensive gifts that Yudhishthira had received, and when he was tripped up by the clever illusions of the palace, his heart felt like it would burst with envy.

In one room he thought the floor was a shallow pond, so he lifted the hem of his dhoti and gingerly stepped into the 'water', only to realize that it was rock solid crystal that only appeared to be water. Embarrassed, he quickly lowered his dhoti and looked around to see if anyone had witnessed his mistake. Draupadi had just come in with a few of her maids, and he heard her snicker, 'Blind son of a blind father.' Then he came to another room that appeared to have a similar crystal floor decorated with water flowers crystalized in it. But when he tried to walk across, he fell into it, because it was actually a pond of water. Here, his cousins Bhima and Yudhishthira saw him fall. Bhima laughed out loud, while Yudhishthira tried to cover his amusement by ordering his servants to quickly bring dry clothes for the Kaurava prince. As Duryodhana left the room, he heard Bhima call out mockingly, 'Be careful, dear cousin. Don't hurt yourself.'

Then, in another room, what he thought was glass was actually an open space, and he fell through it, and in yet another room, he walked into a glass wall that was almost invisible. Not only was Duryodhana distressed because he was getting trapped in the illusions of this palace, but to his great chagrin, wherever he stumbled into the illusion, there was always someone present to witness his embarrassment. The whole experience of Indraprastha was so belittling for Duryodhana that by the time he left for Hastinapur with his uncle, Shakuni, he was consumed by a rage he didn't know how to subdue.

'What are you thinking about, Nephew?' Shakuni asked him a number of times, but Duryodhana didn't know what to say. Finally, he told his uncle, 'I want to throw myself in the fire, or drink poison, or drown myself. I can't live like this. Thoughts of Indraprastha are killing me.'

'Your cousins have worked hard for their success,' Shakuni advised. 'You shouldn't be upset at their good fortune.'

'I don't want to be jealous. But I am. What man is there in the world who can bear to see his enemies prosper? I saw the wealth that they spent on the sacrifice and also the riches that they received in gifts, and then there is their palace built by the master of illusions, Maya himself, in which I was tricked at every step. And their derision and laughter. The more I think about it, the more unbearable it becomes. Tell me what to do, Uncle. I am so consumed, I see no other way but to kill myself.'

'Instead of taking your own life, why not think of taking from them what they have?'

'But how? Should I declare war and conquer them? Then all that they have will become mine.'

'No, Nephew. It's impossible for you to conquer those cousins of yours in battle. You may have a larger force, but they're supported by Krishna. They're invincible. But I know of another way in which you can vanquish Yudhishthira.'

'Tell me quickly, Uncle. I want to ruin that righteous Yudhishthira, but I don't want to hurt any of our friends and relatives in the process. Do you know of such a way?'

'I do. They have created a city of illusions, let's defeat them with illusion.'

'Tell me what you're thinking.'

'Call them to a game of dice. Yudhishthira is very fond of gambling and never refuses a game, but he's the worst player in the world. Invite him and let me play on your behalf. You know my skill with dice, they're puppets in my hand. Can you imagine Yudhishthira playing against me?' Shakuni said with a laugh. 'Go tell your father to organize a game of dyut. He won't refuse you, because he loves you too much. Besides, it's tradition to end the Rajasuya with a friendly game of dice.'

Dhritarashtra didn't quite approve of the game, but he couldn't refuse his son, and so orders were issued to build a special assembly hall for it. It was two thousand dhanushas in length and two thousand dhanushas in breadth; inside, it was supported with one thousand pillars studded with Vaidurya gems, and it had one thousand doors of crystal. When it was completed, Dhritarashtra sent Vidura, his half-brother and adviser, to invite Yudhishthira, the newly crowned king of Indraprastha, to come and see the new assembly hall and also to play a friendly game of dyut with Duryodhana.

Vidura disapproved of gambling in general, and he was always suspicious of Duryodhana's motives. He was also a Pandava supporter, and he loved Yudhishthira like a son. He tried to dissuade Dhritarashtra from holding the game, but when that didn't work, he went to Indraprastha, and, along with presenting the invitation, advised Yudhishthira to be on his guard. 'Be careful,' he said. 'I hear that Shakuni will be part of the game. You know how skilful he is at cheating.'

'I won't play with him,' Yudhishthira said. 'Unless he challenges me.

I can't refuse a challenge.'

When the Pandavas arrived for the dyut, the assembly hall was full of male guests, and the game was already laid out in the centre of the hall.

'Dear Yudhishthira, welcome,' Shakuni said, gesturing to him and his brother to take their assigned seats at the game. He himself was sitting directly across. 'Shall we fix the rules before we begin?' When Yudhishthira sat down, Shakuni continued, 'Come. Let's test our mettle, and may the best man win.'

'You speak of gambling as though it's a glorious battle between warriors,' Yudhishthira replied. 'You know there is no glory or morality in gambling, and cheating in it is even more of an evil. I trust that you will not defeat us through deceitful play.'

'The true player is he who knows how to baffle the opponent, and knowing this, he is ready for victory or loss—as in battle. The skill is in knowing how the dice falls. Are you ready? Shall we fix the stakes?'

'Gambling is not a righteous battle. But I'm asking you not to cheat us of our wealth that we have worked so hard to obtain.'

'It is with the objective of defeating his opponent that one warrior fights another. In dyut, too, the objective of a player skilled in dice is to defeat the opponent. In every contest, victory is the motive. If you think that I'll cheat, and if you're afraid to lose, then withdraw from the challenge and don't play,' Shakuni said.

'I've sworn not to refuse a challenge, so I'll play. Who'll be my opponent?' Yudhishthira asked.

Then Duryodhana spoke for the first time: 'Cousin, I'll stake my gems and jewels and wealth, but my uncle, Shakuni, will play on my behalf.'

Yudhishthira had been worried about this very eventuality. 'It already seems like the rules are being broken,' he stated.

'Then refuse to play,' Shakuni offered.

And Yudhishthira's response was, 'Let the play begin.'

'What will you stake?' Duryodhana asked.

'I'll begin by staking this beautiful necklace of gold and pearls, which are the finest that the ocean can yield,' Yudhishthira said, removing his necklace. 'What is your counter stake?'

'I have many such necklaces, but I'll accept your stake and counter it with double the wealth.'

Shakuni, whose fingers had been caressing the dice, now threw them. And he won. Yudhishthira watched his play, which he knew was manipulated, but it was so skilfully done, it did not appear to be a foul. 'I can already see that you are cheating,' he said to Shakuni. 'But no matter. I now stake gold jars filled with coins.'

Shakuni won again.

'I have a prized chariot that is unmatched in the world. It's drawn by eight white horses, is adorned with jewels, and it has been specially designed for speed and safety. I wager that,' Yudhishthira said and threw the dice. But, once again, Shakuni had the winning throw.

'I have one hundred thousand serving girls decked in jewels—the most beautiful in the country; they have voices like nightingales and bodies like heavenly nymphs. I stake them all.'

Again Shakuni threw the dice and called, 'I have won.'

'Thousands of serving men, strong, wise, self-controlled, obedient,' was Yudhishthira's next stake.

Shakuni threw the winning dice again.

One thousand elephants with golden girdles and tusks like plough-shafts; an equal number of elephant chariots with golden shafts; trained horses, steeds of the highest quality; wagons full of gold and jewels; draught animals; thousands of trained soldiers; the best of milch cows... One after another, Yudhishthira placed them in the game, and for each one, Shakuni's throw beat Yudhishthira's. 'I have won! I have won! I have won!' were the words that Shakuni declared again and again.

By this time, Yudhishthira was in a state of frenzy. His face was flushed and his eyes were dazed, and when he snatched up the dice to make a play, his fingers shook.

'You have lost much of your wealth,' Shakuni said to him. 'Do you still wish to play?'

'You have no idea of the wealth I have,' Yudhishthira retorted. 'Tens of crores—all my wealth. I stake it here.'

When Shakuni threw the dice, he won again.

'My city, my kingdom! I stake them!'

'And you have lost them!' Shakuni soon declared.

Yudhishthira looked around, frantically, and his feverish eyes fell upon his brothers who were staring at him, aghast. 'My brother, this Nakula with mighty arms and a lion's neck, the handsomest of men. I stake him.'

'O king, Prince Nakula is dear to you. Are you sure you want to stake him?' Shakuni asked.

'He is staked,' Yudhishthira cried. 'Haven't I said so?'

'Then, here's my winning throw' Shakuni said. 'And now Prince Nakula is our slave. With what will you play now?'

'Sahadeva, my youngest brother, who is known for his sense of justice and learning. He's so dear to me, but I place him in the game.'

'Are you sure?' Shakuni once again asked. 'This is your mother, Madri's second son. You have placed both her sons in the game, and now you'll surely lose both. It appears that your own brothers, Arjuna and Bhima, are dearer to you after all, since you have not staked them.'

'Don't say another word, fool. I know you're trying to create disunity among us. But nothing will divide us.'

'I don't need to do anything, O Yudhishthira. You're doing it all yourself,' Shakuni replied and threw the dice and won.

'This Arjuna is the greatest hero in the world. I stake him next.'

Shakuni was ready with his dice, and as soon as he threw it, he called another victory.

'My brother who is the foremost fighter, whose strength is equal to ten elephants, who wields the mace better than the gods themselves. This Bhima, I stake him.'

'And he is won,' Shakuni declared. 'O king, you have lost your wealth, your kingdom and even your brothers. You have nothing else to stake?'

'I still have myself, and I stake myself.'

'You do understand that if you are won, you and all your brothers, who are already won, become our slaves,' Shakuni warned.

'Of course I understand. Do you take me for a fool?' Yudhishthira bit back. 'Stop talking and throw the dice.'

And when Shakuni made the throw, the dice were, once again, in his favour. 'You've lost yourself, O king,' he said. 'You shouldn't have wagered yourself. Now how will you stake anything else, because by winning you, we have won all your remaining assets? But wait,' he said softly, a cunning smoothness in his tone. 'You still have Draupadi, your wife. She, like the embodiment of Shri, is the very essence of your kingship, your prosperity and your good fortune. You could bet Draupadi and, with her, win yourself back.'

'Ah, Draupadi,' Yudhishthira exclaimed, his eyes losing some of their delirium and exuding a different kind of passion. 'Slender-waisted, with eyes like leaves of autumn lotuses, fragrant like the lily; the goddess Shri herself in body and grace. Soft-hearted and beautiful and virtuous, with sweet voice and sweeter disposition. The princess of Panchala, my queen, Draupadi. Yes. I'll wager her.'

A gasp arose in the assembly hall at Yudhishthira's words, and it soon turned into an agitated buzz. The elders broke into a sweat, and Vidura held his head between his hands, despairingly. Karna and Duhshasana broke into nervous laughter, and others, of weaker hearts, began to call out to Yudhishthira and Shakuni in distress.

The only ones who did not react were the four Pandavas. They sat behind their elder brother in meek silence; only the muscles in their forearms twitched, as they clenched and unclenched their hands.

Shakuni brought Yudhishthira's attention back to the game. 'Just to make sure. You're staking your wife to win yourself back? Are you sure you want to play this stake?'

'I'm sure,' Yudhishthira said clearly, and threw his dice.

Shakuni held the dice in his hand for a moment, as though making a secret deal with them; then he gently released the pieces. And he won.

For a full minute, everyone in the assembly hall sat in stunned silence. Even Shakuni lost his words. Finally, Duryodhana took a deep breath and stood up, and straightening his shoulders, he turned to Vidura. 'Go and fetch Draupadi and take her to where the serving women are. She'll now sweep the rooms like a servant.'

'Oh wicked man,' Vidura cried. 'Do you know what you're saying? Do you not know that you're provoking tigers with your words? They'll tear you apart for saying such words about their wife.'

'If they were tigers, they would have pounced already—when their wife was wagered. They're nothing but meek lambs being led to the slaughter by their brother. Besides, she's not their wife any more. Is she?' Duryodhana replied, his voice now full of mockery, 'Now she's my slave.'

'Won with deceit! You'll cause the destruction of this race with your ways. Pay heed to my words and stop your wicked ways,' Vidura warned.

Duryodhana smiled disdainfully at Vidura, and then turning to his man, Pratikamin, commanded, 'Go and fetch Draupadi. Don't fear the Pandavas. They can't touch you; they are slaves.'

Pratikamin went inside to Draupadi's chamber and knocked on her door. She was sitting on her bed in the single garment that women wore during their menstruation, and was surprised at the intrusion. She bid Pratikamin to enter and asked him why he had disturbed her.

'O Princess of Panchal, King Yudhishthira has lost you in a dice game, and you have been won by Prince Duryodhana,' Pratikamin told Draupadi with lowered eyes.

'You are to come with me so that I can show you the menial work that you will do as Duryodhana's slave.'

Draupadi was shocked. 'What are you saying, Pratikamin?' she said, her voice shaking in disbelief. 'Is there any king who wagers his own wife in a dice game? Surely, you're mistaken.'

When Pratikamin didn't respond, she asked, 'Could Yudhishthira not find anything else to stake? Surely, he must have been intoxicated with the dice to stake his wife.'

'The king first wagered his brothers, then himself, and when he had nothing else to stake, he bet on you.'

'Do me a favour, Pratikamin,' Draupadi said, steadying her voice. 'Go back to the assembly and ask that gambler, my husband, whom he lost first—himself or me. When you have the answer to my question you may come and fetch me.'

Pratikamin returned to the assembly and repeated Draupadi's words to Yudhishthira, 'She wants to know whose lord you were when you lost her in play? Did you lose yourself first or her?'

But Yudhishthira had no answer for Pratikamin.

'Let the Princess of Panchala come to the assembly herself and pose the question,' Duryodhana ordered. 'Let the whole assembly hear the exchange that happens between Yudhishthira and his wife, whom he has lost in dice.'

Pratikamin went back inside to Draupadi's chamber and repeated Duryodhana's command. 'Forgive me,' he said, bowing his head. 'I'm only obeying orders.'

'Surely the Kuru elders will not act against dharma and morality,' Draupadi stated, still in disbelief. 'Please go back and ask the Kuru elders. Tell them I'll do as they say. If they ask me to come to the assembly, I will, but surely they don't condone this?'

Pratikamin once again returned to the assembly and conveyed Draupadi's request to the Kuru elders. But they all remained silent and with downcast eyes—Guru Drona, Pitahmah Bhishma, Guru Kripacharya,

King Dhritarashtra—not one elder said a word.

By this time, Yudhishthira had sent this own separate messenger to Draupadi with a message: 'Panchali, appear before your father-in-law, King Dhritarashtra. Even though you may be weeping and dressed in the garment of your menstruation, come at once to the assembly hall.'

When Yudhishthira's messenger conveyed this message to Draupadi, she fell on her bed in horror and anguish. In the meantime, Pratikamin asked the assembly what he should tell the Pandava queen.

'Bring her here,' Duryodhana ordered, 'Let her ask her question to the elders here in the assembly.'

Now Pratikamin hesitated, so Duryodhana turned to his brother, Duhshasana. 'Go yourself, dear brother, and bring Draupadi here. This man is afraid. But our enemies are now our slaves. What can they do?'

Duhshasana got up immediately, and with eager steps went inside to Draupadi's room. 'Come. You have been won by us,' he commanded, reaching to grab her. 'Stop being modest. You've been won in an honest game.'

Draupadi got up hurriedly from the bed and backed away from Duhshasana. 'Don't take me there,' she begged. 'I'm having my period, and I'm dressed in this single garment. Have some shame.' She covered her face with her hands and ran towards the inner rooms, but Duhshasana followed her, and grabbing her by her long, curly hair, began dragging her towards the assembly hall.

Trembling like a banyan tree in a storm and crying from the pain of being dragged by the hair, she still begged Duhshasana, 'Where is your shame? The assembly hall is filled with elders and gurus—men whom I honour and respect. How can you take me before of them like this? You may not have any shame, but I do. You're a wicked man. Let me go so that I can return to my room.'

'I don't care if you're in your monthly flow, or one garment, or even naked. You've been won at dice and have become a slave. Your place is now with our serving women.'

'My husbands will never forgive you, even if Indra himself becomes your ally. They'll destroy you.'

Duhshasana laughed, 'What husbands? Those who watched quietly as you were staked? And now they're bound to us as slaves.'

Her hair dishevelled, her single garment soiled and loose, her face streaked with anger and pain, Draupadi was hauled into the assembly hall. She saw the elders watch Duhshasana drag her there, and yet no one rebuked him, no one said a word.

'Shame!' Draupadi screamed, pulling free from Duhshasana and standing straight with head held high, looking pointedly at the assembly of the most respected men of the Kuru clan. 'When all the Kurus in this assembly look silently on this vile act and say nothing, what morality, what virtue, what justice remains? Shame on the scions of the mighty Kuru kingdom!' Then she turned to look at her five husbands with raging eyes. 'Husbands!' she spat. 'You swore to protect me—the wife you married with Vedic rituals.'

'Wife no more. Slave!' Duhshasana laughed, and grabbing her again, pulled her further into the hall.

Draupadi ignored him, and breaking free once again, turned to the elders. 'I want the elders to answer me. How could Yudhishthira have wagered me if he lost himself first? How can I be lost, when he had already lost himself?'

Bhishma Pitahmah finally spoke, his voice sounding hesitant and unsure. 'Dear lady. It is true that one who has no wealth cannot stake another's wealth. But wives are always at the command of their husband and at their disposal. I am unable to decide what is right and what is wrong. The ways of dharma are subtle.'

A sob broke from Draupadi's throat at Bhishma's words. Tears flowing down her cheeks, she begged the other elders to answer her question, and when no one replied, she turned to look at her husbands again, her weeping eyes no longer filled with rage but with the pain of broken promises. Seeing his beloved Draupadi in this pathetic state, Bhima could not bear it anymore and finally gave vent to his anger. 'You wretch,' he lashed out at Yudhishthira, 'Gamblers have in their house many mistresses, but even they don't stake those women. Even they show more kindness to them than you have shown to our delicate-as-a-flower wife. This woman gave herself to us in body and soul when she became our wife, and we swore to protect her. Now look at what you've done to her. I'm so filled with rage at the way you've treated her, I want to burn your hands. Sahadeva, bring me fire, I'm going to burn the hands that wagered Draupadi.'

'Have you lost your mind?' Arjuna scolded Bhima. 'Have you forgotten all respect for an elder brother? Remember your dharma, Bhima.'

'My dharma? And what he did to Draupadi was dharma? If I had known what he intended, I would've broken those arms from his body and burnt them before he had chance to play her so callously.'

There was in the assembly hall. When none of the elders answered Draupadi's questions, a younger brother of the Kauravas, by the name of Vikarna stood up and began speaking: 'First, it is said that hunting, drinking, gambling, and womanizing are vices, and people who are engaged in these can't be taken seriously. Second, Draupadi is the common wife of all five Pandavas, then how could Yudhishthira stake her? She didn't belong only to him. And third, Shakuni himself asked Yudhishthira to stake Draupadi, so it wasn't entirely by free will that Yudhishthira staked her. Therefore, I think that Draupadi has not been won.'

There was an uproar in the assembly hall at Vikarna's words. Then, Karna silenced everyone and turned to Vikarna. 'You're just a boy. You don't know the subtleties of dharma. If the elders here can't say whether Draupadi is won or not, how can you? But, my dear Vikarna, you aptly remind us that Draupadi is a common wife to the Pandavas. The shastras say that a woman should have only one husband, and since this woman has five, it's clear that she's a whore. So it doesn't matter if she's brought here in one garment, or if she's stripped of her clothes. In any case, she's a slave now, along with the Pandavas, who, by the way, are still standing dressed in their kingly robes. Duhshasana, why don't you help them remove their silks?'

Duhshasana was happy to oblige. And after he made the Pandavas strip down to their undergarments, he went to Draupadi and, grabbing the end of her single garment, began to pull it.

Draupadi screamed, holding on desperately to the fabric.

'Duhshasana, you wretch,' Bhima roared. 'I swear that in the battlefield, I'll rip open your chest and drink your blood.'

Duhshasana only laughed and pulled harder. As Draupadi felt the folds of the garment begin to loosen, she let go, and then she began to pray. 'O Hari. O Krishna. Save me. Save my modesty. I am sinking in this ocean of immorality. Be my anchor.'

Not only Krishna, but all the other gods also heard her plea. 'Something must be done,' they said to each other, and looked towards Dharma, who had suffered such violations. Dharma called his maya and sent it to the assembly hall of the Kuru palace: as Duhshasana pulled at the loose garment covering Draupadi's body, yard after yard of fabric began to get added to it. Duhshasana kept pulling and the fabric kept extending, till a pile collected at his feet. His arms became exhausted, his body began to sweat, the breath in his lungs became laboured but still the garment kept coming. Witnessing this miracle, everyone in the assembly hall fell silent in awe.

Vidura then brought the attention of the assembly back to the question Draupadi had asked. 'Great men of wisdom,' he said, 'Draupadi's question still remains unanswered. The rules of dharma require that you resolve the issue.'

Bhishma Pitahmah once again spoke, his voice subdued. 'No one doubts your virtue or your dharma, dear lady. But the ways of dharma are subtle. I'm unable to answer your question, but your husband is himself Dharmaraja. He can say with authority whether you are won or not.'

'That's right,' Duryodhana immediately added, 'let Yudhishthira, Dharmaraja himself, say that he is not your lord, and you'll be free to go. In fact, if your other husbands also declare in this assembly that Yudhishthira is not their lord, they, too, are free to go.'

'It's obvious that your former husband, Yudhishthira, didn't care for you,' Karna added. 'Otherwise why would he have staked you in the dice-game in front of this assembly of men? O beautiful lady, choose another husband who won't make you a slave or stake you in dice.'

'Yes, choose another, dear lady,' Duryodhana said. Then he pushed up his dhoti and, exposing his strong, muscular thigh, patted it in a gesture to invite Draupadi to come and sit on it.

'Duryodhana!' Bhima roared again. 'I'll break that thigh which you so shamelessly show to Draupadi. I vow I'll find no peace in the three worlds till I've done it.'

Duryodhana threw back his head and laughed.

Suddenly a jackal cried out, the ominous sound coming from somewhere nearby, as if it was in the palace itself. Then asses began to bray and birds began to screech. At these evil omens, the men in the assembly hall grew very quiet—afraid. 'Take heed, O king,' Vidura warned Dhritarashtra. 'This bodes destruction for the kingdom.'

Just then Gandhari, Dhritarashtra's queen, whose eyes were covered with a veil that she had vowed to keep for life so as not to be superior to her blind husband, came into the assembly hall with the help of her maids, and making her way to the king, said to him, 'Husband, what you allowed to happen here today violated dharma codes so gravely that misfortune has come looking for us. Make amends and maybe you'll be able to avert it.'

Gandhari's words finally struck Dhritarashtra with the reality of the situation. 'You wretch,' he said mildly to his son. 'You have invited destruction upon the Kuru kingdom by using such derogatory language for Draupadi, who is your cousins' wedded wife—this family's daughter-in-law.' Then he consoled Draupadi. 'You are the foremost of all of my daughters-in-law. You are virtuous and devoted. Ask me for any boon you desire.'

'If you want to grant me a boon, Father, then let Yudhishthira be freed from slavery,' Draupadi said.

'He is freed, daughter, but I think you deserve a second boon. What else do you desire?'

'Let Bhima, Arjuna, Nakula and Sahadeva also be freed.'

'They are free, dear daughter. But, you have not been honoured enough. Let me grant you another boon. Ask me for anything that you desire.'

'Greed destroys virtue. I don't need another boon. I'm happy with what you have given me. With my husbands freed, we'll restore our own prosperity.'

The men gathered in the assembly hall applauded Draupadi for her wisdom and selflessness. Then Karna said, 'When the sons of Pandu were sinking boatless in an ocean of despair, this Panchali became their boat and brought them safely to the shore.'

Myth from the Mahabharata

◆

47

YA'JUJ AND MA'JUJ

Ya'juj and Ma'juj are powerful, and they do not believe. They have small, evil eyes and faces like shields, and they will appear at the time of Qayamat. Their appearance is ordained.

In the past, Dhul Qarnayn, the two-horned one, was established on earth by Allah and given divine inspiration. He had knowledge of the constellations and the means to conquer the east and west. Once, during his travels he came to the place of the setting sun, where its reflection could be seen in a spring of muddy water. There were people all around it, and Allah said to him, 'O Dhul Qarnayn, either you can punish them or you can treat them with kindness.' Dhul Qarnayn invited the people to become believers, and when they did, he treated them with kindness. Then he went in an easterly direction to a place of the rising sun and found people for whom Allah had provided no shelter against the sun. He left them as they were.

Then Dhul Qarnayn went another way, till he reached a place between two mountains. Here, he found people who did not understand a word he said. They explained to Dhul Qarnayn, 'Ya'juj and Ma'juj are doing great mischief in the land. We will pay you a tribute if you erect a barrier between us and them.' Dhul Qarnayn agreed to erect the barrier, but he did not want a tribute. 'Allah has established in me the power to do what he wants me to do,' he said to the people. 'But you can help me erect the barrier.' When the people agreed, he asked them to bring him pieces of iron, and with those he filled up the gap between the mountains. Then he asked them to blow, and with their breath, he heated the iron. 'Bring me molten copper to pour over it,' he said, and with that he sealed the gap and created a strong wall. Ya'juj and Ma'juj were left powerless and could neither scale the wall nor dig through it. 'This is Allah's mercy,' Dhul Qarnayn told the people. 'But when it is time for him to fulfil his promise, He will reduce the wall to dust. On that day Ya'juj and Ma'juj will break lose and surge on one another, like waves of water. That will be the Day of Judgement, when Allah will gather all the people and send unbelievers to hell.'

One day the Prophet woke up with fear in his heart and told his wife, Zainab, that in his sleep he had seen that the destruction of the Arabs was upon them, because evil was fast approaching. 'Today, a hole has been opened in the barrier of Ya'juj and Ma'juj,' he said, making a circle with his index finger and thumb to describe the size of the hole.

Ya'juj and Ma'juj dig every day into the barrier that Dhul Qarnayn erected, until the light of the sun is almost visible to them. Then the one who is in charge of them says: 'Go back home and dig again tomorrow.' So they go home, and the wall is repaired back to its thickness. Ya'juj and Ma'juj return the following day and dig again to make a hole, but again they are told to go back, and, once again, the wall repairs itself. But they will surely return and resume digging the next day and the next.

Ya'juj and Ma'juj will dig until sunlight is almost visible, and the one in charge of them will say, 'Go back home and dig again tomorrow, if Allah wills.' But this time, when they return, they will find the wall exactly as they left it, with sunlight almost visible; and henceforth, every time they go back, they will leave a bigger hole and return to make it even bigger. This will continue until that day when Allah wishes to set them upon the people. That day they will dig through the wall. They will drink all the water of the earth, and people will flee to their fortresses with their herds. Ya'juj and Ma'juj will shoot their arrows into the sky and the arrows will fall back stained with blood, and they will think, 'We have killed the inhabitants of the earth, and now we have conquered the inhabitants of the heaven.' Then Allah will send down upon them a worm that will eat into their necks and kill them.

The Muslims, hiding in their cities and fortresses, will call out to each other to see who among them is brave enough to venture forth to see what Ya'juj and Ma'juj are doing. Then a brave man, hoping to be rewarded by Allah, will volunteer. He will see that Ya'juj and Ma'juj are dead, and, returning to the people, he will give them the good news. Then the people will come out of their fortresses and let their animals loose, who will then feed on the flesh and blood of Ya'juj and Ma'juj for nourishment. Then, for seven years, the Muslims will use the bows and arrows and shields of Ya'juj and Ma'juj for kindling. After Ya'juj and Ma'juj are gone, other signs that the Day of Judgement is arriving will be seen, one after another, until the trumpet, harkening the end of the world, is blown.[23]

Myth from the Holy Quran

48

ANOTHER KRISHNA?

Vasudeva Krishna had a contender, who claimed that he, not Krishna, was the true avatar of Vishnu.[24] His name was Vasudeva Paundraka, and he was the monarch of the kingdom of Pundra. When the belief first spread that Vishnu's new avatar was Vasudeva, and people began to see Vasudeva

Krishna in this role, Paundraka contended that he, too, was Vasudeva; therefore, who was to say which Vasudeva was the true avatar—Vasudeva Krishna or Vasudeva Paundraka?

Just as Krishna received the emblems of his divinity—the golden mace, the pink lotus, the shining discus, and the white conch, so did Paundraka. The only difference was that while Krishna received them from Vishnu, Paundraka obtained his from Shiva. Then he sent a message to Vasudeva Krishna: 'You fool, relinquish the chakra, give up your false claim to my badge of honour, my name, and my attributes that make me Vasudeva, and come and pay me homage, and I'll spare your life.'

When Krishna heard this message, he laughed. Then he sent his own messenger to convey to Paundraka: 'I will certainly dispatch my emblem and discus to you right away. Can you guess my meaning? I'll come to your city with my chakra and release it at you. Instead of paying you homage, I'll make sure that I never have to deal with you again.' Then summoning Garuda, Krishna mounted the bird and set off for Pundra.

The two Vasudevas met in the battlefield. Standing in his chariot, facing the enemy, Krishna saw that the king of Pundra had all the attributes needed to make him Vishnu's avatar, just as he himself had. He, too, was riding a chariot with the Garuda banner. He was also holding a golden mace, a lotus, and a bow that looked like the Sharanga bow, which Krishna had received from Varuna. Like Krishna, he was dressed in yellow pitambar and was wearing a garland of Vaijayanti flowers. He even had the mark of Srivatsa on his chest. There seemed no difference between the two, and Krishna realized that this Vasudeva could indeed be seen as Vishnu's avatar, especially since his claim was endorsed by the powerful king of Kashi. In fact, Kashi's forces were supporting Paundraka even in the battlefield. The only way Krishna could establish himself was by defeating the contender.

And so the battle began. Swords, maces, tridents and spears clashed, and arrows flew. Soon, bloodied warriors on both sides began to fall, and the battlefield became littered with arms and legs, severed heads and writhing humans and animals. For a while, both sides were equally matched. Then Krishna took up his mace and discus and wreaked havoc on the enemy's forces. Coming face to face with the king of Pundra, he challenged him, saying, 'Paundraka, you wanted me to surrender my insignia to you. I now deliver them to you. Here is my Sudarshana; here,

I give you my mace, and here is the real Garuda for your banner.' And so saying, he let fly the chakra and the mace. Paundraka's body fell to the ground in pieces, his chariot lay shattered, and his Garuda banner was shredded by Garuda himself.

The brave king of Kashi, a true friend to the last drop of blood, continued to fight Krishna, but, finally, Krishna shot an arrow that was so powerful that it sliced off the king's head and flung it all the way across the battlefield into the city of Kashi. When the inhabitants of Kashi saw the decapitated head of their king lying in the city, so far from the battlefield, they were flabbergasted.

Kashi's prince, Sudakshina, was enraged by his father's killing and wanted revenge. Taking the family priest with him, he went to pray to Shiva, who had furnished Paundraka with Vishnu's attributes to support his claim as the new avatar. Shiva manifested himself before the prince of Kashi and asked him what he desired. 'Through your favour, O Lord, let my revenge arise in a formidable form and destroy Krishna who has murdered my father,' Sudakshina begged.

'Granted,' Shiva said, and, immediately, from the southern fire, a vast and formidable female spirit sprang up. She was like a blazing fire, with her hair streaming like flames. Enraged, she yelled Krishna's name and sped towards Dwaraka, Krishna's city, to which he had returned after the battle. The people of Dwaraka were terrified to see this apparition, and they ran for protection to Krishna. He released his Sudarshana Chakra. When the creature with flaming hair saw Sudarshana spinning towards her, she tried to escape, but the chakra pursued her all the way to Kashi, Shiva's city. There, the army of Kashi and the hosts of demigods that attend to Shiva opposed Sudarshana with all kinds of weapons, but the divine and radiant chakra discharged such a terrible apocalyptic fire that flames consumed the fierce creatures and engulfed the city of Kashi. Kashi burned. All its inhabitants—elephants, horses, men, women, and children—died in the fire; its treasures, too—granaries, houses, palaces and markets—went up in flames. When the city of Shiva, that used to be inaccessible to even the gods, was nothing but ashes, Sudarshana Chakra returned to the hand of Krishna, the Vasudeva.

Myth from the Puranas

◆

49

THE ELEPHANT IS...

Once a royal retinue stopped at a village. It included many horsemen, who were the king's attendants, and an elephant that the king was riding. The village folk came to see the cortege. Amongst them were six blind men. All six had heard a lot about elephants but none had ever come across one. They requested the mahout to allow them to touch the elephant so that they might be able to get a true picture of the beast. When the mahout agreed, the first blind man stepped forward. He reached out his hand and found the elephant's ears. 'This beast is like a winnow,' he stated. Then the second man, who was standing near the front, reached out and touched the elephant's trunk. 'The beast is actually like a big wooden pestle,' he said. The next man found the tusks. 'These feel like windpipes,' he said. 'I think this beast is like a large windpipe.' The fourth man, who was crouching, reached out and made contact with the elephant's legs. 'No. No. This animal is like a big pillar.' When the fifth man extended his hand, he felt the stretch of the stomach. 'You're all wrong,' he declared. 'The elephant is actually like a water-bag.' The sixth man was standing in the rear and when he put out his hand, the animal was swishing its tail, so he caught hold of it. 'I don't know what you're all talking about,' he said. 'It appears to me that this beast is really like a thick rope.'

Now a quarrel broke out between the men, because each one thought that he was right, and the others were wrong. Then the mahout intervened: 'Each one of you has only perceived one limb, and you have jumped to a conclusion about the whole elephant.'

The blind men stopped quarreling and went their way.

Jain/Buddhist parable

◆

50

OLD AGE IS CHILDHOOD

A grandfather took his three-year-old grandson to the park. The grandson sat between his grandfather's knees and looked around him with wonderment, pointing at everything he saw. When he pointed at the roses, the grandfather said, 'Those are roses. They're red.' When he pointed at the grass, the grandfather said, 'That is grass; it's green.' When he pointed towards the sky, the grandfather said, 'That is the sky; it's blue.' Then a crow flew down from the top of a tree and landed in the grass before them. The boy pointed at the crow, and the grandfather said, 'That's a crow. It's black.'

Soon the crow flew away, and the boy was sad, but then another crow landed near their feet.

'Look, Dada. Crow,' the boy said excitedly, pointing at the crow.

'Yes, child, a crow,' the grandfather replied.

The crow continued to peck in the grass.

'Look, Dada. Crow,' the boy pointed again at the crow.

'Yes, child, a crow,' the grandfather repeated with a smile.

The crow pecked on, hopping closer to where they were sitting.

'Look, Dada. Crow,' the boy said again, his finger pointing at the bird.

'Yes, child, a crow,' the grandfather said, nodding and smiling.

All afternoon, whenever the child saw a crow, he exclaimed. 'Look, Dada. Crow,' and the grandfather acknowledged it patiently. Eventually, the sun began to set and all the crows flew away. The grandfather took his grandson by the hand, and they both walked home.

Thirty years passed. Now the grandfather was ninety years old and the boy, an adult. He lived away from his parents, had a rewarding career, and a successful marriage. Occasionally, he came home to visit his parents and his old grandfather, and whenever he came, he spent a few minutes on the terrace, where his grandfather often sat in a wheelchair, his mind wandering.

One day, when the young man was visiting his grandfather, a crow landed on the parapet.

'Look son, a crow,' said the grandfather.

'Yes, Dada, that's a crow for sure.'

The crow took flight briefly and then landed back on the parapet.

'Look son, a crow,' the grandfather said.

'It sure is,' the young man affirmed.

Once again the crow fluttered its black wings and took off, and then landed in the terrace at their feet.

'Look son, a crow,' the old man said.

'I know it's a crow, Dada. I can see it. You don't have to keep repeating it,' the young man snapped.

The grandfather looked at his grandson with a sad smile and said, 'When you were three, I listened to you say "crow" all afternoon.'

Folktale from Punjab

◆

51

MOTHERS, BE CAREFUL WHAT YOU SAY TO YOUR CHILDREN

Maharaja Ranjit Singh was a great proponent of Punjabi; however, his Empire's official language remained Persian, which was the language of the Mughals. Hence, if anyone aspired to become a court official, he had to formally learn Persian, which was taught only at elite schools. In Dipalpur there lived a middle-class, Punjabi Khatri family, who wanted their young son, Lalu Jas Rai,[25] to learn Persian, so they enrolled him in an expensive school. The boy was very smart and quickly picked up the language. One day, returning from school, he decided to test his skills on his illiterate mother.

'Mother, give me aab,' he said, using the Persian word for water.

The mother, who was busy in her kitchen, had no time to figure out what he meant. 'What?' she said, impatiently. 'What do you want?'

'Aab,' the boy said.

'I don't have time for this. Just tell me what you want.'

'Aab,' the boy repeated loudly. 'Give me aab.'

'Why are you bothering me? Ja nigar ja,' she said. (Go, vanish)

'Nigar jaavan?' (Should I vanish?) The boy asked his mother.

'Ja nigar ja,' she repeated.

The kitchen floor suddenly opened up and the boy began to sink into it.[26] The mother tried to grab her son, but all she could grasp was his bodi—his tuft of hair—and soon that, too, slipped out of her fingers, as her son slowly disappeared.

The mother was left lamenting:[27]

Aab aab kar moya bacha
Parasiyan ghar gale
Jo tu mang-da muyon pani
Bhar bhar dendi pyale

(The boy died saying, aab, aab
May the Persians be damned
If you had asked directly for water
I would have given you cups full)

Folktale from Punjab

◆

52

THE CITY OF MICE

There was a ruined city, whose human population was long dead, but mice had moved into it and made it their home. They lived there for generations, breeding and multiplying, till every nook and cranny and hole and crevice of the decaying buildings was occupied. The mouse community was happy and content, celebrating births, deaths, feasts, festivals, marriages, and life.

Time passed. One day an elephant chief, the lord of a thousand elephants, heard about a lake that was beyond the ruined city. He was told that it never dried, and its water was always cool and sweet. However, no one told him that the city was no longer uninhabited. Thereupon, the elephant chief led his huge herd through the city, not realizing that its streets were teeming with mice. As the herd passed through, the little creatures tried everything they could to save their lives, but the onslaught was just too immense. That day, hundreds and thousands of mice died, crushed under the massive feet of the elephants.

The whole city went into mourning. Wails and cries came from every corner, because each mouse family lost at least one or two of its members; in some households, whole families were wiped out. Then the mice elders called a meeting of the mice who remained, to discuss a recovery plan for the calamity and to strategize how to save the mouse race from elephants, in case the herd decided to return. Many plans of action were discussed, most of them concerning retaliation in some form, but they were all ultimately rejected for a simple reason: the undeniable physical difference between a mouse and an elephant. Finally, it was decided that the best course of action would be negotiation. 'I've heard that they're intelligent creatures who understand logic,' one of the elders said.

'And if logic doesn't work, we plead and beg,' said another.

'Maybe we should try a combination of both,' another elder advised.

Hence, a few of the mice elders went down to the lake and approached the lord of the elephant herd. 'We have a humble petition,' the eldest among the elders squeaked in a voice as loud as he could manage.

The lord of the elephants was just then spraying water from his trunk to cool his back and didn't hear the mouse.

The elder tried again, raising his voice till it cracked, 'May it please Maharaj, we have a humble petition to make.'

This time the elephant heard the small voice, but he couldn't see anyone. Then one of his herd gestured to the ground, and he looked down to see a dozen little creatures standing with their tiny hands folded.

'We are inhabitants of the city that you and your herd crossed on your way to this lake,' one of them said in a voice that the elephant had to strain his ears to hear. 'We have lived there for many generations, perpetuating our community, and we have prospered. Perhaps Maharaj and his companions did not see the members of our community who were going about their daily business. But when Maharaj and his companions crossed the city, hundreds and thousands of our community were crushed under your feet. We're afraid that if Maharaj returns to the lake with his herd, we'll be wiped out. Our humble request to Maharaj is that if it is not too much trouble for you, kindly take another path to the lake.'

As the elephant chief stood thinking about this request, another elder among the mice added, 'Although we are small, we may prove useful to Maharaj someday.'

The elephant chief thought about this some more and then consented. 'You have my deep apologies for having hurt your community,' he said. 'And you have my word that it will not happen again.'

The mice elders breathed a sigh of relief. 'We humbly offer you our friendship,' they said, their tails twitching in gratitude. The elephant chief raised his trunk in acceptance, and the mice elders returned to their city to convey the good news to their community.

Many months passed. Then a king of a nearby kingdom ordered his mahouts to capture more elephants for his stables. The men went into the forest, and using the allurement of a fake water-tank, captured the same herd of elephants that had crossed the city of mice. They lassoed each elephant with a thick rope and tied it to a tree, so as to bring the whole herd under control, before driving it to the king's stable. The lord of the elephants tried everything in his power to break his bonds, but after three days of captivity and many lacerations, he lost his energy and fighting spirit. Then he thought about his friends, the mice. Calling the only cow elephant that had escaped captivity, he told her to rush to the city of mice and tell them of their predicament. 'Tell them that in the name of friendship, we seek their help.'

The cow elephant sped to the city of mice and conveyed the chief elephant's message to the mice elders. Within minutes the elders had gathered their whole clan, and together they hurried to the forest where their elephant friends were tied up. Quickly climbing the trees, the mice gnawed through the ropes, and, soon, they had freed all the elephants. Then, together—mice and elephants—celebrated their friendship.

That is why it is said that one must make friends with both the powerful and the weak, because one never knows when one will need a friend.

Folktale from the Panchatantra

◆

53

TO HONOUR A FRIENDSHIP: THE LION AND THE JACKAL

Once upon a time, the Bodhisattva was a Lion living in a mountain cave. At the foot of the mountain was a water tank, and above it, the incline was covered in mud and soft green grass. Rabbits and deer and other such small creatures came there often to graze. One day the Lion came out of his lair and looked around, his eyes searching for food. On that day, there was a deer grazing on the incline. I'll eat that deer, thought the Lion, and he sprang towards it, but the deer scampered away, and the Lion landed in the mud. He tried to grab on with his great paws, but the muddy soil began to shift under his weight, and he slipped—all the way to the bottom, coming to stop only a few feet from the water. He now tried to pull himself out, but he realized that his paws had sunk in, and the more he tried, the deeper he sank. He was stuck. Seven days passed, with his paws fixed like four posts, and not a morsel to eat.

Then a Jackal, hunting for food, suddenly came upon the Lion, and seeing him, ran off in fear. But the Lion called out to him: 'Hey, Jackal, don't run away. I'm caught in the mud. Can you save me?'

The Jackal approached the Lion most cautiously. 'I could pull you out,' he said. 'But I'm afraid that as soon as you're free, you'll eat me.'

'Don't be afraid. I won't eat you,' the Lion promised. 'On the contrary, if you get me out somehow, I'll be very grateful and do you a great service.'

Accepting the Lion's promise, the Jackal began digging around the Lion's four paws, till the water from the lake seeped in and softened the mud some more. Then, sliding underneath the Lion, he said, 'You'll have to make one big effort, sir,' and pushed his head against the Lion's belly. Straining every muscle, the Lion pulled himself upwards and was finally able to scramble out of the mud. Once he was on dry land, he took a deep breath, and then he plunged into the lake and washed and scoured the mud from his body.

Soon, a buffalo came to drink at the tank, and the Lion leapt on it and killed it. Then, tearing up its flesh, he offered some to the Jackal. 'Friend,' he said. 'Come. Have some food.'

The Jackal took a few hesitant steps, and stretching its neck, grabbed some of the meat. The Lion then tore off a piece of meat for himself and settled down to eat it. Seeing him engrossed in his meal, the Jackal lost his fear, and soon the Lion and the Jackal were both eating in camaraderie. After the Jackal was satiated, he took another piece of meat in his jaws and turned to go. 'Who is that for?' the Lion asked.

'If you will allow me, respected sir, I'd like to take this for my mate, who is waiting for me at home.'

'What a great idea,' the Lion said and tore off a piece of meat to take to his own mate. Then he said to the Jackal, 'You don't have to leave right away. Come, sit with me on the mountain-top for a while.'

By this time the Jackal was feeling comfortable in the Lion's company, so he went with him. At the top of the mountain, the Lion showed him a cave that was adjacent to his own. 'Bring your lady and come and live next to me,' he said. 'We'll be great friends and I'll take care of you.'

The Jackal liked that idea very much and brought his mate to live in the second cave, beside the Lion's. The Jackal and the Lion began to hunt together, leaving their mates behind. They killed all kinds of creatures and feasted on them and then brought the leftover meat for their mates. They soon became great friends; however, the Lioness never quite accepted their friendship. In time, the she-Jackal and the Lioness each gave birth to two cubs, and while the she-Jackal urged her cubs to make friends with the lion cubs, the Lioness would not allow it. Yet, with each passing day, the Lion became fonder of his friend and his family, and the Lioness's resentment towards the Jackal family grew. When the two males left for the hunt, she plagued and threatened the Jackal's mate. She also told her cubs to frighten the Jackal cubs. Then one day, she told the she-Jackal. 'I'm telling you this for your own good and for the good of your children. Leave this place.'

That evening when the Jackal returned to his cave, his mate told him what the Lioness had said. 'I think she's trying to warn us,' she said. 'The Lion must be planning to kill us. I'm scared for my children. I think it's time for us to leave this place. Let's go back to our old cave. We were safe there.'

The Jackal was very distressed to hear this and decided to talk to the Lion. 'Friend,' he said to him the following morning, 'We've been here a long time. I don't want to outstay our welcome.'

'What're you saying?' the Lion replied. 'This is your home now.'

The Jackal thought it best to be honest. 'Actually, your Lioness has been scaring my mate and telling her to leave. Your cubs, too, have been bullying my cubs.'

The Lion was pained to hear what the Jackal was saying. 'I'm sorry, my friend,' he replied. 'I'll talk to my wife.' And that evening he said to the Lioness, 'Do you remember how once I was out hunting and didn't come back for a week?'

'Yes, I remember.'

'Do you know why I stayed away all that week? I was trying to catch a deer, and I made a miscalculation and got stuck in the mud instead. For seven days, I couldn't get out—a whole week without food. It was the Jackal who saved my life. I made him my friend and gave him my word that I would take care of him. A friend in need is a true friend—no matter his size or strength. Promise me that you'll never again dishonour my friendship by frightening his wife and children.'

When the Lioness heard this tale, she made peace with the Jackal's mate, and from then on, they all lived happily together. The young ones began to play together, and even after they grew up and their parents passed away, they remained friends. Through seven generations, their friendship remained unbroken.

Folktale from the Jatakas

◆

54

A PINCH OF SINDHUR

One morning, watching Sita put sindhur in the parting of her hair, Hanuman asked her, 'Why do you do that, Mata?'

'It's to ensure a long life for my husband—your Lord.' Sita replied.

'Really, Mata? Just by putting on sindhur one can do this?'

'That's what I've been told,' Sita said to him, smiling at his simplicity.

Hanuman bounded out of Sita's room and rushed to the market to find a pansari shop, and there he bought all the vermilion the grocer had—a gunny sackful. Then he tore open the sack and poured the red powder on himself.

That day, Sri Rama was holding court, and when Hanuman arrived in the assembly hall covered in vermilion from head to tail, the courtiers burst out laughing.

'What happened to you, dear friend,' Rama asked. 'Did you fall into a pit of sindhur?'

'No, my Lord. I poured it on myself.'

'Why would you do that?' Rama asked, surprised.

'If just a pinch in Mata's hair can extend your life, then surely a sackful will give you a long long life.'

When Rama look confused, Sita, who was sitting beside him, whispered in his ear the conversation that she had had with Hanuman that morning. Rama's eyes filled with tears at his friend's loving gesture. He got down from his throne and embraced Hanuman. Then he turned to the assembly and announced. 'This day—Tuesday—will henceforth be the day to honour the love that my dear friend, Pavanaputra Hanuman, feels for me. Whoever offers him oil and sindhur on this day, will please me, and I will grant his wishes.'

Folk-myth

55

THE SOURCE OF RIVERS AND HEROES IS UNKNOWN

When the Pandava and Kaurava princes completed their education in weaponry, their guru, Dronacharya, told the Kuru king, Dhritarashtra, that the time had come for them to showcase their talents before an audience. The blind king of Hastinapur was gratified to learn that his sons and nephews had become so accomplished, and he proudly commanded that preparations be made for a tournament.

An appropriate field was selected on the outskirts of Hastinapur, and after it was cleared and levelled, it was consecrated with mantras. Then the king's artisans built an arena and two gold-panelled, gem-studded pavilions—one for the king and his entourage, and one for the royal ladies and their attendants. They also built many spectator platforms around the arena for the citizenry of Hastinapur.

On the day of the tournament, amidst trumpeters and drummers and spectator cheers, Drona announced the name of each competitor, and, one by one, the young princes came into the arena to display the skills in which they were most proficient. Arjuna, who was the most accomplished of the princes, was the last to demonstrate his prowess. At the command of his guru, he entered the arena, wearing golden armour, holding his weapons, and slipping on his finger protectors. A shout of joy went up in the crowd. As the music from the musicians' stage started up and conch shells began to sound, the auditorium started to buzz: 'This is the son of Pandu.' 'He's the son of Indra deva.' 'He's the one who will protect the Kuru race.' 'The greatest archer!' 'The protector of virtue!' Hearing these high praises for her son, Kunti's heart swelled with pride and tears flowed down her cheeks.

Arjuna's skills were superlative: adeptly calling the Bhumi weapon, he created land that covered the arena like a second earth, and then, at his behest, it disappeared. When he called upon the Parvata weapon and uttered a mantra, a mountain arose in the centre of the stadium. Then, moving on to demonstrate his finesse in archery, he shot arrows at targets big and small, far and near—always hitting dead centre. He shot five arrows at one time, all hitting one target, followed by five hitting different targets. Then he shot twenty-one arrows, one after the other, in quick succession, into the hollow of a cow horn hanging from a rope swinging back and forth. After that he showed his dexterity with swords and clubs, beating his opponents in record time. With every feat he accomplished, thunderous applause hailed him as the greatest warrior, and the shouts of 'Bravo!' 'Bravo!' that arose from the stadium echoed in the three worlds.

Finally, Drona announced the end of the tournament. But as the musicians began to put away their instruments, the king's attendants started to queue up in order of rank, and the spectators began to quieten down, a distinct sound filled the arena. Everyone had heard it all day, but no one was expecting to hear it after the tournament concluded. It was the sound of someone slapping the muscles of his arms, declaring a challenge. All eyes turned to the gate of the arena, from where the sound was coming. Drona stood up, surrounded by the five Pandavas, and looked towards the gate, and Duryodhana, surrounded by his ninety-nine brothers, also peered keenly in that direction. Everyone wondered who this opponent was who had come to challenge the Kuru princes?

The sun was in its last length, but as the challenger walked into the arena, it seemed to brighten, lingering on him like the caress of a loving parent, highlighting the gold of his armour, and the jewels in his earrings. He was a handsome man with a face that had the complexion of burnished gold and arms with bulging muscles that flexed mightily as he sauntered into the centre of the arena.

This was Karna. He was Kunti's eldest son, born from Surya, the sun god, but nobody knew this, not even Karna himself. Kunti had conceived him at a very young age through a liaison-invoking mantra to the sun, but for fear of society's condemnation, she had abandoned him at birth, placing him in a basket that she put in the river. A charioteer, Adhiratha, had found the basket and brought the boy home to his wife, Radha, and they had adopted him. He grew up as a suta—a charioteer's son, and for the rest of his life, the suta race defined his status and role in society. However, deep in his heart, Karna felt like a fake, he didn't feel like a charioteer; he felt like a warrior, and all his inclinations were that of a warrior. This crisis of identity tortured his soul all his life.

Now, standing in the centre of the arena, Karna bowed indifferently to Drona and to the Kuru family's chief priest, Kripa, and issued the challenge—specifically to Arjuna. 'Oh Partha, I can perform all the feats you have performed, but better.' And he proceeded to do exactly that, performing every single feat that Arjuna had performed but with more artistry, precision, and better timing. Arjuna watched the hero with mounting disbelief and anger. On the other hand, Duryodhana, the Kaurava prince, was thoroughly impressed. He applauded every display of the warrior's superior prowess. Then he descended into the arena and embraced the hero. 'Welcome,' he said. 'The Kuru kingdom is at your service. You deserve whatever you desire.'

'Your saying so has already fulfilled all my desires,' Karna said to Duryodhana, gratefully. 'I only desire your friendship. And I want to engage Arjuna in single combat.'

'You have not been invited to this tournament,' Arjuna snapped.

'But the arena is meant for all. Kshatriya dharma is proved by prowess. Isn't it?' Karna asked.

Arjuna nodded peevishly, and obtaining permission from his guru to compete, he descended into the arena and faced his opponent. At that moment, clouds began to form in the sky, as though Indra was excited to see his son, Arjuna, perform his greatest triumph. Then the sun, in support of his own son, dispersed the clouds and spotlighted Karna, caressing him with his rays, glistening in his armour and earrings. Suddenly, Kunti stood up and stared at the hero. That armour and those earrings—her first son had been born with them. Her shock at seeing the son she had abandoned was so immense that she fainted. When her attendants revived her, her eyes darted again to Karna, and realizing that one brother was facing the other with weapons drawn, she almost fainted again. She tried to say something to stop them, but then she wondered what she would say; how would she explain it. Finally, she just sat there silently, dread pounding in her heart.

Kripa introduced the competitors: 'This is Partha, the youngest child of Kunti. He will duel this competitor who has issued a challenge.' Then, turning to Karna, he asked, 'O mighty-armed hero, who are you? Tell us your lineage. From which royal family do you hail? Who is your father? Who is your mother?'

A deep flush rose to Karna's cheeks, and then all colour drained from his face. His gaze, which had been proud, defiant, and clear, turned away, and his eyes clouded with an old angst.

Kunti saw Karna's distressed reaction to the question of his parentage and understood that he had been adopted by some lower caste family. Her heart went out to him. She was aware that all she had to do to give her son his rightful place in society and end his torment was to claim him, but she didn't. She remained silent, abandoning him to his fate again.

'Why ask the hero his lineage?' Duryodhana came and stood beside Karna and loudly questioned the audience. 'Our shastras state that three classes of men can claim royalty: a person of noble birth, heroes, and commanders of armies. But if Arjuna is unwilling to fight with someone who is not a king, I'll instal this hero on a throne this instance. I give him the kingdom of Anga.' Right then, Duryodhana called for a golden seat for Karna. A golden umbrella was raised over his head and yak tails were waved at his side. Brahmins began to utter mantras and consecrated water, rice, and flowers were showered on him, as he was ritually installed as the king of Anga.

As soon as he was anointed, Karna got up and embraced Duryodhana, his eyes moist with gratitude. 'What shall I give you in exchange?' he asked. 'I'll do whatever you command.'

'I only want your friendship,' Duryodhana replied, embracing him back, and then re-seating him on the throne.

Just then an old man entered the arena. His upper garment was hanging loose, and his body was trembling, as he walked hesitantly, with the help of a staff, towards the centre. Seeing him, Karna quickly got up from his golden seat, and rushing to him, touched his feet. 'Father!' he said. Adhiratha smelled his son's hair affectionately and embraced him, the tears from his eyes mingling with the drops of consecrating water of coronation on his son's forehead.

'A charioteer son?' the Pandavas jeered. 'He's a charioteer's son.'

'Take up the whip, my man,' Bhima mocked. 'A warrior's bow does not suit you. You are as unworthy to be the king of Anga as a dog is of receiving ghee from the sacrifice. Go back to your chariots. You don't belong here in this arena of Kshatriyas.'

Karna looked up at the sun with quivering lips, and sighed. But Duryodhana rose up again in anger, like a maddened elephant. 'The cardinal virtue of Kshatriyas is strength,' he declared to Bhima. 'You speak of birth? Is yours known? The source of heroes and rivers is unknown. Drona, our guru, was born in a water vessel, our priest Kripa, from a clump of earth. This mighty warrior here has all the marks of a Kshatriya—his armour and earrings, his proud countenance, his handling of weapons. Who says he's not a Kshatriya? This warrior with his most excellent talents deserves to be king of not just Anga but of the whole world. If anyone here has doubts about his royal status as king of Anga, get into your chariot and prepare to face me on the battlefield.'

The crowd cheered, and the sun, as though satisfied at the outcome of the day, finally descended. The stadium was lit with lamps, and people began to return home. Duryodhana took Karna's hand and led him out of the arena to his palace, the path to it lit with a thousand lamps.

Myth from the Mahabharata

◆

56

MURDAN KHAN

A soldier, who used to work for the East India Company, lived with his old, widowed mother. For a while they lived on the salary he had received from his service, but when that money ran out, they fell on hard times. One day the son said to his mother, 'If I had fifty rupees, I would go and search for work.' The old mother took out the money from her meagre savings and handed it to her son.

Bidding his mother farewell, the young man took the path that led out of town. He had gone only a short distance when he saw a large crowd by the side of the road. As he came closer, he saw a corpse lying on the ground and a grave already dug, but there was a man in the crowd who was not allowing the corpse to be buried. People remonstrated, but the man seemed adamant.

'Why won't you let him be buried?' the young man asked the man who was protesting.

'Because he owes me fifty rupees. If someone here can repay that debt, I'll let him be buried.' No one in the crowd was willing to pay the dead man's debt. Without a second thought, the young man pulled out all the money from his bag and paid the debt, and, finally, the corpse was buried.

When he returned home, his mother was surprised to see him and asked him what happened. 'I bought goods worth lakhs of rupees with that fifty rupees, but now I have no money to hire a carriage to bring it all home,' the young man replied. 'I need fifty more rupees for that.' His mother only had fifty rupees remaining in her savings, but she gave him the money.

The young man started out again. When he came to the spot where the corpse had been buried, he met a soldier armed with a sword and shield. They began talking and sharing stories about who they were and where they were going:

'I had fifty rupees,' the young man told the soldier. 'But I paid a debt for a corpse that is buried near where you are standing, so I had to return home. But now I have fifty more rupees, and I'm going somewhere to look for work.'

'My name is Murdan Khan,' the soldier told the young man. 'I, too, have fifty rupees, and I, too, am going to look for work.'

The two soldiers decided to join forces and, together, they arrived in a certain town that had a river running through the middle of it. It divided the town into two, and no one crossed from one bank to the other. When the two young men asked why this was so, the townspeople told them that there used to be a time when people crossed freely and often, but no one had crossed for the past fifty years, and if anyone did attempt to sail across, the boat sank as soon as it got to the middle of the river.

'This means that people on one side don't have access to goods that are sold on the other side,' Murdan Khan said to his partner. 'That means, if we can take goods from one side to the other side, we could really build our profits.'

The young man agreed. So they bought goods worth seventy-five rupees, but when they tried to hire a boat to take them and the merchandise across, no boatman was willing. Murdan Khan then rented an old boat and decided to row it himself. After they had loaded all the goods in the boat, Murdan Khan set out with a drawn sword. This news spread rapidly through both sides of the town, and people came to watch the tragedy that would surely happen. When the boat was half way across, a hand rose out of the water, grabbed the boat, and tried to pull it under, but Murdan Khan was ready. He struck at the hand with his sword, and cut it off, and the severed hand fell into the boat.

Finally, the boat made it across, and the crowd burst into applause. Amidst loud cheers and much back-slapping, Murdan Khan offloaded his goods, which he then sold at a profit. When he went back, his partner asked him how he had managed all this and whose hand he had cut. 'That's a jinn's daughter,' Murdan Khan told him. 'She had vowed to marry a man, but he died. Now she sinks all boats that cross the river in the hope of finding another suitable man.'

'How do you know this?' the young man asked.

'I know the science by which secrets are disclosed,' he replied.

The two men then picked up the severed hand, and removing the jewellery from it—a bracelet, two finger rings and a thumb ring—went to a jeweller. When they showed the bracelet to the jeweller, he was flabbergasted. 'This is so valuable that it's worth a year's revenue of a kingdom,' he said. 'Where did you get it from? Who did you steal it from?'

The two young men tried to explain, but the jeweller called the kotwal. Murdan Khan then explained to the policemen about the jinn's daughter in the river. 'I also have three rings that belong to her,' he stated. The kotwal grabbed the two young men and took them to the king, and, once again, Murdan had to explain how he had severed the hand of the jinn's daughter and got the jewellery. 'She won't bother the town anymore,' he added. 'People can now freely cross to the other side.' The king not only believed Murdan Khan, but also he was so pleased to hear that his town had been liberated, he gave Murdan Khan a large reward. Murdan Khan then presented the bracelet and the rings to the king. 'For the princess,' he said.

When the king presented the jewellery to his daughter, she was entranced by its beauty, but she complained that it was only half a set. 'I want the other bracelet,' she demanded.

The king sent the bracelet to all the jewellers in the city to see if they could make a replica of it, but none of them could do it. The princess was very unhappy to learn this and refused to eat or drink till she could wear the pair of bracelets. In a quandary then, the king called Murdan Khan back and told him that if he got the other bracelet, he could marry the princess.

'That's very generous of you, Maharaj,' Murdan Khan replied. 'But I can't marry yet. However, I have a brother, who is with me, and whose marriage I am eager to arrange. If I get you the bracelet, will you accept my brother as your son-in-law?'

'Yes, yes,' said the king. 'Just get the bracelet.'

Murdan Khan went to the river's edge and dove in. He went deeper and deeper into the water, till he reached the jinn's palace. There he presented himself as a physician. The jinn's daughter was suffering from the excruciating pain of a severed hand, and the jinn had announced a large reward for anyone who could cure her. Before diving into the water, Murdan Khan had put the hand he had severed into his pocket, so when he was taken to the bedchamber of the jinn's daughter, he quickly sent everybody out and told the jinn's daughter to close her eyes. As soon as he fixed the hand on to he stump, it became whole.

The jinns were astonished at his skill and wanted to reward him handsomely, but he only wanted the second bracelet of the pair. The jinn gave him that and also many other jewels, and Murdan Khan returned to the king's palace, where he handed over the bracelet. He also gave the king all the other jewels he had received from the jinn. 'For the princess,' he said. 'A wedding gift.' The king was very relieved and, keeping his end of the bargain, married his daughter to the young soldier that Murdan Khan presented as his brother.

When the young man went home with his new bride and new friend and all the expensive presents he had received from the king, everyone in his town wanted to know how, in such a short time, he had gone from being a destitute soldier to the king's son-in-law. 'It's all because of my friend, Murdan Khan,' he said.

Murdan Khan stayed with the soldier and his family for a few days and then took his leave, but the young man was loath to let him go. 'What kind of a man do you think I am that I'll keep all this wealth to myself?' he said. 'Stay here with me and we'll enjoy it together.'

'It's not in my power to stay,' Murdan Khan replied.

'Why?'

'I'm the corpse whose debt you paid and helped bury. Now I've repaid my debt to you, and it's time for me to go. May Allah be with you,' he said and disappeared.

Folktale from North India

◆

57

HOW MAN AND DOG BECAME FRIENDS

There was once a happy family of a mother dog and her two young puppies. One day, a deer killed the mother dog without any reason. The orphaned puppies, angry at the callousness of the deer, wanted to avenge their mother's death. They approached the biggest animal in the forest, the elephant, and begged him to help them kill the deer. The elephant was very sympathetic to their cause and agreed to help. So together, they went looking for the deer, but soon the elephant discovered that the dogs barked at every sound in the forest. 'You have to stop barking,' he told the pups. 'I'm afraid that your barking will draw the tiger's attention, and this will put all of us in danger. If you can't stop barking, then I'm sorry I can't help you.' The puppies tried very hard not to bark, but how could they not bark? It was their instinct.

Leaving the elephant, the dogs went to the tiger and begged his help in avenging their mother. The tiger also agreed, but he, too, could not abide the dogs' constant barking. He prided himself on his stealth, and he was afraid that their barking would render that useless and give away his location to man, who was always hunting him. So he, too, refused.

Now the dogs went straight to man and told him the story of their mother's death and how they were seeking revenge. 'Can you please help us kill the deer?' they asked.

Man was filled with compassion, and he promised he would help them. 'Come and stay with me,' he said to them. 'I'll give you food and shelter.'

Every night, when Man and his family slept, the dogs remained alert to every sound, barking at anything that sounded out of the ordinary. Man felt very safe with the dogs watching his house and appreciated their behaviour. Soon the dogs and Man became good companions. Man fed them and took care of them and they, in return, followed him wherever he went during the day, and guarded his house at night. Then, one day, the dogs reminded Man about his promise.

'Sure. Let's find the deer,' Man said, and the three of them went into the forest and soon found the deer. While Man hid behind a tree, the dogs chased the deer in his direction, and when the animal drew near, Man shot an arrow at it and killed it. The dogs were ecstatic. They came to the man with their tails wagging, and then bit off the right leg of the deer. Man brought the dead deer home, and his family roasted its meat and had a feast.

From that day onwards, Man promised the dogs that if they would watch his house and help him hunt, he would give them shelter, feed them, and also give them the right leg of every animal he killed. The dogs happily agreed, and ever since then, man and dog have been friends.

Folktale from a Naga tribe

◆

58

GOPAL, MY FRIEND

There was an eight-year-old boy who lived with his mother on the outskirts of a town. His mother worked all day, cleaning dishes in other people's houses. She barely made enough to feed her son, but she always put aside money to pay for his school fees. The boy went to the only school in that town, but to get there he had to cross a small forest. Every morning, he would beg his mother to accompany him to school, because he was afraid of being alone in the forest, which was full of fearful sounds and dark shadows.

'I can't come, my dear child,' the mother would reply, holding her son in her arms, her eyes filling with tears. 'If I'm late, that sethani will throw me out. Then how will we eat?'

'But I'm all alone,' the boy would cry.

One day, sick at heart, the boy's mother told him. 'Why don't you make friends with Gopal? Then you won't be alone any more. He'll come and help you cross the forest.'

'I don't know any Gopal. Where is he? Where does he live?'

'When you feel frightened in the forest, just call his name, and he'll come and meet you; he'll also hold your hand and help you cross to the other side.'

That day, as the boy passed the first line of trees in the forest and heard the roar of an animal close by, he squeezed his eyes shut and called, 'Gopal. Where are you? Ma says you'll be my friend. I could really use a friend right now. I'm so scared.'

Suddenly, he felt someone take his hand, and when he opened his eyes, he saw beside him a boy who was a few years older than him. He was wearing a yellow dhoti and was holding a flute. Smiling, he said to the boy, 'I'm here. You have nothing to be afraid of. Come. I'll walk you across to the other side.'

'Where'd you come from?'

'I live right here in the forest. That's why when you called, I heard you right away.'

From that day onwards, the boy called his friend every morning when he reached the forest, and he came and walked with him to the other side. After school, too, the boy found his friend waiting at the edge of the trees, and the two walked back, laughing and playing games. They became fast friends, and the forest became a happy playground for the boy.

Seeing her son's transformation from a fearful, timid little child to a cheerful and confident boy the mother wondered. She was sure it had to do with his gaining courage to cross the forest by himself. 'Are you not scared of the forest now?' she asked one day.

'Not at all,' the boy replied. 'Because my friend, Gopal, comes every day, and I'm not afraid when he's with me.'

Fear struck the mother's heart. 'What does your friend look like?' she asked urgently, afraid that some stranger with bad intentions was meeting her son every day.

'I don't know. He's a boy,' her son said, simply.

'How old is he? What does he wear? What does he say to you?'

'I don't know. I think he's older than me. He's taller than me, and I don't feel afraid when he's with me.'

'What do the two of you do?'

'Nothing. He holds my hand and we walk through the trees. Sometimes, we kick stones, and sometimes, we just talk. I tell him about you and how hard you have to work.'

'What does he wear?'

'A yellow dhoti. Oh, and he has a flute. Sometimes, he plays it for me.'

Listening to her son describe his friend, the mother felt a strange sense of joy replace her fears. She had a feeling that the Lord himself had befriended her little boy.

One day, the school's headmaster announced that there was to be a celebration at the school, and every student was to contribute either money or food.

Getting ready for school on the morning of the function, the boy remembered that he was supposed to bring something as contribution and asked his mother. 'Oh, my child, I have nothing to give you,' she replied, gathering him up in a hug. 'I'm sorry.'

He pushed her away. 'All the other boys will make fun of me and the teachers will get angry. They said everyone had to get something.'

'Why don't you ask your friend, Gopal, to help you? Perhaps, he'll give you something to take to school.'

'He looks pretty poor himself,' the boy said dejectedly, knowing he had no choice but to suffer the jeers of his schoolmates and teachers.

When Gopal joined him in the forest that day and asked him why he looked so morose, he told him about the celebration in school and how everyone was supposed to bring something. 'Ma has nothing to give me,' he said in a small voice. 'Everyone will make fun of me.'

'Wait here a moment,' Gopal said to him. 'I'll be right back.' He went away and then returned shortly with a small jar filled with milk. 'Here,' he said, handing it to the boy. 'You can contribute this.'

In school, the headmaster was making kheer in a large pot, and when the boy handed over his jar of milk to him, he looked disdainfully at it and said, 'One tiny jar of milk. That's all? Other students brought sacks of rice and platters of mithai.' Then he poured the milk from the jar into the pot and was about it set it aside when he saw that it was full of milk again. Shaking his head in confusion, the headmaster emptied it into the kheer one more time, but as soon as it was empty, it was full again. the headmaster kept emptying jar after jar of milk, till his arm became tired and the pot became full to the brim, but there was no depleting the milk. 'Who gave you this jar?' he asked the boy suspiciously.

'My friend, Gopal.'

'Gopal? Who is this? Some magician?'

'No masterji. He's my friend. He lives in the forest and helps me cross it every day. When he's with me, I'm not afraid.'

'Tomorrow, I want you to bring your friend, Gopal, to school,' the headmaster ordered the boy.

The next day, when the boy met Gopal, he told him that his headmaster wanted to see him. 'Will you come with me?' he asked. Gopal didn't reply, and when they reached the other end of the forest, he went away.

'I tried to bring him,' the boy told the headmaster, 'but he didn't want to come.'

'I knew you were lying yesterday.' The headmaster grabbed the boy by the arm in a punishing grip, and twisting his ear with the other hand, yelled, 'Now tell me the truth; who gave you the magic jar? I know your mother is too poor, so you obviously stole it. Tell me who gave it to you?' he shouted, and reached behind him for the jar that he had placed on a table. But the jar had disappeared. Then, the headmaster heard a voice in his head: 'I'm here. I'm everywhere. Your own evil prevents you from seeing me.'

The headmaster dropped the boy's arm as though it had burned him, and without saying another word, he rushed into his office and locked the door.

That evening, after school, the boy stood at the edge of the forest and waited for his friend, but he didn't come. The boy called his name: 'Gopal! Gopal!' a number of times, but his friend didn't even respond. Somehow, the boy knew in his heart that he would never see his friend again, but, strangely, he wasn't sad. After a while, he began walking home by himself. The shadows in the forest were long and the calls of wild animals were all around him, but the boy wasn't afraid anymore.

Children's folktale

◆

59

A QUARREL THAT CREATED A CLAN

Devayani and Sharmishtha were best friends and bitter rivals. They had grown up together and were now young women trying to outdo each other in every way they could. Sharmishtha was the daughter of the asura king, Vrishaparva, and Devayani was the daughter of Shukra, the chief priest and guru of the asuras. One day the girls went with their friends to bathe in a lake. At that time, Indra, in a mood of mischief, took the form of the wind and swept into disarray all the girls' clothing that was lying near the lake. When the girls emerged from the water, they quickly put on whatever fit them. Sharmishtha had on a garment that was Devayani's, and the two got into a fight. The Brahmin's daughter confronted the king's daughter: 'How dare you wear my clothes?' she said. 'My father is your father's guru. How dare you show such disrespect to me?'

'You're the one who knows no respect,' Sharmishtha replied. 'I'm a king's daughter; you're a beggar's daughter. Your father chants my father's praises, and my father is the one for whom praises are chanted. Your father lives on alms, and my father gives alms. You can cry and weep or get all huffy. I don't even need to listen to you, because you're below me in every way.'

Sharmishtha's words made Devayani so angry that she grabbed her shirt and tried to tear it off, but Sharmishtha pushed her away and then shoved her until she stumbled and fell into a dry well. Then, warning her maids and friends about the consequences of tattling, she went home. Devayani sat in that well for hours, crying for help and weeping. At last, she heard someone say, 'Who are you, beautiful young lady, and what are you doing in the well?' When she looked up, she saw the handsome face of a young man peering down at her. This was King Yayati. He had been hunting and was looking for water.

'I'm Guru Shukra's daughter,' Devayani told him. 'I fell in. My father doesn't know where I am and will be worried. Can you pull me out, please?' she said, extending her right hand.

Yayati grabbed her hand and pulled her out of the well, and after making sure she was unhurt, got on his horse and left. Devayani sat down by the well, deciding not to go home. In fact, she decided she would have nothing more to do with the city of Princess Sharmishtha. And that is exactly what she told her friend, Ghumika, who came looking for her.

'Go home and tell my father everything that happened and tell him that I'm never returning,' she declared.

When Shukra heard what had happened to his daughter, he rushed to the forest, but seeing Devayani unhurt, he tried to pacify her. 'Friends quarrel sometimes,' he said, 'but then they also forgive each other and make up. Besides, in a quarrel, there's fault on both sides. I'm sure that you must have done something that hurt Sharmishtha.'

'But she called you a vandi—someone who chants the praises of others. She said that people hire you to chant praises and that you live on charity. She said I was a beggar's daughter. Am I really the daughter of a hired chanter and a beggar who lives on charity, Father?'

'Of course not. You are the daughter of a Brahmin, who everyone respects, even King Vrishaparva. Come now, let's go home.'

'I'll never go to that city again. My enemy, Sharmishtha, lives there, and her father rules there.'

'Dear daughter, one who can subdue anger is the one who can rule the earth. Come now, spit out your anger and make up with your friend.'

'I know the difference between anger and forgiveness, Father, and in this instance, I can't forgive, because I was insulted. Sharmishtha's cruel words are still burning inside me and will probably kill me. I'll not go back to that city—ever. If you don't care about your daughter, you go. I'll stay right here till I die.'

Try as he might, Shukra could not appease his daughter, so, finally, he asked, 'What can I do to make you change your mind?'

'If that asura king really bows before you, then let him come personally and tell me himself.'

Shukra was aware that his daughter was being stubborn and unreasonable, but he loved her very much and had always catered to her wishes. He also knew that he was indispensable to the asuras, because without his mystical knowledge and cosmic secrets, the asuras stood no chance against the devas. Hence, he did not hesitate to tell Vrishaparva about what had happened between the girls and also Devayani's condition for returning home. 'If you don't do this,' he warned, 'I'll have no choice but to leave the asura kingdom, as my daughter desires.'

Vrishaparva acquiesced, and the two fathers went to the forest where Devayani was still sitting with a puffed up, angry face. 'Dear daughter,' Vrishaparva said, bowing before her. 'Accept my apology on my daughter's behalf. Your father is the most revered in this city. No one is more powerful than he. Let alone myself, even Indra bows to him in reverence. Tell me what you want. No matter how difficult it may be to acquire it, I'll give it you.'

'I want Sharmishtha to be my maid-servant, along with her one thousand maids—for the rest of her life. Even when I marry, she must follow me to my house of marriage.'

The asura king was taken aback at the girl's harsh demand, but he knew he had no choice. He sent a maid to fetch Sharmishtha and then appealed to his daughter, 'The fate of the asura race is in your hands, dear child,' he said to her. 'Think carefully and make good decisions that will benefit our clan.'

'I'll do it, Father, even though I'll suffer for the rest of my life.'

Hence, Sharmishtha came to live with Devayani as her hand-maiden. Her one thousand maids also came with her and lived with the one thousand maids that Devayani owned.

Many months passed. Then one spring morning, Devayani took Sharmishtha and all their maids to the forest for a picnic. They all wandered about, eating fruits from the trees and drinking honey from the flowers, and then they lay around languorously, slightly intoxicated. It so happened that Yayati, too, was in the forest that day. He had been hunting and was thirsty, and searching for water, he came upon the glade where the women were enjoying their leisure. There, he saw Devayani, who was reclining on the grass surrounded by her maids—an alluring princess decked in beautiful ornaments, voluptuous in her languor. He didn't recognize her, because the last time he had seen her, her clothes had been torn and her face had been streaked with dirt. 'Who are you, beautiful maiden?' he asked.

Devayani had recognized Yayati as soon as he had come into the glade, and she had already sent a maid home to fetch her father and Vrishaparva. 'I'm the daughter of Rishi Shukra, who is the guru of the asuras,' she replied to Yayati. 'My name is Devayani, and this is Sharmishtha, the daughter of the asura king, Vrishaparva. Don't you recognize me? You pulled me out of the well.'

Yayati did remember that maiden and was mystified by the change in her. 'How is it that a king's daughter is taking care of you like a maid-servant?' he asked.

'It's all fate,' Devayani smiled. 'And it's also fate that you're here. I want to be your wife and serve you, along with my two thousand maids. Be my husband.'

'I'm honoured, but how can I? You are the daughter of a Brahmin, and I am a Kshatriya. We're not matched. You are far superior than I.'

'I don't care about that, and my father will never oppose my wishes. Besides, Kshatriyas and Brahmins have been mixing ever since the caste orders were created. In any case, you and I are already bound. Don't you remember, you took my right hand when you pulled me out of the well?'

Just then Devayani's father and the asura king arrived, and she told them of her desire to marry Yayati. Shukra had no objection and bestowed Devayani on Yayati, and the asura king presided over the auspicious ceremony. 'Take care of her with virtue,' Shukra told his son-in-law. Then he gave Sharmishtha to Yayati, as well, because she was bound to Devayani. 'Always respect her,' he said to him. 'And do not take her to your bed.'

Devayani and Yayati left for Yayati's capital, along with Sharmishtha and their two thousand maid servants. Yayati set up his wife in his palace and, at Devayani's request, he also had a house built for Sharmishtha. It was at a distance from the main palace, in the grove of Asoka trees, and Sharmishtha lived there with her one thousand maids. Many years passed in happiness. Then Devayani gave birth to a son. In the meantime, Sharmishtha, too, came of age. However, the older she got, the more despondent she became; she had no prospects of finding a husband or having children, and she wondered if her youth and beauty would be in vain.

Then, one day, finding herself alone in the palace with Yayati, Sharmishtha decided to do something about her situation. 'Do you find me beautiful?' she asked the king.

'Of course. You're very beautiful and you're also of high birth,' Yayati replied.

'Then let me have a child with you.'

'I can't. You know as well as I that Rishi Shukra specifically instructed me not to take you to my bed.'

'Think of it as a permissible lie. You are a king who knows virtue. You must know that there are occasions when speaking a lie is more virtuous than telling the truth. A lie is sinful only when the object to be accomplished is harmful.'

'I know what the scriptures say about truth and lies. But, as you have so aptly pointed out, I am also king. A king should be a model in the eyes of his people. If I lie, my people will think of me as flawed.'

Sharmishtha could see that she would not win the argument on ethical grounds, so she tried a different tactic: 'I'm Devayani's slave, and since Devayani is your wife, anything she owns is yours; therefore, I'm yours.'

Yayati smiled at Sharmishtha's logic; it was hardly persuasive, but he could not deny his growing attraction to the asura princess, so he himself presented a way by which he could have Sharmishtha and also escape the blame. 'It's one of my strict vows to grant whatever is asked of me. So, ask me, and I'll have to give it you.'

'I ask that you save me from sin. By becoming a mother, I'll perform one of the most pious acts. Because if I can't have you, I may never take another man to my bed, and I'll remain childless, which is a grave sin for a woman. '

Yayati took Sharmishtha out of the palace and deep into the trees where he made love to her till their desire was satiated. After that, he began to visit her regularly in the Asoka grove. In time, Sharmishtha gave birth to a son who had eyes like lotus leaves. When Devayani heard about this, she was distressed on Sharmishtha's behalf. 'Oh, dear girl,' she said to her, 'What is this sin you have committed out of lust.'

'I would never indulge in such sin,' Sharmishtha assured Devayani. 'I asked a rishi who was learned in Vedas and capable of granting boons to grant me a son. All very virtuous.'

Devayani believed her and the two friends continued to live their lives, watching their two sons grow. Years passed. Devayani had one more son from Yayati, and Sharmishtha, who continued her clandestine affair with Yayati, bore two more sons, but she kept them secret from Devayani. However, one day, while Devayani was riding in her chariot with Yayati in an area of the royal grounds that she had never seen before, she saw three beautiful boys and was quite surprised. 'Who are these children?' she asked her husband. 'They look like they have royal blood. In fact, they quite resemble you.' Then she called the boys to her and asked them who was their father. All three boys pointed at Yayati. 'And your mother?' Devayani asked in a trembling voice. 'Our mother is Sharmishtha, the asura king's daughter.'

Devayani rushed to Sharmishtha's house and confronted her. 'How dare you steal my husband?' she screamed. 'Shame on you, you asura woman. You have today proved your asura nature.'

'I've done nothing wrong,' Sharmishtha replied calmly. 'You had a right to choose your husband and you chose the king. I, too, had the right, and I too chose my husband.'

Devayani then turned to Yayati, who had followed her. 'I'm leaving you,' she screamed at him. 'How dare you cheat on me?' Then she got into her chariot, and directing her charioteer, sped to her father's house. Yayati followed close behind in another chariot, calling her, beseeching her to stop and listen. At her father's house, Devayani fell into Shukra's arms, sobbing. 'O Father, once again that two-faced asura girl has hurt me. She stole my husband and has borne three sons. I have only two sons. And that man—who promised you that he wouldn't take Sharmishtha to his bed, who everyone says is full of virtue—is nothing but a cheat and a liar.'

By this time, Yayati had arrived at Shukra's house, and he stood shamefaced before the rishi. Shukra first upbraided him, 'O king, you have made vice your favourite pursuit even though you know the tenets of virtue.' Then, he cursed Yayati: 'Since you have cheated on my daughter with your youthful libido, I curse you that you will lose that youth and become decrepit.'

'Please listen to me, venerable Rishi,' Yayati fell at Shukra's feet. 'I was solicited by that asura woman. She begged me to make love to her. She said it would be my sin not to grant her a child when she asked me for it. The scriptures say that he who doesn't grant the prayer of a woman in season commits the sin of killing an embryo. And he who doesn't fulfil a woman's sexual desire also commits a grave sin. I was only following the injunction of the scriptures and following the path of virtue. It was out of my fear of committing sins that I listened to Sharmishtha. I'm begging you to take back your curse. Think of your own daughter. She's still young, and we still desire each other. If I'm decrepit, she too will suffer.'

Shukra realized the truth of what Yayati was saying—that by cursing him he had basically condemned his daughter to live with a decrepit old man for the rest of her life. But a curse once uttered can't be taken back, so Shukra had to quickly think of an alternative. 'My words will not be falsified,' he said, 'but, if you wish, you can transfer this decrepitude to another man. That is, if someone is willing enough to take it. But my words will be true.'

Suddenly, the handsome Yayati was attacked by old age. His face grew wrinkled, his teeth and hair fell out. His eyes, that used to shine like jewels, became sunken and cloudy. His body, that used to stand tall, erect, and strong like a mountain, became hunched and sagging, and his limbs that used to be muscular and supple, became limp and weak.

Staggering under the weight of old age, Yayati returned to his palace and sought out Yadu, his eldest son from Devayani. 'Dear son,' he appealed. 'Shukra's curse has turned me into an old man, but I'm not done enjoying my youth. Lend me your youth. I promise that after one thousand years,

I'll return it to you. Will you do this for your father?'

'It's no fun being old,' his son replied. 'All kinds of problems with eating and drinking occur in old age, and an old man becomes cheerless; even friends abandon him, because he becomes a burden. I'm sorry Father, but I can't accept your old age.'

'Oh Son, you have sprung from my heart. Since you won't fulfil this small request made by your father, I curse you that your offspring will never be ruling kings.'

Then Yayati called Turvasu, his second son from Devayani, and made the same request. 'I don't like old age,' the boy replied. 'It destroys all pleasures and enjoyments, strength and beauty, intellect and memory. I have no desire to be old. Sorry, Father.' And Yayati cursed this son too: 'Your line will be extinct. All the people in your kingdom will practice immorality; they'll be Mlechhas.' Then he called Druhyu, the eldest of Sharmishtha's children, and made the same request to him, but Druhyu also refused him, and Yayati cursed him: 'Your cherished desires will never be fulfilled. You'll be king only in name. You'll rule over a region where there will be no roads for horses, elephants, and chariots; the only means of transportation will be rafts and floats.' And when his next son, Anu, refused him, he cursed him, as well: 'Your sons will die as soon as they become youths, and you won't be able to perform any fire sacrifices to absolve your sins.'

Finally, Yayati called Puru, his youngest son from Sharmishtha. 'Dear Son, as you can see, I have been transformed into an old man because of Shukra's curse. But I'm not yet ready to enter old age, I'm still enjoying my youth. If you take my decrepitude upon you, I can enjoy the pleasures of life for one thousand more years. After that, I'll return your youth to you and take back my old age. Will you do this for me, Son?'

'You're my father, and it is my duty to fulfil your desire. I'll take on your decrepitude.'

'My dearest son, you are dearest to me.' Yayati embraced his son, his heart brimming with gratitude and love. 'I grant you a boon. You'll be a great king. The people of your kingdom will be happy and prosperous, and your reputation will spread far and wide.'

As they embraced, Yayati's old age slipped off his body like a snake sloughing off its skin and shrouded Puru's body.

After one thousand years, when Yayati returned Puru to his youth, he also named him his successor. Puru became a great king and was the progenitor of the famous Puruvansha, from which the Kuru heroes of the *Mahabharata*—the Pandavas and Kauravas—hail.

Myth from the Mahabharata

◆

60

DISTRIBUTION OF INDRA'S SIN

Tvashtri was a powerful asura and a great ascetic. He created Trishiras—a mysterious son who had three faces that were like the sun, moon, and fire—a whole universe in himself. With the intellect of one, he read the Vedas, with the mouth of the second, he drank wine, and with the eyes of the third, he looked upon the eight cardinal points. Trishiras was a gentle ascetic—controlled, truthful, and austere in his practices. In fact, his asceticism was so exemplary that Indra was afraid he would surely replace him as king of gods, so he began to devise ways to make him falter. He commanded his apsaras to go to him and entice him. 'Do everything in your wiles to bewitch his three heads and make him restless with lust,' he said. The beautiful damsels tried very hard to break Trishiras's discipline with their graceful hips, luscious curves, and sensual gestures, but the equanimous ascetic did not lose a breath or move a hair.

When sexual allurement didn't work, Indra decided to use physical force. He struck Trishiras with his thunderbolt and the three-headed ascetic fell to the earth, like a summit loosened from the mountain. But, even seeing him felled, Indra felt no peace, because although dead, Trishiras' lustre still shone bright. His three heads still looked vital and his eyes still looked at Indra with a fiery gaze. Blinded with the energy that was still emanating from Trishiras, the king of gods felt defeated, despite his victory, so he began to contemplate how he could annihilate the dead ascetic. Just then, a woodcutter came by, carrying his axe on his shoulder.

'Quickly. Cut down the heads of this being,' Indra ordered the woodcutter.

'This man has huge shoulders,' the woodcutter replied. 'My axe won't go through them.'

'I'll make your axe equal to my thunderbolt, and it'll be able to deliver the cut. I've already killed him, I just need you to cut off his heads,' Indra told him.

'But how can I perform an act that is considered wrong by virtuous people? Who are you and why have you committed this cruel act?'

'I'm Indra, the king of gods. Don't question me. Just do as I ask.'

'O Indra, how is it that you aren't ashamed of this cruel deed? You've killed this son of a Brahmin. Are you not afraid of the sin of Brahminicide?'

'Don't worry about me. I'll do some penance or other to absolve myself. He was my enemy and had great strength. Cut off his heads and I'll grant you this favour: from now on, men will offer the heads of beasts in sacrifice, and they will owe it to you. Now quickly do as I ask.'

The woodcutter then lifted his axe and cut off Trishiras' three heads in one fell swoop. From the severed heads, all manner of birds flew out. From the mouth of the head that used to read the Vedas, came the kapinjala birds. From the head that used to look upon the cardinal points, the titara came out. From the head that used to drink wine, flew out the kalavinka birds of prey. Finally, Trishiras' body lay lifeless on the ground, its fiery energy expelled through the birds. Indra released a sigh of relief and headed home to Indraloka, and the woodcutter went home, too.

When Tvashtri heard about his son's murder, his eyes burnt with sorrow and wrath. He called out to the cosmos: 'My son was devoted to knowledge; he had his passions under control and was all forgiving. He hadn't committed any crimes against Indra, yet Indra killed him. I will avenge my son. I'll create another son, Vrta, whose sole purpose will be to destroy that vicious Indra. Let the world witness my ascetic power in this creation. Let the king of gods also see who it is that deserves to die.' So saying, Tvashtri purified himself with water, and making an offering to fire, created a heroic being—Vrta. When Vrta was born, Tvashtri said to him, 'O enemy of Indra, grow through the strength of my asceticism.'

Vrta began to grow, until his form reached beyond the sky, and there it shone bright like the sun—a doomsday sun. 'What shall I do?' he roared.

'Kill Indra,' Tvashtri commanded.

Vrta then went to the third heaven and engaged Indra in a fierce battle. Both heroes were equally matched and fought ruthlessly, but then Vrta opened his mouth wide, and, grabbing the lord of the three worlds, threw him in and swallowed him. Watching their king disappear into Vrta's mouth, Indra's host of gods were flabbergasted. They then created the yawn and threw it at Vrta, and when that warrior opened his mouth, Indra reduced himself to a miniscule size and quickly jumped out. Since then, yawning has remained in the breath of men.

Realizing that Indra had escaped, Vrta became even more enraged. He threw himself at the king of gods and the fighting between the two resumed. They fought for a long time, but Vrta, fired up with Tvashtri's ire-filled energy, was unassailable. Finally, Vrta overwhelmed Indra, and that peerless god turned his back and fled from the battlefield. The gods were dismayed to see Indra's retreat, especially because they, too, were terrified of Tvashtri and his supremely powerful son. Hoping to salvage the situation, they sought out the defeated Indra to discuss options.

'This whole universe has been pervaded by Vrta,' Indra told them. 'He has no equal to oppose him. Before this, I was capable of doing it, but he has rendered me incapable. He has immeasurable strength and his prowess in battle is unmatched. I'm afraid that before long, he'll absorb the three worlds, along with all the gods, asuras, and men.'

Hearing Indra's words, the high rishis and the gods began to tremble in fear. 'There is no one who can protect us now,' they cried. Then one of them suggested that perhaps Vishnu could save them. So all the heaven-dwellers went to the summit of Mount Mandar, where Vishnu lived. Standing before that god with folded hands, they first praised him for his past deeds of valour and maya, and then they pleaded, 'O slayer of asuras, save us and also Indra and the world. Vrta has pervaded the whole world and is undefeatable.'

'Helping you and preserving the world is my duty,' Vishnu responded. 'I'll tell you the means by which you can defeat Vrta. Go to him, and with the help of rishis and gandharvas, who are the best negotiators of heaven, conciliate with him. Declare a truce and request him to make friends with Indra, and this way you will be victorious. I'll help you. When the time comes, I'll make myself invisible and enter Indra's thunderbolt.'

Thereupon, all the heaven dwellers, with Indra leading them, went to Vrta. Even the sight of him terrified them: from where he was, it appeared that the eight cardinal points were on fire, and as he looked at the sun and the moon, it appeared that he was swallowing them. They approached him with great humility and spoke to him in dulcet tones, praising him and his strength. 'All beings, including gods and asuras and human beings, are suffering because of your extended battles with Indra,' they said. 'We beg you for a truce. We request you to make friends with Indra and live happily in heaven with us.'

Vrta was somewhat appeased to see the gods so chastened. 'I hear what you are saying,' he said to them. 'But tell me, how can there be peace between Indra and myself. How can there be friendship between two gods who are of equal strength?'

'One should always seek the company of those who are full of virtue,' the heaven-dwellers said. 'You should not refuse the opportunity of friendship with the virtuous. That is what we are offering you. Such friendships are like wealth and can prove to be beneficial during times of difficulty. Indra is much sought after by men of virtue in all three worlds. Don't refuse this offer of friendship; it'll benefit you and also the world.' Vrta was still suspicious of the offer that the heaven-dwellers were making, but he was willing to give them the benefit of the doubt. He also thought it prudent to secure some insurance for himself in case things went wrong. 'I'll accept your offer,' he said. 'Provided you grant my wish: I cannot be killed by a dry thing nor a wet one; not by stone nor by wood; not by a long-range weapon nor by one that is used in hand-to-hand fighting. Not during the day, nor at night. Not by a Brahmin, nor by Indra, nor by assistance of the gods. If you agree, then I'll make peace with Indra.'

'Agreed,' the rishis said, very pleased by the outcome of the negotiations. Vrta, too, was pleased, and so was Indra, but secretly the king of gods now began to think of ways in which to kill Vrta within the terms of the agreement. He anxiously looked for a loophole. Then, one day, he saw Vrta near the seacoast. It was evening; neither day nor night. Then he saw foam, as high as a mountain, rising out of the sea. It was neither wet nor dry, nor was it a weapon. This was the perfect opportunity. He quickly called Vishnu, who entered his thunderbolt, and Indra, hiding this weapon in the foam, flung it at Vrta. Vrta was slain.

All the creatures of heaven—gandharvas, yakshas, rakshasas, pannagas and rishis—celebrated his death and began to sing praises of Indra and Vishnu. But Indra felt no triumph; instead, he was overpowered by the weight of the treachery he had perpetrated, which was compounded by his old sin of killing a Brahmin—the three- headed Trishiras. And then, from the slain body of Vrta, rose the sin of Brahminicide, fierce and dreadful, striking all the worlds with fear. Of terrible teeth and ghastly face, hideous and ugly, and dark and tawny, with dishevelled hair and dreadful eyes, with a garland of skulls around her neck, looking like an incantation of the incarnate, bathed in blood and clad in rags and tree barks, she came out of Vrta's body and sought the wielder of the thunderbolt.

Indra fled, with Brahminicide pursuing him. Wherever he went, she followed him. Finally, with nowhere else to go, he reduced his size, and in infinitesimal form, slipped inside the stalk of a lotus flower. He lived there for many years, but Brahminicide waited, and when he emerged, she seized him. Possessed by Brahminicide, the illustrious king of gods became so disfigured by his sins that he was hardly recognizable. Stumbling and falling, he found his way to the Grandfather, Brahma, and stood before him in shame.

In the absence of Indra, who is the giver of rain, the earth had become desolate; plants had withered, and the rivers had lost their water. Human beings on earth had begun to suffer, and the rishis and gods had begun to fear for the three worlds. Without the protection of their king, anarchy had broken loose among the elements, and natural disasters were destroying the worlds. So when Indra came to him, Brahma knew that he had rid him of Brahminicide. Speaking gently, Brahma addressed the terrible lady with honeyed words: 'Dear powerful one, free the king of gods. He's very dear to me. Tell me what you wish. What can I do that will appease you?'

'Since you, Creator of the World, have requested me, I'll free Indra, but you must find a place for me to reside. Now that I have been born, I need a place to live.'

'Have no fear, dear lady. I'll find a place for you to live. But there is not a single place or being in the three worlds that can bear your full weight; therefore, I'll have to divide you into four parts.' Brahma then called Agni and asked him, 'Will you take one of the four portions of Brahminicide?'

'If you ask, I will. But please tell me how will I be safe from her?'

'She'll live in you, but when any man does not offer herbs and seeds to you, she'll leave you and enter that man.'

Then the Grandfather called the trees and herbs and grass and requested them to take a portion of Brahminicide. They, too, agreed but wanted to know how they would be saved from this sin. 'We are already victims of nature's vagaries and man's cruel hand, don't afflict us anymore,' they implored Brahma.

'The man who, through lack of judgement, will cut or tear any of you on a full moon day, Brahminicide will leave you and be transferred to him,' the Grandfather assured them.

Then the Grandfather called the apsaras and requested them to take a portion of the sin upon themselves.

'We are willing, but tell us how we may be rescued from this sin?'

'Any man who has intercourse with a woman during her menstruation will take over the sin from you.'

Finally, the Grandfather called the waters and requested them to take the last quarter portion of Brahminicide. The waters bowed before him and agreed but also wanted a means by which to be rid of her.

'She will live in you. But any man who spits in you or pollutes you with urine and excrement will take this sin from you.'

Fire, the trees, herbs and grass, apsaras, and waters all left carrying a portion of the sin of Brahminicide, but they were assured that they would be saved from her, because there would always be men who will lack judgement and intelligence. And Indra, freed of the terrible Brahminicide he had caused to be born, performed the horse sacrifice to regain his former glory.

Myth from the Rig Veda and Mahabharata

◆

61

HOW THE CAMEL WAS DUPED

In a forest, there lived a lion called Madotak. He had three sycophantic friends—a panther, a crow and a jackal. One day the lion saw a creature he had never seen before. It was a camel that had wandered away from a caravan and had come into the forest. The lion asked his friends if they knew what this ridiculous-looking beast was. Only the crow knew, because he had travelled the world and had seen all sorts of creatures. 'It's a camel,' the crow informed the lion. 'It lives among people.'

Madotak, being kind-hearted, summoned the camel. 'I want to assure you that you'll not come to any harm in the forest,' he said and offered his friendship. The camel gratefully accepted.

One day Madotak got into a terrible brawl with an elephant and was badly wounded. He was able to return home to his lair, but he didn't have the strength to hunt, for himself and his friends. Day by day he got

weaker, yet his friends still expected him to procure their food. So Madotak
went hunting every day, even in his condition, only to return without
prey, hungry and exhausted. 'We have to think of another way,' he said
to the panther, crow and jackal, who had come to see him one evening.

'We're your friends, and we'll give you good advice,' they said to him.
'Tell us, what relationship do you have with the camel? Is he even your
friend? Where is he in your time of need?'

'What are you saying?' the lion said, catching the drift of what his
friends were suggesting.

'He's a grass-eater—meant to be eaten by lions.'

'But I promised him safety,' Madotak said, distressed. 'How can I
now break my word?'

'If your promise is all you're concerned about, then we'll think of
something, and he himself will absolve you of the promise. Will that be
all right with you?' they asked, and when the lion agreed, they came up
with a plan.

The crow went to the camel and said to him, 'Have you seen how
our dear leader, Madotak, is dying of hunger? But he's so noble that he
won't say anything to us. There's nothing more precious in the world than
friendship. And, for the sake of friendship, we have all decided to offer
ourselves to him. If you consider yourself his friend, then you should
also do the same.'

'Of course,' said the camel. The crow took him to where the panther
and jackal were waiting, and together, they went to see Madotak. The
crow then said to the lion, 'Eat me and appease your hunger, dear friend.'

'Don't be silly, friend. I can't eat you,' the lion said. 'Besides, you're
so small, your flesh will hardly even wet my throat.'

'Then eat me,' the jackal said.

'No, no, I can't eat you,' was the lion's response. 'You're my friend.'

'I am at your service,' the panther then said. 'My meat will surely
satisfy your hunger.'

Madotak once again shook his head and said, 'No, my friend. You're
very generous, but I can't eat you.'

The camel saw how when the crow, jackal, and panther had offered
themselves, the lion had not only refused to eat them, he had even
reaffirmed their friendship. So, he, too, offered himself to the lion. 'Eat
me,' he said. And immediately, Madotak pounced on him and killed him.

Then he divided the meat among his other friends and everyone enjoyed
a delicious camel meal.

Folktale from the Kathasaritsagara

◆

62

THE PROMISED LAKE

An old crane lived beside a lake. He was losing his eyesight and dexterity
and couldn't really catch his food anymore. More often than not, when
he tried to catch a fish, it slipped away, leaving him snapping his beak at
empty air. 'There has to be an easier way to eat,' he said to himself, and
after much thinking, he hit upon a plan.

The next day, he stood at the edge of the lake, looking very feeble—
his wings hanging loose by his side and his long neck slumping—not
attempting to even catch the fish that swam up close to the lakeside.

A crab, who also lived in the lake, noticed the crane and crawled up
the side to talk to him: 'What's wrong, Uncle Crane. Aren't you hungry
today? How come you're not catching any fish? I thought that was your
favourite pastime.'

'Dear Nephew, you're right. For many years I've lived by this lake
in comfort and contentment, and I've enjoyed the delicious meat. But
today I'm very dejected, because I've heard terrible news about a disaster
that will kill all of you.'

'What disaster? How do you know about it?'

'Yesterday I heard some fisherman talking about this lake and how it
abounds with fish. They're planning to spread many nets here and catch
all the fish. When all of you are gone, where will this old crane go? I'll
surely starve and die. Just the thought of this is making me so sorrowful
that I have no appetite left.'

Terrified by this news, the crab jumped back into the lake and told
everyone. All the fish and other lake-dwellers rushed to the lakeside and
begged the crane to advise them. 'Save us, dear Uncle,' they cried. 'You're
old and wise. You're not only our uncle but also our trusted friend. We've
spent many happy days together and now you must think of some way

to help us escape the fishermen's nets.'

'My dear nieces and nephews and also friends. I'm only a bird. What can I do against those mighty humans? I'm also old now, and I hardly have any strength left. But because you're all so dear to my heart, I can offer one solution. It'll take much out of me, but I'll do it for you. I can carry all of you, a few at a time, out of this lake to another lake far, far away. Its deeper and bigger than this one, and there's no danger there.'

'You're the best! So selfless and caring.' The lake-dwellers all thanked the crane most profusely, and they all clamoured to be the first to be carried to this danger-free lake far, far away. 'Take me! Take me!' they all cried.

'Patience, my dear ones,' the crane said. 'I'll take all of you in turn,' and stepping into the water, he filled his bill with as many fish as he could, and then flew off towards the other side of the plateau.

Of course, the crane had no intention of taking the lake-dwellers to another lake. Reaching the far side of the plateau, he perched on a rock and ate up the fish, spitting out the bones. Then he returned to the lake and took some more eagerly awaiting creatures, and ate them too. In this way, he made many more trips and enjoyed many more sumptuous meals over the course of a few days.

One morning, the crab climbed over all the other waiting creatures and implored the crane: 'Why aren't you taking me?' he cried. 'I was the first one to ask you, and yet I've been waiting for days to be saved.'

The crane liked the idea of adding variety to his meal that day, and his mouth began to water at the thought of juicy crab meat. Swallowing his saliva, he reached for the crab with his beak and flew off across the plateau.

Noticing that the crane had flown across many water bodies but was now getting ready to land on a sun-bleached rock, the crab asked him. 'What's this place, dear Uncle, and why are we stopping here? Where's the big lake that you talked about?'

'Ah, the lake!' the crane laughed. 'It's here, Nephew. Look around and you'll see your other companions, all resting peacefully.'

The crab looked around him and was horrified to see a ghastly scene of execution—piles and piles of fish bones on the rocks. Realizing the crane's treachery, the crab's heart began to pound, and he desperately began to think of how he could save his life and possibly even the lives of the remaining fish in the lake. Just then the crane raised his neck to throw the crab on the rock to dash him to death. Acting quickly, the crab drove his pincers into the crane's throat. The pained bird threw his head this way and that, trying to free himself from the claws, but instead, those sharp, knife-like pincers sliced his throat from one end to the other, till his head fell off.

The crab grabbed the crane's head with its pincers, and with great difficulty, made his way back home. When he finally reached the water's edge, he jumped into its coolness and took a deep breath of relief. Then he gathered all the remaining fish and told them about the crane's treachery and showed them his head as evidence. 'You have nothing to worry about now,' he assured the others. 'We can all live happily, but always remember this lesson we have learned: if you're somebody's food, don't trust him to save your life.'

Folktale from the Hitopadesha

◆

63

THE INTERPRETER OF DREAMS

One night Yusuf dreamt that eleven stars and the sun and moon were prostrating before him. He ran to his father excitedly and told him his dream. His father, Yaqub, realized that Yusuf's dream foretold the greatness that Allah had ordained for him—that one day he would be exalted above the eleven stars—his brothers—and the sun and moon—his mother and father. But Yaqub also feared that Yusuf's half-brothers who were jealous of him, would try to get rid of him. Yusuf was young and innocent and was not aware of the guile of his brothers, so Yaqub advised him, 'Dear Son, don't relate this vision to your brothers, or they will plot evil against you.'

Yusuf's ten stepbrothers felt that their father loved his other sons, Yusuf and Benjamin, more; they also knew that Yusuf, particularly, was his favourite. So they decided to get rid of Yusuf. First they thought of slaying him, then they said, 'Let's not kill him. Let's cast him away in some faraway land. That way we'll have no rivals to our father's love, and we'll remain honourable men.' One of the brothers suggested they throw him down a well, somewhere beide a much travelled path, so that some passing caravan of travellers could take him. Agreeing on this plan, the brothers then asked their father to let Yusuf accompany them. 'He'll play and enjoy himself. And we'll take good care of him,' they told their father. But Yaqub was reluctant. He suspected that the ten step-brothers were planning something to hurt the boy. 'I'm afraid that when you are not paying attention, a wolf will get him and devour him,' he said to them, trying to find an excuse not to send Yusuf.

'We are so many in number, Father,' they reassured him. 'If the wolf eats him, despite all of us, then surely we, too, will have perished.' And Yaqub, unable to refute the brothers' argument, relented.

The brothers took Yusuf with them and threw him down a well. Then, waiting till nightfall, so that it would appear that they had been searching for him, they came to their father, weeping, and told him that they had gone racing with one another, leaving Yusuf with their things, and the wolf had come and devoured him. When Yaqub looked at them in disbelief, they pulled out the shirt that Yusuf had been wearing— it was stained with blood. They had taken it off him before pushing him into the well, and had killed a goat and used its blood to stain his shirt. Yaqub could tell that it was fake blood, and he was grateful for that, but he could do nothing to refute his sons' story. He could only trust in Allah's mercy and pray that He would take care of his son.

Meanwhile, a caravan of traders passed by the well. When their water carrier threw in the bucket and pulled it up, Yusuf came with it. The merchants saw his innocent, angelic face and thought he would fetch a good price in the slave market. They sold him for a few dirhams to an Egyptian court official, who brought him home and told his wife, Zulaikha, to look after him. 'We may adopt him,' he told her.

However, the merchant's wife had other plans for Yusuf. She took care of him for many years, and when he grew into manhood, she called him into her room one day and locked the door. Beckoning to him seductively, she said, 'Come to me. I'm burning with passion for you.' Yusuf, too, felt passion for her, but he was an honourable man. 'Allah forbids this,' he replied. 'Your husband is my lord. He has been kind to me. I can't wrong him like this.' Saying this, he rushed to the door to leave. She tried to grab him, but she could only catch his shirt from behind. It tore down the back.

Suddenly the door was pushed open and there was Zulaikha's husband. Immediately, Zulaikha changed her tune. 'Oh husband,' she said tearfully. 'When someone has evil designs on your wife, how will you punish him? Send him to prison or do something sterner?'

'She's the one who tried to seduce me,' Yusuf appealed to the merchant.

By this time, the whole household had arrived on the scene, and someone saw Yusuf's torn shirt. 'If his shirt were torn in the front, her story would be correct, but his shirt is torn in the back, which means that he's telling the truth.'

'I see that this is one of your tricks,' the merchant admonished Zulaikha. 'You're a cunning woman. Obviously you're at fault. Now ask for his forgiveness.'

News about this incident spread in the city, and all the women gossiped about how the wife of the great Aziz tried to seduce her slave. When Zulaikha heard about the malicious things the women were saying about her, she called them to her house for a banquet. When the women were seated, she gave each of them a knife to cut fruit. Then she ordered Yusuf to come before them. When the women saw Yusuf, they were so astounded by his angelic looks that they cut their fingers instead of the fruit, and Zulaikha felt vindicated. 'See,' she said. 'And you blamed me for trying to seduce him. I did, but he refused. Now if he doesn't do what I ask him to do, let him be thrown into prison and suffer the advances of the vilest women.'

Finding himself in moral jeopardy, Yusuf began to pray: 'Oh Lord, save me from this snare of temptation. Send me to prison, instead.' The men of the community also realized that Yusuf was guiltless, but the situation was very perilous, so they thought it was best to send Yusuf to prison.

At the time that Yusuf went to prison, two other men were sent there as well. One day, they both shared their dreams with him, because he had told them that he could interpret dreams—an ability that he had received from God. One of the men had dreamt that he was pressing wine and the other saw that he was carrying bread on his head and the birds were eating it.

To the latter, Yusuf said, 'You'll hang from the cross, and the birds will peck your head.' And to the one who had seen himself pouring wine, he said, 'You'll be a cup-bearer.' Then Yusuf made a request to this inmate: 'When you are serving your lord, will you mention me to him?' The man agreed, but when he was found innocent and released and began to serve as the Pharaoh's cup-bearer, he forgot his promise to Yusuf. However, it so happened that one day the Pharaoh shared a dream with his councilmen, and his cup-bearer was also present. In this dream the Pharaoh saw seven fatted cows being devoured by seven lean ones. He also saw seven green ears of corn and seven others that were dry. 'Tell me, Councilmen, what this dream means?' he asked, but none of the councilmen could interpret it. The cup-bearer then remembered his fellow inmate. 'I know someone who can accurately interpret your dream,' he told the Pharaoh, and the Pharaoh sent him to the prison to ask the man.

When the cup-bearer met Yusuf and related the Pharaoh's dream to him, Yusuf replied, 'Tell the Pharaoh: You will sow for seven consecutive years. Leave in the ears of the corn you sow, except for the little you need for food. These seven years will be followed by seven years of dreadful famine, which will devour everything in the stores. But, even during famine, when you consume all grain, leave a little for seed. This will be followed by a year of abundant rain, in which people will press the grape.'

When the cup-bearer related this interpretation to the Pharaoh, he said, 'Bring this man to me,' and a messenger was sent to fetch Yusuf. But Yusuf sent the messenger back with the message: 'What of the ladies who tried to cut their hands. My master is aware of how they tried to trap me.' When the ladies were asked if Yusuf was to blame for their behaviour, they exonerated him. Aziz's wife also confessed. 'He's blameless,' she said. 'And true and virtuous.'

The Pharaoh removed all allegations against Yusuf, and employed him in his service with honour and trust. Yusuf asked to be in charge of the granary, and he was awarded that position. And so it was that Yusuf began to live in Egypt as an honoured man, overseeing the royal granaries.

One day, Yusuf's brothers came to the granary for provisions. Yusuf recognized them, but they didn't know who he was. When they presented themselves to Yusuf, he gave them their provisions in full measure and said to them, 'Bring me your other brother from your father. Next time, if you don't bring him, you'll not receive any corn. Don't come and see me again without him.'

'We'll try,' the brothers promised. When they left, Yusuf asked his servants to put their money back into their saddlebags so that they would discover it when they returned home. He hoped that this would be incentive for them to come back. Reaching home, the brothers told their father what had happened and said, 'We'll have to take Benjamin with us next time.' Yaqub became very concerned at his sons' words. He was loath to trust them with Benjamin, considering what they had done to Yusuf. But then when the brothers opened their saddlebags and discovered the money that had been returned to them, they showed it to Yaqub. 'Look. Now do you believe us?' they said. 'We promise we'll take care of our brother, and we'll also buy at least one more camel-load of food.'

'Then swear a solemn oath in Allah's name that you'll bring him back, unless you yourselves are in grave danger and powerless,' Yaqub insisted.

They took the oath, and taking Benjamin with them, presented him to Yusuf. He was very pleased to see them, and treating them with honour, invited them for a feast. As they were being seated, Yusuf took the seat next to Benjamin. 'I am your brother, Yusuf,' he said softly. For an instant Benjamin's face lit up with joy, but then he remembered how his father and he had suffered at losing Yusuf. 'Our stepbrothers…' he began angrily. 'You must forgive them,' Yusuf said. 'Don't hold the past against them.'

After the meal, when Yusuf's brothers prepared to leave, he gave them the provisions they had come for. He also directed his servants to put a drinking cup in Benjamin's saddlebag.

When the brothers' caravan neared the gates, it was stopped by the Egyptian guards. 'You are thieves,' they said to the brothers.

'What have we stolen?'

'The pharaoh's drinking cup. There's a reward for it. Whoever brings it will receive a camel-load of provisions.'

'We're not thieves. We haven't come to make mischief,' the brother pleaded with the guards.

'If you are proved wrong, what should be your punishment?'

'In whosoever saddlebag you find the cup, he'll serve as a bondman for his crime. That's how we would punish the thief,' said the brothers.

And so, with Yusuf watching the proceedings, the guards began to search their belongings and found the cup in Benjamin's saddlebag. 'We're not surprised,' the brothers immediately declared. 'His brother before him was also a thief.'

Yusuf knew what his stepbrothers were thinking: having rid themselves of Yusuf, they hoped to also get Benjamin out of the way. However, to show that they cared for their brother, the stepbrothers pretended to lament: 'We have an ageing father,' they cried. 'He'll grieve at losing his son. Take one of us, instead,' they pleaded, knowing full well that Yusuf would not.

What they didn't know is that this is how Yusuf had planned to keep his brother safe. He could not have kept his brother except by the law of the land.

When the brothers returned home without Benjamin, Yaqub asked them where he was. 'He committed a theft,' they said.

'You have made up a story,' Yaqub accused them.

'We bore witness to it with our own eyes,' they said.

Yaqub turned away from his sons in despair. 'I must be patient,' he said to himself. 'For all will surely be revealed and Allah will bring me back my lost sons.' But he grieved—first for Yusuf and now for Benjamin, and in grief for his sons, his eyes turned white. Soon the brothers grew tired of their father's grieving and told him to stop. 'You'll ruin your health or die from it,' they said.

In time, when food grew scarce and their people began to starve, Yaqub sent his sons into town again to get whatever provisions they could and also to enquire about Benjamin. They went to Yusuf and pleaded with him to be charitable, because they had little money. Yusuf then asked them, 'Do you remember what you did to Yusuf and then to Benjamin?'

'How do you know? the brothers asked fearfully.

'I am that Yusuf, and my brother, Benjamin, is, indeed, with me. Allah has been gracious to us. He rewards those who deserve it.'

'Allah has exalted you above us,' the brothers exclaimed, and then said, shamefaced. 'We are guilty. We wronged you.'

'Today, no one will put blame on you. Allah will forgive you,' Yusuf said to them in generosity. 'I'm just happy to see my family.' Then he gave them his shirt and advised them to throw it over their father's eyes. 'It'll restore his vision. Then bring all your people to me.'

At home that day, Yaqub felt Yusuf's presence. 'I feel his breath,' he said to those near him.

'It's nothing but your old illusion,' they said to him. But then the brothers came and gave him the good news, and when they threw Yusuf's shirt on his eyes, he regained his sight.

'Forgive us, Father,' the brothers said.

'Allah is forgiving and merciful,' Yaqub replied. 'I'll implore Him to forgive you.'

When they all returned to Yusuf, he welcomed his parents into Egypt and seated them on thrones. 'This is the meaning of my dream,' he said, 'Allah has made it come true!'

Myth from the Holy Quran

◆

64

THE THEFT OF SANJIVNI

Devas and asuras were constantly at war with each other to gain sovereignty of the three worlds. The weapons they used in battle were all-powerful and anointed by their gurus—Brihaspati, the guru of the devas, and Shukra, the guru of the asuras. Both these Brahmins were bitter rivals, not only because they represented opposing factions, but also because they were on a par with each other in Vedic learning and in their expertise of sacrifice, weaponry, and maya. However, Shukra possessed a specific secret knowledge, which made him superior to Brihaspati. He knew the science of Sanjivni, with which the dead could be revived. And so the devas could never win, because, while their numbers decreased with each battle, the asuras never lost anyone; just by uttering a mantra, Shukra brought the dead asuras back to life. With every losing battle, the devas became more and more dejected, until, finally, one of them suggested a plan.

They asked Kacha, Brihaspati's son to become Shukra's disciple. 'You must discover the secret mantra,' they told him. 'Shukra never rejects a disciple. He also has a beautiful daughter, Devayani. Use these two weapons to gain what we need.'

Kacha then went to the court of the asura king, Vrishaparva, where Shukra resided, and prostrated himself before the guru of the asuras. 'I am the grandson of Rishi Angiras, son of Brihaspati,' he said. 'My name is Kacha. If you accept me as your disciple, I'll take a vow of brahmacharya—celibacy—for one thousand years and diligently learn from you with all my faculties.'

Shukra not only accepted Kacha as his student but also gave him a place to stay in his own ashram, where he and his daughter, Devayani, lived. She was a beautiful maiden of impressionable age, very fond of song and dance, and full of romantic notions. When she saw Kacha, she was enchanted. Kacha took full advantage of her feelings and made sure he encouraged them by bringing her flowers every day, listening to her sing, and praising her voice, her beauty, and her grace. As he expected, in no time at all, Devayani was madly in love with him.

Five hundred years passed. Kacha learned many skills from Shukra, but not once did the guru bring up the subject of Sanjivni, even though Kacha tried often to coax him into revealing it. He would pose questions such as, 'Can victory be guaranteed?' or, 'Other than having a strong defence, is there another way to prevent the loss of warriors?' But Shukra always evaded the topic, so, one day, Kacha just asked him straight out. When Shukra concluded his lesson about battle strategies, Kacha enquired, 'I've heard that evolved Brahmins have the knowledge of bringing the dead back to life. Is this correct?' As Kacha was asking his question, some asuras who were standing nearby, heard him. They had always suspected the motive of this son of Brihaspati, but now they were certain that he was a deva spy who had come to Shukra to steal the secret science. The asuras then decided to kill Kacha, but without telling Shukra.

One morning when Kacha was out by himself, tending the cattle, the asuras shot an arrow through his heart and killed him and then threw his body to the wolves. That evening, seeing the cattle return without Kacha, Devayani became concerned. Going to her father, she said, 'The evening fire is kindled and the sun has set. The cattle have also returned, but there's no sign of Kacha. I fear for him.' Tears filled her eyes and spilled down her cheeks. 'If something happens to Kacha, I'll die,' she cried. 'I can't live without him.'

Shukra could not bear to see his daughter cry. 'My dearest child, if something has happened to Kacha, I'll revive him with my Sanjivni science. Wipe your tears and sit here while I summon him.' And as soon as Shukra called Kacha, using his mantra, the young man tore open the bellies of the wolves and joyfully returned.

The asuras were irked by Kacha's resurrection and decided that next time they would kill him in such a way that it would be impossible for him to return. Another day, Kacha was roaming in the forest, gathering flowers for Devayani, when the asuras pounced on him and killed him again. This time, they pounded his body into powder and sprinkled it in the ocean.

That evening when Kacha didn't return to the hermitage, Devayani went to her father in tears again. Reassuring his daughter, Shukra, once again called Kacha's name and uttered his mantra to summon him. He immediately arose from the ocean and ran to the ashram.

The asuras killed him a third time, and now they burned his body and mixed the ashes with wine, which they fed to Shukra himself. This time, when Devayani wept and told Shukra that Kacha was missing again, Shukra replied, 'Dear Daughter, forget him. I keep reviving him, but the asuras have a real enmity with him and will not let him live. No matter how many times I revive him, they'll kill him. You are sought after by the celestials themselves, why do you pine for him? Don't weep for him anymore.'

'I swear to you, Father, that I, too, will follow him into death,' Devayani sobbed. 'I love him and can't live without him. How can you talk so callously about him? He's a Brahmin of the highest order—grandson of Angiras himself. Are you not ashamed that your asuras have killed such a Brahmin?'

'You're right, dear daughter,' Shukra replied. 'These asuras will surely bring sin upon me. Don't weep, I'll try to bring him back to life.' Saying this, Shukra called Kacha. But this time, Kacha did not return; instead, his voice spoke from Shukra's stomach: 'I am here.'

'How have you entered my stomach?' Shukra asked.

'The asuras burnt my body to ashes and gave me to you in your wine.'

Shukra smacked his forehead in frustration. 'Oh Daughter,' he said to Devayani, 'How can I revive him now? Kacha is within me. If I revive him, I'll have to die myself. There's no other way for him to come back to life except by ripping my stomach open.'

Devayani threw herself on the floor, wailing. 'I can't live without Kacha, and I can't live without you. If he dies I'll also die, and if you die, my father, I'll not be able to live. My life is doomed.'

Shukra could not bear to see his daughter so distraught. Taking her in his arms he calmed her. 'There's one way,' he said, and then he spoke to Kacha in his belly. 'You're a very lucky man that my daughter loves you so much. Today I'll give you knowledge of Sanjivni. Come to life again, my Son, and when you do, act with gratitude.' And so Shukra taught Kacha the secret science of reviving the dead and then read the mantra to resurrect him. Kacha ripped apart his guru's body and emerged. Then he used the knowledge that he had just acquired to put together the shreds and bring him back to life. Shukra had his life back, but he was traumatized by the experience, and he blamed the alcohol. 'If I had refrained from drinking,' he said to himself, 'I wouldn't have swallowed the Brahmin, and I wouldn't have been forced to divulge my secret science. Brahmins of the world need to be of higher intent.' And so Shukra made an injunction for the world: 'From this day, any wretched Brahmin, who, unable to resist the temptation, drinks liquor, will be considered to have committed the sin of killing a Brahmin.'

Knowing that Kacha now possessed Sanjivni, the asuras did not make any more attempts to kill him, and he successfully completed his one thousand years of training with Shukra. When he prepared to return to his home, Devayani said to him: 'Now that you are no longer my father's pupil and no longer under the vow of celibacy, I've come to propose to you. Take me as your wife.'

'Devayani, we have spent wonderful years together, enjoying each other's company, but it's now time for me to go,' Kacha replied. 'Please don't stop me, and don't ask me to marry you. I can't.'

'Why not? We're both Brahmins; we enjoy each other's company, and I'm certain that we'll be happy together.'

'We may be well matched, but marriage is something else.'

'What do you mean? How can you be so indifferent—after all that I've done for you? Let me remind you that you would have died three times over, but for me.'

'It's true, you saved my life three times. I'm grateful, but I can't marry you.'

'Why not?' Devayani demanded.

'You're my sister. I lived in your father's stomach, just as you did before you were conceived. We are born from the same body; we're brother and sister. How can I marry you? It'll be a sin.'

Realizing how Kacha had manipulated her, Devayani flew into a rage. 'The danavas were right,' she screamed. 'You are a treacherous man. All you really wanted was to learn the secret of Sanjivni and you used me. I curse you that the knowledge that you have learned from my father—for which you betrayed me—will never serve you.'

'Don't do this to me,' Kacha tried to reason with her. 'I made no promises. You can't blame me for this. I don't deserve your curse. Take it back.'

Without saying another word, Devayani turned away from him.

'I'm doing my duty as a rishi; whereas, you're acting from desire,' Kacha called after her, and when she kept going, he shouted back at her, 'I, too, will curse you: Your desire shall never be fulfilled. You will never marry a Brahmin. As for me, you may have cursed me that my knowledge will not serve me, but I can still teach it to others; so I've achieved what I came to do.'

Myth from the Mahabharata

◆

65

TILOTTAMA

Sunda and Upsunda were two danava brothers who were as alike and as close to each other as two peas in a pod. They performed the same actions, they sought the same achievements, and they shared equally of joys and sorrows. When they spoke, it was only to agree with each other, and when they engaged in various activities, it was to be with each other. Their bodies, too, were similar in muscularity, and their disposition was identical. Even the way they reacted was similar. It was like they were one individual in two bodies.

As they grew older, they both had just one desire—to subjugate the three worlds that the devas had created and establish their own cosmic order. To fulfil this desire they decided to invoke Brahma through tapasya and ask him for a boon. Going to the Vindhya Mountain, they stood on a peak for hundreds of years, wearing only bark, withstanding scorching heat and bitter cold, controlling their bodily needs of hunger and thirst, and subsisting only on air. Then, for another hundred years, they stood only on the toes of one foot, and for the next hundred, on the toes of the other foot. For one hundred more years, they stood with their arms raised above their head and gaze fixed on one spot.

The combined austerities of the danava brothers generated so much heat that Vindhya Mountain started to melt. As vapours rose from its summit and reached the heavens, the gods became frightened of the ascetic power of the danavas. 'They have to be stopped,' they urged Indra. 'If they continue with their asceticism, the mountains will be levelled and rivers will become dry. And what if the heat reaches heaven? What will happen to us?'

'I'll see what I can do,' Indra said, trying to calm them down. Then, he called his beautiful apsaras and sent them to Vindhya to distract the brothers. He also threw down gems and precious stones. But even though alluring, scantily clad maidens wandered around them and brushed against their bodies and glittering gems twinkled at their feet, the brothers' gaze remained fixed in meditation. Now Indra tried a different tactic. He used maya to create an illusion in which Sunda and Upsunda saw their mothers and sisters running towards them, screaming, begging for help, trying to escape the terrifying rakshasas that pursued them with sharp lances. 'Save us!' the women cried, reaching their helpless arms towards Sunda and Upsunda, but the brothers were so oblivious to the world, they didn't blink an eye.

Indra could not discompose the danava brothers, and they completed their tapasya. By now their hair was matted like ropes, reaching down to their ankles, and their bodies were emaciated, bare-boned skeletons, but in all the years of tapasya, their minds had not forgotten their purpose, so when Brahma manifested himself before them and asked, 'Tell me what you desire?' they immediately said: 'We wish to possess the knowledge of the weapons and all the powers of maya. We also wish to have the ability to assume any form, and we wish to be immortal.'

'I grant you all that you desire, except for immortality, for that is not possible for any being,' Brahma said. 'Instead, you can choose your method of death.'

'Then grant us that we will not be killed by any created being—mobile or immobile—except by each other.'

Brahma knew that the danavas had so much faith in each other that they trusted each other with their lives, and he realized that granting them this wish was tantamount to making the asuras immortal. But he had no choice, because the danavas had earned this reward, so he declared, 'Granted.' But he returned to Brahmaloka with a strong misgiving that he would regret this.

The danavas, on the other hand, possessing the power of all known weapons and knowing that no one could kill them, returned to their palace in high spirits. They cut their matted hair and put on crowns. They burnt the bark and donned costly silks and ornaments. They ordered their chefs to cook enough food to feed a whole city and invited their friends to celebrate with them. And, when the celebrations came to an end, they embarked on conquering the worlds with their complete knowledge of weapons. Determined to establish a new order, they gathered an army of asuras and, going to heaven, defeated all the celestials. Then they mounted an attack on the underworld and gained victory there, as well. After overpowering the two worlds, they returned to earth and began oppressing the Brahmins, who facilitated the supremacy of the gods through ritual sacrifice. Sometimes they took the form of maddened elephants and trampled the sacrificial sites, and, at other times, they became lions and devoured the rishis. Soon, no rishi dared venture out to perform a sacrifice, and when sacrifice ceased, the gods were not honoured, and people began to forget them. In consequence, the gods ceased their benevolence of rain and fertility, and without fertile lands, there was no agriculture, which, in turn, brought trade to a halt. Ultimately, god-given prosperity vanished from the earth.

Diminished beyond recognition, the gods gathered in conference in Brahmaloka. 'These danava brothers have to be killed,' they beseeched Brahma. 'Or there won't be any trace left of us.'

'I, too, have been thinking about this ever since I granted them their choice of death.'

'Divide and rule!' Vishnu declared. 'You have to devise a way to make them turn on each other.'

'I think I know what to do.' Brahma suddenly had an idea. He summoned the divine architect, Vishvakarma, and said to him: 'Make a woman so beautiful that the very metaphors of beauty will change.'

Vishvakarma loved a challenge. When he heard Brahma's request, his mind began buzzing with ideas about how to create beauty that surpassed all other beauty on earth. He began by collecting loveliness from every mobile and immobile creature on earth and, with that immense stockpile of exquisiteness, he shaped a woman. Then he covered her body with millions of gems and jewels, until every bit of her shimmered like a million tiny lights illuminating her from within.

When the Grandfather saw her, he named her Tilottama (til-uttam-a)—

because every til—every sesame seed bit of her was uttam—unique. When the gods saw Tilottama, their own attributes changed. Shiva grew a head in every direction that she went, and he sprouted four faces. Indra grew a thousand eyes, because two were not enough to look at her.

'Go, Tilottama,' the Grandfather instructed. 'Cleave the bond between Sunda and Upsunda with the blade of your beauty.'

In the meantime, Sunda and Upsunda, having conquered the three worlds, had decided to take it easy and enjoy life. The Vindhya Mountain, which had once served as their field of meditation now served as their pleasure ground. At this time of the year, it was verdant with sala trees and fragrant with wild flowers. Here, they roamed around in woods and gardens, drinking wine and enjoying the company of seductive women, whose sole purpose was to sing, dance and please the brothers.

One day, as the brothers were savouring their inebriation, they suddenly saw at the river's edge a maiden dressed in a single red garment. As wisps of breeze lifted the garment, they got tantalizing glimpses of her voluptuous body, which was radiant with jewelled light. Both brothers watched her for a while as she walked on the river's bank, swaying her near-naked hips, bending over occasionally to pick up a cowrie. Every step she took and every movement she made was like a jolt of intoxication that the brothers had never experienced before. Finally, they both jumped up and approached her on unsteady feet. Sunda grabbed her right hand and Upsunda her left. 'Be mine!' they each begged.

'Whose shall I be? Yours?' she placed a flirtatious fingertip on Sunda's chest, 'Or yours?' she beguiled Upsunda with a smile.

'Let her go,' Sunda hissed at his brother. 'She's mine.'

'You let her go,' Upsunda hissed back. 'I saw her first. She's mine.'

Then Sunda lifted his club and struck Upsunda, and Upsunda struck him back. Soon, the two were fighting each other with all the weapons whose knowledge they had, and, within no time at all, they became bloodied and broken-boned, and yet they fought on.

Seeing the danava brothers caught in a death-dealing battle, all their companions fled. Only Tilottama stood there, smiling and shining, watching them destroy each other.

Myth from the Mahabharata

◆

66

FROM HEAD TO TOE

In the Kurukshetra war, Duryodhana commanded a force comprising eleven akshauhinis, with each akshauhini unit consisting of 21,870 elephants, 21,870 chariots, 65,610 horses, and 109,350 foot soldiers. After seventeen days of combat, almost all his forces were wiped out. His ninety-nine brothers had also been killed, and his four commanders-in-chief—Bhishma, Drona, Karna and Shalya—were dead. Grieving for his men and realizing the certainty that he would lose, Duryodhana decided to take over the command of his remaining forces and continue fighting, if only to honour the sacrifice his men had made for him.

Gandhari, the mother of the Kauravas, had watched ninety-nine of her brave sons die in the war whose result would decide the ruler of Hastinapur. Although the Pandavas constantly reviled the Kauravas and questioned their legitimacy, Gandhari truly believed that her sons were the legitimate heirs. But Gandhari was also a realist. She knew that because Krishna sided with the Pandavas, victory would most likely be theirs. Even though Krishna had sworn to remain unarmed in the war, his presence in the war, as Arjuna's charioteer, was enough of a guarantee. Besides, Krishna had divine maya, which he used to manipulate events, whenever Arjuna's victory seemed in jeopardy.

But Gandhari, too, had one piece of magic in her mother's arsenal, which she had kept secret all her life. This was the tejas, the fiery power of her gaze that she had gained from being a true pativrata. All her life, she had lived in voluntary blindness by wearing a veil over her eyes, so as not to be better than her blind husband, Dhritarashtra. Her vow was so austere and self-sacrificing that its merit had built up. She knew that this shakti had made her gaze so powerful that when she removed her veil, whomever she looked at would be made indestructible.

The evening before Duryodhana was to take command, Gandhari called him to her chamber and said to him, 'Son, tomorrow morning, wake up early and take a dip in the Yamuna, but before putting on any clothes or your armour, come to my room.'

'What are you saying, Mother?' Duryodhana couldn't understand his mother's strange request.

'Just do as I say. A mother commands you. Don't question me. Make sure that when you come to me, you are as bare as the day you were born.'

The next morning, just before sunrise, Duryodhana went to bathe in the Yamuna. Then, wiping himself dry and removing his loincloth, he began to walk towards his mother's chamber, grateful for the half-light which had enough darkness to cover his nudity. He wondered again why his mother had made such an extraordinary request.

As he hurried across the bank, he heard someone say, 'Did you lose your clothes, dear prince?' Duryodhana's hands instinctively reached to cover himself. It was too dark to see who it was, but he recognized the voice immediately. It was Krishna's.

'No,' he muttered, wondering how Krishna had seen him in the dark. 'It's my mother's request that I come to her without any clothes on. I'm sure it's for some ritual or the other, since I'm taking command today.'

'Ritual or not, won't you be embarrassed to go in your mother's presence in the nude? She may want to see you in your birthday suit, but did you forget that you're no longer an infant?'

'My mother does not see,' Duryodhana stated the obvious.

'That may be so, but she'll sense it. You are aware, of course, that it's against all rules of propriety. You may have misunderstood her. When she said, 'without any clothes on', surely, she didn't mean *completely* in the nude. Why don't you at least cover up the genitalia? Besides, since your mother can't see, she won't know the difference, and you won't have disrespected her.'

When Duryodhana hesitated, Krishna added, 'It's your call, sweet prince. I just wanted to wish you all the best for today. Surely, such an important day should not start by dishonouring one's mother.' Duryodhana saw a shift in the shadows as Krishna left. But what he had suggested made sense to him, so he decided to put on his loincloth.

As soon as Duryodhana reached his mother's chamber, he announced himself.

'Welcome, Son. I've been waiting for you,' Gandhari called from inside. 'Come in and stand just in front of me.'

Duryodhana entered the chamber. In the dim early morning light, he could see his mother sitting on the bed with her eyes veiled.

'Are you standing before me, son?' she asked.

'Yes, Mother. I am.'

Gandhari reached behind her head and removed her veil. Her gaze, fired up with decades of pent up shakti, shot at Duryodhana like a razor-sharp laser beam—from the tip of his head down his naked torso. It halted for a moment at the loin cloth, but then continued down to his toes. When her energy was spent, Gandhari covered her eyes again and lay down exhausted. With a deep sigh, she addressed her son: 'I told you to come in the nude,' she said sadly. 'I wanted to look upon your whole body. Why did you cover yourself?'

Duryodhana hung his head in shame. 'I'm sorry, Mother. I felt embarrassed. Krishna...'

Gandhari shook her head in regret. 'That devious divine realized what I was about to do and tricked you. Go and take command, my son, and be careful. Your whole body has become indestructible, except your groin.'[28]

Folk-myth from the Mahabharata

◆

67

THE GREAT DELUDER

VISHNU'S BUDDHA AVATAR

After a battle that lasted a Mahayuga of four million, three hundred and twenty thousand years, the devas were defeated by the asuras, who were commanded by Hiranyakashipu's son, the great asura, Hrada. The devas fled to the shores of the milky ocean and prayed to Vishnu, calling upon his glory and beneficence. When Vishnu appeared, riding on Garuda, armed with his conch shell, discus, and mace, the devas prostrated themselves before him and begged him to help. 'They've seized the three worlds and intercepted every single sacrifice. But we can't defeat them because they practice dharma to the utmost. They follow the commands of the Vedas, and they practice rigorous asceticism. How can we destroy them, when they are more righteous than we are? Have mercy on us and guide us. What can we do to destroy them?'

In response to the entreaty of the devas, Vishnu emitted from his body an illusory form, which he gave to the gods. 'This deceptive form is the Great Deluder. It will beguile the asuras and lead them astray from the path of Vedas and virtue. Then you can kill them, because they will become destructible. The Vedic order is the only true order, and I am its preserver. Whoever breaks this order is susceptible to my destruction. Go now. Take my deluding form to the asuras and then wait and watch!'

The Great Deluder stood on one bank of River Narmada and observed the asuras engaged in pious practices of tapasya and meditation. Then he disguised himself as a naked, shaven-headed Jain monk, carrying a broom of peacock feathers to sweep the ground before him, and spoke to the asuras in a gentle tone, 'Lords of asuras, tell me why you are practicing this asceticism. Is it to gain benefits in this world or the next?'

'We hope to gain rewards in the hereafter, gentle ascetic,' the asuras replied.

'If the reward you hope for is final liberation, then pay attention to what I have to say. What I will teach you is a secret path to liberation; it is far superior dharma than what you are following. '

Then the Great Deluder began to persuade the asuras through many specious arguments, leading them away from the tenets of the Vedas. He taught them that any thing or action can be for virtue or for vice; it might be; it might not be. It might bring liberation; it might not bring liberation. It might be the effect; it might not be the effect. It might be the duty for those who go naked; and it might be for those who wear clothes. So on and so forth, the Great Deluder seduced the asuras with many such arguments of contradiction, which deviate from the synthesis of the Vedas. And the asuras, completely deluded, abandoned the dharma of the Vedas and became Arhats[29] of the false doctrine. Not only that, these asuras became such staunch advocates of the Delusion that they became teachers of this heretic order and taught other asuras, who began to teach the same false doctrine to more of their kind, and, in a short time, the whole asura clan became deluded and gave up adherence to the Vedas.

Then the same Great Deluder put on a red garment, and appearing like a benevolent Buddhist monk went to another section of asuras and said, 'O powerful asuras, if you wish to go to heaven to achieve moksha, then stop killing animals for sacrifice. Understand that this whole universe is unsupported and is perceived by knowledge, but, wandering in the straits of existence, people want to achieve what they mistakenly think is knowledge, because they are impaired by passion and desires.' He also said to them, 'Words of wisdom do not fall from heaven. You should only accept words that are logical.'

The asuras listened and were deluded.

'Know!' the Great Deluder said, 'Budhyadwam!'

'It is known' (Budhyate!) they declared, and forgot their own dharma. Then they went into their community and disseminated this knowledge to others, who, in turn, taught these lessons to many others, and soon all the asuras were persuaded to abandon their Vedic beliefs and practices.

Now, some began to speak evil of the Vedas, others began to denounce the gods, and still others began to scorn sacrifices and fire ceremonies, and they all began to calumniate the Brahmins and also to proscribe brahmanical practices. 'Injury to animals is reprehensible,' they cried. 'To say that pouring butter into fire during the sacrifice will produce results is a childish belief,' they declared. They also posed many logical questions: 'If an animal when slaughtered finds a place in heaven, would not the sacrificer lead his own father to be sacrificed to expedite his entry into heaven?' 'If the food eaten at a shradha feeds another, then it would not be necessary for people who are travelling to carry food.'

In this way, when the asuras began to think for themselves about precepts and understood the logic in the words, they completely abandoned the authority of the Vedas and became evil. This is what the devas had been waiting for. Gaining courage from this delusion of the asuras, they gathered again for battle, and this time, they were able to easily defeat the asuras, because Buddha, the Great Deluder,[30] had dispossessed them of the protective armour of Vedic dharma that they used to wear. And so the deluded asuras were destroyed.

Myth from the Puranas

◆

68

TARA

Avalokiteshvara, the Lord who Contemplates, the Refuge from the three realms of Desire, Form, and Formlessness, saw that no matter how many beings he removed from the suffering of samsara, their numbers did not decrease. He wept. In the water of his tears of compassion grew an utpala—a blue lotus—from which appeared a shimmering sixteen-year-old woman. She was dressed in silks and adorned with ornaments. Her face had the brightness of a hundred autumn moons. Her complexion had the lustre of a thousand stars, and she had a glance like flashing lightning, with which she could see the three worlds instantaneously. Her name was Tara—she who helps one navigate the ocean of suffering. She said: 'I will save them from samsara. I will destroy the army of Mara. Do not cry.'

Buddhist prayer

◆

69

THE RHYTHM OF THE SOUL

HOW VALMIKI BECAME THE ADIKAVI

One day, deep in thought about how he should compose the story of Rama and Sita, Valmiki came to Tamasa river. It was early morning, and this tributary of the Ganga appeared to the rishi as clear as a virtuous mind, so he decided to take a bath in it. Laying his kamandalu on the bank, he asked one of his students to find him an appropriate piece of bark that he could wear after this bath and then dove into the laving water.

After he had bathed and dressed, the rishi walked leisurely along the river bank, watching the sun's rays glisten on the water and listening to the animal and bird calls coming from the surrounding forest. He was thoroughly enjoying the play of nature, when he heard a rolling and purring, as though someone was coaxing another with a secret language. At a short distance, on the river bank, Valmiki saw a pair of krauncha birds. They seemed to be engaged in a love duet with their bodies, bowing and dipping in the air and circling each other with widespread wings, their elegant legs hopping and skipping, as though they were puppets on a string. When the male uttered a cry, the female fondly responded with two, and with each call, the red patches on their faces brightened like emblems of attraction. Seeing them so in love, Valmiki felt elated with the joy of living.

As Valmiki stood contemplating this beauty of life, a Nishada bird-hunter arrived. Seeing the two magnificent krauncha birds, he quickly notched an arrow on his bow and shot the male crane in the chest. For a few minutes, the bird hopped erratically, with its wings distended and blood pouring down its grey chest. Then it toppled over and died. The female crane hovered over her mate, beating her wings, stroking her beak on his wounded chest, and calling out piteously. Watching her in grief, Valmiki's heart filled with compassion, and instinctively he uttered the words:

'Oh fowler, may you find no peace for long years till eternity

For you killed one crane of a pair intoxicated with passion for its mate.'

As soon as he spoke the words, Valmiki realized what he done; he had cursed the fowler to be bereft of peace for eternity. He had been so tormented by the event that he had unwittingly hurt another human being. Anguished though he was, Valmiki couldn't help but be amazed at the sheer poetry he had created. 'Note the couplet down,' he said urgently to his student, Bhardwaja. 'Put it in four metrical feet of thirty-two syllables,' he instructed. 'I think we may have something exciting here.'

Later, sitting with his pupils in his hermitage, Valmiki tried to draw his mind away from the anguish of the dead bird and the regret he still felt for his impulsive curse on the fowler. Just then, Brahmaji came to the ashram. 'Why do you look so morose?' he asked the rishi. Valmiki then related to him the incident on the bank of the Tamasa river. 'But the outcome, Brahmaji,' he concluded, 'was surprising, because from my mouth spilled a couplet with a metre so rhythmic that I think it can be set to music.'

Brahmaji smiled, knowingly. 'It is I who planted the seed of poetic expression on your tongue,' he said. 'Use that honest, soul-wrenching grief of the human condition as the theme to tell the story of Shri Rama and Devi Sita and the loyal Lakshmana. And use the metre you have discovered as your expression.'

And so the Anushtubha metrical form of poetry, in which the twenty four thousand shlokas of the *Ramayana* are written, came into existence.[31] The rhythm of the metre is so true, it is like a heartbeat, and the pathos it contains is so honest that it touches the very soul.

Myth from the Ramayana

◆

70

FIFTY PRAYERS A DAY

Once, during Hijr,[32] when the apostle was sleeping, Gabriel came and woke him up by nudging him with his foot. Sitting up, the apostle looked around, but he didn't see anyone, so he went back to sleep. Gabriel came again to wake him up, but this time, too, the apostle did not see him and returned to sleep. When Gabriel came a third time, he first stirred the apostle awake and then took his arm and guided him to the door of the mosque in Mecca. There the apostle saw Buraq, the white half-mule-half winged-mount that could leap as far as its eye could see. With Gabriel's help, the apostle mounted the animal, and he was carried by night from the mosque at Mecca to the Masjid Al-Aqsa in Jerusalem.

When the apostle had completed his business in Jerusalem, a ladder was brought to him. It was a splendid ladder, such as the one a dying man sees, and the apostle ascended it, accompanied by Gabriel. The ladder reached the gate of heaven, that is called the Gate of the Watchers, and is guarded by the angel Ismail and his army of angels. As Gabriel took the apostle through the gates, Ismail asked him whom he had brought. 'Muhammad,' Gabriel replied. 'Has he received a mission?' Ismail asked. 'Yes,' said Gabriel. After that, in each of the heavens, Gabriel had to seek permission for the apostle to enter. Gabriel stated his name and the mission he had been given, and each gatekeeper angel wished the apostle well, with the words, 'God grant him life, brother and friend!'

Then they reached the seventh heaven, and here the Lord laid upon the apostle the duty of fifty prayers a day.

On his return, the apostle saw his brother, Moses, in the sixth heaven. As he was about to pass by him, Moses asked, 'How many prayers has your Lord laid upon you?' 'Fifty,' the apostle replied. Moses said in compassion, 'Your people are weak and will not be able to bear the weight of so much prayer. Go back to your Lord and ask him to reduce the number.'

The apostle went back to the Lord and made the appeal, and the Lord took off ten. But, again, when the apostle passed by Moses and told him the new number that had been prescribed, Moses gave him the same advice: 'Go back to your Lord and ask him to reduce the number.' And so it went on until the number of prayers for the whole day and night became just five. This time, when the apostle met Moses, and he still urged him to return to the Lord with the same request, the apostle replied: 'I have returned to the Lord so many times to request him to reduce the number of prayers that now I am embarrassed to do it again.'

And so, the apostle told the people, 'He who performs five prayers a day in full faith and trust will reap the reward of fifty prayers.'

Myth from the Hadith

◆

71

A COCONUT WILL SUFFICE

When Sati immolated herself in Daksha's fire, and Shiva wandered the worlds like a mad man, carrying his wife's dead body in his arms, fifty-one parts of the goddess's charred, disintegrating body fell on the earth. These spots became fifty-one Shakti peeths. Sati's tongue fell in the hills of Kangra, and there the goddess manifested in the form of a flame that is inextinguishable. Hence, that Shakti peeth came to be known as Jwala Mukhi.

In the sixteenth century, during the reign of the Mughal Emperor, Akbar, there was a great devotee of the Jwala Mukhi Goddess. His name was Dhyanu, but everyone called him Dhyanu Bhakta, because people believed that his devotion to the Goddess was true.

Akbar was deeply curious about this Goddess. He had once tried to extinguish the flame at Jwala Mukhi by having it covered by an iron disc, but the flame had burned even hotter. So, when Akbar heard about Dhyanu Bhakta, he summoned him to Delhi and asked him about this Devi he worshipped.

'Who is she and why do you worship her?' he asked.

'She is all-powerful—the Supreme Ruler of the world.'

'If she is so powerful, can she bring the dead to life?'

'She is the Compassionate Mother who cares about her devotees. She fulfils all desires.'

Akbar then had one of his horses decapitated and, giving the horse's body and the severed head to Dhyanu, commanded him, 'Go then and pray to this Devi to put my horse's head back and bring him back to life.'

Dhyanu brought the headless horse and his head to Jwala Mukhi and began to pray. He prayed day and night, not losing even a moment's concentration, but the Devi was unresponsive. Dhyanu remained praying for many more days and nights—without eating, drinking, or sleeping, but to no avail. Finally, in anguish at the Goddess's disregard, he cut off his own head and offered it to her.

When the Devi saw this, she was moved to compassion and manifested herself before him. Joining the heads of both Dhyanu and the horse with their bodies, she brought them back to life and then asked Dhyanu to name a boon.

'Ma,' Dhyanu said, 'you are compassionate and all-giving, then why do you test your devotees with such hardship? I only ask that you make it easier for your devotees to receive your benevolence.'

The Devi smiled at Dhyanu and blessed him. Then she promised him that from that moment on, she would consider the offering of a coconut as equal to that of a head.

When Akbar heard about the miracle at Jwala Mukhi, he immediately ordered preparations for a visit to the Devi temple. When he arrived there, he offered a gold parasol at the shrine, but even as the parasol was raised, its gold turned to base metal. Akbar then offered a coconut, realizing that there is no room for scepticism in faith.

Folk-myth

72

THE HALF GOLDEN MONGOOSE

After the Mahabharata war, King Yudhishthira performed the Ashvamedha yajna. In the war, one billion six hundred and sixty million, and twenty thousand men had been killed. Among these were the Pandavas' own grand-uncle, Bhishma, guru, Drona, and eldest brother, Karna, all of whom the Pandavas had killed through treachery. So this horse sacrifice was to help Yudhishthira and his brothers expiate the sins they had incurred in the war. The yajna was a grand affair in which Yudhishthira invited hundreds of Brahmins, all the citizens of Hastinapur, his remaining relatives, and the warriors who had survived the war. He also gave away a vast amount of wealth to the Brahmins.

Just as the sacrifice was concluding, an uninvited guest appeared—a blue-eyed mongoose whose body was gold on one side. He declared in a thunderous, human voice: 'This sacrifice has no merit!'

Everyone was shocked. This was the most magnificent yajna they had attended. The horse had been anointed and decorously sacrificed according to scriptural injunctions, mantras had been uttered with absolute accuracy, Brahmins had been richly rewarded, celestials had been properly propitiated, and all attendees, from Brahmins to Shudras, had been treated duly with the respect they deserved.

'Explain yourself,' the Brahmins, who were overseeing the yajna, demanded of the mongoose. 'Who are you and how can you declare this most excellent sacrifice unmeritorious?'

The mongoose responded with a disdainful smile, 'I tell you, truly, this grand sacrifice is not equal to the handful of powered barley I received from a poor householder.' And he told them a story:

> In Kurukshetra there was Brahmin householder who was observing the Unchcha vrta, which required him to live like a pigeon, eating from grain that he picked from fields after the crop had been collected. He and his family—his wife, son, and daughter-in-law— ate only once a day, and that too only in the sixth division of the day, and if there was nothing to eat at this time, they fasted that day, and ate in the following day's sixth division. It so happened that a dreadful famine hit the land, and that Brahmin and his family

went hungry day after day. But, one day, the Brahmin was able to get a prastha[33] of barley, which his wife ground into powder to make saktu. That day, after the family completed their rituals and prayers, they divided the little quantity of powdered barley among them. As they sat down to eat it, a guest arrived in their house. They welcomed him with honour, giving him water to wash his feet and laying out a seat of kusha grass for him to rest. Then the Brahmin offered his share of powdered barley to the guest. The guest ate that barley, but his hunger was not satisfied, and he asked for more. Now the Brahmin became concerned because he had no more food to offer the guest. But his wife, seeing his distress, handed over her share to her husband to give to the guest. When his hunger was still not appeased, the son and then the daughter-in-law both gave up their share without hesitation so that the father could fulfil his duty towards the guest.

This guest was none other than Dharma. Witnessing the family's compassionate bond and their observance of dharma, even in the midst of such adversity, Dharma was moved. 'With this prastha of barley you have conquered the celestial regions,' he told the Brahmin and his family. Right then he called a heavenly vehicle and, seating the Brahmin's family inside it, he sent them to heaven. As they ascended, celestial flowers showered on them, scented with the barley with which the Brahmin had gained merit.

'That Brahmin's guest was I,' the mongoose informed the audience. 'And as soon as I was touched by that merit, one half of my body became gold. Now I visit hermitages of ascetics and sacrifices of kings, hoping to make the other side of my body golden. When I heard about this grand sacrifice that is being performed by Yudhishthira, the son of Dharma himself, I came here with great hopes. But, alas, I will have to return disappointed. Merit is not in the opulence of wealth, or in the killing of animals, or in grandiose sacrifices. True merit is in self-control, observance of duty, and compassion.'

Putting Yudhishthira's grand yajna to shame, the blue-eyed mongoose left, still searching for true merit that would turn his whole body golden.

Myth from the Mahabharata

◆

73

THE WEIGHT OF A DOVE

One evening, King Sibi was sitting in the lotus garden of his palace, when suddenly, something streaked across the sky and fell into his lap. It was a dove. Its little heart was pounding in its delicate chest, and its fragile wings were trembling. 'Save me, O king,' the dove pleaded in a human voice.

'You have nothing to fear, little dove,' Sibi said, soothing the bird and gathering it in the soft folds of his silk shawl. 'You are in my protection now, and I will not allow anyone to hurt you.'

Just then a fierce-looking hawk swooped down and landed before King Sibi. 'Surrender my prey,' the hawk demanded, also in a human voice. 'That dove is my food.'

'The dove is frightened and exhausted, and it came to me for refuge. I can't surrender a creature whom I have promised to protect,' the king replied.

'Of course it's frightened and exhausted—I was pursuing it. I'm a bird of prey, and I eat tender flesh, like that of this bird; that is my subsistence. If you don't hand over my food, I won't be able to satisfy my hunger, and I'll starve. Where's the justice in that? Surely a king of your fame and stature can't be the cause of a creature's starvation.'

The bird in Sibi's hand trembled at the hawk's words, and Sibi held it more protectively in his shawl. 'I will not give up the dove, but I can't let you go hungry either,' he said to the hawk. 'I can give you other meat, but I can't hand over a creature who is in my protection.'

'Fine,' said the hawk. 'Then give me meat equal in weight to this bird—from your own body. Can you do that?'

'With pleasure,' the king replied, without hesitation, and asked his minister to arrange for a butcher's knife and a scale. When the items were placed before him, King Sibi gently placed the dove on one side of the scale and, carving out a chunk of flesh from his own thigh, placed it on the other side. However, even though the piece from his thigh was large and fleshy, the bird was heavier. So, picking up the knife again, King Sibi cut out another piece from the other thigh and added it to the scale, but the bird still weighed more than the two chunks of his meat.

King Sibi kept adding more and more pieces of his flesh, until his thighs, arms, stomach, shoulders, and shins had gaping holes in them, and his whole body was one big mass of bleeding flesh. And yet the weight of his meat could not match that of the bird. Finally, King Sibi put himself on the scale against the bird.

'Now this is equal to the dove,' the hawk declared and then, suddenly, disappeared. In its stead stood Indra, the king of the gods. The dove, too, vanished from the scale, and standing beside Indra was Dharma. The gods smiled at King Sibi and folded their hands in respect. 'Your fame of bravery, generosity, and compassion has reached even Indraloka,' Indra said. 'The gods are calling you a true dharma king and saying that you will serve as an example for all humans. Lord Dharma and I wanted to see for ourselves if you are deserving of your reputation. This was a test, and you have not only passed it, but you have also raised the qualities of courage and generosity to a new level. You are truly a worthy role model for humanity.'

The gods restored King Sibi's body to its original state and went back to heaven, and King Sibi continued to rule his kingdom with justice and compassion.

Folktale from the Kathasaritsagara

◆

74

AHOI MATA

There were two sisters, Ahoi and Bahoi. Both were happily married, but their lives were sorrowful, because they had no children. They wanted to become mothers, more than anything in the world.

One day, the sisters heard that a very holy man had come to their village, and that through the power of his blessing, he could fulfil any desire. New hope burgeoning in their hearts, the sisters took their sorrow to the holy man, who, they heard, had laid his deerskin mat under a peepul tree just outside of the village. When the sisters arrived there, dozens of people were already waiting their turn to talk to him, and so they, too, got in line. All day they watched the fakir listen to people's entreaties and hand out talismans—dried flowers, a pinch of ashes, a strand of blessed thread—each with a nod and a few words. When, finally, it was their turn, they fell at the holy man's feet and begged him to help them.

'We want children, oh man of God. Give us some magic flowers or ashes or something that can make us conceive,' they implored.

'Flowers or ashes will be of no use to you,' he said. 'Still, I can help you. But first you must pass a test. Go into the village and grab as many children as you can and bring them to me.'

Ahoi and Bahoi ran to the village green, where many children were playing. First they stood on the side of the field and called out to them, but the children were too busy with their games and did not even hear them. Then the sisters went into the green and, interrupting their play, requested the children to come with them, but the kids turned away from the sisters and continued their activities.

'Oh please, come with us,' Ahoi begged. 'We must take you to the fakir baba so that he can bless us with children of our own. If you come with us, we'll give you mithai and toys.' But the children were too involved in their play to be enticed.

It became clear to Bahoi that if they wanted to take the children, they would have to do it by force. So, she grabbed a couple by their arms and another couple by their hair and began pulling them out of the playground. The kids cried and tried to get away, but she held onto them more tightly, calling to Ahoi, 'Do as I do. Take them by force. We must pass the holy man's test.'

Ahoi saw the children struggling to break free from her sister's painful grip. They were sobbing and screaming, and their faces were smeared with tears and mucus. Her own eyes filled up at their suffering, and she said to Bahoi: 'I can't do it. If I have to remain childless, so be it, but I can't hurt children. You go ahead, dear sister, and take the children. I'll be happy for you when you have kids. I won't be a mother but at least I'll be an aunt.'

'You're too soft, Ahoi,' Bahoi scoffed, and tightened her grip on the kids.

The two sisters returned to the peepul tree, Ahoi empty handed, and Bahoi dragging a few wailing and screaming children. She deposited them before the holy man with a triumphant smile, while Ahoi just stood to one side, wringing her hands in despair.

The holy man gave the children some mithai and let them go. Then he turned to Ahoi and asked her why she had not brought any children with her.

'They were playing and didn't want to come, and I didn't want to force them,' Ahoi said. 'I'm sorry. I know I failed the test. But I can't hurt children, no matter what the purpose.'

The holy man then turned to Bahoi and said, 'You have no compassion in your heart. You are not fit to be a mother. You'll remain childless all your life, because that is what you deserve.' Then he called Ahoi to him and blessed her. 'You have the caring and compassionate heart of a mother. May you have many healthy children and may they be successful and renowned.'[34]

Vratakatha folk-myth from North India

◆

75

THE BARTER

There was a poor man, named Patil. All he and his wife had were two ageing buffaloes. When the couple was younger, Patil would to take the animals for grazing, and his wife would milk them, and together they made a living by selling the buffaloes' milk. However, as Patil and his wife grew older, this became difficult. Patil didn't have the stamina to take the animals to the grazing ground outside the village, and there was no money to buy fodder, so the underfed, ageing buffaloes stopped giving milk. The couple hardly had enough to feed themselves and their animals, and to make matters worse, their son and daughter-in-law passed away in a cholera epidemic, and two grandchildren came to live with them.

'Why don't you sell one of the buffaloes?' Patil's wife said to him one day. 'That'll lighten the load, and we can certainly use the money.'

Patil was loath to sell either one of the buffaloes. He had had them for many years and they had become family. But he saw the wisdom of his wife's words and agreed. So, the next morning, he started for the market with one of the buffaloes in tow.

On the way, Patil met a man who was leading a horse. 'Where are you going?' the man asked Patil.

'I'm on my way to the market to sell this buffalo,' Patil replied.

'I could use a buffalo. I'll sell you my horse for the buffalo, if you're willing?'

'Why not?' said Patil. 'A horse is certainly less trouble than a buffalo. Besides, my grandchildren will enjoy riding on it.' So he bartered the horse for the buffalo. But when Patil tried to ride the horse, he realized that the animal was blind. 'Oh well,' he said to himself, and continued on his way to the market, leading the blind horse by the reins. Soon, he met a man who was leading a cow.

'Where are you going with that horse?' the man asked.

'I was actually going to the market to sell my buffalo, but then I met a man who bartered his horse with me for my buffalo. Now I'm going to the market to see if I can sell the horse.'

'If you want to barter your horse for my cow, we can do the exchange right here, and you don't need to go to the market.'

'That sounds like a fair deal. The cow is certainly less trouble than a horse.'

Then the man and Patil exchanged their animals, and the man went on his way. But Patil realized that the cow he had bought was lame in one leg. 'Oh well,' he said to himself and began to lead the cow to the market.

He had gone only a short distance, when a man leading a she-goat stopped him. 'Where are you going with that cow, Uncle?' the man asked.

'Young man, when I started from home, I was going to the market to sell my buffalo, but then a man sold me his horse for my buffalo, and then another man sold me this cow for the horse. Now I'm going to the market to sell the cow.'

'I could use a cow,' the young man said. 'Would you consider bartering your cow with my she-goat?'

'A she-goat will hardly be any trouble, and she can provide milk for the children. I think this is a good deal. Sure. Let's barter.' But after the young man had left, Patil realized that the she-goat was very sick. 'Oh well,' he said to himself and began to walk towards the market with the thought of selling it.

Soon enough he met another man who had a rooster under his arm. 'Where are you taking that she-goat, Grandfather?'

'Well, Son, I had a buffalo that I was going to sell in the market, but then a man sold me his horse for her, then a man with a cow bought the horse and left me his cow, but then a man with this she-goat bartered her for my cow. Now I'm headed to the market to sell the she-goat.'

'I have this rooster that I want to sell. Do you want to barter her for my rooster?'

'That sounds a like a fair deal, Son. A rooster will be no trouble at all. In fact, my wife will enjoy its morning call.'

By this time it was the middle of the afternoon. Patil was hot and hungry, but he had no money. All he had was the rooster. So he went into the market and sold the rooster for one rupee and bought a banana platter of rice and vegetables. After washing himself at the stream, as he sat down under a peepul to enjoy his meal, a beggar in rags stopped in front him and looked at the banana-leaf platter with hungry eyes. 'Would you share your food with me? I'm starving. I haven't eaten in days,' the beggar asked.

Patil couldn't bear to see the beggar's condition and handed him the whole banana leaf. Then he went home. His wife met him at the door. She had cleaned and cooked and had been waiting for him. 'You must be exhausted,' she said. 'How was your day at the market? Were you able to sell the buffalo?'

'Yes and no,' said Patil coming into the house and sitting down. 'I bartered it for a horse.'

'Oh, that's just fine. 'We can certainly use a horse. The children can ride it.'

'But wait, that's not all. Then I bartered the horse for a cow.'

'That's even better. I've always wanted a cow. The children can now have cow's milk.'

'I don't have the cow, because I bartered her for a she-goat.'

'That's not a bad deal at all. A goat's milk is really healthy. The children will grow strong. Besides a she-goat is hardly any trouble.'

'But I don't have the she-goat either. I exchanged her for a rooster.'

'A rooster. Oh that's even better. Now I can wake up with the sun.'

'But, Wife, there's no rooster, because I got hungry and sold it to buy food.'

'Oh, good. What use would a rooster have been? It's better to have food after a long day of hard work.'

'But wait till I tell you what happened after that. As I sat down to eat, a beggar asked me to share the food. The poor man looked so starved that I gave him all the food.'

'And you went hungry yourself? Oh, you poor man. You must be starving yourself. But I'm glad that you didn't turn away a hungry man. Now go and wash and I'll serve you the food I've made.'

Patil ate with relish the simple food that his wife had cooked. Then, with his belly full and his mind at peace, he had a good night's sleep.

The next morning Patil and his wife were woken up by the loud cock-a-doodle-do of a rooster. Surprised at the sound, they got up and went to look. When they opened the front door, even more surprises awaited them. Outside was a buffalo in its prime, a horse with sharp brown eyes, a young, sure-footed cow, a fat, healthy she-goat, a rooster with a bright red cock's comb, and a banana leaf with a shiny rupee coin sitting on it.

'Who do you think has left all these fine gifts for us?' the wife uttered in awe. 'Do you think it was the beggar?'

'Who else?' Patil said.

Folktale from Maharashtra

◆

76

THE RAINBOW PRINCE

In a land far away there lived a princess called Rupanjali who, as her name suggested, was a true gift of beauty. Her face glowed like the moon on a moonlit night, her eyes shone like a cluster of a hundred stars, and when she laughed, it was as though flowers had suddenly sprouted. She was so exquisite that her mother was afraid that they would never find a suitable groom.

'I'll send bards in every direction of the world to find a man worthy of her,' the king consoled his queen. 'Surely, we'll find someone.'

The bards travelled to kingdoms far and near and brought back portraits of the most handsome princes they could find. The king had all the portraits mounted and hung on a wall in a gallery, and then he and his queen invited Rupanjali to choose the one she liked. 'We'll wait outside in the garden and let you decide on your own,' the king told his daughter. 'And when you find the one you like, come and tell us.'

Rupanjali walked around the gallery, but she couldn't find a single portrait that she liked. Joining her parents in the garden, she declared, 'Not one of them is worthy of me.'

Her parents were very disappointed. 'These are the most handsome princes in the world. If you don't like any of them, who will you marry? Who will be worthy of you?'

Rupanjali looked up at the sky, which was clearing up after a rain shower. Just then a rainbow was forming, its spectacular colours stretching from one end of the sky to the other. 'The prince I marry should be as beautiful as the rainbow,' Rupanjali said.

The king and queen returned to their chambers very worried, wondering how they would find a rainbow prince. Then, one day, a minister informed the king that a bard had arrived in the kingdom, who sang about a rainbow land and its handsome rainbow prince. The king commanded that the bard be brought to him immediately, and when the man arrived, he asked him: 'Where are you from, and who is this rainbow prince you extol?'

'I am from the land of the rainbow. I am looking for a bride for our prince. We heard that Princess Rupanjali is seeking a rainbow prince, and I've come with a marriage proposal for her.'

The king was overjoyed. He gave the bard a seat of honour, thanked him for the proposal, and happily accepted it.

'Wait, Maharaj,' the bard said. 'Before you accept the proposal, I must tell you that our prince is under the spell of an evil witch. She has taken his soul and put it in the body of a red parrot. The prince sleeps, but the bird roams free. Our prince will not awaken until the parrot is found and his soul returned to his body.'

The king's shoulders slumped in dejection again. How could he marry his beloved daughter to a man who might never wake up? But by this time, Rupanjali had already heard the news. She rushed to her father and declared that she would marry only the rainbow prince and no one else.

'My daughter, we may never find the red parrot.'

'Order your men to catch every single bird and put it in a cage. The red parrot will surely be caught.'

'But how can we do that? We can't cage all the birds. That would be cruel.'

'I don't care,' Princess Rupanjali stamped her foot. 'If you love me, you'll do this, Father.'

The king had been fulfilling his daughter's every wish from the first time her soft lips turned down in a pout, so there was no question of him refusing her. That very day, he gave orders to trap all birds and put them in the huge iron cage that he had his men construct. Soon nests and tree branches and balustrades became empty. No longer was the evening sky dotted with flocks returning to their nests, and no longer was the morning awakened with excited twittering.

Bird catchers worked day and night, netting birds, and soon the large cage began to fill up with winged creatures of all kind. Their wings were bound with a string before they were put into the cage, and they hopped around awkwardly, screeching in fright. And, every day, more birds arrived. Each morning, Princess Rupanjali came to inspect the cage herself to see if the red parrot had been captured.

The princess had a maid, Nilanjana, whose soft heart filled with pity at the sight of the trapped birds. One morning, seeing a flock of little chicks, hardly old enough to fly, being thrown into the cage with bound wings, she couldn't bear it anymore and went to plead with the princess.

'Please, I implore you. Free the birds.'

'Are you questioning me?' the princess shouted, enraged.

'No, Princess. I'm only asking you to be kind to these creatures. To find one bird you are torturing thousands. How can you build your happiness on the sorrow of so many?'

'Since you're so concerned about those creatures, why don't you go and live with them in the cage,' the princess said, and ordered her guards to throw Nilanjana in with the birds.

Lying in the cage without food or water, when Nilanjana began to weep, all the birds came to her and picked her tears with their beaks. Then they sang sweet, heartbroken songs for her, and, soothed by these, Nilanjana fell asleep. When she awoke, she saw a red parrot perched on her shoulder.

'Oh, you're the red parrot for whom the princess has been searching,' she said excitedly. 'She'll be so happy to see you.'

'Please set me free, Nilanjana,' the parrot spoke to her in a human voice. 'See how the string is hurting my wings?'

'But you're the red parrot for whom my princess has been waiting.'

'I have no wish to meet your cruel princess. When she finds me, who knows what she'll do to me. Please set me free.'

Nilanjana gathered the parrot in her hands and cooed gently. 'I'll cut the string and set you free. I don't care what the princess does to me,' she promised.

Just then Rupanjali arrived to inspect the catch of the day and saw Nilanjana holding the red parrot. 'Oh, you found him!' she cried, clapping her hands. 'Nilanjana, you smart girl. You deserve a reward. Hold on to him while I come inside.' And she ordered the guard to open the gate of the cage. But even before the guard could release the latch, Nilanjana pushed open the small window near the top of the cage, through which the bird catchers deposited their catch, and set the red parrot free.

Rupanjali was beside herself with rage. 'You wicked girl. You've let him fly away. You'll pay for this with your life.' She then ordered the guards to take Nilanjana to the top of the mountain and throw her into the gorge below. Following the princess's orders the guards carried Nilanjana to the mountaintop and pushed her over. Nilanjana screamed and shut her eyes, but even as she began to fall, she felt two strong arms catch her and swiftly deposit her on the ground.

'Open your eyes, Nilanjana,' a gentle, male voice said to her.

When she opened her eyes, she saw that she was back on the top of the mountain, and a very handsome man was standing before her, smiling.

'Who are you?' Nilanjana asked in awe.

'I am the rainbow prince.'

'Oh! You're even more handsome than we imagined,' Nilanjana said. 'Have you come to meet the princess? She's been waiting for you.'

'I haven't come for your princess, Nilanjana. I've come for you. *You* are my princess.'

'But I am only the maid.'

'Now you will be my princess.'

Together they went to the palace, where the prince told the guards to inform the princess that the rainbow prince had come to see her.

When Rupanjali heard this news, she ran to meet the man of her dreams, but when she reached the gate, she stopped in shock. Standing with the prince was her maid, Nilanjana.

'How are you still alive, you wicked girl?' she screamed at Nilanjana. Then she turned to the prince and said. 'You've made a mistake. She's only the maid. I'm the princess, Rupanjali. I'm the one who found the red parrot.'

'The red parrot was only a test to see the worth of the girl I would marry,' said the prince. 'And you failed the test. It is Nilanjana who passed it, and she'll be my bride. You are a princess only in name, and your beauty is only skin deep. You have no heart. I have no wish to marry a woman as cruel as you.'

Nilanjana and the rainbow prince married, and together they released all the birds that the cruel princess, Rupanjali, had caged.

Folktale from Bengal

◆

77

NOT ON THE SABBATH

One Sabbath, Jesus was teaching in a synagogue, when a crippled woman entered. For eighteen years, she had been suffering from a painful degenerative disease that had twisted her spine, until she was almost bent double and could hardly stand. When Jesus saw her, he went to her and gently placed his hands on her. 'You're cured!' he said. The woman's disease vanished and she stood up straight. Filled with joy and gratitude, the woman began to praise Jesus, but the priest in the synagogue stopped her and said angrily to Jesus, 'You cannot heal on the Sabbath. God has made this day for rest.' Then he turned to the congregation and announced. 'There are six working days in a week. If you must, come and be cured on any one of those days, but not on the Sabbath.'

Jesus asked the congregation: 'Do you not take your cattle to drink water on the Sabbath? Do your animals not wander out of the manger on the Sabbath? And do you not go looking for them on the Sabbath?' Then he said to them, 'This poor woman has been suffering and has been in pain from a devil's disease for eighteen years. Why should she have to wait another day? Why can she not be freed from it on the Sabbath? All days are good to do good work.'

Parable from the New Testament

◆

ARROGANCE

78

BETWEEN HEAVEN AND EARTH
TRISHANKU

Trishanku, the king of Ayodhya, had a burning desire: he wanted to live in heaven with the heaven-dwellers, but not as a virtuous, bodiless spirit after his death; he wanted to go there in his living, breathing, handsome physical form. He believed that he had earned the reward of ascending to heaven: he had disciplined his sense organs; he lived by his resolve to never lie; he was a Kshatriya par excellence and had brought much glory to the celebrated Ikshvaku clan. Besides his accomplishments, he had superlative skills of performing yajnas with absolute accuracy, which kept the gods content and benevolent. Because yajna was a means to fulfil desires, and he had perfected the science of sacrifice, he was certain that the best way for him to get to heaven was to have a yajna with the sole purpose of ascension to heaven. There was no doubt in Trishanku's mind about his success; he just needed to find the right priest to officiate over this unusual sacrifice.

The officiating priest for the Ikshvaku kings was the most revered Rishi Vasishtha, one of the Saptarishis—the seven rishis born from Brahma's mind—created to populate the earth with the human race. Vasishtha was, in fact, such an exalted rishi that he was already installed in heaven as one of the seven stars in the Big Dipper. Trishanku couldn't ask for a more appropriate chief priest to execute the yajna; however, when Trishanku broached the subject with Vasishtha, the rishi refused, unequivocally. 'No ritual sacrifice, no matter how long or how grand can take anyone to Indra's heaven in bodily form,' he informed the king. 'Give up this foolish desire, O king, and concentrate on being the good king that you are. That will get you into heaven after you die.'

'Anyone can get to heaven after he dies,' Trishanku replied, disdainfully. 'The glory is in ascending to heaven while one is still alive.'

'One must not hanker after that which is beyond reach. You're a mortal,' Vasishtha reprimanded Trishanku. 'There are rules.'

As a Saptarishi, Vasishtha had to ensure cosmic correctness. A mortal ascending to heaven was a violation that could lead to cosmic disorder, and he couldn't be a party to that. But Trishanku thought that the aged rishi just didn't have the gumption anymore. 'I need someone as skilled as him but young and adventurous,' he said to himself and drew up a list of possible candidates. The first names on his list were Vasishtha's hundred sons, who were not only well trained by their father but were also rapidly gaining acclaim as officiating priests and were always seeking to enhance their reputation. Trishanku was sure that they would jump at the chance, because a yajna like the one he desired, would put them at the top of the totem pole of yajna priests.

But when the king proposed the yajna to Vasishtha's sons, they, too, refused. 'How could you even think that we would act against our father and guru?' they admonished Trishanku. 'Besides, if the ageless Vasishtha, who is able to successfully perform any sacrifice, has said that the sacrifice you desire is not possible, then it's not possible. Take our advice and give up this foolish desire and concentrate on the dharma of being a good king. That'll surely get you into heaven after you die.'

'If you won't do the yajna, then someone else will,' Trishanku told them. 'I'm determined to perform this sacrifice and claim my place in heaven—with or without your help or your father's. Or is it that you and your father are afraid to test your ascetic prowess? You're all afraid you may fail. Perhaps, you're just not as skilled as you claim to be.'

The sons of Vasishtha felt so insulted by Trishanku's innuendo that they cursed him: 'Since you don't seem to recognize the Kshatriya dharma of loyalty; since your ambition has made you aspire to equal the peerless gods; and since you are so attached to your body, may you lose your high caste and elevated status in society and become a Chandala, a person who deals with dead bodies in cremation grounds.'

That very night Trishanku's fair Kshatriya complexion turned dark, and his perfumed skin became coated with the ash of pyres and began reeking of burnt human flesh. His thick, curly hair fell out, and his eyes became sunken and red, like someone who looks upon fires all day. His amber silken dhoti became coarse cloth, blackened with dirt and ashes, and the flowers in the garland around his neck suddenly withered. The kingly rings he wore slipped off his bony fingers, and the necklace that sat on his chest in a glittering bib of gold and diamonds, became an iron choker around his neck.

When Trishanku's attendants saw that their king had become a Chandala who disposes of dead bodies, they ran away from him in fear and revulsion. Trishanku himself was horrified at the change in his appearance, but that did not deter him; he still wanted to go to heaven, Chandala body and all. And now he knew that there was only one man who could help him accomplish his goal—Vishwamitra, whose life's mission it was to make possible anything that Rishi Vasishtha deemed impossible, even if it meant changing the very order of the cosmos.

The rivalry between Vasishtha and Vishwamitra was legendary.

Vishwamitra used to be a king—the radiant and victorious predecessor of the great king, Gadhi. He used to be a warrior ruler with a force of 21,870 elephants and an equal number of chariots, 65,610 horses and 109,350 foot soldiers. With this force, he conquered most of the earth. One day, travelling through his vast kingdom, he stopped at Rishi Vasishtha's hermitage. The rishi welcomed him, as befitting his status of king, giving him a sandalwood seat plated with gold and silver and preparing a feast of a hundred different delicacies, served in utensils of gold. Vishwamitra was amazed at how the rishi, who himself lived without material comfort, had managed to put all this together at a moment's notice. 'How did you do it?' he asked the rishi.

'I have Sabala,' Vasishtha revealed to Vishwamitra. 'She's Kamadhenu, the cow of plenty—the one that arose from the ocean during the great churning. She was given to the Saptarishis so that we will always have milk to make the ghee we need for ritual sacrifices. But she can also produce anything else we may need.'

'She can fulfil anything, no matter what you desire?'

'Yes. No matter what I desire.'

Vishwamitra wanted that cow. 'A hundred thousand cows for Sabala,' he offered the rishi.

'Sabala is my most treasured possession,' Vasishtha said. 'I won't part with her for a hundred crore cows, or a hundred crore pieces of silver. She's not only my means of subsistence but also my means to perform sacrifices. And she's the source of my delight. I will not part with her.'

'My best elephants, my most pedigreed horses, enough gold and silver to buy a kingdom...' Vishwamitra kept sweetening the deal, but Vasishtha's answer remained the same: he would not part with Sabala. When all deals failed, Vishwamitra stole Sabala. Putting a noose around her neck, he took off with her, but Sabala escaped and found her way back to Vasishtha. 'Why have you abandoned me?' she wept before Vasishtha. 'I was happy with you. I don't want to serve that evil Kshatriya.'

'I haven't abandoned you, my Sabala, but what am I to do? Vishwamitra is not only a powerful Kshatriya, but he also commands a mighty force.'

'You're a Brahmin of the highest order,' Sabala reminded Vasishtha. 'You've been building your ascetic power since the beginning of time. That upstart evil Kshatriya is no match for you. You can burn him to ashes with just one mantra. Let's fight him together. I'll create the means to fight his forces, and you take care of the king and his sons.' And so, Sabala conjured up a military force equal to Vishwamitra's and wiped out the king's entire army, and when his hundred sons rushed towards Vasishtha, all the rishi had to do was roar, and the princes fell down dead.

Vishwamitra was dismayed at losing his sons and his entire force, but more than that, he was astounded at the power a Brahmin could wield. Just one roar, and poof! his hundred sons became ashes. The only power in the universe that could equal that had to be divine power, he thought to himself, and made up his mind that he would acquire all the divine weapons that he could. Hence, Vishwamitra began a severe course of austerities by living in the Himalayas, eating only roots and leaves and meditating for hundreds of years. Finally, Shiva, the god he was propitiating, appeared before him and asked him what he desired.

'Celestial weapons,' he declared. 'I want the knowledge of how to call all the weapons of all the gods—Indra's thunderbolt, Shiva's Pinnaka bow, Vishnu's Vajra, Kaala's noose, Brahma's Brahmastra, the gandharvas' weapons to induce instantaneous sleep, Swayambhu Manu's sword that stuns, Agni's fire...I want every single weapon under my command—to call to my service whenever I desire. And I also want to know the complete science of how to use each weapon.'

'Done!' Shiva granted his wish in an instant.

Armed with the knowledge of divine weapons, Vishwamitra faced Vasishtha in battle once again. He threw deadly tridents and fiery thunderbolts; weapons that burst into flames, and arrows that showered snakes. But every weapon he discharged either shattered and fell to the ground or vanished into thin air. All Vasishtha had to do to combat any weapon thrown at him was to utter a mantra and raise his Brahmin's staff. When Vishwamitra ran out of weapons, Vasishtha uttered a final mantra, and a streak of fire shot out from every pore of his body and the tip of his staff, creating a mass of flames that roared across the earth and up into the sky, threatening to devour the universe, like the cosmic fire at the end of the yuga.

'Stop, O great Brahmin. We beg you,' the celestials cried, quickly gathering at the line where earth meets heaven. 'Calm your wrath,' they pleaded with him. 'Or Vishnu's Creation will be destroyed.' Then they begged Vishwamitra to concede, and the king reluctantly bowed before the Brahmin to acknowledge his superiority. Vasishtha then took one long inhalation and, with it, he breathed in the fire to the last ember.

Vasishtha went back to his ashram, but Vishwamitra returned to the Himalayas; this time to acquire Brahminhood, because he realized that not even the gods could match Brahmin power. For thousands of years, he endured the most extreme hardships, keeping his senses under control, and subsisting only on air. Finally, when all that remained of him was a skeleton held together with some sinews, Brahma manifested himself before him. 'You have proved your asceticism, O Vishwamitra,' he declared. 'Go. You are now a rajarishi, a royal sage.'

Vishwamitra was deeply disappointed. He had hoped that his severe tapasya would earn him the title of the rishi of cosmic order—a brahmarishi—like Vasishtha—but it seemed that that was still beyond his reach. But he was determined to not give up, so he became a hermit and began to live in seclusion to continue working towards his ultimate goal.

It was at this time that Trishanku, bearing his Chandala burden, having his desire thwarted by Vasishtha and his sons, sought Vishwamitra's help.

Vishwamitra was moved by Trishanku's story, but when he heard that the person responsible for his condition was Vasishtha, he was delighted. 'Listen to this, O king,' he said bombastically. 'With the power of all the ascetic merit I have built, I vow today that I will send you to heaven in your body, even in its Chandala form.' Then he sent his messengers in every direction to summon to his hermitage all the rishis and holy sages of the land, and they all came, because they feared Vishwamitra's wrath. The only rishis who refused to come were Vasishtha's sons. Instead, they sent him a message: 'How do you expect the holy sages and rishis to participate in a sacrifice in which a Kshatriya is masquerading as the chief priest and the offerings are being made by a Chandala?'

Vishwamitra was so enraged at this that he cursed the sons of Vasishtha to die instantly and be reborn seven hundred times successively in the wombs of mothers of the Mutika caste—a clan even lower than the Chandala—who ate dog meat and lived by selling the shrouds of dead bodies. Despairing at the hopeless state in which his sons had been thrust, Vasishtha decided to commit suicide and jumped into River Hemavathi to drown himself. But his asceticism was so formidable that the river split into a thousand streams.

In the meantime, Vishwamitra commanded the rishi forces in his hermitage to begin organizing a grand yajna to send Trishanku to heaven. All the preparations went according to plan, and the yajna started faultlessly, but when Vishwamitra invoked the gods to come and receive their share of the sacrifice and carry Trishanku to heaven, none of them came. In fact, there wasn't so much as a stir in heaven.

Beside himself with anger at the rejection by the celestials, Vishwamitra picked up the ghee ladle and brandishing it like a magic wand, declared: 'With the energy of my mental prowess and the power of my thousands of years of asceticism, I, Vishwamitra, send you, Trishanku, to heaven in your bodily form. Ascend!'

To everyone's amazement, Trishanku began to rise, his body erect, his head pointed upwards, towards the sky.

Sitting on his throne in Indraloka, Indra watched in horror and disbelief, waiting to see what would happen next. Soon he saw the crown of Trishanku's head, crossing the line that separated heaven and earth. 'Stop!' Indra shouted, standing up in panic. 'Return to earth, mortal. You do not belong in my heaven. Cursed by Vasishtha's sons and doubly cursed by your impossible desire, I doom you to fall back to earth.'

Trishanku's body did a flip in mid space, and now, with his head downwards, he began to fall. 'Help,' he screamed. 'Save me, Vishwamitra.'

'Stop!' Vishwamitra commanded from earth, fuming at Indra's attempt to thwart him. And Trishanku's body stopped right there, suspended between heaven and earth, his head pointing earthward, his feet pointing heavenward. 'If Indra will not allow you entry into his heaven, to hell with him,' Vishwamitra stated. 'I'll create another heaven for you. In fact, I'll also create another Indra for that heaven, or better still, I'll create a heaven without the arrogant Indra.' Then, as everyone watched in astonishment, Vishwamitra created seven new constellations and a new galaxy around Trishanku.

The gods, too, looked on, bewildered. 'How is this possible?' they asked each other. Then they said to Vishwamitra. 'Your ascetic powers are truly unmatched. No one on earth is capable of doing what you have done,' they proclaimed. 'But, why have you done this?'

As soon as the gods acknowledged his prowess, Vishwamitra's anger abated, and he responded, 'I promised Trishanku that I would send him to heaven. I had to fulfil that promise. I ask you to let Trishanku's heaven remain and leave him intact in his heaven.'

'So be it,' they stated. Since then, Trishanku's heaven has existed, and Trishanku himself has remained suspended between heaven and earth.

Myth from the Ramayana

◆

79

A PARADE OF INDRAS

Indra, the king of gods, fought numerous battles with the danavas, and in each battle, his beautiful city, Indraloka, suffered damage. After winning a particularly difficult battle with the great asura Vrta, Indra decided to rebuild his Indraloka. This victory against his most powerful enemy made Indra feel invincible, and he began to see himself as the utmost exalted being in heaven. He wanted his abode to be a true reflection of this glory. Calling Vishvakarma, the divine architect, he described his vision to him and instructed him to build a city that would be unmatched in magnificence.

Vishvakarma worked for a whole year and built just such a city— aesthetically designed yet grandiose and luminous with precious stones and diamonds studded in its walls. Indra liked it, but not enough; he wanted something more—an additional palace here, a more intricately latticed wall there, a different pattern of jewels somewhere else. So Vishvakarma went back to work on Indra's new requirements; however, when the architect completed the improvements, the king of gods was still not satisfied. 'I am king of gods,' he shouted at Vishvakarma. 'There is no one in this universe as powerful, valorous, and laudable as I. My city needs to reflect who I am.'

A dozen modifications later and exhausted in body and mind, when Vishvakarma found himself back at the drawing board, he sought Brahma's advice. 'What should I do?' he asked the Grandfather. 'Nothing I create will match his elevated sense of self. But how can I refuse him? He is the king.'

'I'll take care of it,' Brahma assured Vishvakarma. 'You go on home and rest. Don't worry about a thing.' Brahma knew exactly who he needed to call to resolve the situation. He first paid a visit to Vishnu and then, together, they went to see Shiva.

The following morning, a young Brahmin boy, no older than ten, arrived at the gates of Indra's palace. The child had a radiant and innocent face, and he was wearing white. He also had a large Brahmin mark on his forehead and was holding a parasol and a staff. 'I've come to see the king of gods,' he told the gateman.

Indra welcomed the Brahmin boy, offered him water, fruits and honey, and then enquired about the purpose of his visit.

'I've come to see Indraloka,' the boy replied in a voice that was surprisingly deep, like a thundering sky. 'I've heard that its beauty is unsurpassed, and it's more beautiful than the cities of any other Indras. Yet, I hear that you are not satisfied with it. How long do you think it'll take Vishvakarma to make the city that you envision?'

Indra was amused at the child's boastfulness. 'Dear boy, how many Indras have you heard of and how many have you seen?' he asked.

'Child,' the boy replied. 'I knew your father Kashyapa, and your grandfather, Marichi. I also know Brahma, born from Vishnu's navel, and I know Vishnu, the preserver of this universe. In fact, O king of gods, I've also seen dissolution, when everything is finished and the world is nothing but water. Again and again, at the end of every cycle, I've seen this dreadful annihilation—fathomless, infinite—nothing but water and darkness. Who can count the universes that have passed and the universes that have arisen afresh, each with its own Brahma and Vishnu and Shiva. They say it's easier to count grains of sand or drops of rain water than it is to count the universes that have been and will be. Like a tiny boat floating on the ocean, universes float by in the primordial ocean. Who can say how many Indras have been? The scriptures say that one Indra lives and rules for seven yugas, and the span of twenty-eight Indras is one day and night of Brahma, and one year of Brahma's life span is one hundred and eight years. You do the math, if you can. In fact, not only Indras, but even Brahmas are countless. Know this, that from each pore of the Supreme Vishnu's body, a universe is born, each one with numerous gods like you.'

Listening to the boy, Indra grew more and more horrified. Just then, a line of ants, each one following the other, as in a procession, crossed the floor. Seeing them, the boy burst into laughter, and then he grew silent, as though in deep thought.

Indra, with his throat quite dry, asked warily, 'Why did you laugh? Who are you—in a boy's body but with the mysterious mind of a divine being? Who are you, ocean of virtues, shrouded in deluding mist?'

'See those ants? I'm laughing at the sight. Each ant was a former Indra,' the boy revealed. 'Like you, each, by virtue of great deeds, became elevated to be king of gods. But now, through rebirth and lack of virtue, they have become ants. This procession of ants is a procession of former Indras. This is a hilarious sight, and it made me laugh. It holds a secret that you should know, but you choose not to know it,' said the boy.

'Please tell me the secret,' Indra said fearfully.

'This secret is the wisdom that dispels darkness: each being in this world is bound by karma. The karma of good deeds releases a person and brings him to heaven, and the karma of bad deeds lands him in the nether world and brings him pain and sorrow and disease and deformity. Or, it causes him to be reborn among pigs and birds and insects. It is deeds that make a person a king or a servant, or even an Indra or a Brahma. This is the secret that carries one across the ocean of life. Life is a cycle of birth and rebirth. Death rules this law of time, and within its domain, beings perish and are reborn, like bubbles. It's an unending cycle of good and evil, and snared in this cycle, people suffer their karmas. That is why the wise remain detached.'

Humbled and in despair, Indra listened to the boy. But now, another person entered the palace. He was a very old Brahmin. His hair was matted, he was wearing deerskin around his waist, and he was holding a parasol of grass over his head. On his chest was a circular cluster of hairs, intact at the circumference but with a bald spot in the middle. Indra welcomed this guest, too, and gave him a seat of honour, as befitting his age and caste, before asking him, 'Who are you? Why are you dressed like that and what is the meaning of that circle of hair on your chest?'

'People call me Lomasha (Hairy), and I'm a mendicant,' said the old Brahmin. 'Life is short. That's why I haven't built a house for myself or collected any material wealth. Pleasures are transient, as are sorrows. All I need in life is this deerskin to cover my body and this grass parasol to protect my head from sun and rain. As for the hair on my chest—each of these hairs corresponds to the life of one Indra. Each time a hair from the centre falls, one Indra dies. Soon the time allotted to Brahma will expire, and the whole circle of hair will fall, and I, too, will die along with everyone else.'

Suddenly, both the boy and the hermit, who were Vishnu and Shiva in disguise, disappeared, leaving Indra sitting in his peerless palace, questioning himself and his desires. Now he was no longer interested in wealth and honour or in aggrandizing his city. He called Vishvakarma and released him from any further work. Then he decided to leave his life of luxury to become a hermit and seek wisdom. When Shachi, Indra's wife, heard that her husband was renouncing the world to become an ascetic, she was horrified. She ran to Brihaspati, the priest of the gods, and begged him to help. Brihaspati explained to Indra the virtues of both a spiritual life and a worldly life. 'The ideal existence is a balance,' he taught him. 'Pursue wisdom but also live life.' And Indra realized his error.

Myth from the Puranas

◆

80

THE FISH THAT WERE TOO CLEVER

Three friends lived in a pond—a fish named Satbuddhi (having the intelligence of a hundred), another fish, Sahasrabuddhi (having the intelligence of a thousand), and a frog called Ekbuddhi (having the intelligence of one). Every evening, as the sun set, the three would meet near the bank to talk about their day and hang out. On one such evening, some fishermen, carrying nets and baskets full of fish on their heads, passed by the pond, and the friends heard one of them say, 'I've been told this pond has a lot of fish. Let's come back here tomorrow morning and set our nets.'

Ekbuddhi, the frog, was stricken with fear. 'What should we do?' he cried to Satbuddhi and Sahasrabuddhi. 'Maybe we should leave this pond. In fact, I think we should leave right away.'

Sahasrabuddhi laughed. 'Dear friend, don't panic,' he said. 'Those were just words. Most likely, those men won't return tomorrow. But even if they do, I'll use my intelligence to figure out an escape route by finding a path through the bottom of the pond. I'll also take care of you, don't worry.'

'I agree with Sahasrabuddhi,' Satbuddhi said and recited:

Intelligence will find a path,
where neither wind nor sun can.
Also, there's no problem on this earth
That intelligence can't resolve.

'Besides, we shouldn't abandon the place where we have lived for generations, just because we heard someone say something. If those men do return tomorrow, I, too, will protect you with the power of my intelligence, Ekbuddhi.'

'Forgive me, friends,' the frog responded. 'I appreciate your concern for me. It's true that I have just the intelligence of one, but right now, it's telling me to flee. I think I'll take my wife and go to some other pond tonight.' And that very night Ekbuddhi and his wife found another pond.

Early the next morning, the fishermen came like messengers of Yama, and spreading their nets in the water, caught all the creatures in the pond. Satbuddhi and Sahasrabuddhi swam frantically, trying to find other paths under the water to escape the nets, but, before long, they were caught, along with their wives and families.

When the fishermen took their catch home in the afternoon, Sahasrabuddhi was hanging dead on a string that one of the men was holding, and Satabuddhi was among the dozens of dead fish in a basket on the head of another man.

Watching them from the embankment of his new home, Ekbuddhi, the one-intelligence frog, said to his wife, 'He who has the intelligence of a thousand hangs from a string, and he who has the intelligence of a hundred sits in a basket on a head, while I, who have only one intelligence, still live and enjoy life in the clear water of this pond.'

Folktale from the Panchatantra

◆

81

THE ARRIVAL OF KALIYUGA

As Dwapara Yuga, the third aeon in the cycle of Great Time, came to an
end, Hastinapur was ruled by Raja Parikshit, who was the grandson of
Arjuna, of *Mahabharata* fame. One day, chasing a deer he had wounded
during a hunt, Parikshit got separated from his men and found himself
deep in the forest. After hours of wandering around, he came upon a
cowshed in which a rishi was drinking the froth that was spilling from the
mouths of suckling calves.

'Respected sir, have you seen a wounded deer come this way?' the
raja asked the rishi.

Let alone respond, the rishi didn't even acknowledge Parikshit.

'My dear man, if you could just tell me whether or not you have
seen a wounded deer, I'd appreciate it.'

The rishi still didn't respond.

Parikshit was already in a foul mood. He was frustrated with the
chase, his throat was parched, his stomach was growling, and his body
was hurting from hours of riding. So this rishi's behaviour was especially
irksome to him. 'Hey. Can you hear me?' he called loudly this time. 'I'm
Raja Parikshit. I command you to answer me.'

Silence!

'You arrogant old man, do you not realize that I'm not only a thirsty
and hungry guest standing at your door, I'm also your king.'

Silence!

'What nature of a rishi are you? What nature of a man? Are you deaf?
Blind? If not, you are an aberration of the very essence of humanity. I'll
show you what I think of you, you old coot.' Parikshit looked around for
something with which he could defile the rishi, and seeing a snake carcass
nearby, lifted it off the ground with the end of his bow and garlanded
the holy man with it. The rishi not only bore it all without so much as
a frown, he also made no effort to remove the dead snake, even after the
king left. This was Rishi Shamika, and he was observing a vow of silence.

Rishi Shamika had a seven-year-old son, Shringin, who, despite his tender age, was quite skilled in ascetic practices. On this day, he was on the village green, boasting about his accomplishments to the other boys, unaware of the insult his father had suffered, when his friend, Krishna, arrived on the scene and said to him: 'You think you're accomplished, but you're not. You don't even know that your father has been shamed. Someone has put a dead snake around his neck. I saw it with my own eyes on my way here.'

Shringin became filled with rage. With his nostrils flaring, he took water in the cup of his hand and, raising his voice to the skies, shot off a curse: 'May he who has defiled my father with a dead snake be bitten on the seventh day by Takshaka, the king of snakes.'

When Rishi Shamika found out what his son had done, he was saddened. 'What have you done, Son?' he said. 'Raja Parikshit is a good king who cares deeply about the well-being of his people, and especially about us Brahmins. By condemning him in your anger, you've endangered this whole land.'

'It's done now, Father. It can't be undone. The words I've uttered have been sealed with the truth of water,' Shringin replied.

'I know your words are true, my Son,' the father said. 'But with the yuga of Kali upon us, perhaps even immutable truth can be made mutable. If we warn the raja, maybe he can find a way to avert the power of truth. Let me send my trusted pupil, Gaurmukha, to apprise him.'

When Gaurmukha informed Parikshit about Shringin's curse, the king was pained—not so much at his own impending doom, but at the thought that he had insulted a faultless rishi who was only observing his vow. 'I beg your guru's forgiveness,' he said to Gaurmukha. 'What can I do to make amends?'

'O Raja,' Gaurmukha replied. 'Rishi Shamika holds no grudge against you and has already forgiven you. You shouldn't worry about making amends to him but about saving yourself from Shringin's curse.'

'Can it be done?' Parikshit was sceptical. As far as he knew, Brahmin curses were irreversible.

'These are uncertain times when yugas are changing,' Gaurmukha replied. 'Everything is uncertain, even the sacrosanctity of water and truth. There's hope. You must do whatever you can to counter the curse.'

That's all Parikshit needed to hear. He ordered his architects to build

a palace erected on one pillar to guard against the serpent, Takshaka.
All around the pillar, he stationed security guards so that nothing—
not even air—could enter without first being breathed by his men. In
this pole-hoisted, fortified palace, he surrounded himself with doctors
and pharmacists and also with Brahmins who were experts in antidotal
mantras.

Six days passed. All was safe. On the seventh morning, security was
doubled around the pillared palace and, inside the palace, doctors and
pharmacists and mantra chanters were put on high alert.

On this seventh morning, Takshaka was also on alert. He was positioned
in a banyan tree in a forest near the pillar that held aloft Parikshit's palace,
and was watching it, the security guards, and the path that led there.
Then he saw Rishi Kashyapa hurrying towards the palace. Kashyapa was
the master of mantras, so Takshaka wondered what he intended to do.
Changing himself into a Brahmin, he appeared before the rishi. 'Where
are you going in such a hurry, respected rishi?' he asked.

'I've heard that today Takshaka will bite Raja Parikshit,' Kashyapa
replied. 'I know the antidotal mantra for Takshaka's fiery poison. I'm going
to the palace so that I can cure the king after he is bitten.'

'I'm that Takshaka, king of snakes,' Takshaka said, changing back into
himself. 'And I will certainly bite Parikshit today, and you can't cure him.
The raja will die. No one survives my poison.'

'O Snake, you dare to equal a Brahmin? King of snakes you may be,
but your poison is no match for my mantras.'

'Prove it,' Takshaka challenged.

'How?' Kashyapa asked.

'See this banyan tree? I'll burn it with my poison. Can you revive it?'

'Go ahead. Give me your best,' Kashyapa accepted the challenge.

Coiling at the base of the grandfather banyan, Takshaka sank his fangs
into the trunk and released all but a bit of the venom he had, saving the
last bit for the king. Within seconds, the massive tree trunk began to
smoke, and then it erupted into flames that engulfed every last branch,
stem and leaf, until only a pile of simmering ashes remained.

'So you have proved that you have fire. We rishis deal with fire every
day. Now watch.' Kashyapa took a pinch of the ashes of the tree and,
mumbling a few words over them, scattered them back on the pile. Within
seconds, out of the ashes appeared a young sapling, which burgeoned and

shot up, and within seconds the banyan was back, even more expansive and verdant than before.

When Takshaka saw what Kashyapa's mantra could do to counter his poison, he knew he needed a different strategy to ensure that the rishi did not interfere in his business. 'What will you gain by reviving the raja?' he asked Kashyapa.

'Wealth and riches. The king will reward me.'

'I'll double the riches and wealth you expect from Raja Parikshit, if you promise to turn back now and not interfere in my business of biting and killing the king.'

'It's a deal,' Kashyapa said, and taking the gold and jewels that Takshaka gave him, he turned back without a second glance at the pillared-palace.

Now Takshaka's path to Raja Parikshit was clear. According to his plan, he disguised some of his cohort snakes as Brahmins and sent them to the palace, bearing fruits for the raja. At the entrance to the pillared-palace, the security guards inspected the fruit and the Brahmins and declared them all legit before ushering them in.

Parikshit welcomed the Brahmins with open arms. 'Thank you for bringing me fruit,' he said. 'And thank you for having faith that I'll escape Takshaka. It appears that I have. The seventh day is almost over and I see no snakes.'

'We wish you the best of health as long as you live, O Raja. Enjoy the fruit,' the snake Brahmins bid Parikshit goodbye and left.

The sun had almost set and the doors and windows to the palace were sealed tight. Sitting back against plump satin pillows, Raja Parikshit took up a rosy red apple from the fruit that the Brahmins had brought and smiled a smile of pure hubris: 'If the curse is true, may Takshaka bite me now—right this minute,' he declared, and bit into the apple.

As his teeth sank into the juicy flesh, a big, copper-coloured bug buzzed out of the apple, which changed into six coppery feet of deadly snake—Takshaka—and, winding himself around the raja's neck, bit him.

Parikshit was the Pandavas' only scion, who had been resurrected from a dead foetus, and now, with his final death, Dwapara Yuga came to an end and Kaliyuga began.

Myth from the Mahabharata

◆

82

GANESHA'S APPETITE

Kubera is chief of the yakshas, Lokapala of the north, and the Lord of wealth. His golden city, Alkapuri, is famed to be the wealthiest and most beautiful in the universe. Once, sitting on his throne in Alkapuri, Kubera became filled with pride about his high position and his immense wealth. Wanting to show off to the other celestials, he said to himself, 'I'll organize an opulent feast in my peerless Alkapuri and invite everybody. In fact, I'll even invite Shiva and Parvati, and give those mountain-dwellers a taste of what it is to live in the most luxurious palace in the universe.'

Shiva and Parvati lived on Mount Kailash, and they rarely left their mountain abode, so when Kubera invited them, they regretfully turned him down. 'But why don't you invite our son, Ganesha, instead?' they said to him. 'He really enjoys a good feast.' And so Kubera extended the invitation to Ganesha, who happily accepted.

Before the feast, Parvati called Kubera and warned him: 'Feed your other guests before Ganesha sits down to eat. My son has a voracious appetite. Once he starts eating, there may not be enough left to feed the others.'

'My kitchens abound with food, Devi,' Kubera replied, affronted. In his mind, he thought, he's a child—how much can he eat?

When Ganesha sat down at the feast, Kubera's servants began to serve him. First, they placed before him a small sampling of all the various dishes that had been cooked. Ganesha emptied all the bowls in just a few mouthfuls and waited to be served more. They then served him another, larger helping of everything, which Ganesha quickly made his way through, before gesturing for more. The servants now brought out additional food, making the portions larger, but, in no time, that, too, was gone. Kubera's servants kept bringing out more food and Ganesha kept eating it all, demanding more and more. Finally, he finished everything that Kubera's chefs had prepared for the entire feast, and yet his hunger was not satiated. 'I'm still hungry. Do you have some more?' he asked the servants. When they shook their heads and stood with folded hands of apology, Ganesha began to eat the empty utensils sitting before him, and when those, too, were gone, he began on the decorations, the furniture, the carpets...everything that was in sight.

At first Kubera was embarrassed that he didn't have enough to feed the child, but as Ganesha began to gobble down the utensils and the furniture, he became alarmed. Afraid that soon all the treasures that he had amassed in Alkapuri would be in Ganesha's belly, Kubera fled to Shiva and begged him to control his son.

'What's wrong?' Shiva asked him.

'He won't stop eating. I've never seen such an appetite. He ate all the food. Now he's devouring everything in sight, and still he keeps saying, "I'm hungry. Give me more." But I have nothing more to give him Lord. Save me.'

Shiva laughed. 'That's because you never really fed him.'

'I don't understand. I fed him all the food my chefs had prepared.'

'Ah, but did you mean it?' Shiva asked, and then he gave Kubera a handful of puffed rice. 'Here. Feed him this with a humble heart.'

Kubera took the rice and rushed back to Alkapuri, where Ganesha was just getting started on the golden pillars that held aloft the palace, muttering in between bites, 'I'm so hungry.'

'Here, Lord,' Kubera called, holding out the handful of puffed rice Shiva had given him. Then, closing his eyes, he prayed aloud, 'Lord, I am your humble servant. Please accept this offering, it is meagre, yet all my wealth is dust before it. If it satisfies you, please shower your benevolence on me.'

The elephant-headed god took the grains of rice with his trunk, and putting them in his mouth, ate them with relish. Then, he rubbed his belly, burped, and declared with a satisfied smile: 'I'm full.'

Folk-myth

◆

83

MALIK BHAGE AND BHAI LALO

On a pilgrimage of the country, Guru Nanak arrived in the town of Saidpur. The official of the town was a high caste, wealthy man called Malik Bhage, who was very corrupt. In the same town there also lived a low caste, honest carpenter, called Bhai Lalo, and it was with him that Nanak decided to stay. The poor carpenter felt honoured to have the Guru and his trusted companion, Mardana, as his guests. He laid out mats for them on the floor and shared with them whatever simple food his wife had cooked.

One day, Malik Bhage held a big feast to which he invited all the influential people of the town. He also invited many holy men, including Guru Nanak and Mardana, but Guru Nanak refused the invitation. Malik Bhage was very offended and summoned the Guru to his house. 'Why did you refuse to come to my feast?' he demanded to know.

'We are poor fakirs,' Guru Nanak said to Malik Bhage. 'Our needs are simple.'

'As it is you have insulted the high caste Khatri community of this town by staying at the house of a low caste man. And now, when you are invited to eat the rich delicacies that my cooks have prepared, you have chosen to eat dry rotis at that poor man's house. Explain yourself.'

Guru Nanak asked Bhage's servant to get a dry roti from Lalo's house, and he also asked Bhage to bring him a plate of the most delicious food that was being served in the feast. When both the plates—one with a roti from Lalo's house and the other with desi-ghee fried puras from Bhage's feast—were placed before him, Guru Nanak took the pura in his left hand and the dry roti in his right. When he squeezed his left hand, blood dripped from the pura, and when he squeezed the right, milk and honey poured out.

'See Bhage?' he said. 'Your food is soaked in the blood you have sucked from the poor; whereas Lalo's rotis are made from honesty and truth. Now you tell me which food is sweeter to me—your sweet puras or Lalo's dry roti?'

Folk-myth from the Janamsakhis

◆

84

HIRANYAKSHA AND HIRANYAKASHIPU

Diti, the daughter of Prajapati Daksha, sought out her husband, Rishi Kashyapa, one evening, just as he was sitting down to meditate. 'The god with the bow and five arrows is tormenting me,' Diti beseeched. 'He's piercing me with this desire. Dear husband, please do me the favour of making love to me.'

'You're my wife and partner,' Kashyapa replied, 'The scriptures say that in a happy marriage, wife and husband are equal partners, because they both need to unite to produce children. It'll be my pleasure to make love to you, but for the well-being of the child that you will conceive, please wait for a good muhurat. This is a not an auspicious hour, because at this time, rudras—the dark spirits—prowl. It is the time when Lord Shiva, smeared with dust and ashes from the cremation ground, rides around on his bull, surrounded by ghouls and spirits. His third eye is vigilant, witnessing everything. If we perform the act at this inauspicious time, it'll not be hidden from him, and it may impact our offspring.'

Diti understood what her husband was saying, but she was so overcome with desire that she pulled Kashyapa's garment off and stood before him in abandon. Kashyapa felt his own heat mounting, and accepting this as providence, he took his wife in his arms. Afterwards, taking a cleansing bath, he sat down to meditate, repeating the Gayatri Mantra, praying to be forgiven the infraction of the untimely act.

When Diti found herself pregnant, she feared for the foetus, 'Will Rudra kill the child in my womb?' she asked her husband.

'You disobeyed me and disrespected the gods. Because of your lustfulness and your inappropriate action at an inauspicious hour, your children will definitely suffer.' Then he looked into the future and told her, 'You'll have twin sons. The most dangerous ever born from a woman's womb. They'll commit so many villainous acts that the world will cry out, and when their arrogance begins to weigh the earth down, the preserver of the world will descend as an incarnation and kill them with his Vajra—his diamond thunderbolt.'

Diti wept at her husband's prediction. 'Forgive me, my children,' she cried in regret. Then she asked Kashyapa, 'Can I change my sons' fate?'

'You can't. Their fate was already written on that evening. However, because you are sorrowful and repentant, one of your sons will bear a son who will be renowned for his devotion to Vishnu. He will be unlike his father—without reproach.'

Diti bore the foetus in her womb for a hundred years, trying to prevent her twin sons from being born for as long as she could, but ultimately, she had to birth them. When the twins were born, many portents appeared in heaven, earth, and sky, boding calamities for the world. The earth with its mountains quaked, there were firestorms all around, meteors and comets showered down, whirlwinds uprooted trees, and dust swirled everywhere. The sun and moon were eclipsed, and such a darkness spread across the sky that even the stars disappeared. Planets swung so close to each other, they almost crashed. The ocean roared and rivers, wells, and tanks grew agitated, the lotuses in them withering. In towns and villages, jackals and owls howled, domestic animals screeched, donkeys brayed, and birds flew out of their nests.

The twins grew up fast, like two nilgiri trees. By the time they became youths, their heads touched the heavens, and their arms were so long and muscular that they could encircle a mountain and squeeze the soil right out of it. Kashyapa named his two sons Hiranyakashipu and Hiranyaksha. Both brothers were asuras, who opposed the supremacy of the gods.

Hiranyaksha took up the mace and went to heaven and challenged the gods to battle, but all the gods hid from him in fear. He then dived into the roaring ocean to war with Varuna's soldiers, but the armies of Varuna also fled from him. Beating down the huge waves with his massive iron club, Hiranyaksha reached Vibhavari, Varuna's city, and challenged the Lord of Waters himself to battle. Varuna refused to battle with him and instead, threw him a counter challenge: 'Go and fight Vishnu. He incarnates to put down wicked beings like you. He'll teach you a lesson and destroy you till you lie on a battlefield, dead, surrounded by dogs.'

At that time, Vishnu had taken birth as a Boar to rescue Earth from the ocean. Just as he lifted her on his tusks, Hiranyaksha arrived, and ridiculing his beastly avatar, challenged him: 'You beast, who lacks personal strength but depends on maya, come and fight me. The Earth belongs to us who were born on earth, not to beasts like you. Leave her and face me.' Vishnu as Boar, gently placed Earth on the water, and infusing her with the power to support herself, faced Hiranyaksha: 'It is true that I'm a wild beast, but I'm in search of domesticated dogs like you. True warriors are not braggarts like you. Instead of spouting words, come and fight.'

The two battled for a long time, each one overcoming the other at various times, and then Vishnu called his Sudarshana Chakra and sliced off Hiranyaksha's head.

When Hiranyakashipu heard that his brother had been killed by

Vishnu, he was maddened with grief and anger. He called an assembly of asuras, and addressed them with fiery words, brandishing his trident, 'I'll avenge my brother, whose death has me thirsting for Vishnu's blood. While I'm accomplishing this, I want you all to go to Earth and disrupt all practices that sustain the gods: kill the Brahmins and desecrate sacrificial sites.' Then, consoling Hiranyaksha's bereaved wife and children, he went to Mount Mandar to do tapasya to become invincible.

For hundreds of years Hiranyakashipu meditated, standing on the tips of his big toes with his arms stretched over his head and his eyes fixed on the sky. His tapasya was so severe that smoky fire emanated from the crown of his head and spread to all the regions of the world. Burning up from the heat of that fire, the gods rushed to Brahma and begged him to stop Hiranyakashipu.

'Give him what he wants,' they begged. 'Just make him stop, or the world will be reduced to ashes.'

'Do you know what his intention is?' Brahma asked the gods. 'Let me tell you—and if you still think I should grant what he wants, then I'll do so. With his yogic power, Hiranyakashipu wants the highest position in the universe. He also wants to reverse the order of the cosmos and the law of cause and effect. He wants sin to result in happiness and merit to lead to misery. He also wants asuras to live in heaven and the devas to be sent to patala. Do you want me to allow this?'

'At this time, our greatest danger is his relentless tapasya,' the gods told Brahma. 'We'll worry about the result of his boons later. Right now, you need to stop him.'

Thereupon, Brahma went to visit Hiranyakashipu in his hermitage on Mount Mandar, but he couldn't see the asura anywhere. Then he spotted a huge anthill in the middle of the compound and realized that that was actually the asura. He had been sitting motionless in that position for so long that grass and weeds had grown on him and ants had made a home over his body.

'Awaken, son of Kashyapa,' Brahma called, shaking the anthill and dislodging the soil and ants. He then poured celestial water on the ant-eaten mass of bones and called again, 'Awaken Hiranyakashipu.' Slowly, like a leviathan rising, Hiranyakashipu threw off the remaining debris and ants from his body and emerged, perfect in limb, golden in complexion, and endowed with the energy of youth.

Seeing Brahma, he was overjoyed and with folded hands asked for boons: 'May my death not be at the hands of any being created by you. Let death not come to me indoors or outdoors, during night or in the day time, or by means of weapons. Let me not die either on earth or in the sky. Let me not be killed by man or beast, by gods, demons or big serpents; by beings living or dead. Also, grant me utmost superiority in battle and absolute rule over all beings. And give me undiminishing glory and unfailing mystical powers. I also want your position and power so that I can be the guardian of the world.'

Filled with trepidation, Brahma granted his boons and returned to Brahmaloka to await the consequences. He didn't have to wait long, because as soon as Hiranyakashipu became empowered, he subjugated the three worlds of devas, danavas and mortal men, and also brought under his control all the beasts, serpents and birds. Having conquered the universe, he established himself in the celestial region and took up residence in Indra's palace, where he had the divine architect, Vishvakarma, build him a pleasure garden, which he named Nandana. Here, he began to live a life of pure indulgence and power. He commanded all the gods and creatures to worship him; gandharvas and apsaras were ordered to always be ready to perform for him; and all sacrifices, performed anywhere in in the world, were only to him. He also became the celestial gatekeeper of the four quarters, and the sole and absolute ruler of the world. Soon, not only the gods but also the Vedas were forgotten.

However, despite this cessation of Vishnu's order and the severance of the relationship between devas and mortals, the world did not erupt into chaos. Hiranyakashipu had gained so much yogic power with his tapasya that he was able to change the cosmic order. At his command, the seven continents yielded harvests without being ploughed, the oceans yielded endless jewels and pearls, and trees bore fruits and flowers in all seasons.

Twenty-one yugas passed in the new order that Hiranyakashipu had established. People on earth were happy in the beginning, but, over time, Hiranyakashipu's practices became more and more oppressive, to the extent that anyone who did not follow his rules was destroyed. When people began to suffer, those who still remembered Vishnu decided to seek his help. Hearing their petition, Vishnu spoke to them. 'I am aware that Hiranyakashipu sees himself as the undisputed ruler of the three worlds. I'm just waiting for the right moment to destroy his arrogance. He'll have a son named Prahlada, and when the asura seeks to injure this son, I'll slay him. '

Hiranyakashipu had four sons, and the youngest was Prahlada. Unlike his brothers, who followed Hiranyakashipu's precepts, Prahlada paid reverence to the Brahmins and honoured the Vedas. He was also a great devotee of Vishnu. Even as a child, he immersed himself in Vishnu bhakti and the highest form of Vedic meditation. Hiranyakashipu tried to instil proper asuric behaviour in him by sending him for instruction to the asura gurus; however, one day, as he sat with his son on his lap, affectionately smelling his forehead, he asked him, 'What did you learn at the guru's ashram, Son?'

Prahlada recited: 'There are nine forms of devotion to Vishnu: to hear the names of Vishnu, to sing his glories, to remember him, to offer service to him, to worship him, to pay obeisance to him, to dedicate all actions to him, to confide in him as a friend, and to offer him everything, body and soul.'

Hiranyakashipu was shocked. He immediately called the asura gurus, Sanda and Amarka to his palace and demanded to know why they were teaching his son such nonsense.

'We didn't teach him that,' the gurus replied, fearfully. 'He speaks his own mind. He doesn't listen to anything we teach him about your greatness, O Great One.'

Enraged, Hiranyakashipu flung Prahlada on the floor and ordered his guards to kill him. 'He is my brother's killer,' he roared. 'If a son becomes an enemy, he should be amputated like an infected limb.'

The asura guards, who had sharp teeth, wild hair, and terrible faces, attacked Prahlada with their tridents. But Prahlada fixed his mind on Vishnu, and the tridents could not even scratch his skin. When his asuras were unable to kill Prahlada, Hiranyakashipu had him thrown in a pit of serpents, but the serpents affectionately curled at his feet and around his body. Hiranyakashipu tried every other means possible to kill Prahlada: he had him flung down a mountain, poisoned, starved, exposed to extreme cold, thrown in a fire. He even used his own asura magic on him, but nothing he did could hurt the boy.

'It's obvious that the boy is fated to live,' Sanda and Amarka advised Hiranyakashipu. 'Let him live, O Great Asura, and let him learn. Give him time. As he grows into adulthood, he will surely imbibe behaviour that is appropriate for your sons.'

Hiranyakashipu consented and sent Prahlada back to school to learn administration and politics, and the Kshatriya codes of dharma, artha and kama, which were a hallmark of all Kshatriyas, whether they were devas, asuras, or men. Prahlada proved to be an ideal student in all respects, except one—he was more interested in the fourth principle of the purusharthas—moksha, the ultimate goal, a goal that went against the asura code. Then Prahlada began to teach his classmates the ideals of moksha through Vishnu bhakti, and soon, the other asura children began to repeat these lessons at home.

When the matter was reported to Hiranyakashipu, he ordered Prahlada to be brought to him and commanded him to give up his allegiance to the enemy, or be prepared to receive the punishment of a traitor. 'Don't you know that I rule these three worlds?' Hiranyakashipu told his son. 'And it is my command that only I be worshipped. How dare you disobey my command? On whose incitement are you violating my command? Who has given you the power to oppose me?'

'Vishnu is the force that controls the universe. You, too, should change your asuric nature, Father, and give yourself to him.'

'Stupid boy. I already know Vishnu. He, like everyone else, trembles at my very name.'

'No, Father. You don't really know Vishnu. He is Eternal and Supreme.

'He is no match for me. Call your Vishnu here and you'll see,' Hiranyakashipu challenged.

'I don't need to call him. He's already here.'

'Where?' Hiranyakashipu looked around him. 'Are you playing with me, boy?'

'No, Father. Vishnu is everywhere.'

'Really? Is he in this pillar?' the asura said disdainfully, pointing at a gold-panelled pillar in the hall.

'He is.'

'Okay then. Let me cut your head off. Let's see if your Vishnu will save you.' And saying this, Hiranyakashipu leapt from his throne with his sword drawn and knocked down the pillar. Then he turned towards Prahlada to kill him.

As the pillar crashed, a sound so terrible and immense arose, the gods in heaven thought it was doomsday. Then a being appeared that was neither human nor animal. It was a terrible man-lion—Narasimhan. He had eyes of molten gold, a majestic face, and dazzling mane. From his mouth protruded razor-sharp tusks, and his ears were erect and sharp. He had a thick, short neck and a wide and powerful chest over a slender waist. He was covered with white hair, like lunar rays, and had hundreds of hands, each with sharp claws. In his hands he held many weapons— swords, the Sudarshana Chakra and the Vajra.

When the asura guards saw him, they fled, but Hiranyakashipu thought to himself, this is surely an illusory being that my enemy, Vishnu, has created with his maya. I'll destroy him in a trice. And he struck Narasimhan with his huge mace, but Narasimhan only laughed and, grabbing the great asura, laid him on his thighs. Then, using only his claws, he first tore him apart, like a child tears apart a rag doll in sport, and then, sinking his jaws into the flesh, chewed him to pieces. When he was done, he licked the blood from his lips and flung the tattered body away.

When he walked across the hall to take his place on the throne, the firmament trembled with his footsteps, and all the celestials bowed in awe before this terrible Narasimhan avatar of Vishnu.

Myth from the Puranas

◆

85

GREATEST DEVOTEE

Narada Muni was very proud of being Lord Vishnu's greatest bhakta. 'There's no one more devoted to him than I,' he would tell everyone. He bragged about it to all the gods in Indraloka; and every time he visited Brahma in Brahmaloka, or Shiva and Parvati on Kailash Parvata, he would make it a point to declare his devotion. One day, he even announced it to Lord Vishnu himself.

Vishnu smiled at Narada and asked, 'How do you know that you are my greatest bhakta? Do you know all my other devotees in this entire world?'

Narada was disconcerted. 'Well, no. But, Lord, who can be more devoted to you than I? I think about you all the time, I even say your name every second of the day. I'm certain there's no one in these three worlds who does that.'

Lord Vishnu nodded serenely. 'You're right, of course,' he said. Then he asked Narada, 'Dear bhakta, would you do me a favour?'

'Of course, Lord,' Narada said, puffing out his chest, pleased at this acknowledgement of his devotion.

Lord Vishnu handed him a bowl filled to the brim with oil. 'I need your help,' he said. 'Can you please circle the world, holding this? But make sure that not a drop spills.'

'What sort of task is this, Lord?' Narada became a little suspicious.

'I'll explain its significance after you complete it, but I can tell you this: it'll be a great test of devotion and will serve to set an example in the world—only if you complete it successfully.'

'Don't worry, Lord. I'll be successful. I'm your greatest bhakta. If I can't succeed in a test of bhakti, who can?' Narada said, carefully taking the bowl in his two hands, and with utmost attention to it, began circling the world. He made sure his steps were measured, his hands were steady, and his eyes remained trained on the oil at the brim, so that not a drop went over it. It took him a long time, but finally, he completed the circumambulation of the world without spilling a single drop. Returning triumphant to Vishnu, he handed him the bowl. 'There you go, Lord. Not a drop spilled.'

'And you circled the whole world?'

'Every inch of it.'

'And you're sure not a drop escaped over the brim?'

'Not a fraction of a drop.'

'And in accomplishing this task, how many times did you think of me?'

Narada looked at Vishnu indignantly. 'How could I think of you? I had to concentrate on the oil. You yourself told me that it was of utmost importance that I not spill a single drop of it. Do you know how hard that was? I needed every bit of my concentration.'

Vishnu smiled and took Narada by the hand. 'Come with me,' he said, 'I want you to meet someone.' And together they descended to earth, right in the middle of a small, two-roomed house. It was early morning, and the family, consisting of a husband and wife and their two adolescent children, had just woken up.

'Watch the man,' Vishnu whispered, making himself and Narada invisible. The divine rishi watched the man as he helped his children pack their school bags, bathe, and get dressed. Then, after bathing himself, he went to the corner of the room where a picture of Vishnu sat on a flower-filled pedestal. The man lit incense before the picture and bowed his head in prayer for a few minutes. Then he walked to the kitchen, where his children were sitting on floor mats, bickering playfully and eating food that their mother was preparing. The man joined his children and talked and laughed with them, as he, too, ate. After he and his children finished their meal, he washed his hands, put on his shoes and went to work. Vishnu and Narada followed him. He worked in a busy loan office where, all day, he listened patiently to people's problems, answered their questions, and gave them advice about their loan applications. In between, he checked files, dealt with his boss, joked with his co-workers, and even loaned his own money to one of them so that he could buy a birthday gift for his daughter. At a quarter after 5 p.m., he left his office and walked home. Vishnu and Narada followed behind him. On the way, the man stopped at a vendor and bought vegetables, and then, after some hesitation, he counted out the remaining few bills in his hand and purchased some sweets.

As soon as he stepped through the door of his house, his two children came running to him and threw their arms around him. He laughed and produced the sweets for them and then peeped into the kitchen to nod at his wife and hand her the bag of vegetables. Next, washing his hands and feet in the bathroom, he went to the picture of Vishnu again and repeated the ritual of the morning—lighting incense and bowing his head in a few minutes of prayer. After that the man sat down with the children and helped them with homework, drinking the tea that his wife had placed beside him. Once the children were engrossed in their studies, he went to the kitchen and began to help his wife shell peas, urging her to tell him about her day. He listened attentively as she talked about her concerns, her joys, and her griefs. A little later, he went back to the main room and spent the rest of the evening immersed in office paperwork. After dinner, he helped his wife lay out the bedding for the night and, finally, around midnight, lying beside his wife, massaging soft fingers in her hair and whispering sweet words to her, he fell asleep.

Vishnu nudged Narada's arm and together they ascended to Vaikuntha.

'So Naradaji, did you enjoy meeting my greatest bhakta?' Vishnu asked.

'Greatest bhakta?' Narada exclaimed. 'Who are you talking about, Lord?'

'That man we just saw on earth.'

'That man? All he did was light incense before your picture twice a day and pray to you for a minute or two, at the most. And you say he is your greatest bhakta? How can that be?'

'Did you not see that every minute of his life is filled to the brim with concerns of living, providing for his family, and being a good human being? While doing all this, every day he makes sure that not a single drop from his life spills over. And yet he finds time in his day to devote to me. All you had to do was watch a bowl of oil once in your life, and you could not spare me even a passing thought. Now, you tell me, who is the greater bhakta?'

Narada fell at Lord Vishnu's feet in shame.

Folktale from North India

◆

86

THE FACE OF A BAD OMEN

Whenever Emperor Akbar wished to escape the tedium of ruling the empire, he went to Kashmir. During one of his visits there, he stayed overnight in a camp that was being considered as a site for a royal garden. The place was a paradise—one end of it had a snow-capped mountain and the other end was a natural lake.

When Akbar woke up the following day, it was dawn. He thought he would go watch the sunrise at the lake, which, he had been told, was spectacular. Without waking his attendants, Akbar picked up a doshala and left the camp. As he walked towards the lake, breathing in the fragrance of lilac and wild irises and seeing soft saffron colours streak the sky, he felt in harmony with the world around him.

When Akbar drew nearer to the lake, he heard a 'thwack! thwack!', at regular intervals, and wondered what it was. Coming closer, he saw that a washerman was whipping clothes on a rock. Akbar looked at the man and the man looked right back at him. For a moment they both looked at each other's faces, then they nodded to each other, and the washerman went back to his washing. Akbar stood gazing at the sky for a few more minutes, but the accord between the sunrise and his solitude was gone.

By the time Akbar returned to camp, everyone was awake, and the emperor got busy with his day's activities. Later that morning, as he was walking with the royal gardeners, discussing fertilizers for rose bushes, a bee stung him in the hand. His attendants immediately rushed him back to his pavilion, and the royal hakim was summoned. The hakim extracted the sting and put a poultice on the swelling, but the emperor's hand hurt all day. That afternoon, Akbar was scheduled to inspect the surrounding areas. As he was walking towards his horse, his foot tripped on a loose stone, and he twisted his ankle and almost fell. His attendants once again rushed him back to his pavilion, and a messenger was immediately sent to fetch the hakim again. While waiting for him to arrive, his attendants tried to make the emperor comfortable by fanning him and putting cold compresses on his foot.

'Someone has looked ill upon the Badshah,' one of Akbar's sycophants stated.

Others agreed and called curses upon this person.

'Who could it be?' someone else asked.

'Maybe the Badshah started his day by seeing the face of someone who brings bad luck,' another attendant suggested.

'Whose was the first face the Emperor saw this morning?' everyone wondered.

'It was a washerman,' Akbar's personal attendant said. 'The Badshah mentioned him when he returned from the lake.'

'Find this washerman,' a minister ordered. 'And bring him here. He should not be allowed to show his face to anyone in the morning. He is obviously an ill omen.'

The royal guards searched the surrounding villages and found the man who had been doing his washing at the lake that morning. When they asked him if he had looked at the Badshah, he replied, 'I saw a man at the lake. He was dressed very finely, but I didn't know that was the Badshah. Forgive me,' he said trembling in fear. 'What have I done wrong?' The guards just put him in chains and dragged him to the camp.

Inside Akbar's pavilion, the minister explained the situation to him. 'We think the man deserves to be put to death. He's obviously a bad omen, and he's a danger to other people.'

'What do you think, Birbal?' Akbar asked his friend and minister. 'We are considering announcing a death sentence on this man whose face is a danger to others.'

'Forgive me for saying this, Jahanpanah,' Birbal replied. 'May God give you a long life. But if the washerman is to receive a death sentence, then the same sentence should apply to you.'

A hush fell in the pavilion. This was treason. Everyone awaited the Emperor's response.

'How so, Birbal?' the Emperor responded, in a voice that was deceptively quiet.

'It's really very simple, Jahanpanah. If you saw this man's face, he also saw yours. If you believe that your mishaps today occurred because you saw his face in the morning, then think how much worse this washerman's day has turned out to be after he saw yours. You only suffered a bee sting and a twisted ankle; this man, on the other hand, is going to lose his life. You decide whose face can be considered more inauspicious. You are the very embodiment of justice and fairness. Superstition has no place in your justice.'

Akbar felt ashamed at his own arrogance and for letting superstition cloud his mind. 'Give the man a hundred dinars with our apology,' he said to his minister. 'And make an announcement that after today, anyone who utters a superstition in our presence will be severely punished.'

Akbar-Birbal folktale

◆

87

KAHAN RAJA BHOJ, KAHAN GANGU TELI

Raja Bhoja was a legendary king of Malwa in the eleventh century CE. He was a highly celebrated Paramara king, reputed equally for his polymathy and his patronage of arts and literature. He was also a great warrior and, through his victories, he had expanded his kingdom from the Sabarmati river to Vidisha, and from Chittor to the Konkan coast.

During a campaign in Kolhapur, he commissioned his engineers to build a fort on a hill at Panhala in the Sahyadri mountains. Architectural plans were laid out according to Vastu Shastra, and the site was duly ritualized. However, when construction began and the first wall went up, it came tumbling down. The masons, who had had years of experience in their profession, couldn't understand what had happened. They checked the ratio of their materials and their building tools, but everything seemed to be in order. So, ascribing the incident to chance, they raised the wall again. But this time too, even before it was completed, it crumbled. The masons made many more attempts to build the wall, but it just would not stay up. Finally, urged by his perplexed masons, Raja Bhoja consulted his astrologers.

'The mountain requires a sacrifice,' the astrologers declared. 'Unless you make this sacrifice, the mountain will not let any wall stand on it.'

'What kind of sacrifice?'

'A human sacrifice—of a new-born infant and its mother.'

It was a difficult demand, but it had to be met. Raja Bhoja needed to fortify Panhala to secure the territory, so he sent out village criers to make the proclamation and seek volunteers for the sacrifice.

It so happened that just a few days prior to this, Jakhubai, the wife of Gangu Teli, the oil presser, had given birth to a son; in fact, theirs was the only newborn infant in the village at that time. When Gangu Teli realized that he was the only person who could help the king, his chest puffed with self-importance. Brimming with pride, he presented himself to Raja Bhoja and offered his wife and infant for the sacrifice.

Jakhubai and her baby were ritually sacrificed, and the fort was finally built. For a while, everyone in the village hailed Gangu Teli a hero, and he gained some renown. However, people soon moved on to other concerns, and Gangu Teli went back to being an insignificant oil presser. And if ever anyone mentioned how the mighty Raja Bhoja had to take the help of the lowly Teli, the scoffing response was: Kahan Raja Bhoj aur kahan Gangu Teli (How can there be an equation between the eminent Raja Bhoja and the insignificant Gangu Teli).

Folktale from Madhya Pradesh and Maharashtra

◆

88

WHEN A SHUDRA ASPIRED TO BE A BRAHMIN[*]

After returning from Lanka, Rama established Rama Rajya in Ayodhya. His strict adherence to dharma engendered prosperity and rightfulness across the kingdom, and this ensured the happiness of every citizen. But, one day, a wailing and lamenting Brahmin arrived at the royal gate. He was carrying the dead body of his five-year-old son. 'Surely some evil has pervaded this land, where children are dying even before their natal rites are completed,' he sobbed. 'This unnatural event is surely a result of an evil deed committed by our king.' Then, laying the corpse on the ground, he shouted, 'Oh Rama, bring my son back to life, or my wife and I will also give up our lives right here at your royal gate. Then the sin of killing a Brahmin will hound you, and your Rama Rajya will become a curse on every citizen of Ayodhya.'

Rama heard the Brahmin's lament with a sense of foreboding. Wondering where he had erred, and if it was possible to rectify it, he summoned all the holy sages to his palace and asked them for advice.

'The untimely death of the child is a result of slippage in dharma,' Rishi Narada explained to Rama. 'In every yuga, dharma loses strength. In Krita Yuga, dharma was in full strength, because Brahmins were superior,

---

[*]Hari Prasad Shastri, (trans.), *The Ramayana of Valmiki*, London: Shanti Sadan, 1957, p. 1585.

and, in that era, men were immortal. In this Treta Yuga, Kshatriyas have gained superiority, and dharma has declined; however, both Brahmins and Kshatriyas still only engage in practices ascribed by their caste dharma, and the other two varnas—Vaishyas and Shudras—have also been following professions according to their own dharma. But, now, as Treta Yuga approaches its end, the Vaishyas and Shudras have started pursuing occupations that violate their varna dharma; so much so that Shudras are practicing asceticism like Brahmins. That is why children are dying untimely deaths. If you want to restore dharma, you must not be tolerant to its violations. Go investigate in your kingdom, and wherever you see anyone breaking the laws of varna dharma, put an end to it. This will bring the Brahmin's child back to life.'

Instructed by the holy rishis, Rama had the body of the Brahmin boy placed in a tub of herbal oils so that it would not decompose. Then, mounting Pushpak, his flying chariot, he began to scour his kingdom to find anyone who was committing unrightful acts. He looked in the north, then east, and then west, and all he saw was pristine land and dharma-abiding people. Then, in the south, on the northern side of Shaivala Mountain, he saw an ascetic, hanging suspended, with his face downwards. Impressed by his formidable discipline, Rama approached him and asked him gently. 'Why are you performing this austere penance, O ascetic? Who are you? Are you a Brahmin, Kshatriya, Vaishya, or Shudra? I am Rama, King of Ayodhya, and I request you to tell me the truth.'

The ascetic, his head still hanging downwards, replied, 'My name is Shambuka. I was born a Shudra, but I aspire to achieve devaloka—the world of the gods. That is why I am performing tapasya.'

As soon as he heard this, Rama pulled out his sword and cut off the Shudra's head. The gods rained flowers on Rama and called down to him: 'O son of Dashratha, you have done a great deed. By preventing this Shudra from achieving devaloka, you have restored dharma. Go back to Ayodhya. The Brahmin child you wish to revive is alive again.'

Myth from the Ramayana

◆

89

ELIMINATING THE COMPETITION: EKALAVYA

Ekalavya was the son of the Nishada king Hiranyadhanu, whose tribal kingdom was in the Aravalli mountains. Ekalavya was passionate about learning the science of archery, and he wanted to learn it from Dronacharya, who was the famous guru of the Pandavas and Kauravas.

To pursue his desire, Ekalavya came to Hastinapur and requested Drona to accept him as a student. Drona refused. 'You are a Nishada—a low-caste fisherman's son,' he stated. 'I am guru of the Kshatriya Kuru princes. If I accept you, it'll jeopardize the status of my other students. In any case, it is not your place in society to learn a warrior's skills.'

Ekalavya touched Drona's feet with his head and went into the forest near Hastinapur. Clearing an area, he set up his own training field, complete with archery range, targets, and a revered guru, in the form of a clay statue of Drona, and began diligent practice. Over time, with utmost discipline and under the guidance of his clay guru, Ekalavya became an expert at stringing a bow and shooting a variety of targets with a light hand.

One day, the Kuru princes went on a hunting excursion in the forest. One of their servants was walking ahead with a dog, when the animal wandered off and suddenly came upon the Nishada prince. Startled by the stranger dressed in black animal skin, the dog started barking. Ekalavya quickly mounted seven arrows on his bow and shot them all at one time into the dog's mouth. Whimpering, the canine turned around and ran back with his tail between his legs. When the princes saw the dog, they were amazed at the precision with which the arrows had been shot into his mouth, silencing him without hurting him. Who could this superior archer be, they wondered, and began searching the forest. Soon they found Ekalavya.

'Who are you?' they asked him. 'Whose son are you?'

'I am the Nishada king Hiranyadhanu's son,' Eklavya replied. 'I'm a student of Dronacharya.'

As soon as the princes returned to Hastinapur, Arjuna confronted his guru, his face contorted with jealousy. 'You promised me that no pupil of yours will be equal to me,' he said sullenly. 'You held me to your bosom and promised me this. But there's a student of yours who is not just equal to me but better than me—the son of the Nishada king.'

Drona was surprised to hear this. 'Take me to him,' he told Arjun, and the Pandava prince led his guru through the forest to where the Nishada prince was practicing. Eklavya's body was smeared with dirt and his hair was matted, but he was holding the bow like a seasoned archer and shooting targets with a hand so light and swift that the action was no more than a blur.

When Ekalavya saw Drona, he stopped and came over to touch his forehead to the guru's feet. Then, presenting himself as his student, he stood before him with folded hands.

'If you are my pupil then give me my dakshina,' Drona said to him.

Ekalavya was overjoyed to hear Drona acknowledge him as his student. 'O illustrious Guru,' he said, his face wreathed in smiles. 'What shall I give you? Command me. There is nothing I will not give to my guru.'

'Give me your right thumb,' Drona replied.

Unruffled, Ekalavya took a knife and at once sliced off his right thumb and, with a cheerful smile, handed the bleeding digit to Drona as his dakshina.

Arjuna, the greatest archer, stood by, watching his guru eliminate his competition.

Myth from the Mahabharata

◆

90

THE PROSTITUTION OF MADHAVI

When Galva completed his education with his guru, Vishwamitra, he asked him what dakshina he desired.

'Give me eight hundred healthy horses that are white all over but have one black ear,' Vishwamitra replied.

Galva was in a predicament. He had no idea where he would procure such a gift. Not only was he a poor man but even if he had the money, where would he find so many horses with the same peculiarity? But to not pay his guru dakshina was even more unthinkable. Then Galva consulted with his wise friend, Garuda, the king of birds, who had seen the whole world and could fly to any region he wished. 'Get on my back,' Garuda told Galva. 'Let's search the earth for such horses.'

They looked for days, but they couldn't find a single horse that fit the requirement.

'I have another idea,' Garuda said to his friend. 'What we need to do is appeal to kings who have wealth. If anyone can provide you these horses, it'll be kings. I have a friend who is a wealthy king. His name is Yayati. Let's go and ask him.' And so the friends flew to Yayati's kingdom.

'Unfortunately, my wealth has diminished quite a bit,' Yayati told Rishi Galva. 'But you're a Brahmin, and I can't turn away a Brahmin empty-handed. I'll try to fulfil your request, as much as I can. I can't give you the horses you require, but I can lend you my daughter, Madhavi. She's beautiful, and astrologers have predicted that she will bear four sons. You can trade her for the horses. My only request is that when your dakshina is paid, bring her back to me, so that she can give me a grandson.'

Galva accepted Madhavi, and taking her with him, he went to another wealthy king, Haryashva, who did not have any offspring and was often performing sacrifices to procure sons. 'I have this girl who can bear you sons,' Galva offered the king. 'Will you accept her?'

Haryashva was immediately moved to passion by Madhavi's beauty. 'Yes,' he said to Galva. 'What do you want in return?'

'Give me eight hundred white horses, each with one black ear.'

King Haryashva had his stables checked to see if he had these particular horses and discovered that he did, in fact, have such horses, but only two hundred of them. 'Take the two hundred,' he told Galva. 'And I'll use the girl to bear only one son. And then I'll return her to you.'

Galva knew that Madhavi was bestowed with another boon—that after giving birth to each son, her virginity would be restored. 'Deal!' he said to Haryashva and left Madhavi with him. Haryashva lived with Madhavi, and in due time, when she gave birth to a son, Galva came and took her back. He also requested the king to keep the horses safe for him until that time when he could come and retrieve them.

The next king Galva approached was Divodasa of Kashi—but when he began to relate to him the story of the dakshina he owed Vishwamitra, Divodasa stopped him. 'Your story is already known to me, and ever since I've heard about Madhavi's beauty, I've been eager to possess her. My only problem is that, like Hiranyaksha, I, too, only have two hundred horses of the kind you need. Therefore, I, too, promise that I'll only have one son from her and then return her to you.'

'Agreed,' Galva said and handed Madhavi over to Divodasa. Once again Madhavi was given to a king for his pleasure and progeny, and in due course, she gave birth to another son. When Galva received the news, he arrived at Divodasa's palace, took Madhavi and requested him to keep the horses safe for him. Once again, Madhavi became a virgin, and once again Galva began to search for a king who needed sons and had horses to trade. In the city of the Bhojas, he heard that King Ushinara was looking for a wife to bear him sons. Galva approached him and told him, 'This girl will bear you two sons. She is a princess herself, and it has been predicted that her sons will be great rulers. I'm willing to give you this girl—all I ask for as the bride-price is four hundred horses that each have a black ear.'

'I have thousands of horses in my kingdom, but I know that there are only two hundred of the kind you seek.'

'That's fine. I'll take the two hundred, and in that case, you can have one son with his girl.'

Ushinara accepted, and Madhavi stayed with him until the time she gave birth to a son. Galva still needed two hundred more horses, so, after he brought her back, he began to look for another king. This time, however, his search proved futile. Finally, he approached his friend, Garuda, again and asked him for advice.

'Give Vishwamitra himself the choice of having a son along with the six hundred horses you have procured,' Garuda advised. And that is exactly what Galva did. Going to his guru's ashram, he presented him with six hundred horses and Madhavi. 'I'm giving you this girl as a substitute for two hundred horses,' he said. 'She has already borne three strong sons, and is a virgin again, and now you, too, can have a strong son. Would you consider a son equivalent to two hundred horses, so that I can be free of debt?'

Vishwamitra saw the beautiful Madhavi, and smiled. 'Why did you not come to me in the first place?' he asked Galva. 'That way all four sons would have been mine.' He happily accepted the girl and the six hundred horses. Then, he set the horses free to roam in any direction they pleased.

Vishwamitra lived with Madhavi and enjoyed marital life with her for some time. After she gave birth to a son, Galva took her away to return her to her father, Yayati, so that he could fulfil his paternal duty towards her. Yayati welcomed his daughter home and began planning her marriage, as all fathers do for their daughters.

With the thought of holding a svayamvara for her, Yayati invited many kings and princes to a hermitage at the confluence of the rivers Ganga and Yamuna. On the appointed day, the family proceeded towards the hermitage in chariots, with Madhavi, decked in flower garlands, sitting between her two brothers. When they arrived at the site of the swayamvara, Madhavi quietly stepped down from the chariot and walked away into the forest, to live a life of celibacy away from people.

Myth from the Mahabharata

◆

91

DISFIGURING SURPANAKHA

Ravana killed Surpanakha's husband by mistake. He had been on a mission to conquer the three worlds and, in a battle in the netherworld, he had destroyed all the Kalkeya daityas, without realizing that among them was his own sister's husband. When he returned victorious to Lanka, Surpanakha confronted him. She was inconsolable at her loss, and blamed her brother for making her a widow.

'I'll make it up to you,' a contrite Ravana promised his sister. 'Go and live with our cousin, Khara, in my Dandaka forest. I'll establish Khara as regent of the Danda kingdom and give him fourteen thousand rakshasas, whose sole purpose will be to protect you. The vast Dandaka will be your leisure ground. Live there in peace, roam around, feast on the forest creatures, and enjoy the beauty of the trees and lakes. All is at your disposal, my dear sister.'

When the exiled Rama, Lakshmana, and Sita came to live in the grove of Panchavati in Dandaka forest, Surpanakha was living there peacefully with her cousin, Khara. One day, wandering in the forest, she came upon a hut, outside which she saw a young human couple. The man was extremely handsome, even though he was dressed in bark and antelope skin and wore no ornaments. He held a bow as adeptly as though it were an essential limb. Surpanakha was immediately attracted to him. She belonged to a matrilineal tribe, where women felt no modesty about choosing their lovers and husbands, and widows had no restrictions. So, without any inhibition, she approached Rama and spoke to him. 'Who are you?' she asked him. 'Why have you come to this region? Don't you know that this forest is not safe for humans? It's full of rakshasas and other wild creatures.'

'I'm Rama, eldest son of King Dashratha of Ayodhya. This is my wife, Sita, princess of Videha, and there, that other young man, is my younger brother, Lakshmana. We've come to live in the forest to fulfil a vow I made to our father. Whose daughter are you? Whose wife? Judging from your appearance...' Ram paused for a moment to think of how to describe her. Then he continued, 'judging from you *beautiful* appearance. I can tell that you are from the rakshasa clan.'

Surpanakha was indeed a rakshasi, a cannibal giantess, fierce-looking, with wild hair, long teeth and big belly. Her name itself spoke of her looks—it meant a woman with nails the size of winnowing fans. As a rakshasi, she was, in fact, beautiful, but to a human, she was fearful. However, she didn't catch Rama's sarcasm and admitted, with poise, to being a rakshasi. 'My brother is Ravana, king of Lanka,' she told him proudly. Then she looked at Sita and said, 'What're you doing with an insipid woman like this, who is ugly and small-waisted. You should leave her and marry me. I find you very handsome and am quite attracted to you. Then you and I can roam this forest together. We'll go to mountain peaks together and frolic in the lakes. This whole forest is mine. I'll share it with you. If you wish, I can change my form into that of a human, if that form is more appealing. My tribe knows the secret of shape shifting, and I can change into any form.'

Rama burst out laughing at her proposal. 'My beautiful lady, with enticing eyes and shining face, I'm already married and have no wish to marry again.' Then, looking at Lakshmana, he decided to play a joke on his brother. 'But my brother, Lakshmana, is single,' he said to Surpanakha, lying about Lakshmana's marital status. 'He's handsome and brave and should make a good husband. Why don't you ask him?'

Surpanakha turned away from Rama, and giving Sita a disdainful look, went to Lakshmana. 'Marry me,' she proposed to him in honey-sweet tones. 'I'll charm you with my beauty and together we'll live happily, roaming through this forest region.'

'You wouldn't be happy with me,' Lakshmana replied, looking daggers at his brother for foisting this rakshasi on him. 'I'm just a servant and completely dependent on my brother. So, as my wife, you, too, would have to live the life of a servant. Why don't you go back to him and ask him again? I'm sure he'll accept you now and give up his ugly wife. What wise man would refuse someone like you, of excellent form with a big belly and lovely complexion?'

Not realizing that that the two brothers were jesting with her, Surpanakha returned once again to Rama. 'I desire you,' she said. 'Let me eat up your hideous wife. Then you'll be free to marry me.' Saying this, Surpanakha tried to grab Sita.

Rama pulled Sita into his arms and called urgently to Lakshmana. 'Stop joking with her, Lakshmana. She took you seriously. Look how she's frightening Sita. Pick up your sword and show this ugly, lusty, big-bellied piece of womanhood her place.' Lakshmana immediately grabbed his swords and struck at and disfigured Surpanakha.[35]

Roaring in pain and bleeding profusely, Surpanakha ran into the forest towards Janasthana, where her brother Khara lived. Khara was sitting in his palace surrounded by his rakshasas when Surpanakha staggered in, covered in her own blood, and fell into a faint. When they revived her, she sobbed out the tale of her encounter with Rama and Lakshmana. Khara sprang up, shaking with fury, and calling Dusana, his commander, ordered him to take fourteen of his fiercest rakshasas and kill the two humans who had dared to hurt his sister. Then, going to Surpanakha, he soothed her: 'Hush. You are the bravest of the rakshasis. No one can withstand your valour. Come, gather yourself together and take Dusana and these rakshasas to the spot where you met these humans. Go and avenge yourself.'

Surpanakha led the fourteen fierce rakshasas to Panchavati. Rama was expecting this retaliation; therefore, as soon as he saw them approach, he strung fourteen arrows on his bow and felled all fourteen rakshasas with one shot. When Khara heard about the fate of his best warriors, he could hardly believe it, and, gathering his whole army of fourteen thousand warriors, he marched into the forest. But Rama and Lakshmana destroyed these rakshasas, too, and the ravaged and helpless Surpanakha fled to Lanka to her elder brother, Ravana, seeking revenge.

'Look at me,' she cried in his court. 'They've humiliated me and disfigured me. They've killed Khara and fourteen thousand of our tribe. They're wiping out our way of life and establishing a Brahmin culture in our Dandaka. If you're a true warrior, rise and fight them, or people will call you a weakling.'

Ravana had already been informed by his uncle, Maricha, about Rama's prowess as a warrior. In fact, Maricha had advised him to leave Rama alone. 'Live happily with your wives in Lanka and let him complete his exile in peace with his wife and brother,' Maricha had said. 'Don't put your head in fire, which is what war with Rama will be.' Ravana had agreed to this advice then, but now, seeing his sister's mutilated body and hearing her challenging words, both his anger and sense of dharma were roused. 'Tell me about these men who have dared to hurt you,' he told Surpanakha.

'They're handsome beyond words, especially the older one, and their arrows are invisible; they discharge them so fast that the eye can't see them. The elder one has a wife—a most beautiful wife. Her complexion is like melted gold, and her eyes are like twin lotuses. Her hair is lustrous, her lips like petals, her body like a swan's. Her name is Sita. Whoever possesses her will surely be the luckiest male on earth. She would be a worthy wife for you. Realize your duty to me and to your slain brothers Khara and Dusana. If you are, indeed, the mighty Ravana that everyone extols, then prove it by making Sita your wife.'

Ravana got up from his throne and called for his golden flying chariot, Pushpak. In his mind he was already planning Sita's abduction to avenge his sister's humiliation and to restore rakshasa pride.

Myth from the Ramayana

◆

92

RAPE OF TAMAR

King David's third son was Absalom, and he had a beautiful sister named Tamar. His eldest son was from another wife, and his name was Amnon. It so happened that Amnon fell in love with Tamar. He was heartsick for being so in love with his half-sister, but he was in even more torment because she was a virgin, and it was impossible for him to approach her.

Amnon had a very shrewd friend named Jonadeb, who was also his paternal cousin. One day Jonadeb asked Amnon, 'Why do you look so dejected every day? Can you tell me the reason?' And Amnon told him that he was in love with Absalom's sister. 'But I can't even approach her, because she's a virgin,' he said.

'I'll tell you a plan,' Jonadeb advised. 'Pretend to be ill and remain in bed. When your father comes to visit you, request him to let Tamar bring you food. Tell him that you wish for her to prepare it in front of you, and then feed you with her own hands. The king won't refuse you."

So Amnon pretended to be sick and lay down in his bed. When the king came to visit him, he said, 'Can Tamar come here and make some cakes in front of me and then feed me?'

David sent a message to Tamar in the palace: 'Go to your brother Amnon's rooms and prepare a meal for him and feed him.'

When Tamar came to Amnon's room, he was lying in bed. She had the attendants set up a little kitchen on one side and began preparing cakes. Taking some dough, she kneaded it, rolled out cakes, and baked them. Then, taking the pan she turned out the cakes before Amnon and urged him to eat, but Amnon refused. He ordered everyone out of the room, and after they had left, he said to Tamar, 'I want you to bring the cakes here and feed me with your own hands.'

Tamar brought the cakes over, and, as she extended her hand to offer them to Amnon, he grabbed her, 'Come and lie down with me, sister,' he said.

Tamar struggled to free herself. 'No brother,' she cried. 'Don't dishonour me like this. How will I hide my disgrace? Besides, in Israel, we don't do such beastly things. Don't sink as low as a beast. If you really want to be with me, then why don't you marry me? Speak to the king. He won't refuse you.'

Amnon wasn't listening to Tamar. Forcing himself on her, he dishonoured her. But after the deed was done, he couldn't stand the sight of her. 'Get out,' he said to her.

'No!' she screamed. 'How can you be so wicked and send me away now? This is worse than what you have done to me. '

Amnon paid no heed to Tamar's entreaties. He called his servant and ordered him to get rid of the woman. 'Throw her out, and bolt the door,' he said. The boy did as he was told and threw Tamar out.

Tamar was wearing a long-sleeved robe, which was the usual dress of virgin daughters of the royal family. She tore the robe and put ashes on her head, and, sobbing, left Amnon's quarters. When her brother Absalom saw her, he knew right away what had occurred. 'Has your brother Amnon done this to you?' he asked.

'Yes,' Tamar replied.

'Don't tell anyone, sister. And try not to dwell on it.'

When King David heard what Amnon had done to Tamar, he was furious, but he didn't punish him, because he loved his eldest son more than he loved anyone else. Absalom, too, didn't say a word to Amnon, but in his heart he hated him for dishonouring his sister. No one paid any more heed to Tamar; she remained in Absalom's house, devastated and desolate.

Myth from the Old Testament

◆

93

OGHAVATI, THE DUTIFUL WIFE

There was once a king called Sudarshana, who hoped to become immortal by being the perfect householder. Sudarshana knew that achieving this goal was next to impossible, but he was quite confident that his knowledge of dharma would help him make the leap from the impossible to possible. He came from a family that, literally, wrote the book on dharma: his ancestor was Manu Vaivasvata—the predecessor of the current human race—who formulated householder dharma. His father was Agni, the sacrificial rite itself and also the celestial liaison between gods and men, and his mother was Sudarshana, who, although a mortal, was no ordinary woman. Her own father was a mortal king called Duryodhana, (not of *Mahabharata* fame) who was an exemplary householder, and her mother was River Narmada, who is so virtuous that even the pebbles that come into contact with her waters become banlingas (stones in the riverbed that are naturally shaped in the form of Shivalinga). Basically, King Sudarshana inherently knew every householder sacrament, and he was certain that if he demonstrated his prowess through practice, Death itself would have to concede.

Taking water in the cup of his hand to evoke the testifier of oaths, Varundeva, as witness, Sudarshana made a vow: 'I will be a flawless householder, and if Dharma is pleased, may I conquer death in this very lifetime!'

Sitting in Kalichi, his palace in Yamaloka, where only truth exists, and the strong who have tormented the weak on earth are themselves tormented by the weak, Yama was intrigued by Sudarshana's vow. Men, who pride themselves in the virtue of householder duties, aim to go to Kubera's region of Mandakini to live in utmost comfort among celestials, sporting in flowering groves and laving in the gentle breezes coming from the Mandakini river. But this young man wanted none of that; he wanted deathlessness! He wanted the impossible, because even those who gain immortality through the most arduous means of knowledge, do so only after they leave their bodies. No human, no matter how virtuous, can escape bodily demise and conquer death; yet this young man hoped to do it. And so Yama, who himself is Mrityu and Dharma, accepted Sudarshana's challenge and began to keep a close eye on him, because he was certain that the king would fail Dharma, and when he did, Mrityu could strike him dead and proclaim victory. So it was that Mrityu, carrying his skull-bashing, death-dealing iron club, began to follow Sudarshana from sun-up to sun-down, noting his every action, every word, and every thought. But, to Mrityu's chagrin, this householder king seemed to know dharma so well, it was as though he breathed it.

Following householder dharma laws, Sudarshana married a suitable princess—Oghavati—who walked as gracefully as an elephant and who had small, pearly teeth, long, supple limbs, and sooty, black hair that was thick and long. Also, she was the daughter of Oghavata, a king appropriately matched to Sudarshana in caste and wealth. The wedding itself was a ritual that exemplified Vedic rites and invoked the blessings of the thirty-three gods. After they were married, Sudarshana honoured his bride every day with his heart and body, as well as gifts of expensive jewellery and clothes on special occasions; basically he epitomized the writ that where women are honoured, there the very gods are honoured.

Every day, at the exact time appointed by the dharma of a householder's daily life, Sudarshana performed the five required ritual sacrifices of divine study, offering ghee to Agni and to the celestials, respect to the twice-born, and food to the ancestors. He also followed a strict regimen, never eating food that causes lethargy or evokes passion, and never defecating or urinating in water, cowshed, animal hole, ploughed field, abandoned temple, or on fire or a hill. He was also vigilant with his senses, avoiding that which was foul smelling and speaking and hearing only that which was true; never allowing himself to indulge in illusion, such as viewing a rainbow in the sky. When he slept at night, he kept Oghavati on his left and his head towards the east, and when she was menstruating, he never slept in the same bed with her, in case he got aroused and couldn't control himself, because he knew that a man's wisdom depletes if he is smeared in a woman's menstrual blood.

Oghavati was proud to be Sudarshana's wife. Not only did she support him, but she also learned to discipline herself so that she never indulged in any action that would jeopardize his oath. Her goal was to be the ideal wife to her ideal householder husband.

Soon after they were married, Sudarshana told Oghavati, 'I have made a vow to be a flawless householder. As my wife, it's your duty to help me fulfil this vow.'

'Of course, dear husband,' Oghavati replied. 'I'll never act in a way that will hinder you, but I'm only an ordinary woman. Your vow is extraordinary. Please give me an example of how I should assist you, so that I will know what standard to follow.'

'For example, honouring guests is one of the highest virtues of a house-holder,' Sudarshana explained. 'You must never refuse a guest anything. No matter what he desires, you must provide it, even at the expense of your own comfort.'

'Of course, dear husband. I'll do whatever is possible to make our guests welcome, and I'll consider their desires above my own, as much as I can.'

'I don't think you quite realize how important this is to me, dear wife,' Sudarshana admonished her. 'I must not fail in this vow. If I'm successful in this vow, I'll conquer death, but if I fail, I'll be dishonoured and will have to renounce my body. That's why, you must promise to do even that which seems impossible. For instance, if you are asked to offer your own body, you must do it, and without hesitation.'

Oghavati thought how hard it would be to give up her body at the request of someone she might not even know—not because she feared death, but because she loved her husband very much and wished to live a long life with him. And how wonderful it was that she would never have to worry about surviving her husband, because he would have conquered death and would live forever. Then she thought that surely her husband had used this extreme example only to make sure she understood the gravity of his vow. Surely, she would never be called upon to give up her body. So, to make her husband happy, because she loved him, she agreed.

'And you accept my words as authority, even if I'm not present to guide you?' Sudarshana asked.

'I accept, O lord and master,' Oghavati replied, playfully. 'What do you want me to do to prove it to you? Take a test?'

'Time and situation will be their own test,' Sudarshana responded, gently pulling her into his arms but keeping the embrace very light, in case he became aroused.

One afternoon, a dishevelled, nondescript looking Brahmin appeared at their house. Sudarshana was out at that time, doing some household task, so Oghavati welcomed the guest and offered him a comfortable seat and cool water to wash his feet. Then she stood before him with folded hands and a respectful smile, 'What can I offer you?' she asked.

'Your self,' the Brahmin replied.

Oghavati's heart began hammering in her chest, but she controlled herself as best as she could and asked in a voice that wasn't quite steady. 'I'm at your service, O revered Brahmin, but may I ask how my death will serve you?'

'I don't want your life,' the Brahmin replied, sounding surprised. 'I want your body. I want to be pleasured by it.'

'What?' The word jumped out of Oghavati's mouth before she could stop herself. 'I mean, are you sure I can't get you food, drink, or some other means of satisfaction?'

'No. Only your body. Only that will satisfy me.'

The Brahmin's words filled Oghavati with shame and fear. All her life she had been taught that a woman's chastity was her greatest virtue and that she must preserve it at all costs or be shamed forever. All her life she had also learned how to be a good wife—how it was a sin for a wife to even think about another man, even after her husband was dead; how if she so much as thought of another man, she would be condemned in both the worlds; in this world, people would call her a whore and in the next world, her soul would be thrust into the womb of a jackal. But then Oghavati remembered her husband's words: 'If it means that you have to offer your own body, you must do it.' She also remembered what he had said would happen to him if he could not fulfil his vow: 'I'll be dishonoured and will have to renounce my body.' Oghavati knew then what she had to do. She knew that even if she herself ended up in a jackal's womb, she must do whatever she could to help her husband achieve his desire of immortality, because to serve him was her greatest duty.

'So, what do you say?' the Brahmin asked. 'Will you give me what I desire?'

Oghavati was repulsed by the lascivious way in which he was looking at her through his beady little eyes, a lewd smile on his thick lips. But without a word, she led him to the bedroom and gestured to the conjugal bed in which she and her husband shared intimacies when she was in her season. Then, with trembling fingers, she began to untie the strings of her blouse.

Shortly, thereafter, Sudarshana returned home. 'Oghavati, I'm home,' he called. 'Where are you?'

Receiving no answer, he called again, and then again, wondering where his dutiful wife was. This had never happened before. Whenever he called her, she came immediately, eager to please him. 'Oghavati,' he called one more time, in agitation. 'What can be more important than heeding your husband's call? Why don't you come to me? Can't you hear me?'

Oghavati could hear her husband loud and clear, but lying naked under the Brahmin, she felt so dirty and sullied that she couldn't respond to him. But the Brahmin felt no such compunction and responded in her stead, 'She can hear you, O son of Agni, but she can't come to you right now, because she's here with me in my arms, pleasuring me. I'm a guest in your house and your wife is showing me great hospitality with due rites, doing what I desired. You should wait until we finish, or you can do whatever you think is right.'

For an instant, something burned in Sudarshana's eyes. And, at that moment, Mrityu began to polish his iron club.

Then Sudarshana called back cheerily, 'Do enjoy yourself, dear guest. It is a pleasure for me to know that my wife has been able to welcome you suitably and provide what you desired. I have sworn to fulfil the virtues of a householder, and I honour you as a guest. My material possessions, my wife—everything I own is at your service.'

At this, the Brahmin, who was, of course, Yama, changed into his dharma form and emerged from the bedroom, applauding Sudarshana. 'Glory to you, O king. You are truly virtuous. Without your knowing it, I've been following you and watching your every move. This last act was your final test to see if you knew how to gain the blessing of a guest, because when a guest is not honoured, he takes the blessing of that house with him. But you have passed this test, too, with great success. You are not only exact in your duties, but you have also controlled your senses and your passions. Congratulations! You have conquered death and will be immortal while in this body. I applaud you. Oh and your wife... she is matchless—in virtue, and...in everything else. Being Dharma and having dharma's authority, I declare that she has not violated any dharma. She will be as chaste and untouched as before. In fact, her virtue is so extreme that she will be a salvation for other people. I ordain that from today, only half of her body will serve you, and the other half will be the river, Oghavati.

And so King Sudarshana got what he desired. His wife, Oghavati, also achieved her goal—in a manner of speaking. Sudarshana became immortal in his body, and Oghavati, split in half, continued to serve—one half served her husband till she died, and the other half served people, cleansing them until her waters dried up.[36]

Myth from the Mahabharata

◆

94

A SAAS-BAHU TALE

Once there was an old widow who lived with her son. The son cared about his mother very deeply, and the mother wanted nothing more than for her son to be happily married, but every marriage proposal she brought to him, he refused. Finally, one day, the mother sat down with her son, and, with moist eyes, said to him, 'It is clear to me that you want me to die an unhappy woman.'

'Why would you say that, Amma? Your happiness is the most important thing for me.'

'The only thing that will make me happy now is your marriage. Why do you keep rejecting every girl I propose? What kind of girl are you looking for? Tell me, and I will try my best to find you that girl.'

'It isn't that, Amma. I have no such preferences. I'm just worried that your daughter-in-law may not look after you well enough.'

'Is that all?' the mother was relieved. 'Why do you worry about that? Not all daughters-in-law treat their mothers-in-law badly. Besides, I'll treat your wife so well that she'll have no choice but to treat me well in return. I'll manage it. You just say yes. It'll make me so happy.'

'Fine, Amma. I'll get married to whomever you choose. But if she treats you badly, don't come and complain to me.'

The mother was delighted and soon found a beautiful bride for her son.

On the very day that he got married, the son told his bride that his first priority was his mother. 'Promise me that my mother's comfort will be your topmost concern,' he said to her. The wife readily agreed, and for a few weeks, she did take care of her mother-in-law's every need. Before long, however, she began to resent the extra work and also the amount of attention her husband paid to his mother. Day-by-day, her resentment grew, until she began to think of ways to rid herself of this burden. She started telling her husband insidious little lies about his mother: one day she told him that her gold earrings had gone missing, and she had found them under his mother's pillow. On another day, she complained that her hands hurt, because her dear mother-in-law had made her massage her back all day. On yet another day, she wept before her husband and told him that his mother had been calling him all kinds of names. 'I can't bear it when she insults you,' she said, laying her head on his shoulder. She acted the ideal daughter-in-law when her husband and mother-in law were both present in the same room, but as soon as her husband left for work, she treated the old woman atrociously—yelling at her for no reason and giving her only morsels to eat.

Although she was sick at heart and half-starved, the old woman said nothing to her son, because she didn't want to create strife in her son's married life; she bore it all in silence. But the son began to notice that his mother was becoming more and more frail each day.

'Are you sick, Amma?' he asked with concern.

'I'm just getting old,' she said to him. 'Don't worry about me.'

Then, one day, the son found his mother crying in her room. 'Something is surely the matter,' he said. 'Please tell me what it is.' But the mother just shook her head and tried to smile. 'It's nothing,' she said. 'I'm just an old woman. Don't pay me any heed.' So the son went to his wife and asked her if she knew what was wrong with his mother.

'There's nothing wrong with her,' she told her husband.

'Surely something is the matter. I know her well. She doesn't cry for no reason. You spend all day with her. You must know what's troubling her.'

'If you must know,' his wife replied. 'Then I'll tell you—only because you are insisting. But you won't believe it. It's really quite embarrassing. Your mother wants to remarry.'

The son was shocked. 'I don't believe it,' he said.

'See? I told you, you won't believe it. That's why I didn't want to tell you.'

'How do you know?'

'I saw her in her room one day, trying on some of my bridal clothes, and when I confronted her, she told me herself.'

'It seems that my mother has lost all sense of propriety,' the son said. 'At her age...chhe chhe.'

'Exactly! Can you imagine what shame we'll have to suffer if anyone finds out?'

'No one must know,' the son said, urgently. 'We need to make sure no one finds out.'

'The only way to put an end to this shamefulness is to put an end to her.'

'What are you saying? She's my mother. I care about her.'

'Well, she obviously doesn't care about you or me, or our good name, dear husband,' the wife, said, sounding tearful. 'Or she wouldn't bring such humiliation upon us. People will look at us with contempt.' She let the tears flow down her cheeks, and then lifting the corner of her sari, making a show of wiping her eyes, she continued. 'I'm mortified just at the thought of the scandal.'

The wife's lies hit their mark. They incited the son to do whatever was necessary to protect the family's honour. How could his mother bring such dishonour on his good name? he thought. How could she make him a laughing stock of the entire community? What face would he show to his friends and relatives? No, this must not be allowed to continue, he resolved. 'What do you suggest?' he asked his wife.

'Put her in a sack and take her to the forest and burn her.'

So the son put his old mother in a sack and carried her to the forest, but he couldn't bring himself to burn her. Instead, he took the sack to an abandoned Kali temple and left it there, with its top still tied with a rope. Then he returned home to his wife and told her that the deed was done.

The old woman struggled all day to get out of the sack, crying for help, but no one came into the temple, and, finally, exhausted, she fell asleep. When she woke up, she saw it was light, and she also discovered that the sack was miraculously untied. As she was crawling out of it, her eyes fell on something glittery at the feet of Kali's statue. It was a pile of gold jewellery and coins. The old woman could hardly believe her luck. She thanked the goddess and, gathering up all the riches in the pallu of her sari, rushed home, excited to give the wealth to her son.

What the old woman didn't know is that much had occurred in the temple in the middle of the night. The ties of the sack had been gnawed by the rats who lived in the temple. Then, a pack of thieves had come to take shelter in the temple and, praying to the goddess, they had promised that they would share half the loot with her, if she helped them in their planned heist. Later, having pulled off a successful robbery, they had returned and left the promised share of the loot at the Devi's feet.

When the old woman arrived home, her daughter-in-law was shocked to see her alive. 'What... How...?' she began.

'Look what I have,' the mother–in-law said joyfully, opening the bundle in her sari and pouring out the riches.

The daughter-in-law's eyes almost popped out. 'Where did you get all this?' she asked with bated breath. By this time, the son had also joined them, and he too was agog.

The mother told them how all day she had struggled to get out of the sack and had fallen asleep, tired and hungry, and how Devi Ma had not only released her but had also rewarded her for her suffering.

'Quickly,' the daughter-in-law said to her husband, her eyes gleaming with greed. 'Bring a stick and beat me until I suffer so much that I cry out in pain. Then tie me up and take me to the temple and leave me there at night. In fact, put me in a double sack so that I have to struggle extra hard. Devi Ma will surely give me double the reward for all my suffering.'

The son now understood that his wife had been abusing his poor mother, and he was furious at what she had made him do. He beat his wife black and blue. Then, stuffing her into a sack, he carried her to the forest and set her on fire.

Folktale from Kerala

◆

95

SONA AND RUPA

There was a young prince who was the only heir to a large kingdom. His parents fulfilled his every wish and never refused him anything, no matter what he asked for.

One day, returning from a hunt, he stopped at a river to water his mare. As he led her to the water's edge, he saw strands of hair floating in the waves—some gold and some silver. Catching the strands in his hand, he pulled them out, noticing that they were long and silky. He ran his fingers through them and began to imagine the women whose heads these hairs must have adorned. Tucking the hair in the folds of his turban, he went home.

When it was time for dinner, the queen sent her maid to summon the prince, but he was not in his quarters. The maid looked in many other places as well, but he was nowhere to be found. The queen then enlisted the help of other servants and had them search every room in the palace. In the meantime, an old maid went into the storeroom for some sugar, and she saw the prince lying on the floor. For a moment she stood there, appalled, and then started to call out to the queen, but just then, the prince whispered angrily. 'Don't tell anyone, or I'll kill you.' The old maid backed out of the room, shaking her head, and quickly going to the queen, whispered in her ear.

The queen went to the storeroom and rattled the door handle before entering. She pretended as though she was looking for something and had no idea that the prince was there. 'Oh,' she said, acting surprised when she saw him. 'What are you doing in here, Son? Why are you lying on the dusty floor? Are you all right? Get up. That floor is dirty."

'Promise me first that you'll get me what I desire,' the prince said to his mother.

'Have we ever refused you anything?' the queen replied.

The prince got up, and, taking out the gold and silver hairs from his turban showed them to his mother. 'I want to marry the girls who have such gold and silver hair.'

The queen looked at the hair and her heart sank a little.

'I must have those girls,' the prince said again.

'We'll find girls who have hair like that,' the queen said and left the room, her steps faltering.

That very day town criers were sent to announce that the next morning all the young women of the kingdom should come to the palace courtyard with their heads uncovered. The following morning there was a parade of young women before the palace. The prince inspected each one, but after many hours, he still didn't see anyone with hair of gold or silver. Frustrated, he was turning to go back to the palace, when his eyes fell on two girls sitting in the women's courtyard. One had golden hair, and the other, silver. Calling his mother in excitement, he pointed to the two women whose heads were gleaming gold and silver in the sun.

'That's them!' the prince declared. 'I want them.'

'Oh God!' the queen exclaimed, holding on to a doorjamb for support. 'They're your sisters, Sona and Rupa.'

The prince felt a moment's misgiving, but then he said obstinately, 'I don't care who they are. These are the two I will marry, or I'll leave the country and never return.'

Every elder in the family tried to persuade the prince to change his mind—to select someone else. The king and queen appealed to him with folded hands, but the prince was adamant. 'I only want those two. If I don't get them, I'll go away forever,' he repeated. The king, whose only heir was the prince, was left with no choice. With a heavy heart, he ordered his men to begin preparations for the marriage.

When Sona and Rupa heard they were to be wed, their hearts leaped in excitement, but then when they learned that their groom was to be their own brother, their chest felt heavy with dread. They begged and pleaded with their mother, tears streaming down their cheeks, sobbing till their breath caught in their throat, but the queen could do nothing. Feeling powerless and forlorn, the two princesses finally went to the river, where they had bathed on that fateful day, and wept their hearts out. On the bank of this river was a sandalwood tree that they had tended from the time it was a sapling and they, little girls. Now it was tall and full grown, just as they were. On the morning of their wedding day, the two princesses returned to the river, and this time, they climbed up the sandalwood tree and hid in its branches. When it was time for the ceremony to begin, the servants came looking for them and requested them to come down, but they refused. At last the king himself came and called to them.

> Come down, come down
> My daughters Sona and Rupa
> The wedding hour is here.
> The girls called back in grief:
> We called you father
> How can we call you father-in-law?
> Take us higher. Take us higher, O sandalwood tree.

And the tree grew taller.

By now the whole family had gathered at the riverbank, and each member of the family implored them to come down. To each call, they responded in the same manner, asking the tree to take them higher, and the tree grew taller and taller.

Then, when the prince came and asked them to come down, they replied:

> We called you brother
> How can we call you husband?
> Take us higher. Take us higher, O sandalwood tree.

And suddenly the sky filled with clouds and thunder roared. Then, lightning flashed and struck the tree, splitting it open. Even as the family watched, Sona and Rupa descended into the tree and disappeared inside it.

Folktale from Madhya Pradesh

◆

96

IF IT WASN'T YOU, IT WAS ONE OF YOU

One day a lion stopped to have a drink at a stream that flowed down the mountain. At some distance downstream, he saw a lamb also drinking from the same stream. 'You are dirtying my water,' he roared at the lamb.

The lamb trembled in fright, but it replied, 'How is that possible? You're upstream, and I'm down here.'

'Then you must have dirtied the water last week.'

'I wasn't even near this mountain last week.'

'Then it must've been your mother.'

'My mother died two months ago.'

'Then it must've been your father.'

'My father was killed some time ago.'

'Your brother, your uncle, your grandfather! I don't care who it was. If it wasn't you, it was one of you, and so I'm going to eat you.' And the lion ate the lamb.

Folktale from North India

◆

97

WHO WILL SAVE YOU?

One day Prophet Muhammad was travelling by himself. It was a hot day, and when the heat became unbearable, he found shade under a tree in a secluded area. One of his enemies saw him sitting there alone and thought it was an opportune moment to kill him. Approaching, the man pulled out his sword. 'Now, who is going to help you?' he jeered at the Prophet.

'Allah,' said the Prophet calmly, without any sign of fear.

Seeing his lack of fear and his total confidence in Allah's protection, the man became afraid, and the sword fell from his hand.

Now the Prophet picked up the sword and pointed it at the man who had threatened him. 'Can you tell me who will save you?'

'No one,' the enemy said, his body quaking.

'You're wrong,' said the Prophet. 'The same Allah will protect you, as well.'

Then Prophet Mohammad laid the sword on the ground and let the man, who used to be his enemy, go.

Luqman Hakim folktale

◆

98

INDRA VS GOVARDHANA

On the fourteenth day of the second half of the month of Kartika, the inhabitants of Braj used to gather to worship Indra. As part of the celebration, Nanda, Krishna's father, who was chief of the Gopa tribe of cowherds, used to hold a big feast in his house to which all the dwellers of Braj were invited.

On one such day, the young Krishna, noticing all the Braj women making mithai, asked his mother, Yashoda, what they would do with so much mithai.

'I've no time to talk to you today, Son,' Yashoda replied impatiently. 'Go and ask your father.'

So Krishna went to his father and asked him, 'Father, are we honouring some god today? Will he fulfil our desires? Will he give us boons? Is he a mighty god?'

'Son, all this is to worship Indra, who is the ruler of the gods and the lord of clouds. He bestows prosperity by giving us water which makes the flowers, fruits and grain grow. If he's happy, then all living beings—human, animal, and bird—are happy.'

'How do you know that Indra does all this because of our puja?' Krishna asked.

Nanda was perplexed. 'It's a custom, Son,' he said. 'We've been honouring Indra on this day since long before you were born.'

'I've never heard of Indra giving anyone a boon. From all the stories you've told me about him, I know that the gods made him their king, but he hardly acts like a king. He runs away and hides when he's scared of the asuras, and someone always has to come and rescue him. If he can't save himself, how can he save us? You also said our prosperity comes from our cows and our Govardhana hill and the forests. Then why do we worship Indra? We should worship the mountains and forests where we live and graze our cows. Why don't we take our sandalwood and saffron and mithai to the Govardhana hill and worship it, instead of Indra?'

Krishna's words struck Nanda with the force of truth. He thought for a long time and then calling an assembly of the cowherds, told them what his son had proposed. 'Don't take these words as coming from a child. Consider them as seeds of truth. Why do we pay homage to Indra? Shouldn't we worship those who give us sustenance? What have we to do with the ruler of the gods? Let's worship forests, rivers and the Govardhana.' The cowherds liked what Nanda said, and so the chief of the Gopas made a proclamation: 'This day, on which Indra used to be worshipped, will now be celebrated as Govardhana Puja.'

The following morning, the Brajvasis rose very early, and bathing and dressing in new clothes and jewellery, they gathered at Nanda's house. Then, in a celebratory procession, everyone walked to Govardhana with platters full of mithai, saffron, sandal, flowers and other puja paraphernalia. They covered the hill with flower garlands, sprinkled it with holy water, and offered it the confections they had made. 'Meditate with pure minds on Govardhana, and he'll appear and eat with you,' Krishna told the people. And, sure enough, as the Brajvasis stood with their eyes closed and their hearts and minds set on the benevolence of the hill, a huge being with massive hands and feet, dressed in a yellow dhoti and wearing a crown on his head and flower garlands around his neck, emerged from the middle of the hill. Ecstatic to see this manifestation of their beloved hill, the people piled all their platters of mithai before him, and he, with his big, open mouth, happily ate up everything and then returned to the hill.

Their hearts content, knowing that their puja had been accepted by the deity they had worshipped, the people returned home, singing and dancing. The festivities continued through the next day, as they feasted in Nanda's house and adorned all their cows and calves, decorating them in bright colours and fastening rings and bells around their necks.

Seeing the Brajvasis reject him and worship Govardhana instead, Indra become enraged. He summoned all the gods and asked them to explain to him what had happened in Braj. Narada, the divine sage, explained to him: 'You are the king of devas. Everyone obeys you, but the people of Braj have decided to listen to Nanda's young son, Krishna, and abolish your worship.'

'It seems that Brajvasis have become excessively proud because of their wealth,' Indra declared. 'But they don't know me. They don't know that by rejecting me, they have invited famine and suffering. They think Krishna is a god and they believe all he says. He's nothing but a foolish, arrogant child who is misleading the people. I'll put an end to it all.' Indra then summoned his clouds and commanded them: 'Pour down so much water on Govardhana and on Braj that everything—hill, town, people, cattle—is washed away; nothing should remain.'

The rains came, unceasing and torrential, flooding houses and sweeping away cattle and crops. The people of Braj ran to Nanda's house in a panic. 'You told us to stop worshipping Indra, and now look what he's doing,' they cried. 'We should never have challenged Indra.'

'Don't be afraid,' Krishna said to them. 'We chose to honour Govardhana, now Govardhana will protect us. Come with me.' And he took all the Brajvasis and their animals to the hill. Then, slipping the tip of the little finger of his left hand under the hill, he lifted it and held it aloft, like an immense umbrella. Astonished, the people gathered under the hill with their families and cattle. Soon, all the animals and birds from the surrounding forests also came there to take shelter.

For seven days, the clouds thundered and rained, but not a drop fell on any Brajvasi—human, animal, or bird. They stood under Govardhana, watching the deluge around them, awestruck by this little boy who, with only his little finger had overpowered Indra.

Sitting in his Indraloka, Indra's wrath turned to consternation. 'Surely this is none other than Vishnu descended upon earth,' he said to himself, and realizing that all the Lord needed was the little finger of his left hand to thwart him, Indra felt greatly humbled. Getting down from his throne, he fixed his mind on Vishnu and begged him for forgiveness.

The clouds suddenly dispersed and the sun shone brightly on Braj. Krishna then placed Govardhana back in its place and all the Brajvasis rejoiced.

Myth from the Puranas

◆

99

MARIAMMA AND YELLAMMA

Rishi Jamadagni was one of the seven chief rishis. He was married to a beautiful royal princess, Renuka, and the couple lived a virtuous and contented life in the rishi's ashram in Peripalayam. They had five sons; the youngest among them was Rama Jamadagnya, who later came to be known as Parashurama—the Rama who wields a battle-axe.

Every morning, Renuka used to go to the river to fetch water for her husband's puja. She never took a vessel with her in which to fill the water, yet she returned every day with a pot full of water. She was such a chaste wife that with the power of her chastity, the water used to settle itself on her head in the shape of a pot.

One spring morning at the river, as Renuka straightened up to adjust the pot-shaped water on her head, she saw a reflection of a very handsome gandharva, who was flying past, probably on his way to Indra's court. It was not an uncommon sight. Spring was the season when nature spirits came to earth for sport, and since gandharvas were known for their musical talents, they were most often on earth, enjoying the symphony of spring. Renuka had seen many nature spirits, but this gandharva was more handsome than any male she had seen, and she was strangely affected— just for a fleeting moment. But, in that split second, the water pot on her head shattered, drenching her. Renuka was ruined. She wondered how she would go home. Surely her husband would ask her why she had returned without the water. Why was she soaked? What would she tell her husband? Her mind in turmoil, Renuka sat by the river, waiting for her clothes to dry and her courage to return so that she could face her husband.

In the meantime, Rishi Jamadagni wondered why his wife was so late returning from the river. With his spiritual vision, he sought Renuka at the river bank and saw for himself what had happened and knew that Renuka was no longer a chaste woman. He was furious, and as he waited for her, his fury grew. As soon as Renuka stepped over the threshold, he commanded his eldest son to cut off her head. Trembling in fear at his father's anger, the eldest son refused. Jamadagni then ordered his second son to do the deed, but he, too, trepidatiously refused. In the same way, the other two sons were also not willing to kill their mother. But the youngest, Rama, followed his father's orders, and picking up a battle-axe, came at his mother.

Terrified, Renuka turned around and ran towards the village, trying to escape her axe-wielding son. When she saw the open door of a hut, she quickly slipped inside and shut the door behind her. This was a washerwoman's hut, and seeing Renuka's panicked face, she quickly hid her. But Rama had seen his mother go into the hut. He broke down the door and cut off the heads of both Renuka and the washerwoman. Then he returned home to tell his father that his command had been carried out.

'You are a good son,' Rishi Jamadagni said to him, patting him on the back. 'For upholding my honour and for your obedience, I'll give you a boon. Ask me for anything.'

'I want you to bring my mother back to life,' Rama replied.

Jamadagni was surprised, but a boon once promised has to be fulfilled. So, giving his son a pitcher of mantra water, he told him to attach his mother's severed head to her body and then sprinkle it with water from the pitcher to bring her back to life. Rama rushed back to the washerwoman's house, and quickly picking up the two heads attached them to the two bodies, and then sprinkled them with anointed water from the pitcher. But, in his hurry, he attached Renuka's head to the body of the washer woman and the washerwoman's head to Renuka's body. Both women came back to life, and the woman who had Renuka's head and mind, accompanied Rama back to the ashram. But when Rishi Jamadagni saw that his wife's body was that of an untouchable, he refused to accept her.

Still anguished for being condemned as unchaste, and now abandoned for being untouchable, Renuka's grief broke the bounds of human forbearance. This extreme suffering rendered her divine and transformed her into the Goddess Mariamma. Also transformed was the washerwoman who, by virtue of sharing Renuka's suffering and then receiving her body, became the Goddess Yellamma.[37]

Both goddesses became symbols of suffering, providing succour to all those who suffer, and they created a bond of sisterhood that transcends caste.

Folk-myth from South India

◆

100

DEATH WILL NOT US PART

King Ashvapati of Madra longed for a child. He was a virtuous and pious king, always working for the betterment of his people and constantly performing sacrificial rituals and worship to keep the gods benevolent. However, no matter how rigorously he fulfilled his dharma as a king and householder, the gods did not reward him with his greatest desire, which was to be a father. His priests advised him to pray to Goddess Saraswati in her Savitri form. 'She is the daughter of Savitr, the sun god, whose rays burgeon life, and she is married to Brahma, the Creator himself. If anyone can plead your case with the Creator, it is she,' the Brahmins told the king

Ashvapati began an eighteen-year invocation of Goddess Savitri. He offered ten thousand oblations to her and observed a fast, eating only one small meal a day and that too, just in the late evening. Finally, Savitri acknowledged the king's devotion and appeared before him. 'O king of Madra, I am very pleased with you,' she said. 'What do you desire?'

'Devi,' Ashvapati said, bowing in reverence. 'I long for children who will carry on my name and be my heirs.'

'I knew your heart's desire even before I came here,' the goddess said to Ashvapati. 'I have already discussed this with Brahmaji. You will have a daughter—a highly virtuous daughter, who will be your delight and a guiding light for all humanity.'

Shortly thereafter, Ashvapati's eldest wife, Malavi, became pregnant, and at the appropriate time, she gave birth to a beautiful daughter with lotus eyes. Filled with joyful reverence, the royal couple performed her naamkaran ceremony and named her Savitri, after the goddess.

Savitri was delightful as a child, and when she became a young maiden, she was like Lakshmi herself—beautiful and generous, with a spark of playfulness. However, despite her attractive looks and good nature, no suitors seemed to be interested in her, and this caused Ashvapati great anxiety. Hence, he decided that if suitors would not come to his daughter, he would send his daughter to them. 'I want you to go and seek your husband,' he said to Savitri. 'Travel to different cities and hermitages and find the man you want to marry. I'll happily give you away to the man of your choice.'

Savitri journeyed to many regions. Seated in a golden carriage, surrounded by ministers and bodyguards, she visited ashrams, where she talked to yogis and sages, went to pilgrimage sites, where she gave away much wealth in charity, travelled to many cities, where she met people of all kinds—scholars, craftsmen, and businessmen. Finally, she started back for Sagala,[38] Madra's capital city. On the day that she arrived home, King Ashvapati was hosting Narada, the celestial priest. When Savitri saw the revered rishi sitting beside her father, she bowed before him and asked for his blessings. Touching the girl's head in benediction Narada asked Ashvapati, 'Where has your daughter come from? Isn't it time that you marry her?'

'That is exactly what she has been doing these past many months, O Sage Narada. She has been searching for a husband, and I think she has come home to tell me who she has selected. Is that right, Daughter?'

Savitri nodded and began to tell her father about the man she had chosen. 'In Shalya, I met a pious Kshatriya, who is blind. His name is Dyumatsena, and he used to be a king, but when he became blind, his relatives usurped his kingdom, and he had to flee to the forest with his wife and infant son. They've lived in a hermitage in the forest for many years, and now the son is all grown up and is very handsome. He takes care of his old parents and considers it his highest dharma to serve them. His name is Satyavan. This is the man I want to marry.'

'This is very sad, indeed,' Narada shook his head. 'O king, your daughter has made a tragic choice.'

'Why?' Ashvapati asked. 'Is this young man not energetic, intelligent, brave, and forgiving?'

'He is as energetic as Surya, as wise as Brihaspati, as heroic as Indra, and as forgiving as the earth.'

'Then is he not charitable, handsome, and generous?'

'He is the embodiment of charity and generosity, and his handsomeness is like that of the Ashwin twins; it makes the apsaras moon-eyed. Satyavan is also truthful to a fault, as his name suggests, and he is humble and modest and patient.'

'If he possesses all the virtues that any father would seek in a husband for his daughter, what defects does he have that makes him a tragic choice?'

'He has only one defect, which has eclipsed all his qualities, and this defect can't be fixed, no matter how hard he tries.'

'What is that defect?' Ashvapati asked with apprehension.

'He has only a short time to live. In fact, a year from this day, he will die.'

Ashvapati's face paled and his shoulders sagged. 'No. No. I can't allow this marriage,' he said to his daughter. 'You must go again and search for another husband.'

'A daughter can only be given away once, Father,' Savitri said. 'You gave me the freedom to find my own husband, and I did, and you have already bestowed me on Satyavan. Whether his life is long or short; whether he's gifted with noble qualities, or not; whether he's rich or poor, I've made my choice. Besides, in my heart, I already consider him my husband. How can I then choose someone else?'

'Your daughter is a very determined young woman,' Narada said to Ashvapati. 'I applaud her for her resolve to do what she thinks is right. I think you should prepare for the wedding.'

With a heavy heart, King Ashvapati began to prepare for the ceremony. He visited the hermitage where Satyavan's parents were staying and made the marriage proposal. But Dyumatsena was hesitant to accept it. 'We are in exile,' he said to Ashvapati. 'We are living like ascetics here in this ashram. How can your daughter bear to live a forest life devoid of luxuries?'

'Happiness and misery are both transient,' Ashvapati replied. 'My daughter is aware of this, as am I. She has decided to marry your son, knowing well enough the kind of life she'll have to live. As for me—I consider you my equal and a friend, and on the basis of that, I ask you to accept this match.'

Dyumatsena agreed, and Savitri and Satyavan were married in the hermitage in a simple ceremony that was attended by the Brahmins who lived there. Giving away his daughter, adorned in silks and jewels, Ashvapati returned home to Sagala.

After her father and his wedding party departed, Savitri removed all her jewels and her fine silk clothes and dressed in a modest cotton garment dyed red. Then she began living the simple life of a forest-dweller with her husband and his parents. In no time at all, her modesty, generosity and caring endeared her to her parents-in-law and everyone else in the hermitage, and her sweet disposition and loving smile, made Satyavan feel like the luckiest man on earth.

However, Savitri herself was troubled day and night. She could not forget Narada's words that her husband had only a short time to live. In her mind, she began a countdown. When only three nights remained in her husband's life, she undertook a very strict vow called Triratri—three nights—which required her to fast continuously for three days and nights. Her husband and parents-in-law asked her why she was observing such a severe vow, but she simply said it was her duty as a wife. Pleased at her devotion to her dharma, they applauded her and let her be.

The night before the morning on which Satyavan was to die, Savitri stayed awake, immersed in deep grief. She sat looking at Satyavan's sweet face as he slept, the peace on his face breaking her heart. As dawn broke, she performed her morning rituals, offering oblation to the fire and bowing to all the elders in the hermitage, but on this day, when the elders called out the blessing, 'Forever be a suhagin—a married woman—' tears welled up in her eyes.

'Your vow is complete today, dear Daughter,' Savitri's mother-in-law said to her, 'Do put some morsels in your mouth. You haven't eaten for three days.'

'I'll eat at sunset,' she replied. 'This is what I have resolved.'

Just then, Satyavan came out of the hut with an axe on his shoulder, ready to leave for the woods. 'Let me come with you,' Savitri said to him. 'Today I wish to spend the day with you.'

'Dearest Wife, you have already seen the woods. Besides, you know that the forest paths are difficult to cross. You're weak from hunger and thirst. You haven't eaten or had a drop of water for three days. You should stay at home today.'

'Don't try to dissuade me,' Savitri said to Satyavan. 'I really wish to spend the day with you. Besides, I feel fine. I'm not tired or hungry. Do let me come.'

Satyavan loved his wife and was quite pleased that she wanted to spend the day with him, so he didn't protest any more, and the two of them, after taking his parents' permission, set off for the forest. It was spring; everything was alive—flowers were blooming, streams were chattering, and peacocks were showing off their plumage to their mates. Inspired by the atmosphere, Satyavan became especially romantic, pausing every now and then to pluck a bloom and put it in Savitri's hair, to point out her reflection in the clear water of a stream, or just to smile at her. Savitri smiled back at him sadly, knowing that every gesture, every word, every smile was the last of its kind.

When they were deep in the forest, Satyavan first gathered fruit to take back home and then he began to cut wood. Savitri sat under a tree, watching him. As he was felling the branches of a tree, he began to sweat profusely. 'I think I'll rest a little,' he said to Savitri. 'I'm tired and my head hurts.'

Trying to hold back her tears, Savitri gestured to him to lie down with his head in her lap so that she could massage it. As she pressed her fingers to his forehead, she began counting the seconds—4-3-2-1...and suddenly a huge man dressed in red garments, wearing a diadem on his head, appeared before her. His complexion was dark and his eyes were red, but his face shone like the sun. When he approached Satyavan and stood above him with a noose in his hand, Savitri realized who it was. Gently placing Satyavan's head on the ground, she stood up and folded her hands before the Lord of Death. 'I know who you are,' she said to him. 'Please tell me why you have come.'

Yamaraja smiled at her question. 'The number of years allotted to this man are over, and I have come to take him.'

'But we hear that you send your emissaries to do this task. Why have you come yourself?'

'This was a virtuous man and his life is being cut down in his prime. I like to honour men like that by receiving them myself.' And even as Yamaraja said that, he drew out of Satyavan's body a tiny person, the size of a thumb, and slipped his noose around him. Satyavan's body shuddered one last time and then became completely still, and within seconds, all the lustre went out of it.

Securing the thumb-sized Satyavan in his noose, Yamaraja proceeded to the south; Savitri, with tears streaming down her face, mindless with sorrow, began to follow him. 'Go back, Savitri,' Yamaraja called to her. 'Go and perform your husband's last rites. Your debt as wife has been paid. You have come as far as possible with him. Now it is time for you to return to your own life.'

'But my life is my husband. Wherever he goes, I go with him. This is the vow I took when I married him, and I'll fulfil that vow in life and in death. The wise say that one forms a friendship with another after walking only seven paces with that person. I have not only walked seven paces with my husband, I have bound myself to him forever. That is the vow of conjugal life and nothing can stop me from fulfilling it. The wise also say that one gains the most virtue by fulfilling the vow of conjugal life. You can't take away my right of seeking this virtue.'

'I'm impressed with your devotion and your wisdom,' Yamaraja said. 'I'll grant you a boon. Ask me anything, except for your husband's life. And then you must go back.'

'My father-in-law has been driven from his kingdom and lives in a hermitage. He has also lost his eyes. Let him regain his sight.'

'It will be as you say. Now go back.'

But Savitri didn't turn back; instead she began talking about the virtues of the wise. 'It's said that one should form friendship with the wise, because such a friendship enhances one's own knowledge.'

'Well said,' said Yamaraja. 'Your intelligence is certainly worthy of praise. Ask me another boon—anything except Satyavan's life.'

'Let my father-in-law regain his kingdom and his former glory.'

'Your father-in-law will be the monarch again and will be hailed for his glory. Now you absolutely must go back.'

'You are a just and fair god. You are called Yamaraja, because you govern through your ordinance. When you carry away creatures, you do so through ordinance, not through caprice or lack of mercy and charity. The wise say, mercy and charity are the highest virtues. People who are truly virtuous show mercy and charity even to their enemies.'

'I applaud you for your understanding of high virtues. Ask me for another boon. I can grant anything but your husband's life.'

'My father has no son to perpetuate his race. Grant him one hundred sons. This will be my third boon.'

'Granted. Your father will have a hundred energetic sons who will perpetuate his race. But now you have come too far. Go back!'

'It'll never be too far for me if I'm with my husband. You are the powerful son of Vivasvata, the sun god. You judge people impartially and rightfully. That's why you are called the Lord of Justice. You are also full of virtue. Virtue gains one glory. People place more trust in the virtuous than they do even on themselves.'

'You are a very discerning young woman. Your words please me. Ask me for one more boon, but remember, I can't grant your husband's life, so ask me for anything but that.'

'Let me have one hundred strong and powerful sons.'

'Granted. You will have one hundred sons who will delight you. Go and be happy with your children.'

'Truthfulness is the highest virtue. The very sun moves because of truth. It is the truthful who cause the past and future. The truth is that you have granted me a hundred sons, yet you are carrying away my husband; without my husband, how can I bear sons? So, grant me my husband's life and make your own words true. You have also said go and be happy with your children, but how can I be happy without Satyavan, whom I love. Grant his life and make your own words true. So, grant me this fifth boon. Return my husband's life.'

Yamaraja paused to think and realized that he had, indeed, been caught in the trap of his own words, and there was no way to extricate himself; the boons had already been granted. 'Dear lady, I release your husband,' he said. 'You have gained him back with your intelligence and virtue and devotion. You'll live together happily for four hundred years and you'll have a hundred strong and delightful sons with him, and those children will be kings. Your name will forever be renowned for what you have accomplished today.' Granting these boons Yamaraja loosened the noose and released Satyavan's soul. Then he vanished.

Savitri quickly returned to the place where her husband's body lay. It was exactly as she had left it. She sat down again with his head on her lap, and even as she watched, Satyavan's body began to show signs of life. Soon, he opened his eyes, and, for an instant, his gaze was distant, as though he was returning from a faraway place. Then he looked at Savitri's face and smiled fondly. 'Oh, you have let me sleep too long, dear one. Why did you not awaken me?'

'You have certainly slept long, Husband, but now you're awake. Welcome back.'

'I feel very refreshed,' Satyavan said, sitting up. 'I had a dream—that a dark and shining person was dragging me away. It seemed so real.'

'What's real is that we are together,' Savitri said, placing her head on his shoulder. 'It's time that we return home.' Then, leading each other through the dark paths of the forest, they went back to the hermitage, where life had miraculously changed for Satyavan's parents.

Myth from the Mahabharata

◆

101

THE RED LOTUS OF FAITHFULNESS

In the famous port of Tamralipti[39] there lived a wealthy merchant named Dhanadatta, who traded in precious stones. He had a son called Guhasena. When the boy came of age, Dhanadatta took him along on a business voyage to Suvarnabhumi,[40] hoping to find a suitable girl for him there. In Suvarnabhumi the merchant met a prominent Brahmin, Dharmagupta, who had a daughter named Devasmita, whose beauty was such that her name—on whom the gods have smiled—was completely suited to her. But when Dhanadatta requested Dharmagupta for a marriage alliance between their children, the Brahmin refused, because he didn't want to send his daughter to the faraway port of Tamralipti. However, by this time Devasmita had met Guhasena and had fallen love with him, so, one night, disregarding her parents' wish, she sailed off with Guhasena and his father.

Guhasena and Devasmita were married in Tamralipti, and they spent many happy years together. Then Dhanadatta passed away and Guhasena took over his father's business, which required him to travel. When he prepared for his first business trip to the island of Yavadwipa,[41] Devasmita became very despondent. She was a jealous wife and was afraid that he would fall in love with another woman, so she begged him not to go. To appease his wife, Guhasena accompanied her to a temple, where they both took a vow of chastity. That night, as the couple slept, they dreamt of receiving a red lotus from Lord Shiva, who said to them, 'Both of you must hold on to this lotus, and if one of you commits adultery, the lotus in the other one's hand will wilt.' When Guhasena and Devasmita woke up, they found that they were each holding a red lotus with the image of the other's heart enfolded in its petals.

Guhasena then departed for Yavadwipa, holding his lotus, and upon reaching the island, he took the lotus with him, wherever he went. This aroused the curiosity of four mischievous sons of a merchant, who wondered why Guhasena always carried a red lotus and why the flower never withered. One evening, they invited Guhasena to their house and, plying him with drink, asked him about the lotus. When he told them about the vow of chastity that he and his wife had taken and how the lotus was a symbol of their faithfulness, the merchant's sons decided to have some fun.

Knowing that Guhasena's business would keep him in Yavadwipa for a while, the brothers set sail for Tamralipti, without telling anyone. There, they found a bhikshuni named Yogakarandika in a Buddhist monastery, and promising her great rewards, enlisted her help in finding Devasmita and carrying out their scheme.

'I don't need your money,' the nun told them. 'But tell me who is this woman you seek, and why do you seek her?'

'Her name is Devasmita and she is the merchant, Guhasena's wife. We want her in our bed. Can you bring her to us?'

'I'll do my best,' the bhikshuni replied, and began to make enquiries. When she found out where Devasmita lived, she managed to ingratiate herself and gain entry to the house. However, when she tried to enter Devasmita's room, a bitch guarding the door began barking. Because she had never barked at anyone before, Devasmita came to the door herself to see who it was, and seeing a bhikshuni, invited her in. 'May I ask why you have come?' she asked.

'I've heard so much about you and have always wanted to meet you,' Yogakarandika replied. 'Then today I saw you in a dream. That's why I've come to pay you a visit. I see that you are separated from your husband, and my heart goes out to you for your suffering. What use are youth and beauty, if they are deprived of love's pleasures?'

Devasmita was gratified to hear these words and the two began talking like old friends. The next day the bhikshuni came again to Devasmita's house, but this time, she was carrying a piece of meat covered with sneezing powder, which she gave to the dog, who immediately ate it and began sneezing.

Entering Devasmita's room, Yogakarandika found a seat across from her and began to weep.

'What is it?' Devasmita asked her kindly. 'Tell me, dear friend. Is there anything I can do?'

'Go and look at your dog,' Yogakarandika said. 'She's crying. Just now she recognized me from a former life. We knew each other well, and this has moved her to tears.'

In disbelief, Devasmita went to the door to see, and sure enough, there was the dog with tears rolling down her cheeks. 'What is this miracle?' she asked the bhikshuni.

'My dear, she and I were co-wives of a Brahmin in our former life. Our husband was a king's envoy and had to travel a lot. I understood that our highest duty as human beings is to fulfil the natural needs of the body and, while my husband was gone, I fulfilled them with other men. That's why I've been rewarded with the ability to remember my former lives. She, on the other hand, curbed her needs and remained chaste. That's why she has been born as a bitch, although she did remember her former life when she saw me.'

Devasmita was aghast at the bhikshuni's words. Never had she heard of this moral duty, and she became certain that the woman was trying to trick her into some evil scheme. But Devasmita was a clever woman, so she decided to play along. 'Thank you, dear respected mother, for telling me about my real duty,' Devasmita said, trying to sound as naïve as she could. 'I've been ignorant of this, but now I must remedy it. Do you have any handsome man in mind for me?'

'There are some merchant's sons who have just arrived from

Yavadwipa and are staying in town. They're very handsome. Shall I bring them to you?'

'Yes. How about tomorrow?' Devasmita said to Yogakarandika, her mind already formulating a plan. After the bhikshuni left, she called her maid and told her to prepare some alcohol mixed with datura and also to get a branding iron with a dog's paw design made at the smith's shop. She had a feeling that somehow these merchant's sons had seen her husband's red lotus and had also found out about the vow that she and her husband were observing. She felt certain that they had come to Tamralipti to create mischief.

The following day, Devasmita had her maid dress up as her, and when one of the young men, sent by the bhikshuni, arrived at the house, the maid greeted him and hosted him, pretending to be Devasmita. In the course of the evening, the maid plied the young man with datura-laced alcohol, and when he was knocked out, she called the other maids. They stripped him until he was clad only in air, like a Digambar, stamped his forehead with the dog-paw, and then threw him in the cesspool. When the merchant's son woke up in the last hours of the night, he found himself in Avichi hell, which is the lowest level of hell, with his forehead burning from the branding. He quickly got out of the cesspool and jumped into a nearby water tank to clean himself, and then, finding a piece of cloth to tie around his forehead, he returned to the bhikshuni's house, deciding not to tell anyone the truth. 'Why should I be the only one to be ridiculed?' he said to himself.

When his brothers saw him naked, except for his head, they slapped him on the back and asked, 'So, what happened?'

'Exactly what I expected,' he said with a sly smile. 'There was also a lot of drink. Then on the way here some robbers took all my clothes. I requested them to spare me the headscarf, because I have a headache.'

The next day, the second bother also went to Devasmita's house and was given the same treatment. He, too, found himself in the cesspool, naked and branded. He, too, returned in the nude with just his head covered with a scarf, and he, too, gave the excuse of a headache and being robbed of his clothing. In this way all four brothers were castigated, branded, and thrown in the cesspool, and all four claimed to have been successful in their mission.

Now Yogakarandika, emboldened by her success, went with her own pupil to Devasmita's house. The lady welcomed them with grateful smiles and offered them drinks. When both the bhikshuni and her pupil passed out, she had her maids cut off their noses and ears and tossed them outside in the sewage dump.

Then Devasmita received news that the merchant's sons had departed for Yavadwipa. 'They may try to hurt Guhasena,' she told her mother-in-law, with whom she had shared the whole story. 'I have to stop them and save him.' Devasmita had men's clothing made for herself and her maids and, masquerading as a rich merchant with business in Yavadwipa, she boarded a ship and left for that port.

When she disembarked in Yavadwipa, Devasmita saw her husband at the port, going about his business, but she did not approach him. Guhasena, too, saw Devasmita, and although he did not quite recognize her, he was surprised by how much this young trader resembled his wife.

Finding rooms for herself and her maids, Devasmita rested that evening, and the following morning, dressed as a wealthy merchant, she went to the local king and requested him to gather all his male citizens in one place. When the king asked, 'For what reason?' Devasmita replied: 'Four of my slaves have escaped and I've been told that they're living here in Yavadwipa, pretending to be merchants.' The king was a lawful man, so he called the gathering and asked Devasmita to identify her slaves. She saw the four men who had come to violate her and pointed them out. 'These four are my slaves. Please surrender my slaves to me, Maharaj!'

'But these are the sons of the caravan trader,' the other merchants vouched. 'We know these men.'

'If you don't believe me, take a look at their foreheads. My slaves are branded with a dog-paw. You'll see that branding.'

And sure enough, when their turbans were removed, everyone saw the branding on the foreheads of the four brothers.

'What's the meaning of this?' the king demanded, caught between what the traders had guaranteed and what this young foreigner claimed. Devasmita then revealed the whole story to the king, and everyone had a good laugh. 'They are certainly your slaves, my lady,' said the king. 'Do with them as you please.' But the father of the four pleaded with Devasmita to allow him to pay a ransom in exchange for his sons. Devasmita agreed and freed his sons from bondage.

Then, reunited with her faithful husband, Devasmita returned to

Tamralipti, flush with the ransom money, and she and her husband were never apart again.

Folktale from the Kathasaritsagara

◆

102

BOPOLUCHI

The village well was where all the young women gathered in the morning. They came to fill their pots and jars with water, but they stayed for a while to chat with their friends, sharing dreams and hopes about prospective husbands and married lives.

One morning, talking about the gifts they desired for their wedding, one of the girls said. 'My father will give me bridal clothes of brocade and my marriage will take place in a palace.'

Another one said, 'My parents will prepare platters and platters of mithai.'

Yet another stated, 'My relatives will give me boxes and boxes of jewellery and gold ornaments, and I'll wear them for my wedding.'

Among the young women was also Bopoluchi, who was the most beautiful of them all. She was an orphan, but she, too, had dreams like her friends. 'I don't have parents, but I have an uncle who'll, one day, he will come to see me,' she said wistfully. 'And like your parents, he, too, will give me brocade and mithai and jewels.'

At that time, a middle-aged robber, who was disguised as a peddler of perfumes, happened to be sitting near the well. He had been watching the girls and enjoying their conversation. When he saw Bopoluchi and heard that she was an orphan, he decided that he would marry her. So the next day, he dressed up like a rich farmer and came to see Bopoluchi, carrying trays full of mithai and jewels and a trunk full of brocade—just as she had described. 'I am your uncle,' he said to her. 'Your father's brother. I've been away in foreign lands, making my fortune. But now I'm back, and I want to give my niece a wedding that the whole village will remember.'

Bopoluchi was overjoyed, but doubt niggled at her. How could this be, she thought? How could my dream come true exactly as I wished it? But its realization was so sweet that she didn't question it too much, and when her uncle said, 'I want you to come and live with me right away,' Bopoluchi quickly packed the few pieces of clothing she owned in a bundle, and, without even informing her friends, went with her uncle.

As they were walking down the path that led out of the village, a crow, sitting high on the branch of a tree, crowed:

Bopoluchi, watch where you go
What he says is not so
Not an uncle you perceive
But a robber out to deceive

Bopoluchi heard the crow, but she had never heard that kind of caw before and she thought she might not have had heard it correctly. 'Uncle,' she said, 'that was a strange caw from a crow. Don't you think?'

'All crows caw strangely in this village, Niece,' the robber said. 'Ignore it.'

A little further, they saw a peacock in the field, and he too screamed:

Bopoluchi, watch where you go
What he says is not so
Not an uncle you perceive
But a robber out to deceive

'That was a strange sound that the peacock made.' Bopoluchi said. 'I'm not sure what he said. Do you, Uncle?'

'All peacocks in this village scream strangely. Don't give it any thought,' the uncle advised.

Still a bit further up, a jackal ran across a field right in front of them, and as it went, it howled,

Bopoluchi, watch where you go
What he says is not so
Not an uncle you perceive
But a robber out to deceive

'I swear I've never heard a jackal howl like that,' Bopoluchi said. 'Uncle, do you know what he said?'

'In this village all jackals howl like that. Don't worry your pretty little head about it.'

Finally, they reached a small neighbourhood, and the robber stopped before a tree, behind which was a hidden door. Quickly unlocking it, he ushered Bopoluchi in, and bolted it. Then he turned to her and said, 'What the crow and the peacock and the jackal said is true. I'm not your uncle; I'm a robber.'

Bopoluchi's heart broke. 'I knew you were too good to be true,' she cried. 'I'm just a poor orphan. I have nothing that you can rob. Why have you brought me here? All I have is in this bundle, and it only contains a few old clothes.'

'I don't want to rob you, ' the robber replied. 'I want to marry you. That's why I've brought you here.'

'But you're old,' Bopoluchi wailed, her heart breaking even more. 'I dreamt of a husband who is young and handsome. I don't want to marry an old man like you. Please let me go back to my village.'

'I'll shower you with jewels and brocades. You can eat as much mithai as you want.'

'I don't want anything from you. I just want to go back to my village,' she begged.

'We'll be married today whether you like it or not,' the robber stated, handing her a bridal salwar kameez. 'I'm going to the village to make preparations. You'll stay here with my mother until I return. While I'm gone, I want you to get changed into these bridal clothes, and, as soon as I return, we'll be married.' Then the robber let himself out, locking the door from the outside.

'Come on, come on. Don't just stand around.' A very old woman with a bald head stepped out of the shadows and scolded Bopoluchi. 'My son will be back soon and he'll be angry if you're not dressed.' Then, waddling up to Bopoluchi, she pulled off the dupatta from her head, and suddenly stood still, staring at Bopoluchi's long and black silky hair that reached almost down to her knees. Then she touched the hair. 'Oooh,' she exclaimed. 'Your hair is so beautiful. How did you get such beautiful hair?'

Bopoluchi stopped crying and looked at the old woman; then a plan began to form in her mind 'My mother used to put my head in the mortar, the pounding of the pestle works wonders on hair growth. You should try it.'

'Really? Do you think if I put my head in the mortar, my hair will grow back?' the bald old woman asked.

'Let's try it, Amma,' Bopoluchi said, deliberately making her tone gentle. Then she located the mortar and beckoned to the old woman with an encouraging smile. The old woman sat down at the mortar and placed her head in it. Bopoluchi, quickly brought the pestle down hard, crushing the old crone's skull. Then she dressed the dead woman in the wedding suit and, covering her head with the red dupatta, straightened her, so that it looked like she was sitting in front of the mortar. After that, Bopoluchi quickly changed into the ragged clothes from her bundle, covered her head with a thick shawl, and finding a window in the house, made her escape.

As she was walking back to her village, she saw the robber returning home. He was carrying a millstone to grind the corn for the wedding feast. Bopoluchi looked this way and that, wondering where to hide, but she had nothing to worry about, because the robber didn't recognize her in her ill-fitting, patched-up clothes and a shawl that covered her hair and part of her face.

When the robber got home, he saw his bride, dressed in bridal clothes, sitting before the mortar. 'Come and help me with this millstone,' he called out, but his bride didn't respond. The robber called again, and when the girl still didn't respond, he became so enraged that he threw the millstone at her head. The bridal figure toppled over, and the robber realized that it was his mother. He thought he had killed her with the millstone, and kneeling before her dead body, he wept and wept. Then he remembered Bopoluchi. Wiping his tears, he began searching for her all over the house, but when he couldn't find her anywhere, it dawned on him that it was the girl, not he, who had killed his mother.

In the meantime, Bopoluchi reached her village, but she knew she was not safe, because the robber would surely come looking for her. At first she tried to get help from her friends and asked each one if she could stay with her, but when all her friends refused, Bopoluchi realized that the only person who could help her was herself. She also realized that she was in this precarious situation because she had been depending on someone else to fulfil her dreams. That's when Bopoluchi decided that it was time she faced the robber and show him that she was not powerless. From that night on, she slept in her own bed, with a billhook under her pillow, waiting for him.

Four big men broke into her house and, lifting up her bed, carried her away, each one holding a post. One of the men, the one holding the bedpost nearest her head, was the robber. Once they reached the forest, the men put the bed on the ground and sat down to rest. All this time, Bopoluchi had pretended to be asleep, but she had been waiting for the right opportunity. When she saw the men doze off, she grabbed the billhook and slipped out of the bed. Coming up behind each sleeping man, she sliced his neck—first one man, then the next, and then the third. When she came to the robber, she saw that he was awake and looking at her with fear in his eyes. He stood up and backed away from her and then quickly climbed up a tree.

'Come down and face me like a man,' Bopoluchi called, brandishing the billhook. When the robber refused, she piled up twigs and dry leaves at the base of the tree, and lit it. The robber was burnt to ashes.

Bopoluchi now went to his house and collected all the gold and jewels and brocades in trunks. Then, hiring donkey and camel drivers, she had them deliver the trunks to her house in the village. She became a rich young woman and could now marry any man she wanted, or not marry at all, if she so desired.

Folktale from Punjab

◆

103

MAY YOUR HEAD SPLIT INTO SEVEN PIECES!

On a mission to conquer the realm of the gods, Ravana camped for a night in Mount Kailash. It was a beautiful night: in the moonlight, the tops of kadama and vakul trees shone like emeralds, and lotus ponds turned silver. Kinnara birds, returning to their nests, sang sweetly, and gentle breezes, wafting through blossomed branches, spread perfume in the air. Lying in the midst of such a sensual environment, the powerful king of Lanka felt a strange pull at his heart, as though of longing, and his virile body burgeoned with acute desire.

Just then, Rambha, the most beautiful of the apsaras, strolled by. Her body was perfumed with sandalwood, and her curly black hair was woven with fragrant flowers. Around her hips she wore a gold girdle, which sat on her sky-blue sari, like a golden disc circling the sky.

'Where are you going, O lady of the lovely limbs?' Ravana said in a deep voice, and springing to his feet, grabbed her hand. 'For whom have you adorned yourself?'

Rambha pulled her hand out of his and stepped away. 'Let me go,' she cried, trying to skirt around him, but Ravana blocked her way. 'Who is the lucky male who will have the pleasure of sipping the nectar of your lips and riding your glorious thighs circled in gold?' he insinuated. 'Is it Indra, Vishnu, or perhaps the Ashwin twins? Why don't you stay with me for a while? Lie here on this fragrant mountain under the silver moon. I am Ravana, king of the worlds, but I stand before you, your humble servant. Let me serve your beauty.'

'I beg you not to speak to me like that. You are my father-in-law.'

Ravana laughed. 'You can't evade me with false words. How can I be your father-in-law? None of my sons are married to you.'

'I'm married to Nalakubera, who is your brother Kubera's son. Just as Kubera is my father-in-law, so are you. I'm going to meet my husband and I've dressed for him. He's waiting for me. Let me go, please.'

But Ravana planted himself more firmly in her path. 'The word "daughter-in-law" applies to women who have only one husband,' he mocked. 'Apsaras have no husband. They pleasure whomever they desire and whoever deserves their desire. I desire you and I deserve you. Be mine tonight, O beautiful lady of sweet lips.' And saying this, he embraced Rambha. 'No,' she screamed, trying to beat him off, but the strength of his arms made her efforts futile She could do nothing as he threw her down on the ground and stripped off her sari.

When his desire was sated, Ravana sauntered off into the trees, without a second look at the apsara, uncaring now about the beauty of the moon and the mountain. Rambha scrambled off the rock, and, trembling like a leaf in a storm, wrapped herself in the discarded sari. Then she staggered to where her husband, Nalakubera, was waiting. When he saw her—her face stricken with pain, her jewellery askew, her hair tangled, the blossoms in it, hanging limply, he knew something terrible had occurred. 'What happened?' he asked urgently, gathering her in his arms.

Tears of injury and insult pouring down her cheeks, Rambha told Nalakubera what Ravana had done. 'I begged him. I told him, "No",' she said brokenly. 'I even told him I was like his daughter-in-law. But he didn't stop.'

Nalakubera's nostril flared in rage. Taking water in his left hand, he pronounced: 'O blessed lady, since Ravana violated you and forced himself upon you against your will, I curse him that he shall never again be able to have sexual intercourse with any other woman against her will. I curse him that if he even approaches a woman against her will, at that very moment, his head will split into seven pieces.'[42]

Myth from the Ramayana

◆

104

DURGA: THE SUM OF ALL GODS

Mahisasura was a mighty buffalo asura. He was the nemesis that his grandmother, Diti, had invoked to avenge the massacre of her daitya sons by the devas. Ravaged at the loss of all her sons, Diti, resorting to her primeval roots, had told her daughter to evoke the powerful buffalo spirit of the land and birth a formidable buffalo son who would overpower the enemy devas. So, Diti's daughter had taken the form of a she-buffalo and performed severe tapasya to compel Brahma to grant her a son; in consequence, Brahma had bid the asura Rambha of great ascetic power to become an ox and mate with Diti's daughter. The son that was born from that union was the mighty buffalo, Mahisa.[43]

Being an asura, he became the leader of the asuras and challenged the devas, and then routed them so thoroughly in battle that they couldn't muster a counter-attack. Then he ransacked the heavens and, usurping Indra's domain, began terrorizing all the heaven-dwellers. In desperation, the gods went to Vishnu and Shiva for help.

'He has subjugated Indra, Surya, Yama, Agni, Chandra and Varuna,' they cried. 'He has thrown all the gods out of heaven and now they wander on earth like mortals. He's so powerful that even our combined forces could not defeat him. You have to help. Think of some way to bring about Mahisa's death, or we'll be annihilated.'

Hearing about Mahisasura's fighting prowess, Vishnu and Shiva realized that because he was invoked from the womb of the primordial mother, their individual male strength would not suffice, they would have to create a force that equalled the energy of the feminine. Evoking fury within themselves, they focused it between their brows, which is the inward third eye, and from the intense frown that settled there, they each emitted energy. Then from the bodies of the other gods more energy emerged. All this energy combined, creating a mass, like a burning mountain reaching the sky. From this mass, a feminine form took shape.

Her face was formed from Shiva's vitality; Yama's potency created her hair; Vishnu's force gave her arms. From the Moon her breasts were shaped; from Indra, she received her waist, from Varuna, her legs and thighs, and the light of Bhudeva made her loins. Her feet came into form through the energy of Brahma, her teeth were created by the brightness of Prajapati, and her eyebrows were shaped by the twilights of Sandhya. Her toes were formed by the rays of the sun, her fingers by the Vasus, her nose by Kubera, her ears by Vayu, and her three eyes by the energy of Agni.

She was the Great Goddess, and, looking at her, the gods felt triumphant. Now they equipped her with weapons. From his trident, Shiva gave her a trident, Vishnu drew a discus from his own and handed it to her. Varuna placed a conch in her hand, and Agni a spear. Marut provided her with a bow and a quiver full of arrows. Indra drew Vajra from his thunderbolt for her and also gave her a bell from his elephant Airavata. Yama equipped her with a rod from Fate and Varuna gave her his noose. Prajapati made her a necklace of beads as white as milk and also earrings, finger rings and bracelets, and Brahma handed her an earthen pot. Kala gave her a transparent sword, Sesha fashioned her a necklace of serpents, and Himavata provided her the lion for her ride.

The Goddess became the warrior supreme. When she pulled the string of her bow, the twang echoed in the three worlds. When she shouted, the whole firmament reverberated with the sound: the worlds shook, the seas trembled, and the mountains quaked. When Mahisasura heard these sounds, he wondered who this was—with power so immense that the universe shuddered. Then he gathered his asura forces and tens of thousands of horses and chariots and soldiers, and they all rushed towards the Goddess, with Chikasura, Mahisasura's general, at their head. Then the gods, too, brought their troops—hundreds and thousands of them—and the two armies clashed in a war, the likes of which the cosmos had never before witnessed.

The Goddess was unassailable. Whatever weapons the asuras hurled, she cut, cleaved, and smashed them. She bound thousands of asuras in her noose and chopped off the heads of thousands more. Mighty asuras, the leaders of mighty troops, were all struck down by her, as she, her face serene, moved through the enemy troops like a whirlwind of weapons. All the while her lion, his mane ruffled in wrath, emitted his own loud roars. The Goddess routed the asura armies in no time at all, and the battlefield of earth became a river of blood, strewn with limbs and heads of both asuras and animals. 'Victory to the Goddess,' the gods shouted.

As the Goddess was destroying his troops, Mahisa himself was in the thick of battle, shattering bows with his snout, crushing heads under his massive hooves, slashing throats with his tail, ripping limbs with his horns and jaws. Then he turned to attack the lion on which the Goddess was riding. When the lion roared, the buffalo struck his hooves on the earth, causing mountains to tremble and seas to overflow their shores.

Seeing her lion under attack, the Goddess threw her noose around Mahisa's neck and bound him. His buffalo body trapped, Mahisa abandoned that body and took the form of a lion to match the Goddess's mount, and when she cut off his lion's head, he appeared before her in the form of a man wielding a sword. When the Goddess struck down the man and destroyed his sword, he immediately became an elephant and grabbed the Goddess's lion with his powerful trunk, but the Goddess cut off the trunk, as well.

Laughing wildly, the Goddess guzzled wine and, smacking her lips, challenged Mahisa once more. The asura, taking his buffalo shape again, began to hurl mountain missiles at her, but she shattered each one with her arrows and mocked him. Then she flew up, and planting a foot on his throat, pierced it with a spear. The blow of her foot and the thrust of the spear was so great that the body of the asura was pushed halfway out of his own mouth, but he battled on, until the Goddess cut off his primordial head with her mighty sword.

When Mahisasura died, the gods and all the inhabitants of the three worlds rejoiced. They praised the Goddess and called her Durga, because she was invincible.

Myth from the Puranas

105

KRISHNA'S SECRET[*]

Once Arjuna asked Krishna to tell him about his divine Rasa Leela. 'What is this place of eternal happiness and love? And what is the nature of your divine sport? Please tell me its secret.'

'This sport cannot be perceived by anyone—not even Brahma, and I don't reveal its secrets, even to those who are very dear to me.' Krishna replied. 'Dear one, don't ask me about it.'

Arjuna fell at Krishna's feet in anguish. 'Please Lord, tell me. I long to know.'

Krishna affectionately raised Arjuna by the shoulders. 'Go then to the goddess Tripurasundari, in whom everything merges. She is the only one who can grant you divine sight.'

When Arjuna worshipped the goddess, she bestowed upon him a vision of Vrindavan where Krishna is constantly engaged in Rasa Leela with the gopis. The sight of the divine dance of love was so overwhelming that Arjuna was rendered unconscious. When he regained his senses, the goddess took him to a lake in the east that was in the midst of a flower garden, where Krishna celebrated the spring festival in honour of Kamadeva. The lake itself was in the shape of a thousand-petalled lotus with a bud in the centre. It was fed by four waterfalls and four streams; the southern stream was of honey and liquor distilled from the madhuka tree. The water of the lake was speckled with pollen from white, red, and blue lotuses and also lotuses that bloomed at night. It rippled with gentle breezes, and its waves caressed the wings of swans, as they swam across.

As soon as Arjuna plunged into this lake, the goddess vanished, and from the lake emerged a smiling young maiden. This was Arjuna himself—transformed. Gone were his rock-hard muscles, bowstring-

---

* N. A. Deshpande (trans.), *The Padma Purana, Ancient Indian Tradition and Mythology Series*, vols. 39–48, New Delhi: Motilal Banarsidass Publishers, 1988–1992, Adapted.

calloused hands, and high-cheek-boned warrior's face. This maiden had a slim and fair body, like rays of pure gold. Her face shone like the autumn moon and her hair was glossy, dark and curly, with jewels woven into it. Her eyebrows resembled Kama's bow, and her eyes were the colour of rain clouds. Jewelled earrings brushed against her soft, round cheeks and ornaments sparkled around her neck and wrists, from which her delicate hands sprouted like lotuses. There was a golden girdle around her hips and golden anklets at her feet. So caught up was Arjuna in this splendid illusion created by the goddess that seeing himself in this form of Arjuni, he forgot his earlier form.

Stepping out of the lake, Arjuni stood bewildered, not knowing what to do. Then she heard a grave voice from heaven: 'O beautiful lady. Go down this easterly path and you will achieve your desire.' As she walked along that path, the tinkling of girdle and anklet bells reached her ears, and she saw a bevy of beautiful young women, shining with ornaments, laughing and engaging in amorous play, coming towards her. Seeing them, Arjuni stood shyly with her head bowed, etching mindless patterns in the ground with a big toe.

'Who are you?' one of the women, whose name was Priyamuda, asked.

'I don't know,' Arjuni replied. 'I don't how I got here or who brought me here. Perhaps it was the goddess. Who are you?'

'We are the beloved of Krishna,' Priyamuda said. 'We are the self-delighted gopis with whom the lover of gopis, the Moon of Vrindavan, sports.' Then Priyamuda introduced Arjuni to all the other maidens, and, together, they brought her to another lake in the east, where they anointed her with flowers and fragrance and taught her a special hymn honouring the goddess Radhika. Arjuni then joined the gopis in worshipping the goddess, whose body is like heated gold, whose face is like a full autumn moon, and who illuminates all three worlds with her lustre.

'What my friends have told you is true,' Radhika said to Arjuni. 'Come with me and I'll help fulfil the desire in your heart.'

Arjuni's body began to tremble in anticipation and her eyes filled with tears. She was so overcome, she could hardly stand. Then one of the other gopis, Priyamvada, took her hand and brought her to Radhika, who taught her how to draw a magical eight-petalled yellow lotus made of saffron and sandal, and how to offer worship to Krishna so that he would grace it.

Pleased with her devotions, Krishna said to Radhika, 'Bring her here quickly.' And Sharada, another gopi, brought Arjuni to the Playful One. Suddenly finding herself standing before him, who was her heart's desire, Arjuni could not bear it and collapsed on the ground like melted gold. Slowly, her heart fluttering and her body perspiring, she raised herself and looked around. Under a desire-yielding tree was a golden temple with a golden throne. On either side of it were two treasures of Kubera—Sankha and Padma. In the four directions were desire-yielding cows, and around the temple was the full bloom of Nandan garden, fragrant with sandalwood and honey. Bees were humming and sounds of cuckoos, pigeons, sarikas and parrots were everywhere. Peacocks, intoxicated with the season, danced in this environment that was slightly shadowed, as though smeared with collyrium, like a maiden's eye.

Slowly, Arjuni dared to look at Krishna himself. He was shining like the petals of a blue lotus. His curly hair was glossy, dark, and fragrant. A peacock feather adorned his head, his cheeks were lustrous, and his nose was like the sesame flower. His lips were the red of bimba fruits, and his gentle smile, a sharp arrow in the heart. Around his neck was a garland of wild flowers, and his chest displayed the Kaustubha gem and the mark of Srivatsa. His waist was slim and his navel deep, and his hips were covered with pitamber, which also partly covered his front. Every part of his body exuded the arrogance of kama, as he reclined on the throne, tired from dancing and sporting.

As Arjuni watched, Radhika offered him a betel leaf, and he accepted it and Arjuni felt her own heart overwhelmed with ardour. Seeing her in that state, Krishna, who knows everything, seized her hand and took her to the solitude of the forest of passion and revelry.

Afterwards, supporting her with his arm around her shoulders, Krishna brought her to Sharada. 'Bathe this beautiful lady in the western lake,' he instructed.

As soon as Arjuni stepped into the lake, he became Arjuna again, and found himself back in Vaikuntha, where he and Krishna had been talking. But now his heart ached and his mind was dejected. Knowing his state, Krishna touched him with a magical hand, and Arjuna finally came back into his own nature again.

'O Dhananjaya,' Krishna said to him. 'You are very dear to me, and there is none equal to you. No one in the three worlds knows my secret except you. Know that you will curse me if you reveal it to anyone.'

Myth from the Puranas

◆

106

ILA'S DOUBLE LIFE

Ila, the king of Bahlika,[44] was famous for his valour and for his love of hunting. One spring season, he went to the vast forest on the mountain with his attendants and killed hundreds and thousands of animals, all in one expedition, but his desire for the hunt did not abate. As he pressed deeper and deeper into the forest, he found himself at the spot where Shiva was sporting with Parvati. To please his consort, Shiva had assumed the form of a woman; therefore, everything in that forest had become female; so much so that even the trees that had masculine names had become feminine. So, when King Ila arrived there, he discovered that he had become a woman, as had every member of his entourage.

Mortified, he approached the great god and implored him to show mercy.

'Aside from manhood, ask for anything, and I'll grant it,' Shiva told him.

But gaining his masculine form back was the only thing the king wanted. So he turned to Parvati and begged her for a boon.

'The giver of one half of the boons is Shiva; I am the giver of the other half. Since he has made you woman, I can only turn one half of you male. Will you accept that?'

Ila thought for a moment and then asked the goddess: 'Is it possible that instead of a half male and half female form, I alternate between male and female from one month to the next. This way, for one month I'll be a woman and the next I'll be a man?'

'Granted,' Parvati said. 'The month that you are female, you'll not remember your manhood at all, and becoming a man, you'll have no memory of being a woman.'

And so, the year round, Ila alternated between being a handsome man and a beautiful woman.

In the first month as a lovely woman, Ila wandered the forest with her attendants, who had also become women. One day, coming upon a still lake, she sat down by the water and began splashing in it, washing her limbs with abandon, not realizing that inside the lake was Budha, Lord Soma's son, deep in meditation. When the waters were agitated, Budha opened his eyes and saw the most alluring woman that he had ever seen, and immediately fell in love with her. And when Ila left the waterside, Budha emerged and followed her into the forest. Along the way, he asked one of her attendants about her—who she was and whether she had a husband or a lover.

'She's single and roams the forest at will,' the woman told him.

Relieved to know that Ila was unattached, Budha used his ascetic powers to learn more about her, and when he discovered her secret, he was even more intrigued. Hoping to press his suit, he went to the attendants and told them, 'I'm Budha, son of Soma, and I intend to make Ila mine. If, through my ascetic powers, I can find you all a home at the foot of this mountain and also husbands, will you then leave her side?' They all agreed, and so Budha turned them into Kimpurushis, who found Kimpurusha[45] husbands and went to live at the foot of that secluded mountain. Then Budha approached Ila, and, professing his love for her, asked her to marry him. She accepted, and they lived together in that mountain forest for an entire spring.

One morning Ila woke up and found himself in a strange bed. No one was around, but when he went outside, he saw a man sitting beside a lake, worshipping the sun. 'Sorry for disturbing you,' he called, 'but could you tell me if you've seen my attendants. I came to this forest on a hunt with a whole army of men, and now they all seem to have disappeared. And also, I just woke up in a strange bed. Do you, by any chance, know what has happened?'

'Your attendants were all killed in a hailstorm,' Budha replied, concluding his rituals. 'And to get away from the hail and thunder, you took shelter in the hermitage and fell asleep.'

Ila was grieved by the tragic news about his attendants. 'How can I return to my kingdom now? All my men are gone,' he said despondently. 'I'll send a message to my son, Sasabindu, and tell him to rule in my absence. But where will I go?'

'Don't worry, brave one,' Budha said. 'You can certainly stay in my hermitage.'

So, for the next month, Ila stayed with Budha, and the two became close friends. Then, when a month passed, Budha once again welcomed his wife.

In this way, alternating between friendship and a spousal relationship, Ila spent eight months with Budha. Then in the ninth month, when Ila became a woman again, she gave birth to a son, Pururavas.

Budha was happy to have a son, but he was sad for his friend and wife, who was living a split life without even knowing it. He wished Ila to live fulsomely, and with this objective in mind, he gathered the best of Brahmins and asked them to help him perform the Ashvamedha yajna to propitiate Lord Shiva. At the conclusion of the yajna when Shiva manifested himself, Budha requested the god to liberate Ila from a dual life and restore him to full manhood. Shiva granted this, and Ila returned to Bahlika, where he lived out the rest of his life as its king.

Myth from the Ramayana

◆

107

THE LANGUAGE WE SPEAK WHEN WE SLEEP

Once upon a time a reputed scholar from Kashi visited Raja Krishnadeva's court in Vijayanagar. He claimed that he knew all the languages that were spoken in India and could converse in them more fluently than the native speakers. Krishnadeva had many brilliant scholars in his court from different parts of the country. One by one, they all spoke with the scholar and came away applauding his skill. Then the savant laid down a challenge: 'Maharaj, can any of your able scholars guess what is my mother tongue?'

Krishnadeva looked expectantly at his men of letters, but they all shook their head, shamefaced. Finally, Krishnadeva turned to Tenali Raman, who was his Vikatkavi and one of his Ashtadiggajas—his humorist among the cadre of eight court poets.

'I would like to give you my answer tomorrow morning, Maharaj,' Tenali replied and left the court to do some planning. He instructed the king's servants to feed the scholar a big meal that evening and also to give him a very comfortable bed. 'But make sure that you put him in the warmest room of the palace,' he told the servant. 'And keep one window in that room unlocked.'

That evening, the Kashi scholar ate more than he usually did, because the food was especially delicious, and he lay down on a bed that was the most comfortable he had ever slept in. But the room was so hot that he had to remove his shirt before he could fall asleep. Tenali was watching him from the window, and when he heard the man begin to snore in deep sleep, he climbed into the room. Then, tiptoeing to the bed, he poked the man gently in the belly with the end of a stick he had brought with him.

'What is it?' the scholar mumbled in Telugu, and then he turned on his side and began snoring again

The following morning, after everyone had assembled in the court and the esteemed scholar had been given a seat of honour, Tenali bowed to Krishnadeva and declared, 'I am ready to answer the question of the able pundit from Kashi.'

The scholar smiled with an air of superiority. 'I would like to hear the answer,' he said. 'Tell me, what is my mother tongue?'

'Telugu!' Tenali announced.

The man was flabbergasted. 'How did you find out my secret?' he asked Tenali.

'A person may be fluent in many languages, and he may keep his mother tongue a secret, but the language he speaks in his sleep is the language he has subconsciously learned from his mother at birth. I heard you speak Telugu in your sleep.'

Everyone applauded Tenali, including the humbled scholar.

Tenali Raman folktale

◆

108

THE DIAMOND PARROT AND THE GOLDEN-HAIRED RANI

There was a king who had seven sons. He arranged marriages for all his sons, and all the brides were beautiful, but the youngest was the loveliest of them all. She had hair of gold. One day she was sitting at the window, drying her hair, when a jogi passed by and saw her. He then went to the palace gates and began begging for alms. The king sent a servant with some coins, but the jogi refused to take the offering from the servant. 'Tell the king to send all who are in the king's household, and I'll select the one from whom I will accept alms.'

'Turn him out!' the king shouted angrily. 'Who does he think he is?'

When the servant tried to push the jogi away, he sent another message for the king: 'I'm a very powerful jogi. If you refuse me, I'll make terrible things happen to your family.'

Hearing the message, the king thought it prudent not to take any chances. And so he sent each of his seven sons to the jogi, one after the other, and then their wives—everyone, except his youngest daughter-in-law. The jogi refused to accept alms from any of them and asked, 'Where's the rani with the hair of gold? She's the only one from whom I will accept alms.'

The youngest queen never appeared before anyone, because it was feared that her rare beauty made her susceptible to the evil eye, so the king refused to send her, but the jogi would not budge. Then it was decided that the golden-haired queen would give the jogi alms, but a sheet would be erected between her and the jogi, so that he could not look upon her directly. However, when the jogi rejected this proposition as well, the royal family gave up and the youngest rani finally appeared before the jogi.

The moment the jogi saw the golden-haired queen, he uttered a mantra, which turned her into a bitch, and she ran to the jogi, wagging her tail. The king had her caught with a golden chain but the jogi turned her into a mare, and the chain broke. Then the jogi got on the mare's back and rode away. He brought her to his house, where he turned her back into the beautiful golden-haired woman again. He lived in a land where he had killed everyone with his mantras, except for a Brahmin and an old woman, who were as skilled in the black arts as the jogi, and had been able to counter his mantras. The old woman lived in the jogi's house, and the Brahmin lived not far away. The jogi went to the Brahmin's house every day to play cards; he loved to gamble.

After the jogi brought the golden-haired rani home, he still visited his Brahmin friend daily, but before he went, he cut off the queen's head and hung it from the ceiling with a rope and put her body to sleep on a couch. When he returned, he waved a magic stick which put her back together, and she came back to life.

The golden-haired rani's family was heartsick at her abduction, but they were determined to find her and bring her home. With great difficulty, they learned where the jogi lived, and the brothers set off to rescue her. When they arrived at the jogi's house, he wasn't at home, but the old woman was there. She heard their story and was very sympathetic, and when they begged her to take them to the queen, she advised them, 'It's the jogi's dinner hour. Wait till he leaves the house again, and I'll see what I can do.' Then she turned the brothers into flies and hid them in the house.

When the jogi returned, he sniffed the air. 'I smell man,' he said. 'I smell man.'

'What a fool you are,' the old woman told him. 'There's not even a shadow of man here.'

The jogi looked in every nook and corner of the house and, satisfied that there was no one, he sat down to eat his dinner. After he left for the Brahmin's house, the old woman hurriedly turned the flies into men again. Then she took the magic stick and, calling down the rani's head, joined it to the body. When the rani came alive, the seven brothers quickly put her in a carriage and rode off, but the jogi saw them. 'Quickly,' he said to the Brahmin, 'Give me a mustard seed.' And with that he blew such a spell on the brothers that they turned the carriage around and rode back to the jogi's house. The jogi then killed all the brothers and gave the rani a sound beating.

One of the brother's wives was pregnant at this time, and a few months after the jogi killed her husband, she gave birth to a son. When the boy was about twelve, he grew curious about his family and asked his mother what had happened to his father and uncles. She told him how the jogi had taken the golden-haired rani and how his father and uncles had gone to search for her and never returned. Listening to the tale, the boy resolved to rescue his family from the clutches of the jogi. Everyone—his mother, his aunts, his friends—tried to dissuade him, but his mind was made up. Thereafter, making many enquiries, he found his way to the jogi's house, where he was met by the old woman.

'What do you want, young man?' she asked.

'My father, my uncles and my aunt are all here, and I've come to take them home.'

'Your father and uncles are all dead, but your aunt is alive. Come. I'll show you.' She took the young prince and showed him the rani's golden-haired head hanging from the ceiling and her headless body lying on a couch. She also gave him the magic stick and showed him how to put the rani back together. When the prince brought his aunt to life, she asked him who he was.

'I'm your nephew and I've come to take you home.'

The rani burst into tears and hugged her nephew. 'You're a brave boy. But this is not possible. He'll kill you, too. Go home, dear nephew. No one can save me. Don't put your life in danger.'

'But I must save you. I have vowed that I will. I just need your help. I have a feeling that the jogi, being such a powerful man, doesn't keep his life in his body. I'm certain that he keeps it secure somewhere very secret. Try to find out from him where he keeps his life.'

'I'll try,' the rani said, feeling hope rise in her heart after many years. All afternoon, aunt and nephew talked, and when it was time for the jogi's return, the young prince cut off his aunt's head again, hung it from the ceiling, and placed her body on the couch. Then he hid himself.

That evening, the rani treated the jogi very affectionately. When they were sitting together, she poured him some wine and asked him playfully where he kept his life.

'Fire,' the jogi, said with a smile.

'Really,' she said, pouring more wine in his cup. 'How is it possible? How does it not burn?'

The jogi laughed. 'It's not really in the fire,' he said. 'It's actually in the body of diamond parrot.'

'I love diamonds. Can I see it?'

'No one can see it. It's hidden far, far away—in a secret place.'

'Tell me,' the queen asked, placing a flirtatious finger on his heart and filling his cup again. 'I won't tell anyone. It'll be our secret.'

'Beyond the seven seas is a forest protected by a fierce tiger and a tigress and watched by nine hundred witches. In the middle of this forest is a sandalwood tree, and hanging from its branches is a golden cage. In that cage lives the diamond parrot that has my life.'

Learning the jogi's secret, the young prince set off on this arduous journey the very next day. With great difficulty, he crossed the seven seas and found the forest. As he was about it enter it, the tiger rushed at him, but the boy called out to him. 'Salaam, Mamu. How are you this fine morning?' The tiger stopped in his tracks and, wondering which of his sisters was the mother of this boy, let him go. Then the boy encountered the tigress, and she too began to pounce on him, but he said, 'Salaam, Mami. I've come a long way to see your forest. Won't you show me around?' The tigress, too, started wondering how she could be related to this young man. She walked with him through the trees up to the boundary from where the witches watched the forest. 'Take care, Nephew,' she said. 'It was good to meet you.' As soon as the boy entered the inner sanctum of trees that the witches watched, they crowded around him, looking at him with hungry, mean eyes. 'Today we'll eat human flesh,' they said, smacking their lips.

'Oh, so you are all my Khalas that I have heard about,' the boy said. 'Seeing you gathered here to welcome me, I can honestly say that you are even more caring than I've heard.'

'This is our nephew,' the witches all said and stepped away from him.

'The jogi has sent me to get his golden cage,' he told them. 'Can you please show me where the sandalwood tree is?' The witches had no reason to doubt that the boy had been sent by the jogi, otherwise how would he know about the golden cage and the sandalwood tree, so they took him to the tree and pointed to the cage hanging from the branches. Sitting on a golden perch in the cage was a parrot whose whole body was made of diamonds that shone and twinkled like a hundred points of starry light. The young man quickly took the cage down and, walking out of the forest, made his way back across the seven seas. When the young man arrived at the jogi's house, he began to call out loudly, 'Parrot for sale! Parrot for sale!' The jogi came out to look and blanched to see a young man holding the golden cage with the diamond parrot that held his life. He rushed towards the boy to seize the cage, but the young prince quickly took out the parrot and twisted one of its legs till it broke. At the same time, the jogi's leg snapped in mid-stride. He screamed in pain and fell down. But he immediately got up and reached for the boy, hopping on one foot. The boy then broke the parrot's other leg, and, instantly, the jogi's other leg also broke, and he came crashing to the ground. Screaming and wailing, he now began to implore the boy to return the parrot to him.

'First bring my uncles and father back to life,' the boy called.

The jogi uttered a mantra, and suddenly, the boy's father and uncles were standing outside the jogi's hut.

'Now bring back to life all the people that you have killed in this land,' the young prince ordered. And soon, the town began teeming with people going about their daily lives, as though the twelve years that they had been dead had not even occurred.

'There. I've done it. Return my parrot now,' the legless jogi shouted at the boy.

'Not so fast,' the boy called back. 'My aunt is still under your control. Give her back.'

In response, the jogi raised his arm to throw a magic spell, but the boy saw his intention. He grabbed one of parrot's wings and tore it off, and the arm that the jogi had raised fell to the ground, severed from his body.

'I'll tear this off too,' the boy threatened, pulling on the other wing. 'if you don't restore my aunt.' The jogi gnashed his teeth and uttered a mantra and the boy's golden-haired aunt came out of the house. Seeing her husband and brothers-in-law, she rushed to them in joy.

'Please,' the jogi implored the boy. 'Give me back my parrot now.' But the young prince tore off the bird's second wing anyway, and then he crushed the diamond parrot to death. As its last breath left its body, so did the jogi's, and he and his magic were no more.

Folktale from North India

◆

109

WHY THE FISH LAUGHED

There was a city called Ujjaini whose king was Vikramaditya. One day, dining with his favourite queen, Vikramaditya offered her some roasted fish. She looked at the platter full of fish and said, 'I can't bear to look at these men, much less touch them.' At these words of the queen, the fish in the platter burst into laughter so loud that it was heard by all the people in the town. The king was perplexed. He asked his astrologers, who were acquainted with the language of the birds and the fish, what the fish meant by their laughter. None of them had an answer, so he sent for his chief priest, who was head of the Brahmins, and warned him, 'If you don't tell me why those fish laughed at what the queen said, I'll banish you and all the Brahmins.'

The priest requested a few days grace and went home. He was quite distraught, because he was certain that he and his team of Brahmins would not be able to figure out why the fish had laughed. His daughter noticed his visible distress and enquired what was worrying him. 'You're a man of wisdom,' she said. 'It doesn't behoove you to lose your equanimity.'

'Of course I'm upset,' he replied and told his daughter the situation. 'I've served the king faithfully for years, and now, for a small matter, he has threatened me. It's true what they say, 'Put not your trust in rivers, or savage beasts, or horned cattle, or women, or kings; they'll turn on you."

'What you say is true, Father,' she said. 'But as you very well know, men of wisdom need kings and other powerful men to survive, or even their wisdom is of no use. As they say, the sandal grove can only flourish on Mount Malaya. Besides, you're the king's chief minister and it's your duty to serve him in every capacity, and if he needs you to answer a riddle, then we must find the answer. But don't worry. I'll help you in investigating what the fish meant by their laughter.'

The minister felt comforted and told Vikramaditya that his daughter would find the answer.

'Splendid,' said the king. 'Bring your daughter to me. Let me pose the question to her directly.'

The following morning, the daughter presented herself in court, and when Vikramaditya asked her why the fish had laughed, she replied with a question of her own: 'Can you tell me what kind of a laughter it was that you heard from the fish?'

'It was loud. That's all I can say.'

'Then can you tell me what this verse means?

The fish! The fish! They lay upon the dish.

And they laughed when the queen called them men!'

But neither the king nor his wise men had the slightest idea what the verse meant, so the minister's clever daughter went away, telling the king that he should call her when he had the answer. Vikramaditya spent a sleepless night puzzling over the meaning of the verse and, in the morning, sent for the girl again. 'I have no idea what the verse meant. Can you tell me?'

'Maharaj, if I tell you, you may regret it.'

'What do you mean?'

The girl told him a story:

There was a town called Jayanti, and a merchant, whose name was Sumati, lived in it with his wife, Padmini. Unfortunately, he lost all his money and couldn't care for his family; consequently his family would have nothing more to do with him. So this merchant started gathering straw and wood to take into the market to sell. One day he couldn't find either, but he came across a statue of Ganesha made of wood. He said to himself, 'This will suit my purpose very well,' and began to break the statue to sell its wood. But then Ganesha came to him and said, 'If you spare my statue, I'll give you five rotis made of sugar and butter every day and you can feed your family. Come here and collect them; only, you mustn't tell anyone how you come by them. If you let the secret out, the deal is off.'

The merchant gladly consented, and Ganesha began giving him the five rotis every day, which he took home and gave to his wife. Padmini fed her family with a portion of them, and gave what was left over to a friend. But then, one day, this friend asked her from where she got such delicious rotis. Padmini couldn't answer that question, and the friend said to her, 'If you don't tell me, then we can't be friends anymore, because friendship is all about sharing secrets.'

Padmini didn't want to lose her friend, so she gave her the only explanation she could: 'My husband gets them, but he won't tell me from where. He says it's a secret.'

'Then all I have to say is that you make very bad use of your youth and beauty,' said the friend.

That evening Padmini asked her husband again, 'Where do these rotis come from?'

'Destiny's favour,' he replied. 'Once upon a time there was a serpent, who was so starved, that he lay with its jaws open under a wooden shed. A mouse, who was making a hole for itself, fell into the jaws of the serpent. So, you see. It's all destiny's favour.'

Thinking about what her friend had said about putting her

beauty and youth to good use, Padmini pouted prettily at her husband. 'I won't eat till you tell me,' she said.

'Don't say that, dearest,' Sumati appealed. 'If I tell you what you want to know, disaster will follow, and you'll be sorry.'

'I don't care.' Padmini pouted some more.

They say when a man's ruin is near, he loses his senses. Sumati, whose name means using good sense, lost his sense on seeing his wife's pretty pout, and told her the secret of the rotis. Padmini went and told this secret to her friend, and the very following day, the friend sent her own husband to the spot where Ganesha appeared, and the god bestowed the rotis on him. A little later, when Sumati arrived at the spot for his daily reward, Ganesha told him that the deal had been broken and now someone else would receive the rotis. Padmini and Sumati were left empty-handed, regretful—Sumati for divulging the secret and Padmini for forcing him to do so.

'So, you see, Maharaj,' the girl concluded. 'In the same way, you should not ask me to explain the meaning of the verse, because you may regret your knowledge. You should figure it out without my help.' And with this, she got up and went home.

That night, too, the king lay awake, trying to figure out the meaning of the verse, and in the morning he called the Brahmin's daughter again. 'No more delays,' he implored. 'I beg you, for God's sake. Tell me the meaning of the verse.'

'You must not importune the gods with entreaties, or repentance will follow, as was the case with the Brahmin, who fell in love with Sthagika.' And she told him another story:

There was a town somewhere or the other, whose king was Virabhya, and in it lived a Brahmin called Keshava. One day a thought occurred to Keshava: why should I not increase the wealth my father has left me; it is wealth from one's own skills that brings a man glory. So he left home with the objective of seeking his fortune. Passing through several towns and pilgrimage sites, he, at last, reached a faraway place where he saw an ascetic sitting cross-legged in meditation. When Keshava came up to him and bowed in obeisance, the ascetic opened his eyes and asked him: 'Who, in the world, deserves favour and protection? Who deserves charity?'

'I do,' Keshava replied. 'I seek wealth in any way possible—even through charity.'

'But you're a Brahmin; you shouldn't be begging. It doesn't behoove you,' the ascetic admonished Keshava. 'Even if a Brahmin falls on hard times, he remains a Brahmin. The sandal tree may be broken into a thousand pieces, but it still keeps its fragrance.' The ascetic then gave Keshava a magic cloak and said, 'Whenever you shake this, five hundred gold pieces will fall from it—but you mustn't give it to anyone else, or tell anyone where the money comes from.'

Thanking the ascetic, Keshava departed with his magical cloak. The next morning he shook the cloak and immediately owned five hundred gold pieces. Then he continued on his journey till he reached a town called Ratuvati. Here he met a young lady called Sthagika and fell violently in love with her. To express his love, he would shower her with gold coins every day, and soon the young lady grew curious about his source of wealth. When she confided in her mother about this, the old woman advised her to insist upon an answer. 'Threaten him that if he doesn't tell you, you'll leave him,' she said. The next time Keshava came to see her, Sthagika told him exactly that, and Keshava, afraid of losing her, divulged the secret of the magic cloak. That night, while he slept, Sthagika stole the cloak and the following morning, her mother showed Keshava the door.'

'You see, Maharaj, we don't need to be very clever to deceive those who trust us. It also doesn't take very much courage to kill one who is asleep. What happened to Keshava may be your fate, too, if you persist in your curiosity.' With these words the minister's daughter got up and went home.

The king was still unable to fathom the meaning of the verse, and after suffering yet another miserable night, he sent for the girl again. When she arrived she said to him: 'Maharaj, be mindful of your subjects. If evil befalls you, it'll affect them. You should not invite evil like the merchant who lost his home and all that he had.'

'How was that?' asked the king, and the minister's daughter told him yet another tale:

There was a city called Tripura. A merchant lived in it, and he had a wife whose name was Subhag. She was frivolous and wayward. One day, wandering about town, Subhag came across a merchant who lived in the house of a yaksha. She promptly fell in love with him, and when he willingly responded to her advances, she decided to spend more time with him. Wondering how she could get away from her husband, she hit upon a plan. Calling her trusted maidservant, she told her, 'I'm going away for a bit. As soon as I'm gone, set the house on fire. My husband will be so occupied in putting out the fire that he'll not even know I'm gone, and before he realizes it, I'll be back.'

The maidservant did exactly as Subhag asked. Ironically, Subhag's husband had been suspicious of his wife and the merchant living in the yaksha's house, all along, and he had been keeping a watch, so when he saw his wife at the merchant's house, he stayed to see what she was up to. When he returned home, it was to a house that was already burnt down.

'So, you see, Maharaj, if you persist, you too could lose everything,' the girl said. 'Try to figure out the riddle yourself. But I promise that if you haven't figured it out by the morning, and you still want to know, I'll tell you.'

The next morning when the girl arrived, Vikramaditya still didn't know the answer, and he still wanted to know, so the minister's daughter told him: 'The chief among your soothsayers and wise men is one called Pushpakara. Tell me why is he called Pushpakara?'

'Because when he smiles it's as though a shower of blossoms falls from his face,' the king replied.

'Call him here,' the girl said.

When Pushpakara came, he neither laughed nor were there any blossoms falling from his face. In fact, everyone now called him 'the face of secrecy'. The girl asked Vikramaditya, 'Do you know the reason why Pushpakara doesn't laugh or smile anymore?'

'I haven't the least idea,' replied the king.

'Then you should make him tell you,' the girl said. 'You have asked me what the fish meant by laughing. Ask Pushpakara the same question. Perhaps he'll give you the answer and also the reason why he doesn't laugh himself.'

When Vikramaditya asked Pushpakara, he replied: 'Maharaj, family scandals should not be talked about. Loss of money, sorrow of mind, difficulties at home, fraud, contempt—these are things which no wise man ever publicizes. Still, you are my king and you have commanded me, so I'll tell you. I found out that my wife was having an affair with someone else—grief has killed my laughter.'

Then the king asked him if he knew about the fish and why they laughed. Pushpakara responded by requesting that the queen be summoned. When the queen arrived, Pushpakara struck her full in the face. The queen pretended to faint, and Pushpakara started laughing. Vikramaditya was furious. 'How dare you strike the queen, and what is there to laugh at? What do you mean by this?' he asked both Pushpakara and the Brahmin's daughter.

'Maharaj,' replied Pushpakara. 'Forgive me. But the queen did not faint the other night when she was struck by the young men in whose company she was. Now when I strike her, she faints, or pretends to faint.'

The king became even more infuriated and roared, 'How dare you make such allegations? How do you know this?'

'I saw it with my own eyes, and if Maharaj is not convinced, I'll prove it to you.' Then Pushpakara gave Vikramaditya information about the young men with whom the queen spent her nights.

The king made enquiries and discovered that Pushpakara was, indeed, telling the truth. 'Now do you understand why the minister's daughter would not tell you why the fish laughed?' Pushpakara asked the king.

The end of it was that Pushpakara and the Brahmin's daughter were sent home, while the queen and her lovers were sewn up in a sack and thrown into the river.

Folktale from Shukasaptati

◆

110

THE SHADOW SITA

When the time came for Rama to challenge Ravana, the king of Lanka, he didn't want Sita to be used as a bargaining chip. So Rama devised a secret plan. He shared this with Sita one day in Panchavati, when Lakshmana was out in the forest, gathering nuts and fruits.

'Listen, beloved,' Rama said. 'I'm about to live a very alluring part of the human life that you and I have taken, but it'll be painful for you, not to mention dangerous. That's why I want you to remove yourself from here and stay safely inside Agni, until I've completed this task.'

Sita then impressed the image of Rama's feet in her heart and entered fire, leaving her own image behind. This shadow image was the same as Sita in all aspects of appearance and disposition, and no one could discern that she wasn't the real Sita—not even Lakshmana or the gods and the sages.

In the meantime, Ravana enlisted the help of his shape-shifter uncle, Maricha, who became a golden deer and lured Rama and Lakshmana away from Sita so that he could abduct her. Little did Ravana know that the Sita he stole with such bravado and hid in his private garden, guarded by fierce rakshasis, was only the shadow of Sita.[*]

After Ravana was destroyed in battle, Rama sent a message to Sita, asking her to come to him. Elated at the prospect of seeing her husband again, Sita bathed, perfumed her body, and dressed in fine clothes and jewels. Then she sat in a palanquin covered in silks and was carried to where Rama was waiting. When the palanquin-bearers put her down, hundreds of curious monkeys, who had fought for her in Rama's army, and also rakshasis, who had cared for her in Ravana's Ashoka Vatika, all gathered around her, but Vibhishana, Ravana's brother, who had betrayed Ravana and joined Rama's camp, began to disperse them. He thought Sita may need to keep her modesty as she reunited with her husband. But Rama stopped him: 'A woman's veil is her character. No clothes, protective walls, or even royalty can be her shield. I don't object to Sita being brought out in public. Besides, these are my own people. Let Sita come to me on foot. Let these people see her.'

Everyone present—Sugriva, Hanuman, Lakshmana, Vibhishana— wondered at Rama's callous behaviour, but they kept their silence. Vibhishana went to fetch her from the palanquin, and she walked to Rama, shrinking within herself in her own modesty. But as soon as she saw her beloved husband, her shyness vanished and she smiled like the full moon in a cloudless sky. She walked eagerly towards him, expecting

---

[*]The motif of Shadow-Sita or Maya Sita appears in *Devi Bhagavata* (Skandha 9), *Tusidas's Ramayana* (Aranya Kanda) and *Adhyatma Ramayana*. This interpolation was to help maintain Sita's purity and also to absolve Rama from the adharma of condemning his wife.

him to welcome her with words of love.

But the words Rama spoke broke her heart: 'Winning you back after conquering the enemy in a field of battle, I have won back the dignity of Ayodhya. I have repaid the enemy for the insult that my manliness suffered. Now my manliness is vindicated. Today I have fulfilled my vow. I have redeemed my honour. I want you to know that I undertook this war not for you but for the sake of my own dignity and the dignity of the Ikshvaku clan and of the kingship of Ayodhya. Your standing here without modesty confirms my suspicion of your character. You are as distressing to me as light is to one whose eyes are sore. I will have nothing to do with you, daughter of Janaka. Go where you will. I give you leave. What man, who has any dignity, would take back a woman who has lived in another man's house. How can I take you back when Ravana must have held you in his arms, as he carried you off and looked at you with lust in his eyes?'

Shock gripped the audience. But Sita looked directly at Rama and straightened her spine. 'Lakshmana,' she called to her brother-in-law, who was standing there, bewildered. 'Prepare a pyre for me. I'll enter the fire and prove that I am pure.'

The rakshasis and monkeys began to wail, and Lakshmana silently appealed to his brother, but Rama commanded his brother: 'Do as Sita says. Prepare the fire.' With a heavy heart, Lakshmana began to build a pyre, which soon began to blaze.

Sita rejoiced to see the flames and felt no fear. Calling upon all the gods to bear witness to her purity and faithfulness, and praying to Agni to bear witness and to become as cooling as sandal-paste, she circumambulated the pyre and jumped into the flames.

Just then a miracle happened. From the midst of the flames Agni appeared in corporeal form, holding the real Sita by the hand. As he handed the real Sita to Rama, the shadow of Sita, as well as the stigma of public shame were consumed in the blaze.

Myth from the Shri Ramacharitmanasa

◆

111

SAY IT TO THE TREES

There was a handsome king who was quite vain about his looks. However, his subjects began to notice that the king always seemed to have his head covered under the crown. His attendants, too, noted that even when he wasn't wearing the crown, he wore a head covering that he pulled down to his ears. Also, servants entering his chamber now had to wait a few minutes outside the door before he gave them permission to enter.

The king had a secret that he hoped to keep concealed. But he needed a haircut. He had waited as long as he could, letting his hair grow, but when it got so long that it started to snag in the embroidery of his royal robe, he knew he could not wait any longer. Calling his barber into his private chamber, he told him to lock the door. Then, before the man could take out his scissors, he gave him a bag full of gold coins. 'This is for your silence,' he warned the barber. 'You must never reveal to anyone what you see here today. Is that understood?'

The barber heard the threat in the king's words and nodded fearfully, wondering what terrible things would be revealed to him. Then the king removed his head covering, and the barber's jaw dropped. On both sides of the king's head, extending from his ears, were erect and pointy donkey's ears. For long minutes, the barber couldn't say anything, then a laugh bubbled out of him, followed by a guffaw. He clamped a hand over his mouth in horror. 'Forgive me, Maharaj,' he said as soon as he was able to. 'But you have…you have…donkey's ears.'

'And this information will not leave this room. Right?' the king said, in a deceptively quiet tone.

'I swear,' the barber said, bowing low. 'I'll never tell a soul.'

The king nodded. 'Then get on with it,' he said. 'And mind the ears.'

Another bubble of laughter rose to the barber's throat, but he swallowed hard and contained it, and then readied his scissors.

After the barber was done cutting the king's hair, he quickly collected his paraphernalia and the bag of gold coins and rushed home, not stopping on the way even once, not even to say hello to his acquaintances. He was afraid that if he talked to anyone, the first words out of his mouth would be, 'Raja ke gadhe ke kaan (The king has donkey's ears).' In fact, he felt so full with the secret inside him that it was brimming.

For days, the barber didn't see anyone. He couldn't eat or sleep. The king's secret swelled inside his body, his head, his throat, and even his eyes, until he thought he would burst. His mother grew quite concerned at her son's condition. 'Why can't you tell me?' she begged.

'I can't tell anyone. I swore.'

'But I'm your mother. Mothers don't count. Just tell me. I promise I won't whisper a word to anyone.'

'I can't. I can't. I can't.' the barber cried, covering his face with his hands. 'But I must, or I'll die.'

'Then go tell it to the trees,' the mother suggested. 'That way, you'll say it and yet no one will hear.'

The barber ran into the forest, which was full of shisham and neem trees, and cupping his hands around his mouth, whispered to the trees: 'Raja ke gadhe ke kaan.' As soon as the words left his lips, his body felt light—so light that it could have lifted in the air and floated away. Whistling a merry tune, the barber walked home with a bounce in his steps.

Many days passed. Then, one day, a tabla-maker, who got the shisham wood for his tablas from the forest, cut down one of the trees to make a new set of tablas for the court's tabla maestro, who was scheduled to play in a public concert for an upcoming festival.

It was a grand concert that the whole citizenry attended. The vocalist sang Raag Darbari, and the tabla maestro played Rupak Taal in perfect rhythmic accompaniment. But instead of the notes tin-tin-na-dhin-na-dhin-na, the tabla sounded very much like ra-ja-ke-gadh-e-ke-kaan.

Folktale from India and many other lands

◆

112

PURURAVAS AND URVASHI

The apsara, Urvashi, was desired by two gods, Mitra and Varuna, at the same time. In their jealousy, trying to prevent each other from acquiring the heavenly nymph, they ended up cursing Urvashi that she would become a mortal and live as the wife of Pururavas, king of Kashi. With this curse looming over her, Urvashi was one day sporting with her friends on a peak in the Himalayas, when the asura, Kesin, abducted her. King Pururavas, who also happened to be on the mountain that day, witnessed the abduction and, pursuing Kesin, he rescued the apsara. Urvashi took one look at the handsome Puraravas and became besotted, losing all interest in the delights of heaven. Pururavas, too, was enraptured by the lovely and delicate apsara, who was full of gaiety and flirtation. Gazing at each other, the two forgot every other purpose in life.

'I love you, woman of the beautiful brow,' Pururavas said boldly to Urvashi. 'Be kind to me and love me, too. Marry me.'

'All right,' Urvashi replied, arching her eyebrows suggestively. 'I'll marry you, but I have a few conditions, and if you fail to meet any one of them, I'll leave you.'

'Anything, sweet lady. Tell me your conditions.'

'I have two lambs, whom I love like my children—they stay by me all the time; even at night they are at my bedside. You must promise to never take them away, and you must always protect them. My other condition is that you must embrace me at least three times a day but never lie down with me against my will. And, finally, I must never see you naked, for this is how men must behave towards us apsaras.'

'These conditions are hardly a challenge, dear lady. Protecting you and your lambs will be my duty. Embracing you will be my pleasure, but I will never do it against your wish. And,' he added with a twinkle in his eye, 'I have no wish to show you my naked self, provided I can see your beautiful golden body.'

And so, Pururavas and Urvashi began to live together, their happiness increasing each day. For sixty thousand years Pururavas made love with Urvashi in Alaka, Kubera's abode, in the groves of Chitarartha and amid clusters of lotuses that grew in beautiful Lake Manasa. But without Urvashi, Indraloka lost its charm for the heaven-dwellers, and the gandharvas, who are the celestial husbands of the nymphs, began to miss her very much. So Vishvavasu, the king of gandharvas, orchestrated a plan to separate her from Pururavas. He knew about her conditions and intended to manipulate them to his advantage.

One night, as Urvashi and Pururavas slept in each other's arms, oblivious to the rest of the world, the gandharvas stole one of the lambs from their bedside. Urvashi heard its bleating as it was carried away through the sky, and she cried out, 'Someone has stolen my son. It seems that I have no hero to protect me.'

When Pururavas heard Urvashi, his first instinct was to jump out of bed and reach for his sword, but then he realized that he had no clothes on and was afraid that the apsara might see him naked. In the meantime, the gandharvas stole the other lamb as well, and hearing its bleating, Urvashi cried out again in anguish: 'I have no protector. It's like I'm married to a coward.'

Feeling insulted at being called a coward, Pururavas jumped right out of bed and grabbed his sword, grateful for the dark that concealed him. He began pursuing the thieves, but just then, the gandharvas shone a brilliant light and Pururavas was revealed to Urvashi in all his nude manliness. She instantly disappeared from earth. The gandharvas, too, ascended to heaven, leaving the lambs behind. Pururavas caught the lambs and returned to his bedchamber, only to discover that Urvashi had left him.

Maddened with grief and longing, Pururavas began roaming the worlds, seeking his beloved, not even realizing that he was still naked. In his wanderings, he came to Kurukshetra and was walking along the bank of the lotus lake, Anyatahplaksha, when four white swans swimming in it, saw him. These four swans were Urvashi and her companions.

'That's the man with whom I was dwelling,' Urvashi told the other apsaras.

'He's so handsome,' they said. 'How could you leave him? Let's show ourselves to him.'

And so they did, and Pururavas, seeing one of the swans transform into his wife, cried out in joy, 'Oh my wife, I've found you at last.' But then he remembered his misery: 'You're so cruel. Why did you leave me? Why didn't you stay and talk to me? These secrets that we have between us are making us wretched. Talk to me. Stay with me.'

'What's the point in speaking with you now?' Urvashi replied. 'I've passed away like the first rays of the dawn. Pururavas, go home. I'm like the wind, difficult to catch. You didn't do what I asked you to do. Now I can't be with you. Go home.'

'If that is so,' Pururavas said, sorrowfully, 'then know this—your lover and friend will rush away, never to return. He'll go to the farthest distance and then lie in death's lap. He'll either hang himself or be devoured by wolves or dogs.'

'Oh, Pururavas, don't talk like that. Don't kill yourself or let the wolves devour you. Surely you know that there's no friendship with women; theirs are the hearts of hyenas. Don't take our parting to heart. Return home to your kingdom.'

'Tell me just this. Did you feel nothing when you were with me?'

'When I walked among mortals and passed my nights with you for four autumns, I was content.'

Pururavas took a deep breath, as though his heart had been bereft of air and now it was receiving breath again.

Then Urvashi took pity on him. 'I'm pregnant with your child,' she said. 'Come back here a year from now—on the last night of the year— and I'll spend it with you and also give you your son.'

His heart singing with joy, Pururavas went back to his kingdom and lived a year in fevered anticipation of the promised night. A year later, when he returned to the same spot, he saw a golden palace in the place where he had met Urvashi. He went in, and there was Urvashi, waiting for him with open arms. They spent many passionate hours together, and before dawn, she said to him, 'Tomorrow morning the gandharvas will grant you a boon, and you must make your choice.'

'You choose for me,' he said to her.

'Then say to them, "Let me be one of you."'

The following morning when the gandharvas granted Pururavas a boon, he said what Urvashi had instructed him to. 'Be it so,' they said, but then they realized that mortals did not have the pure form of sacrificial fire that would allow them to transform into gandharvas. So they put the special fire in a pan, and handed it to Pururavas, saying, 'By sacrificing with this, you'll become one of us.' Pururavas took the pan full of fire and the boy that Urvashi had put in his arms, and went on his way, but in the middle of the forest, he began to think about the bargain he had made. He asked himself, 'What if this pan of fire is just a trick of the gandharvas. What a fool I am. I should have asked for Urvashi directly, instead of asking to be one of them. Now I'm carrying around this useless pan of fire like a fool.' So he left the fire pan in the forest and went home with his son. But, that night, his mind was still conflicted. Lying in bed, he thought: that fire pan that the gandharvas gave me was to allow me to become a part of Urvashi's world. And I left it in the forest. What have I done? He quickly got up and rushed back to the forest to retrieve the pan, but it had disappeared. What had been the fire was now an Asvattha tree and what had been the pan was a Sami tree.[46]

Myth from the Rig Veda

◆

113

USHA AND ANIRUDHA

The great asura king, Bana, of a thousand arms, had a beautiful daughter named Usha. She was of marriageable age and often thought about who she would marry. One night she dreamt that a handsome young man was making love to her, and she woke up, disturbed and agitated. She had never seen or heard of the man that she saw in her dream, yet she was madly in love with him. Sitting up in her bed, she wondered if such a man even existed, or whether he was just a figment of her imagination. Her heart ached at the thought of never meeting him in reality, and this made her cry.

Usha's best friend was Chitralekha, who was the daughter of one of Bana's ministers. The night that Usha saw her dream man in her sleep, Chitralekha was sleeping in Usha's apartment. When she heard the princess crying, she woke up.

'What's wrong?' she asked.

'What if he doesn't exist?'

'Who?'

'That man who made love to me in my dream. I want to be with him. But what if he's only in my mind?'

'If he exists, I'll find him for you,' Chitralekha said. She was an excellent artist and started making portraits of all the known gods and demi-gods and asuras and serpent princes. She drew for seven days and showed each portrait to Usha, but the princess shook her head at each one, becoming more and more morose at every picture that was not of her lover. Then, Chitralekha asked Usha to describe her dream man to her, and as Usha described his features, Chitralekha drew a portrait of a man with dark complexion and flirtatious lotus eyes. His arms were long and he was wearing yellow garments. His lustrous face was made more so with jeweled earrings that shone on either side of his face, and he had curly locks of hair that fell to his shoulders. Even as Chitralekha etched the final stokes, Usha blushed. 'That's him,' she said softly, her face suffused with colour as she recalled the passion they had shared in her dream.

Chitralekha, being the daughter of an asura, had inherited powers of yoga and maya. With her mind's eye, she identified the man in the portrait as Anirudha, the son of Pradyumna, who was the incarnation of Kama and was born as Krishna's son. 'He's Krishna's grandson,' she told her friend. 'He lives in Dwaraka. I'll bring him to you before the night is up.' Usha hugged her friend, and Chitralekha took off, flying through the air, borne by the vehicle of her mind. At the speed of thought, she reached Krishna's palace in Dwaraka and quickly found Anirudha's room. The prince was sleeping peacefully on a jeweled bed with silken sheets strewn with crushed flowers—the aftermath of lovemaking. Around him were the sleeping forms of many woman in various stages of undress and abandon. Without disturbing anyone, Chitralekha moved the women away and, raising Anirudha's bed, flew it all the way back to Sonitpur, Bana's capital city, and then, making him invisible, she flew him into Chitralekha's apartment.

When Anirudha woke up, he found himself in a strange room decorated with gold panelling and silver filigreed screens. The air was redolent with the perfume of flowers and soft, rosy light filtered in through silk curtains.

'Welcome, sweet prince,' said a dulcet voice, and he turned to see two beautiful women, one of whom was staring at him quite unabashedly, her eyes filled with amusement. The other one, who was more beautiful, had downcast eyes, but she kept sneaking glances at him from under her long eyelashes.

The immodest one gave him one more playful smile and then got busy bringing trays laden with fresh garments, fruits, flowers, incense and diyas. The shy one stood before him, gently biting her lips, a blush tinting her cheeks.

'Who are you, beautiful maiden?' Anirudha asked the shy one. 'Are you an apsara?'

A tinkling laugh came from her petal-soft lips. 'No,' she shook her head. 'I'm Usha, the daughter of the asura king, Bana.'

'Where am I? How did I get here?'

'You're in my apartment in my father's capital city, Sonitpur. As to how you're here? I don't quite know. My friend Chitralekha brought you here with her mayavi power.'

'Why did she bring me here?'

Usha lowered her head, blushing deeply. 'I dreamt about you,' she whispered.

Anirudha laughed softly and, getting off the bed, gathered Usha in his arms.

Usha kept Anirudha concealed in her apartment for many days with Chitralekha's help, and the prince was happy to remain there, because he was utterly captivated by Usha. But, eventually, Usha's other attendants discovered that there was a man living with her. Afraid that if Bana found out, he would punish them for failing to guard the princess, they went to Bana and told him about Anirudha. 'We don't know how he got in. We kept a strict guard so that no male eye would fall on her. But your daughter has thwarted all our efforts.'

Bana was livid. He rushed to his daughter's apartment, and there he saw his daughter with the Yadava prince. They were sitting across from each other, playing dice. Anirudha's chest was smeared with saffron that adorned Usha's forehead, and his body smelled of the jasmine flowers that Usha wore around her neck. Bana had no doubt about what had transpired.

When Anirudha saw Bana standing there with his fierce-looking soldiers, he stood up, and, grabbing an iron bludgeon, positioned himself like Yama, the wielder of the rod, ready to finish off anyone who would touch either him or Usha.

'No! No!' Usha cried. 'That's my father. Please don't hurt him.'

But then Bana gave a command to his soldiers, and they attacked Anirudha from all sides. The Yadava prince had no choice but to fight back. He was a seasoned warrior; within minutes he had bludgeoned them and kicked them all away till they fled, wounded and broken-limbed.

Furious, Bana now conjured up serpent ropes and tied Anirudha with them.

'Stop! Please, Father,' Usha ran to her lover in tears. 'I love him,' she wept. But Bana was relentless. He commanded Usha to step away and had the serpent-bound Anirudha imprisoned.

Back in Dwaraka, when four months of the rainy season passed with no trace of Anirudha, his relatives began to worry. Then Narada, the wandering ascetic, told them about his liaison with Usha, his valorous fight with Bana, and his imprisonment in Sonitpur. 'How dare he worry us like that?' Krishna shouted. 'Doesn't he know who is dealing with? That Bana is a formidable asura.'

Krishna then gathered Balarama and twelve akshauhinis of soldiers, and, declaring war against Bana, surrounded the city of Sonitpur.

This city was under the protection of Shiva. Thousands of years ago, when Shiva had danced the Tandava, Bana had provided musical accompaniment with his thousand arms playing a thousand instruments. Pleased at his devotion, Shiva had granted Bana's boon that he himself would be the guardian of his capital city. Hence, when the Yadava army attacked Sonitpur, Shiva arrived there with his own troops and his warrior son, Skanda.

The battle that followed between the forces of Shiva and Krishna and between the two gods themselves was cosmic—terrible yet marvellous to behold—and the other celestials came to watch it in their aerial cars. Shiva used his Pinaka bow and Krishna his Saranga—the twang of both cosmic bows continuously echoing through the three worlds. They also used one celestial weapon after another in combat, each one with the power to destroy the world, and each one neutralized by the other. When Krishna called the Brahmastra, Shiva, too, called it. When one called the Agnaastra, the weapon of fire, the other one called the rain missile. When Shiva threw his beloved Pashupata, Krishna produced the Narayanastra. Finally, Krishna stupefied Shiva with the Jrumbhanastra, which makes the enemy yawn and fills him with lethargy. Then he slaughtered the rest of Bana's army, while his son, Pradyumna, gravely wounded Shiva's son, Skanda, forcing this greatest of warriors to retreat from the battle. Now Bana himself came to face Krishna, simultaneously holding five hundred bows, ready to shoot an equal number of arrows, all at once. But Krishna snapped his bows, killed his charioteer and horses, and shattered his chariot. Then when he blew his conch in preparation to kill the enemy, Bana's family goddess, Kotara, suddenly appeared—completely in the nude, her open hair falling around her shoulders. She came and stood before Bana, guarding him with her body, and Krishna turned his face away in embarrassment.

When all of Bana's army was destroyed and Shiva's troops had either been killed or had fled, Shiva, in a last ditch effort, called his Jvara, his Fever weapon, that had three heads and three feet, and is always ready to spread fire to the very cardinal points. To counter it, Krishna let lose his own Vaishnava fever and a battle between Vaishnava and Shaivic fevers broke out. The latter was no match for Narayana's fever and, screaming in terror, it took refuge at Krishna's feet. In the meantime, Bana, his energy replenished, returned to the battlefield and began discharging missiles with his thousand arms. But by this time, Krishna had had enough, so he called the Sudarshana Chakra and began lopping off Bana's arms with the discus. When he had lopped off all but four of the arms, Shiva reappeared before Krishna and requested him to stop.

'Bana had no idea that you are the Supreme Lord,' he said. 'I, too, bow to you. Please spare Bana's life. He is my devotee and I have promised him protection.'

Krishna withdrew his discus at once. 'He does not need to be fearful anymore,' he assured Shiva. 'In fact, I give him a boon: the four arms that are left on his body shall never suffer age or destruction.'

Shiva then left for Kailash, and Bana invited Krishna into his palace, treating him as an honoured guest. He also released Anirudha and summoned his daughter.

Everyone approved of the union of Usha and Anirudha, and Krishna and Balarama happily took the young couple back to Dwaraka.

Myth from the Puranas

◆

114

VASAVADATTA AND UDAYAN

King Udayan of the kingdom of Vatsa was a descendant of the legendary
Pandavas. He ruled from his capital city of Kausambhi, and his subjects
adored him, because not only was he kind and caring, but also he was
a handsome young man. However, he was more of a romantic than a
warrior, preferring wine, music, and hunting to battles. He was also a
master musician and had a veena called Ghoshavati on which he produced
music so divine that he could charm any creature with it, especially
elephants. He was not much of a statesman and left most of the kingdom's
affairs in the hands of his two trusted ministers, Yaugandharayana and
Rumnavan.

Vatsa's neighbouring kingdom was Avanti that was ruled from Ujjaini
by the very powerful Pradyota, who had the title of Mahasena, because
he had a vast standing army. Mahasena had heard about King Udayan's
divine knowledge of music with which he could charm elephants, and
he wanted to acquire that knowledge so that he could use it in war. So
Mahasena decided to have Udayan abducted. One day, a guard in an
outlying forest post of Kausambhi saw a stunning white elephant. He
immediately sent word to the king, and Udayan, excited at the prospect
of making a new conquest, quickly mounted his horse, carrying his veena.
When he arrived in the forest, he saw the elephant from a distance; it
appeared to be exactly as his guard had described: pure white with broad
sides, a long, elegant trunk, ears like winnowing fans, and curved proud
tusks. Dismounting, Udayan crept up to within a few yards of the majestic
beast, and there he sat down on the ground with his veena on his lap
and began to play. All of a sudden, the side flank of the elephant flew
open and Mahasena's troops jumped out and captured Udayan.

When Mahasena came to see Udayan in prison, he said to him: 'I
want you to teach me your music. After that, I'll release you.'

'I'm happy to teach my music to anyone who will learn it like a
pupil,' Udayan replied. 'Are you ready to accept me as your guru?'

Mahasena was a proud man and could not conceive of bowing to
anyone, even if it was to learn. However, he had captured Udayan for
this very purpose, so he came up with a strategy. 'Will you teach it to

one of my relatives?' he asked. 'The poor woman is a hunchback and will come to you in gratitude. But you must promise never to look upon her—you will teach her from behind a curtain.'

Udayan agreed to this.

Mahasena then summoned his daughter, Vasavadatta, and told her that he had arranged a music teacher for her, but he had leprosy, and she mustn't look upon him; he would teach from behind a curtain. Vasavadatta had always wanted to learn music, so she was happy to comply.

The music lessons began. Every day, Udayan and Vasavadatta would sit in the room with a heavy curtain between them—Udayan teaching Vasavadatta raga notations on his veena, and Vasavadatta learning the sweet notes on her own instrument. She was a bright student and quickly picked up everything he taught. However, one day, Vasavadatta just could not play a string of notes that Udayan was demonstrating, so, in a moment of impatience, he lifted the curtain, and the two looked at each other—speechless. Instead of an ugly hunchback, Udayan saw the most beautiful woman in the world, and Vasavadatta, too, saw not a leper, but a man as handsome as a god.

'Who are you?' Udayan finally asked.

'I'm Vasavadatta, King Mahasena's daughter. Who are you?'

'I'm Udayan, king of Vatsa.'

'You're *the* Udayan,' Vasavadatta said in awe. 'The veena player, whose music is known throughout the land? Who can charm the very birds off trees? It's you who has been teaching me all these days?'

Udayan nodded, his cheeks turning red in modesty.

After that, Vasavadatta and Udayan began to spend all their time together, playing music and falling deeply in love. 'I want to take you to my kingdom as my queen,' Udayan would say to Vasavadatta. 'I want to marry you, but I can't do it as your father's prisoner.'

'Why don't you ask my father for my hand?'

'He'll never agree. The man didn't even want us to see each other, do you think he'll agree to our marriage? Besides, I'm his prisoner. But don't worry, beloved, I'll find a way to escape from here. Will you come with me to Vatsa as my queen?'

'Of course,' Vasavadatta responded. 'I can't imagine life without you.'

With Vasavadatta's help, Udayan sent a message to his ministers Yaugandharayana and Rumnavan, and within a few days, he received a response. 'My ministers have a plan,' he told Vasavadatta. 'But I will need your help. Tell your father that you are ready to test your music and you need an elephant at the gate to see if you can charm him.'

Mahasena was delighted to hear that his daughter had acquired what he sought and ordered an elephant to be brought to the gate the following morning. 'But there can't be any soldiers or guards around,' Vasavadatta warned her father. 'I don't want anyone distracting him.'

When Mahasena heard this request, he became suspicious, so to his daughter he said, 'It'll be as you say,' but, secretly, he instructed his chief minister to post guards in the vicinity of the gate. However, Yaugandharayana, Udayan's wily minister, had anticipated this; he had already planned for the elephant's mahout to be his own man, who would be able to evade the secret guards. Hence, Udayan and Vasavadatta safely escaped from Ujjaini, and when they arrived in Kausambhi, they were immediately married. They lived happily for many years.

Udayan's love for his bride consumed him to the extent that he began to completely ignore affairs of state, and soon a neighbouring king, Aruni, began to eye Vatsa. Yaugandharayana attempted many times to remind the king of his duties, but when Udayan dismissed his concerns, the minister became worried. He feared that if Aruni attacked, Vatsa would not be able to defend itself. Finally, Yaugandharayana decided to seek help from other kingdoms. Avanti was out of the question, because it appeared that Mahasena was still furious at his daughter's elopement. The other kingdom that Yaugandharayana could petition was Magadha, which was one of the most powerful kingdoms in the region; its king, Ajatasatru, was formidable. Yaugandharayana knew that with Magadha's support, no one would dare to even look at Vatsa. With this in mind, he called a meeting with some of the other ministers, and asked for suggestions about how to approach the intimidating Magadha king. The royal astrologer informed him that Ajatasatru had a sister, Padmavati, who was not only beautiful but also whose horoscope predicted that whomever she married would become emperor. Everyone agreed that this was the perfect solution—to make an alliance with Magadha through the marriage of Udayan and Padmavati. But the question was—how to get Udayan to agree to the marriage. The king of Vatsa was so single-mindedly in love with Vasavadatta, he wouldn't even entertain the thought of another woman.

'There has to be a way to draw him away from the queen,'

Yaugandharayana said to his friend and colleague, Rumnavan. 'We have to come up with a plan, or all will be lost. Today it is Aruni threatening us, tomorrow, it'll be someone else.'

'What if the Queen Vasavadatta is no more,' Rumnavan suggested.

'What're you saying?' Yaugandharayana hissed, reaching for his sword. 'Are you suggesting that we have the queen killed? I'll separate your head from your body for just suggesting that.'

'No, no, of course not. Calm down. All I'm saying is what if the king is made to believe that she is dead.'

'He'll be destroyed and so will she, if you so much as part them.'

'Only till he marries the princess Padmavati.'

'Well...' Yaugandharayana said thoughtfully, and the two ministers hatched a plan.

One day Yaugandharayana suggested to Udayan that he and Queen Vasavadatta should go on a holiday to the forest resort of Lavanka. 'Show the queen the beauty of the forest. And you can also enjoy a hunt or two.'

Udayan liked the idea very much and left with his wife for Lavanka the very next day. He and Vasavadatta spent glorious days together, wandering in the forest, holding hands, picking flowers like young lovers, and making love, bathed in the rays of the rising and setting sun. A few days into the holiday, Udayan was urged by Yaugandharayana to go on a hunt, and he agreed.

'Don't miss me too much,' Udayan said affectionately to his queen. 'I'll be back before sunset.' Vasavadatta, who was sitting in their pavilion adorning herself with gold ornaments, gave him a fond smile of farewell.

But that evening, when Udayan returned, his world had been destroyed. The pavilion in which he had left Vasavadatta was burnt to the ground.

'We tried to save her,' Rumnavan wept. 'Yaugandharayana jumped into the fire to get her out, but they both perished.'

Udayan fainted, and when he came to, he tried to drive his sword through his heart, but Rumnavan caught his hand. 'No, Maharaj. I beg you. Think of Vatsa. Think of your subjects. They'll be orphaned. You must live for Vatsa.'

'My Vasavadatta. My heart. How can I live without my heart?' he wailed. 'And Yaugandharayana, my best friend. What will I do without him? How will I manage Vatsa?'

Rumnavan placed Vasavadatta's ornaments in Udayan's lap. 'We were able to retrieve these,' he said. 'Keep the queen's memories alive, but come away, back to Vatsa, Maharaj. Be a good king for the citizens of Vatsa. That's how you will honour Yaugandharayana.'

For a long time, Udayan sat on the forest floor, the gold ornaments in his lap glinting obscenely in the sunset. Then, holding them tightly to his heart, he lay down and slowly drifted off to sleep. Rumnavan quietly covered him with a blanket and posted guards around him. In the morning when Udayan woke up, he gathered his wife's ashes in an urn from the gutted pavilion and returned to Kausambhi with Rumnavan.

Vasavadatta and Yaugandharayana, were, of course, alive. The fire had only been a ruse to separate Udayan from Vasavadatta. She had agreed to go along with the ministers' plan only for the sake of Vatsa, although her heart wept bitterly for herself, and for her grieving husband. While Udayan and Rumnavan went to Kausambhi, Vasavadatta and Yaugandharayana went into hiding near Lavanka.

Back in the palace, everything reminded Udayan of his beloved. The courtyards smelled of her fragrance, the corridors tinkled with the sounds of her bangles and anklets, and his bedchamber, littered with her clothes, her creams and powders, and her ornaments, was like the inside of his mind—filled with her. For days, he remained locked in his room, sometimes weeping into a pile of her clothing, sometimes hanging up her jewellery all around the room like mementos, and sometimes, tearing the silken bedsheets into shreds. But, eventually, with Rumavan's soft cajoling and strict reasoning, he was able to leave his private quarters and go into the courtroom, where he forced himself to get involved in matters of state. Udayan slowly began to live again, although every beat of his heart still felt like a blow.

Rumnavan let a few months pass before he brought up the subject of Padmavati before Udayan. 'Will you consider it, Maharaj,' he said. 'You know we really need the support of Maharaja Ajatasatru. Magadha will help thwart our enemies' designs. Besides, I hear that Princess Padmavati is very beautiful.'

'Oh, Rumnavan. I know you mean well. But love's quiver had only five arrows and all five struck me when I saw Vasavadatta. From where will I get a sixth arrow?'

'At least say you will consider it. For Vatsa's sake.'

Udayan considered what his friend and minister suggested and finally asked Rumnavan to send word to Magadha, because Aruni's threats were growing bolder by the day. Ajatasatru knew Udayan's repute and had heard many stories about his ability on the veena, so he invited Udayan to Pataliputra, Magadha's capital, to discuss the possibility of a matrimonial alliance.

This was the news that Vasavadatta and Yaugandharayana had been waiting for, and as soon as they confirmed it, they started for Pataliputra, arriving there many days before Udayan was expected. The plan was that Vasavadatta would influence Padmavati's mind so that she would fall in love with Udayan and persuade the king to accept the match.

When they arrived in Pataliputra, Yaugandharayana was dressed like a Brahmin, and Vasavadatta was posing as his sister. At the palace, they asked to see the Princess Padmavati. 'We have come to you for refuge,' Yaugandharayana told Padmavati. 'This is my sister, Avantika,' he said, introducing Vasavadatta. 'Her husband is away. He left her with me for safe-keeping, but now I, too, have to go to a foreign land for business, and I have nowhere to leave my sister. May I leave her with you, under your protection? I'll be back soon.'

'Of course,' Padmavati replied, 'Avantika will be my very special handmaiden.'

And so Vasavadatta, as Avantika, began to live with Padmavati. Every day, while taking care of the princess's needs, she would extol the virtues of the Vatsa king—how he was as handsome as Indra, how his music was sweeter than the music of the gandharvas, how he had learned to love from Kamadeva himself.

One day, as they talked, Padmavati said: 'I've heard that King Udayan eloped with the princess of Avanti.'

Avantika responded: 'It's true. I've heard that too, but haven't you heard about the tragedy that struck King Udayan? Vasavadatta perished in a fire.'

'Yes, and I've heard that King Udayan loved her very much and grieved for her for a very long time.'

Vasavadatta's eyes filled with tears. 'Forgive me,' she said. 'I always tear up when I think of the pain that the king must have suffered.' Then, forcing a smile, she continued, 'But I also hear that he is recovering very well and is coming here to see you and meet Maharaj Ajatasatru.'

Soon, word arrived in Pataliputra that Udayan was on his way there. Vasavadatta was ecstatic at the prospect of seeing her beloved husband again, even though the thought of him marrying another woman pierced her like a dagger in the heart. For a moment, she thought she would appear before him just to see his eyes sparkle with joy, but she knew she could not let him see her, otherwise the plan that she and the two ministers had worked so hard to bring to fruition would be ruined. But none of this logic could prevent Vasavadatta from wondering if Udayan still loved her or whether his heart was now only filled with thoughts about his new bride.

When Udayan and Ajatasatru met, they liked each other instantly, and after they had Padmavati's consent, the marriage negotiations were concluded. All these days, Vasavadatta had not caught a single glimpse of Udayan. Then, a day before the wedding, Padmavati asked Avantika to accompany her to the pleasure garden to get sephalika flowers. As the two women wandered in the garden, picking the red flowers that grew on bushes like bunches of red crystal, they heard male voices. Vasavadatta quickly pulled Padmavati into a grove covered with madhavi creepers. It was Udayan, with one of his men.

'Your betrothed was here a short while ago, Maharaj,' the man was saying.

'How do you know?'

'I see that flowers have recently been plucked from these branches, and see here—under the seat—soft petals of sephalika.'

A few steps away, hidden among the creepers, Padmavati felt her heartbeat increase. She wanted to step out and look at her groom-to-be, but she didn't want to seem forward, so she moved the vines just a bit to steal a few glances.

'Isn't he like Kamadeva himself?' Avantika whispered.

'O hush,' Padmavati quietened her maid, her cheeks burning.

Then Udayan's man spoke again. 'May I ask you a question Maharaj? Right this moment, who do you love more, your new bride-to-be—Princess Padmavati—or Queen Vasavadatta, who was taken from you so cruelly by fate?'

Udayan sighed deeply. 'I treasure Padmavati, because she's beautiful and kind and sweet, but my heart is still in captivity. Vasavadatta captured it the moment I looked upon her behind the curtain. I'm still caught in that moment.'

'Oh, he is cruel,' Vasavadatta's heart leapt at Udayan's words, and she blurted out the words without even thinking.

'No,' said Padmavati. 'It's so romantic. His heart grieves because he loves so deeply. I'll be honoured to be his wife, and I pray that one day he'll love me just a little bit. Do you think he'll learn to love me?' she asked, turning to look at her friend. When she saw tears in her eyes, she grew concerned. 'What's the matter?' she asked.

'It's nothing,' Avantika replied, wiping her tears. 'The pollen from these kasa flowers has made my eyes water.'

On the morning of the wedding, a maid came to fetch Vasavadatta and take her to Padmavati, who had woken up with a headache and had gone to lie down in the ocean house. Udayan, too, been informed by his man that Padmavati was unwell and was in the ocean house, so he decided to call upon his bride-to-be to see how she was doing. When he and his man, Vidushak, arrived there, he saw that the bedroom was empty and it seemed that the bed had not been slept in.

'Maharaj, why don't you sit for a while?' his man said, 'and I'll go and check to see where the princess is?'

Udayan sat down on the bed to wait, but the sound of the ocean was so relaxing that he lay down and soon feel asleep. As he slept, he began to dream about the day that he and Vasavadatta had spent at the river. In the meantime, Vasavadatta also came to the ocean house, looking for Padmavati, but instead of the princess, she saw Udayan sleeping on the bed. He was murmuring softly, 'Vasavadatta, Vasavadatta.' Her heart broke at the pain in his voice. She knew she should leave, but she couldn't stop herself from going to him. As she sat beside him, looking at his beloved face, she heard Udayan murmur agitatedly. 'Oh my dearest heart, why don't you answer me?'

'I'm here,' Vasavadatta whispered.

'Are you angry with me?'

'Why would I be angry?' she said.

'I was thinking about us in Virachika,' he murmured and reached out his hand, but when she didn't take it, it fell on the side of the bed. Gently, Vasavadatta lifted the hand and put it back on the bed.

Suddenly, Udayan opened his eyes, 'Vasavadatta,' he cried, but Vasavadatta quickly ran out.

Udayan jumped up and ran towards the door and, not realizing that it was closed, hit his head against it. Just then, Udayan's man came back. 'Vidushak, Vasavadatta is alive!' Udayan cried excitedly, barely able to contain his joy. 'I saw her. Her fragrant hair was open around her shoulders, her lotus eyes looked lovingly at me. She touched my hand. I felt her touch. My beloved is alive.'

'What are you saying, Maharaj?' Vidushak replied. 'You must have been dreaming. Queen Vasavadatta perished in the fire.'

'No. Rumnavan lied to me. She did not perish. I just saw her.'

'It was an illusion, Maharaj. They found her ornaments. Don't you remember?'

An illusion! Doubt filled Udayan's mind, and he came back and sat down heavily on the bed, holding his head in his hands. He could still smell the sweet fragrance of Vasavadatta, but perhaps his mind had been affected when he hit his head.

Later that day, as Udayan prepared for the nuptial ceremonies, two messengers arrived—one was from Vatsa to tell him that Aruni's forces had been repelled by the joint armies of Vatsa and Magadha and that Vatsa was once again safe. The other messenger was from Ujjaini and had been sent by Mahasena, Vasavadatta's father. He was accompanied by a lady—Vasundhara, who used to be Vasavadatta's nurse. They brought with them Udayan's veena, Ghoshavati. It had fallen off the elephant, when Udayan and Vasavadatta had eloped from Ujjaini.

'Who found her?' Udayan asked the messenger, taking his veena in his arms. He had missed his beloved instrument and had thought she was lost to him forever.

'A few nights ago, the king heard strains of the veena coming from the banks of Narmada. He hurried there and found the veena buried in the sand. After news of Vasavadatta's death the king has been a broken man, but when he found this veena, it was like a part of Vasavadatta had returned. He ordered that it be brought to you so that you can play it, and in your music Vasavadatta will live again.'

Udayan embraced Ghoshavati like a long lost love. 'Oh Ghoshavati,' he cried, a sob caught in his throat, 'You have been found but your Queen Vasavadatta, on whose lap you used to sit as she played your strings, is no more.'

Then the old nurse drew something from a bag and handed it to

Udayan. It was a portrait of Udayan and Vasavadatta. 'When was this made and why?' Udayan asked, surprised.

'Oh Maharaj. It was all a big misunderstanding,' the nurse said. 'Maharaj Mahasena always desired to have you as his son-in-law, but he was too proud to ask you, so he had you captured. He would have eventually made the proposal, but before that could happen, you and the princess eloped. So the king and queen had this portrait made of the two of you, and with this, they celebrated their daughter's marriage with you.'

'I wish we had known. It would have saved Vasavadatta the grief she felt for betraying her parents.' Udayan said, touching Vasavadatta's face in the picture. 'She looks so alive,' he said sadly. 'See Padmavati. This was Vasavadatta.'

Padmavati stared at the portrait. 'But that is...that is...Avantika,' she said, 'my handmaiden, placed in my care by her brother.'

'Surely you are mistaken, Padmavati. Vasavadatta died in a fire,' Udayan said.

'No. I'm certain. Go quickly,' she said to one of her maids. 'And call Avantika here.'

Even as Avantika was summoned, Padmavati was informed that Avantika's brother had come to take her back.

'What perfect timing,' Padmavati exclaimed. 'Now all will be clear.'

When Udayan learned that his ministers had orchestrated everything, but only for the sake of Vatsa, he forgave them. Mostly he forgave them because he was beside himself with joy at finding Vasavadatta alive. He also married Padmavati, as planned, and brought his two wives home to Vatsa, where they all lived happily.

Folktale based on Bhasa's play, Svapanavasavadatta

◆

115

A PRINCESS, A MECHANICAL GARUDA, AND A COUNTERFEIT VISHNU

In the region of Gauda was a city called Pundravardhan, and in it lived two friends, a weaver and a chariot-maker, who were fine craftsmen. They were very successful in their professions and were quite wealthy, and they also liked spending their money. They dressed in fine clothing, chewed the finest betel nut, and wore perfumes of musk and aloe and camphor. All day they worked at their jobs, and in the last quarter of the day, they bathed and preened to attend all-night parties with their friends. Another activity that the two enjoyed was participating in celebrations and festivities that their city often held in public squares.

Attending one such festival, which was being held in the city square near the king's palace, the two friends, dressed in their finest clothes, were wandering around, people-watching, when they walked past the palace. By chance, the weaver looked up and saw in the balcony a sight that held him transfixed. It was a woman of incandescent beauty. She was surrounded by her companions, who were also very lovely, but she shone like a moon among stars. Her breasts were firm and vibrant, like twin flowers budding in the springtime. Her waist was slender, curving out into rounded hips, like a matki. Her hair was glossy and blue, the colour of rain clouds. Her face was like a lotus that has just bloomed, and the gold hoops that she wore in her ears swung around her face like a charming invitation.

The weaver was fascinated by this woman of incomparable beauty, and he felt his heart pierced by all five flower-arrows of Kamadeva— red lotus, blue lily, jasmine, asoka, and mango. Somehow, the weaver extricated himself from this vision and returned home, but he could not think of anything else. The whole day he only saw the woman, and all he could do was lie in his bed, sighing—lovesick. Sometimes he would moan in despair, and, sometimes, remembering her beauty, he would smile, imagining himself within the perfumed circle of her arms. And when he realized how impossible it would be for him to attain her, he would lament, 'You live in my heart, yet you burn it with cruelty.' At these times, he would break out in song:

> She has stolen the moon's lustre of pearls
> But the moon is a cold, hard block.
> Her eyes glow like moon-lotuses.
> She has stolen her gait from a spirited elephant
> And the poor animal does not even know of his loss.
> From me she has taken

My heart…
She is everywhere; here on earth
Up in the sky, far in space in every corner.
She pervades my universe.
I'll remember her until I draw my last breath.

And sometimes, he would wax philosophical:

Buddha says all things are transitory,
What a lie!
When I think incessantly about my love,
My life seems infinite, each moment an eternity.

Thus, impassioned and smitten, the weaver spent the night in a dream state of effervescent joy, anguish, and longing. The next morning, his friend, the chariot-maker, came to his house as usual and was utterly surprised to see his friend's unkempt appearance and unmade bed, and his friend lying on it, sighing and murmuring. 'What's the matter?' the chariot-maker asked, but the weaver was so lost in his world, he didn't respond.

The chariot-maker checked his friend's forehead to make sure he wasn't running a fever, but then he saw the faraway look in his eyes and realized the truth. 'Oh, my friend,' he exclaimed. 'This is no ordinary fever. You're suffering from the worst fever of all—the fever of love. Do tell me. I promise you, you'll feel better. Who is she? Where did you meet her?'

The weaver then told his friend his sad love story.

'I see your problem,' the weaver's friend said. 'She's the daughter of a Kshatriya and a king, and you, my dear, are a lowly artisan, lowest of the merchant class. I see the transgression of law.'

'How do you know that she's a princess? She could very well be the daughter of someone of my class. Maybe she's one of the princess's companions. I don't know. I only know that I'm deeply in love. And love transgresses all classes and laws.'

The chariot-maker realized that nothing he said would dissuade his friend. 'So what's to be done?' he asked.

'How should I know? You're my friend and you have to help me.'

'Okay, I'll think of something. But you have to stop being so gloomy. Go take a bath and clean yourself. You stink.'

The weaver felt much better after talking to his friend and took his friend's advice. He bathed, dressed, and even went to work, although he couldn't concentrate very much on anything.

The following day, when his friend came to see him, he was carrying a large, man-sized, wooden bird, painted golden.

'What this?' the weaver asked.

'This, my friend, is your ride into your princess's heart,' said the chariot-maker. 'I've made it for you.' He put the bird on the floor and, to the weaver's growing amazement, began to show him what an ingenious contraption it was. On its sides were pegs, which when pushed in, made the bird rise and fly, and when pulled out, made it descend. They could also be used by the operator to manoeuvre the machine and make it go wherever he wished. 'This is your Garuda, Vishnu's ride, and tonight, dressed as Vishnu, you're going to ride your Garuda bird up onto the terrace of the princess's apartment. By the way, I've found out that the woman you saw is, indeed, the princess, and she sleeps on the terrace. I'll help you look like Vishnu, and when you land on her terrace and meet her, you can make whatever other arrangements you like,' he said with a wink. Then, telling his friend to be ready in the evening, the chariot-maker left.

The weaver spent the whole day dreaming, and, in the evening, long before his friend was supposed to arrive, he began to get ready. He spent an hour on his bath and then burnt incense to perfume his body with the fragrant smoke. He also rubbed scented cream on his skin, dusted himself with sandalwood powder, and popped a betel nut in his mouth to make his breath fragrant.

When the chariot-maker arrived, he helped the weaver dress in a silk pitambar, like Vishnu's. He also placed a diadem on his head and flower garlands around his neck. Then he added all the other touches that were part of the disguise and, by the end of it, the weaver was transformed into Vishnu.

That night the princess, lying on her bed on the terrace that was bathed in moonlight, was gazing at the moon, dreaming romantic dreams, when suddenly she saw Vishnu's Garuda in the sky and, in bewilderment, watched it land on her terrace. Then she saw Vishnu himself alight. Jumping out of bed she fell at the feet of the divine being, her head bowed, her body trembling in shock and excitement. 'O Lord, why have

I been graced with your divine presence? Command me, O Lord! How shall I worship you?'

Reaching down, Vishnu tenderly grasped the girl's shoulders and helped her rise. 'Gracious lady,' he said in a gentle, modulated voice. 'It is you who have brought me here.'

'Me? But I'm just a simple, mortal woman.'

'You are my very own divine consort who was banished to the earth by a curse. I have protected you all these years, but now the curse is over, and I've come to make you my own once again. I'll marry you this very night. It'll be a gandharva marriage in which all we'll need is each other's consent—no rituals, no family, no ceremony. Just me and you and our love. Are you ready?'

The princess was, at first, incredulous, and then she was filled with happiness, 'Yes,' she whispered.

Vishnu took his consort in a tender embrace and the two consummated the marriage.

Many nights of bliss passed. Every night, the weaver would fly in on his Garuda bird, and every morning, just before daybreak, he would leave for his 'Vaikuntha'—Vishnu's realm. But soon, the attendants in the princess's apartment began to notice things—sounds of lovemaking, a male voice, laughter, and the princess herself looking different—radiant, yet weary. 'She's seeing a man at night,' they realized and rushed to tell the king. 'We have no idea how he comes in, because we're vigilant at the gates,' they said. The king, shocked and saddened at his daughter's dishonourable behaviour, went to his queen. 'We have been shamed,' he cried. 'Ask her if it's true that she has dishonoured our name.'

The queen, in deep distress, went immediately to her daughter's room and saw the evidence for herself: her daughter's lips swollen from kisses, her shoulders and back marked with tiny love bites and scratches. 'Shameless girl!' she hissed. 'What have you done? 'Who is it with whom you have blackened your face?'

Her head hanging in shame, her eyes full of tears, the princess recounted the whole tale. 'It's Lord Vishnu,' she said. 'I had a curse on me which made me a mortal, but I'm really his consort. He came to me one night on his Garuda and we were united in a gandharva marriage. Now he comes to me every night on his celestial bird.'

The queen was incredulous at first, but her daughter didn't seem to be lying; in fact, the more the queen heard, the more she believed, and her heart began to fill with joy. She clasped her daughter to her bosom and kissed her, and then rushed back to the king. 'O husband,' she said excitedly. 'It's time to celebrate the prosperity that will be yours. You have been blessed. It's Vishnu himself who visits our daughter at night. He has married our daughter in a gandharva marriage. Tonight we will delight our eyes by seeing him ourselves. Let's hide behind the windows and watch as he alights on the terrace of our daughter's apartment.'

The king was exultant. He could hardly wait for the daylight hours to pass so that it could be night and he could see for himself. He and his queen hid in a niche by the windows and waited. In the deep of the night, they saw the large golden Garuda in the sky, and when it alighted on the terrace, they saw Vishnu dismount. Seeing him, there was no doubt in their minds that it was the Supreme Lord himself. He bore all the emblems with which he is described: he wore a yellow pitambar; on his head was the signature gold and jewel diadem, his chest was adorned by the Vaijayanti garland, and in his four hands, he held the lotus, the conch, the discus and the mace.

The king felt as though amrita was flowing through his limbs instead of blood. He turned to his queen and whispered in awe, 'When the Supreme Lord himself waits on my daughter, who in the world can be more blessed than I? Everything we hoped for her has come true. I am now content. Moreover, now with Vishnu as my son-in-law, my reign will extend over the whole earth.'

The king of Gauda was a vassal of the Emperor Vikramsena of the southern region, who reigned over nine times ninety lakh villages. When Vikramsena's envoy came to Gauda to collect the quarterly tribute, the king refused to pay and sent the man packing. At this rebellion, Vikramsena gathered his army, complete with elephants, chariots, horses and infantry and mounted an attack on Gauda. The people of Gauda fled, seeking refuge in the palace, begging the king to retaliate. The king's ministers, too, met with him to plan a strategy. However, the king sat on his throne, calm and at ease. 'I already have a plan,' he informed his ministers.

'Tell us,' they were impatient to know.

'You'll find out at dawn,' the king said mysteriously. Then, commanding a heavy guard at the city's gates and ramparts, he summoned his daughter.

'Darling child,' he said to her when she arrived. 'As you know, we're at war with Vikramsena, who has arrived with his army to crush us. I want you to talk to your husband tonight and ask him to destroy our enemy.'

The princess nodded, and when her divine husband came at night, she apprised him of the situation. 'Lord, my father is depending on you to destroy his enemy,' she stated.

'Dear lady, this battle of mortals is a trifle,' Vishnu said, smiling indulgently. 'In the past I've crushed asuras like Madhu and Kaitabha and thousands of other powerful danavas. Vikramsena is a mere mortal. So, be at peace, dear lady, and tell your father not to worry. At dawn, I'll let fly my Sudarshan Chakra at the enemy and the war will be over in a blink of an eye.'

Brimming with pride, the princess informed her father, and he, in turn informed the citizenry. In fact, he felt so benevolent that he made an announcement: after the enemy was defeated, the citizens of Gauda could keep anything they acquired of the spoils.

Now, while the citizens of Gauda eagerly awaited dawn, the weaver in Vishnu's guise, sat in the princess's apartment in total dejection, wondering what he would do at dawn. I could simply get on my mechanical bird and get out of here, he mused to himself. But in that case, I'll lose my precious pearl—my wife—and die in grief. Or, I could fight the enemy, in which case, I will surely die in battle. Therefore, since death is certain in either case, I would rather die for her and her father than away from her. But then, he thought…perhaps, when the enemy sees me on Garuda, dressed as Vishnu, they may actually believe that I'm the divine Vishnu and flee in terror. Who knows!

As the weaver battled with his thoughts and arrived at his decision to fight, someone in the sky was watching his inner struggle. This was the real Garuda, the true divine ride and companion of Lord Vishnu. When the weaver came to his decision that he would confront Vikramsena's vast army in his disguise of Vishnu, Garuda flew to Lord Vishnu in the celestial city of Vaikuntha and told him of the situation that was developing on earth: 'There's a city on earth called Gauda. In it lives a weaver who, assuming the guise of your divine self, loves a princess and visits her every night on a wooden replica of me. Now Vikramsena the overlord of nine times ninety lakh villages, of whom the king of Gauda used to be a vassal, has attacked Gauda, and the weaver has resolved to fight in the battle for his father-in-law—dressed as you, my lord. Please consider this: if the weaver dies, the people of earth will think that you have perished, killed by the mortal Vikramsena. When people on earth hear this, they will lose faith in you. There will be no more sacrifices on earth and religious ceremonies will cease. Heretics will destroy temples and shrines, and your worshippers will stop worshipping you. In this situation, please think what should be done.'

Vishnu thought for a while and then spoke, 'It seems that this weaver has something special in him—a divine spark. Let him defeat the enemy and kill Vikramsena. But the only way this can be accomplished is if you and I help him. So I'll let a part of me enter his body and you must do the same and enter his wooden bird. Also, I'll let the power of my Sudarshana enter the fake chakra he carries; the power of my mace will be in his mace, and the power of my conch in his conch.'

Finally, dawn, for whom everyone on earth was waiting, arrived, and the sun rose, glistening like a jewel in the forehead of the eastern sky. At the gates of Gauda, the sounds of battle rent the air—trumpets and drums and roars of men challenging the enemy.

Then the true Garuda, invisible to the mortal eye, flew to the centre of the battlefield, awaiting the weaver. Soon, the weaver, mounted on his wooden bird, flew off the parapet of the terrace and circled the sky. People looked up and hailed the Supreme Lord. The weaver then put his lips to his conch and blew on it. The sound that it emitted was so terrifying that elephants and horses and men broke formation in fear. Hearing the sound of the celestial conch, the other gods of heaven came out in surprise and, seeing Vishnu mounted on his Garuda ready to do battle, asked Brahma. 'Are we at war with the asuras again?'

'I don't know,' Brahma replied, equally surprised to see Vishnu ready to battle with mortals.

The weaver then let fly his discus at Vikramsena and, in the blink of an eye, that emperor fell to the ground, decapitated. Seeing their overlord killed, and by none other than the Supreme Lord Vishnu himself, the other kings fell to the ground in obeisance. 'Command, O Lord,' they said.

'Be without fear,' the weaver-Vishnu said, raising his hand in the blessing gesture of fearlessness. 'From today, the king of Gauda is your overlord. That is my command.'

'So, be it,' all the kings pronounced.

The weaver bestowed all the bounty of war on his father-in-law, and he himself, lived happily ever after with his princess.

Hence, it is aptly said:

A hoax that is well crafted
cannot be detected even by the Creator himself.

And so, it was that the weaver, disguised as Vishnu, was able to win his love.

Folk-myth from the Panchatantra

◆

116

MARU BIHAG

In the eighth century, Narwar and Poongal were two small kingdoms in Rajasthan. Nal, the king of Narwar, created an alliance with King Pingal of Poongal by marrying his two-year-old daughter, Maruwani, to the three-year-old Poongal prince, Salehkumar, who was nicknamed Dhola.

Since the bride and groom were so young, only the nuptial ceremony was completed. Then the children returned to their homes, until the time when Maruwani would come of age, and the young couple could proceed with the remaining wedding customs. For many years, the families hardly interacted, and communication between them was limited to perfunctory invites for formal events, which were mostly attended by emissaries of the two kingdoms.

In Maru's family, Dhola's name was mentioned quite often, and Maru herself knew that she was married to the prince of Narwar. However, Dhola had no recollection of a wife. His family never talked about Maru, because no one remembered the marriage. A few years after the ceremony, Raja Nal died and shortly thereafter, the queen, too, passed away and soon, even the memory of Dhola's marriage to Maru faded in the minds everyone else in Narwar. Therefore, when Dhola became king and his ministers advised him to form a marriage alliance with the powerful kingdom of Malwa by marrying the princess Maluwani, Dhola readily agreed, and marrying Maluwani in an elaborate ceremony, brought her to his home in Narwar.

Maluwani was a beautiful woman and she loved Dhola passionately. Dhola, too, was deeply in love with his wife, and the couple lived a happy life. But then one day Maluwani heard an old maid, who used to serve the queen mother, talking to one of the younger maids: 'I hear she has really blossomed,' the old woman said.

'My sister saw her at the fair in Poongal, and she said her beauty is unmatched—like a full moon shining on the sand,' the younger maid replied, and then asked, 'Kaki, what will happen now? Will Pingal Raja send a message to our raja?'

'That is the custom, but the question is, will our raja honour it?' the old maid replied.

Maluwani became very curious to know who they were talking about. Who was this woman as beautiful as the full moon and why would her Dhola be informed about her? So she summoned the young maid and promised her a bag full of coins if she told her the truth about this woman.

The young maid divulged whatever little she had heard from the older women about King Dhola's childhood marriage to the princess of Poongal. 'She has now come of age, Maharani,' she informed Maluwani.

Maluwani's heart sank with each word that the maid spoke. Just the thought of Maruwani made her want to tear out her eyes. She wondered if all this while that Dhola had been married to her, he had actually been waiting for a message to bring home his other bride, who was as beautiful as a full moon. No message will ever reach him, she promised herself, and was determined to do whatever was necessary to keep this information from him.

Maru had, indeed, reached puberty, and she did have an ethereal beauty, like moonlight on sand. Within her family now, more and more conversations related to her marital status. A month before the festival of Hariyali Teej, when newlywed brides go to their husband's house, her father sent a letter to Dhola, reminding him of his obligation to Maruwani. 'It's time to take your bindni home,' he said in his letter. 'We will await your response to this letter and your confirmation that you will come to Poongal on Hariyali Teej.' But that monsoon festival came and went without so much as an acknowledgement from Dhola. In fact, even the messenger that Raja Pingal had sent did not return. Maruwani's parents were very distressed, and they were glad that they had not told Maru about the message they had sent.

'Perhaps, the messenger didn't make it to Narwar,' the queen said
to her husband. 'Something may have happened to him. Why don't you
send another letter with another messenger?' And so the king sent another
messenger, and then another and another, but let alone a response, the
messengers, too, seemed to disappear. In actuality, what was happening
was that Queen Maluwani was intercepting all the messengers and having
them killed before they could reach town.

In the meantime, one night, Maru had a dream about Dhola. She
had never dreamt about him before, and she didn't know what he looked
like, but in this dream he became real for her. She saw him clearly—his
handsome, smiling face, his proud moustache twirled upwards at the edges,
and his molten brown eyes looking lovingly at her. After that night, she
couldn't stop thinking about him and became so lost in thoughts about
him that she forgot to eat and sleep. She heard his voice in the whispering
of leaves, she saw his form in the shadows cast by the sun, and she felt
his presence around her wherever she went. Everything made her think
of Dhola, and she felt that if she didn't meet him soon, she would die.

Raja Pingal and his wife grew worried about their daughters. She
had begun to lose weight, and her eyes were sinking in their own dark
shadows. 'Can't you see that Maru needs to be with her husband?' the
queen admonished her husband.

'What can I do?' the king replied. 'I've sent five messengers. Besides,
I've learned that Dhola is married to the princess of Malwa.'

'If it's our daughter's fate to have a sauten, a co-wife, to share her
husband's love, then so be it. But, as parents, how can we keep a married
daughter at home after she has come of age? The world will shame us.
Please send another message to Narwar.'

'It will be useless. Who knows what has happened to the others I
sent? I don't want to jeopardize another life.'

'I have an idea,' said the queen. 'Why don't you send bards this
time, rather than a court messenger? Let them convey our message, very
subtly, through songs. They can also gauge what is going on in Narwar,
and why Dhola will not come to take his bride.'

Raja Pingal liked that idea. 'I know just whom to send,' he said, thinking
about a plan. 'Veer-ji and his group of singers are perfect for this task.'

When Maru heard the news about Dhola's marriage to the princess
of Malwa, she lost consciousness. But when she came to, she had new

resolve: it is of little consequence if my Dhola loves another, she thought. My love for my Dhola is true, and I want to be with him, even if he has another wife. Then, getting up hurriedly, she summoned the bard, Veer-ji, who she knew would be going to Narwar. She had known Veer-ji since she was a little girl; her father often invited him and his group of singers to the palace to sing before honoured guests. 'Kako,' she said to him, 'when you see my Dhola, sing this couplet to him: "Dhola Narawar seriyan, dhan Poongal galliyan. (Dhola of Narwar, remember the wealth in the streets of Poongal)."'

Veer-ji memorized the couplet and assured Maru that he would do his best to bring back Dhola. 'If I come back, I promise it'll be with your Dhola, and if I can't bring him back, I'll die in Narwar.'

Veer-ji and his group reached Narwar safely, because they appeared to be ordinary gypsy bards, travelling from city to city, singing folk songs to make a living. After they had secured their belongings in a guest house, Veer-ji went to the palace to reconnoitre the place and see how he would implement the plan he had in mind. Evening had descended and the weather had become dark and stormy, so Veer-ji felt that this might actually be the perfect evening to initiate his plan. Standing under a tree, beneath the window of Dhola's bedchamber, he began to sing. He started with Raga Malhar, to welcome the clouds and rain, and then deftly slipped into notes of a new Raga he composed right then: Raga Maru Bihag, and into this, he wove the couplets of Maru's separation from her Dhola: 'Dhola Narawar seriyan; dhan Poongal galliyan.'

Sitting in his room, Dhola had been enjoying the soulful voice of the bard, quite caught up in the romance of the rain mingled with the monsoon raga. Then, when the notes shifted into a different raga—one he had never heard before—he listened more attentively. Suddenly, he heard the words Dhola and Poongal, and he was struck dumb. Faint memories stirred deep inside him, and, as the bard repeated the couplet, more and more memories of his childhood began to flood his mind. He began to recollect women in colourful ghagras, singing and dancing, a ritual fire and a ceremony, and then he remembered a little girl sitting in her mother's lap. As the bard continued to sing, describing Maru's moonlike beauty and her angst at being separated from her beloved, Dhola was filled with a strange sorrow and desperation. He sent for his servant and asked him to find out who was this bard singing near the palace and to summon him to the king's chamber, first thing in the morning.

The following day Dhola learned the whole story—about his childhood marriage, his no-show at the Teej festival, the mysterious disappearance of the five Poongal messengers and his waiting bride.

'Princess Maru is dying bit by bit,' Veer-ji told the king.

'Take me to her right away,' Dhola said, getting up in agitation.

When Maluwani found out that her Dhola was leaving for Poongal, she refused to let him go. 'How can you go now? It's the rainy season. I've heard that the road to Poongal becomes impassable at this time. I won't let you go,' she cried, holding on to her husband. Dhola loved Maluwani very much but, by now, his heart was pining for Maru. So that night, soon after Maluwani fell asleep, he slipped out of the palace and into the stables, where a groom was waiting with his most trusted black camel readied to make the long journey. 'Will you get me to my Maru, safely?' he whispered to the camel, rubbing his hand on her long black snout. Soon the two were headed towards the desert.

He was gone only a short distance, when he heard hoof-beats behind him. Dhola stopped and waited, quite sure he knew who this was. Sure enough, he saw a guard from the palace riding towards him at break-neck speed. When he reached the king, he hurriedly got off the horse and informed him: 'The queen. She collapsed after you left and died.'

Seeing a complete lack of grief on the guard's face, Dhola smiled. 'Go back and collect nine-maunds[47] of sandalwood and cremate the queen with all due ceremony.'

The guard lowered his eyes and folded his hands apologetically, 'I'm only following the queen's order, Maharaj.'

'I know and you have done your duty. Now return to the palace and tell the queen that you have conveyed her message.'

By this time, Dhola's quest to claim his bride had also reached the ears of another man—a powerful leader of a band of robbers. His name was Umar Sumaru, and he had been pursuing his own quest to marry Maru. He had sent many proposals for her to Raja Pingal, but the king had refused each one with the honest response that Maru was already married. Now, Umar Sumaru posted his men in the desert, along the path that he knew Dhola would take to go to Poongal. As Dhola made his way along this path, one of Sumaru's men met him, disguised as a traveller. He was on horseback, and coming abreast of Dhola's camel, he called out, 'I've heard that the bride that you're hoping to bring home is already married. Raja Pingal sent you many messages, but when you didn't respond to any of them, he married his daughter to someone else.'

'Who?'

'A rich merchant called Umar Sumaru.'

Dhola had heard about Umar Sumaru and knew that he led a band of robbers, and he was certain that Raja Pingal would never marry his daughter to a robber. 'Thank you for warning me,' Dhola replied to Sumaru's man. 'I will now go to Poongal and bid the princess farewell and give her my blessings.' Then, hefting his whip, he urged his camel to pick up the pace.

Raja Pingal and his wife were overjoyed to see Dhola. As soon as he arrived, they completed the wedding rituals, honouring their son-in-law with fitting ceremonies and gifts. Dhola and Maru were finally together. After spending a few days in Poongal, Dhola announced that it was time for him to return to Narwar, so Poongal began to prepare for the doli. On an auspicious day, the women of the town gathered to sing Bhadawo and bid a tearful farewell to their princess, who was, at last, going away to her husband's house.

Raja Pingal wanted to send his daughter off with an elaborate ceremonial caravan of royal guards, but Dhola refused this, deciding instead to take Maru on his camel's back. 'It'll be quicker and safer this way,' he told his father-in-law. He seated Maru before him on the back of his trusted camel, and the two set out for Narwar. They made good time the first day, but that evening, as they were resting in an oasis, a snake bit Maru on her heel. The poison spread slowly and Maru writhed in pain all night. Distraught, Dhola tried every herb he could find in the oasis, but nothing seemed to work, and as he watched the delirious Maru, he swore that if she died, he would drive his dagger into his heart and die along with her. Sometime during the night, he dozed off and had a dream: Shiva and Parvati were standing at Maru's side and telling Dhola not to give up hope. 'She'll be cured,' Parvati assured him. 'The world will tell the story of Dhola-Maru.' Dhola awoke with a start to find that Maru was, indeed, breathing more normally. The poison in her body seemed to be losing its potency, and within a few hours, she was fully recovered. Holding her in his arms, Dhola wept with relief. 'I can't lose you now,' he said. 'You were lost to me all my life, but now that

I've found you, you have become my life.'

Soon, they resumed their journey, but it was strenuous; although Maru had recovered, she was weak. Also, the sun was getting hotter by the minute and even though Dhola's black camel had an endless reserve of energy, carrying the weight of two had slowed her down.

Around midday, they came upon a camp with colourful pavilions. As they approached it, a man in fine merchant's clothes hailed them. 'Come and rest for a while,' he offered.

Dhola gratefully accepted his invitation. He let Maru go with the maids to the women's enclosure and, leaving his camel outside the pavilion, accompanied the merchant to the male enclosure, where he was offered a comfortable seat and a tall glass of amal.[48] Dhola began to take long swallows of the cool opium water, not realizing that the water was laced not with just a smidgen of opium, as was the custom of hospitality, but a heavy dose of it. He also didn't know that the host himself was no ordinary merchant; it was Umar Sumaru himself. His intention was to put Dhola into an opium daze, kill him, and then claim Maru.

As soon as Dhola finished his drink, Sumaru filled his glass again, and then again. With every glass, Dhola became more relaxed. Lying back against the silk pillows, he began to lose himself in the music of the bards. Sumaru had taken the chief singer into his confidence so that he would be able to help him with his plan. However, Sumaru did not know that the bard's wife was from Poongal and her husband had divulged Umar Sumaru's intention to her. Now, in the women's enclosure, this women took Maru aside and told her everything. 'Save your husband, Princess,' she advised.

Maru immediately ran outside, and mounting the camel that still stood near the pavilion, she kicked it hard. The camel gave a high-pitched bleat and took off at a trot. Hearing the bleat and recognizing it as his camel's, Dhola stood up.

'What happened? Sumaru asked. 'Come, sit down and finish your drink.'

But just then the camel grunted loudly, and Dhola realized that something was wrong. Dropping his glass, he ran outside.

'Get on,' Maru yelled. 'That's Umar Sumaru. He intends to kill you.'

Dhola leapt onto his camel's back, and he and Maru fled the camp. Sumaru followed in hot pursuit with his men, but Dhola's trusted camel, feeling the urgency, flew across the desert like the wind.

Dhola and Maru reached Narwar safely. By this time Maluwani had accepted the fate of a co-wife, and she welcomed her husband back and embraced Maru. Maruwani and Maluwani soon became like sisters and they lived happily with their Dhola.

Folktale from Rajasthan

◆

117

THE CREATION OF NIGHT

Yama died. Yami was bereft. The gods tried to console her many times, but each time she said to them, 'He died only today.' At that time there was only day, and no night; therefore, her grief was continuous and unabated. Then the gods said to each other, 'She will not be able to endure this. Let us create night.' The gods created night, and the following day, Yama's death was yesterday. Now, Yami could endure her bereavement.

Myth from the Yajur Veda

◆

118

LEAP OF KA LIKAI

In Meghalaya, near Cherrapunji, is India's highest waterfall, with the water plunging down 1,115 feet. This waterfall is called Nohkalikai, which, in the Khasi language means the leap of Ka Likai.

Ka Likai was a woman who lived in the village of Rangjyrteh, which is located above the falls. At that time, it was only a plateau of land. Ka Likai was happily married and had a lovely daughter, but a few years after her daughter was born, her husband died. She tried to fend for herself, but often she couldn't even feed her child, so her relatives talked her into marrying a local man, who had shown great interest in her.

The new husband took good care of Ka Likai, but he was very jealous of the little girl and grudged every minute that Ka Likai spent with her. Soon, he became so resentful that every time his wife left the house, he beat the little girl. However, in Ka Likai's presence, he pretended to love the child just as much as she did; hence Ka Likai never suspected anything.

One day, when Ka Likai returned from work, she saw that her daughter was not in the house. 'Where is she?' she asked her husband, who was cooking the evening meal. He greeted her with a loving smile and replied, 'She's just gone out to play. Why don't you eat? You must be hungry after your long day of work.'

Ka Likai was, indeed, quite hungry so she decided to eat first and then go out and fetch her daughter. After she finished her meal, which was very delicious, she reached for her jute box, in which she kept betel leaves. When she opened the box, she screamed, because sitting on top of the pile of betel leaves was a tiny little hand covered in blood. Ka Likai knew immediately that it was her daughter's. 'What have you done with her?' she asked her husband fearfully.

'You just ate her for your dinner,' her husband replied.

Ka Likai ran out of the house, crazed with shock and grief. She ran and ran, and, in her madness, she ran right off the edge of the plateau. Her grief was so crushing that water burst out of the top of the plateau and plunged down into the valley, sounding like Ka Likai's cries.

Folktale from the Khasi tribe

◆

119

SHIVA'S GRIEF

One day, Sati was sporting with her friends on Gandhamadana mountain when she saw a number of celestial sages on their way to some place. Soon, she saw a group of devas along with their sons and wives and attendants, all going in the same direction. They were followed by another party of celestials, and then, another. In fact, it seemed that everyone in the cosmos was headed to the same destination.

When Sati saw her sister, Rohini, with her husband, Chandra, also making their way to this place, she sent Vijaya, her friend and chief maid, to find out from Rohini where everyone was going.

Rohini told Vijaya that Daksha, their father, the leader of the Prajapatis, had organized a grand sacrifice at Kanakhala, the sacred town by the Ganga, to which everyone in the universe was invited.

When Vijaya conveyed this information to Sati, she could hardly believe it. 'Daksha is my father. How can he have such a grand sacrifice and not invite me, his own daughter, and my husband, Shiva, who is the Lord of Sacrifices?' Sati was sure that there was some logical reason behind this and went to Shiva to ask him what it was.

'Daksha is your father, my dear,' Shiva said, taking Sati on his lap, affectionately. 'But he thinks that because he is a Vishnu devotee, I'm his enemy. That's why he didn't invite me.'

'Are you his enemy?'

'Of course not. It's the people who have placed me and Vishnu on opposite sides. Those who believe they are on Vishnu's side reject me—like your father.'

'But you are the lord by whom sacrifice becomes fruitful. How can my father not invite you? In any case, I don't care whether we're invited or not, I want to go.'

'Dearest, one should not go where one is not invited.'

'I don't need an invitation to go to my father's house,' Sati insisted. 'I know that when he sees us, he'll be very pleased.'

'Dear one, even Indra would be belittled if he went uninvited,'

'Fine. If you feel belittled, don't go, but I'm certainly going. It's my father's house.'

Shiva feared that Sati would not be welcome at Daksha's sacrifice, but he also knew that he would not be able to dissuade his wife. He only hoped that Daksha would at least treat her with the love of a father and not upset her too much.

At the sacrifice, Daksha and Sage Dadhichi, who was Shiva's great devotee, were having a similar conversation. Dadhichi advised Daksha to immediately invite Shiva to the sacrifice, along with his wife, Sati. 'This sacrifice cannot be considered perfect and complete without the presence of the noble-souled, trident-holder, Shiva,' Dadhichi advised. 'Only he can sanctify the sacrifice. So, do yourself a favour and send Indra and the guardians and other important Brahmins to bring Shiva and Sati here immediately.'

'No,' said Daksha. 'Vishnu, in whom all the Vedas, sacrifices, and the rites are founded, has graced the sacrifice with his presence. Brahma, the grandfather of the worlds, has come from Brahmaloka. Indra, the king of gods, is here with his host of devas. What need do we have for Shiva? Yes, he's married to my daughter, but I was forced to give him my daughter on Brahma's insistence. He's not noble. In fact, he's the lord of goblins and ghosts and spirits. He's also conceited and arrogant and hostile. He's unworthy in all ways. I see no need to invite him.'

'Your sacrifice has become a non-sacrifice without Shiva,' Dadhichi declared, and, storming out of the palace with his followers, returned to his hermitage.

In the meantime, Sati quickly got dressed in her finest clothes and jewels. Then, with Nandi and sixty thousand attendants accompanying her, she left for her father's house, excited to be part of the festivities. At Kanakhala, Sati's mother and sisters welcomed her, but Daksha hardly spared her a glance. When Sati went to the sacrificial site, she saw roles allotted to all the important dignitaries. Vishnu was the presiding deity, Brahma was the director and guide of the Vedic rituals, and the Lokapalas of the quarters—Surya, Chandra, Vayu, Agni, Yama, Varuna, Indra and Kubera—were the gatekeepers. There were also eighty-six thousand ritvik priests to perform the sacrifice and sixty-four thousand udgatra priests, to sing the sacrificial hymns. Narada was the adhvaryu priest to ensure the accuracy of the sacrifice, and thousands of other priests were there to invoke the gods and sanctify the sacrifice. In addition, the seven sages were present to recite the hymns of the Sama Veda, and Sacrifice itself was present in its embodied form. However, there was not even a seat designated for Shiva.

Hurt and angry, Sati confronted her father, 'How is it that the highly auspicious Shiva, by whom the entire universe of the mobile and the immobile is sanctified, has not been invited? What is a sacrifice without Shiva, when he himself is sacrifice?' Then she turned to Vishnu and the other devas and said disdainfully, 'How is it that you, Vishnu, Brahma and others are present without your Lord Shiva?' She reminded them about all those incidents in which Shiva had proven superior to each one of them. 'Did you forget,' she admonished, 'that this entire universe was once burnt by his Linga?'

Vishnu and all the other gods heard Sati's words, and, although their minds were unsettled, they remained silent. But Daksha waved his daughter off. 'The inauspicious Shiva has been excluded from Vedic sacrifices. He is indecent and wicked and doesn't know our customs.'

'My husband may have matted hair and he may dress in deerskin and wear a garland of skulls, but sages and devas smear their foreheads with the dust of his feet. You are a sinner for not recognizing his greatness.'

'You are an uninvited guest in my house,' Daksha told his daughter. 'And yet you have the audacity to insult me. Your husband is not welcome here, and by association with him, neither are you. I didn't invite you. You can stay or leave, it's up to you.'

Sati was infuriated and in a dilemma. She wanted to leave, but she didn't have the courage to face Shiva. How would she tell him about the humiliation she suffered at her father's house? But if she stayed, she would continue to suffer the ignominy that her father had heaped on her. In fact, she felt so debased that she decided she would give up her body that was born of Daksha. She said to her father, 'I'm Dakshayani because I am born in your race, but no more. I'll abandon your race and you and my body.' So saying, Sati took a sip of sanctified water, removed her jewellery and fine clothing, leaving on only a single garment. She closed her eyes, and, focusing her thoughts on Shiva, entered a yogic trance. She generated so much heat in her body that it spontaneously combusted and flames broke out. Sati's body burned in the flames and she fell down, dead.

Mayhem broke loose at the sacrificial site. Those who witnessed Sati cast off her body, sat stunned. Some of Shiva's attendants, who had accompanied Sati, were so steeped in sorrow at seeing their mother kill herself that they cut off their own heads, but many others, fuming, attacked Daksha's guests with sharp weapons. Bhrigu, one of the priests, began pouring offerings into the sacrificial fire until thousands of ribhus—beings with superhuman powers—holding firebrands as weapons, arose from the fire and began fighting Shiva's attendants, killing many of them.

The remaining few attendants fled to Shiva, and wailing and sobbing, told him what had happened at Kanakhala. Shiva could not believe what his attendants were saying, so he called upon the divine sage, Narada, to confirm it. When Narada arrived and recounted the incident of Sati's immolation, such immense sorrow swelled in Shiva, that it transmuted into fury, and Shiva assumed his Rudra form of destroyer of the world. From his furious breath a hundred fevers and thirteen humours flew out in embodied form. Then he plucked out a clustre of his matted hair and struck the top of the mountain with it causing a loud, explosive reverberation that sounded like dissolution. From the first half clump of that hair, arose the powerful Virabhadra. He had a thousand heads, a thousand eyes, a thousand feet, and two thousand hands holding two thousand clubs. He was dressed in tiger skin, dripping with blood, and he bore a blazing bow and a battle axe. His massive form enveloped the world and he towered ten inches over it. He was Shiva's wrath.

From the other half of the clump of matted hair, Bhadrakali was born. She had black skin and a hideous countenance. Snakes were dripping from her whole body, and hanging around her neck were skulls and human heads. She was the fury of the Goddess.

'Oh Lord, command me,' Virabhadra roared.

'Destroy Daksha's sacrifice completely,' Shiva ordered, his eyes burning like copper. 'And if the devas, gandharvas, yakshas, or others interfere, reduce them to ashes. If Vishnu, Brahma, Indra, or Yama come in the way, destroy them. Burn them all with your fires, along with their wives. Even if someone comes and pleads with you to spare him, kill him. After you have burnt Daksha and all his kinsmen and their wives, drink up all the water and destroy the paraphernalia of the sacrifice.'

Virabhadra bowed to Shiva and quickly sped to Kanakhala, accompanied by crores more of Shiva's ganas, now also transformed into rudras. As his chariot rode across, the mountains crumbled, the earth quaked, the winds whirled, and the ocean grew agitated.

Bhadrakali, too, accompanied by nine Durgas—Kali, Katyayani, Isani, Chamunda, Mundamardini, Bhadrakali, Bhadra, Tvarita and Vaishnavi, and their sixty-four attendant yoginis, went ahead of Virabhadra to witness the destruction.

When Virabhadra, looking like apocalypse itself, arrived at Kanakhala with his massive force, Daksha became terrified. He fell at Vishnu's feet and begged him to save him. 'I started this sacrifice under your auspices. You are the only one who can save me.'

'I can't,' Vishnu told him, trembling in fear himself. 'I have no power to prevent this. Because of you, I myself have become an enemy of Shiva's. My Sudarshana Chakra will not cut him, because the Sudarshana itself belongs to Shiva. Even if Virabhadra had not arrived, this discus would have killed us all and returned to Shiva. Destruction is imminent. Even if we flee from this place and hide, Virabhadra will drag us out.'

Virabhadra, looking like a black fire, burst onto the sacrificial site. The ganas who came with him, uprooted the sacrificial posts and hurled them away and put all other paraphernalia into the flame. Virabhadra gouged out the eyes of Bhaga and smashed in Pusan's teeth. He killed the moon and cut off Indra's head. He cut off Agni's hands and pulled out his tongue and then kicked him on the head. He then smashed Yama's staff and hit the lord of the guardians, Ishana, with his trident. He killed three thousand, three hundred and thirty-three devas. When Vishnu lifted his discus, a terrible fight ensued, but Virabhadra rendered his discus immobile and cut his bow in three. Then he cut off his head and flung it into the netherworld. Sacrifice itself made to flee towards the sky in the guise of a deer, but Virabhadra caught it and beheaded it. He killed all the other devas too, and then he chopped off Daksha's head and threw it into the fire, where it burned to ashes. He also sliced off the tips of the noses of Saraswati and Aditi. Then he stood among the destruction like Rudra himself, ready to do more damage.

Finally, Brahma bowed before Virabhadra and begged him to stop. 'Calm your wrath,' he implored. 'All the heaven-dwellers are already destroyed.' At Brahma's words, Virabhadra quietened down. Then Shiva appeared, and at the request of Brahma, he restored all the gods to life and gave back the tips of the noses of Saraswati and Aditi. He couldn't restore Daksha's head, because it was reduced to ashes, but he placed in its stead the head of a goat. The gods then eulogized Shiva with glowing words and, begging his forgiveness, promised him that from then on, he would be allotted a share of the sacrifice.

His fury spent, Shiva was left with only his grief. He took Sati's charred body in his arms and went away. Inconsolable, maddened with sorrow, he began roaming the world, clutching Sati's decaying corpse close to his chest. He forgot everything else, even his divine function of death and destruction; consequently, the earth began to sink under the weight of people, who continued to be born, but did not die. Vishnu realized that as long as Shiva held Sati in his arms, his grief would consume him. Therefore, to restore the natural order, Vishnu hastened the decay of Sati's body by making it fall apart, bit by bit.[49] Wherever the body parts of the goddess fell on the earth, they became Shakti Peethas. To protect these portions of the goddess, Shiva created Bhairava from his being and entrusted him with the task. He himself, in his Shiva form, returned to Mount Kailash, where he transmuted his intense bereavement into yogic quietude, so that cosmic order could be restored.

Myth from the Puranas

◆

120

DASHRATHA'S CURSE

Dark, moisture-laden clouds spread across the sky. Frogs croaked and peacocks danced, and chitaka birds, their wings drenched, landed on trees that were dripping with raindrops. Rivers and lakes swelled with abundance and waterfalls cascaded from mountain-tops. It was the monsoon season, and the king of Ayodhya, Dashratha, was excited. He loved hunting in this season, because all the forest creatures came out of their lairs and filled the woods.

Early one morning, Dashratha set out to hunt elephants. These beasts normally came to the fords at the dark hour before dawn. Dashratha drove his chariot to the river Sarayu and, parking it near a bank, waited, ready with his bow. He could hardly see anything, but the king was renowned for his marksmanship—able to shoot accurately, just by sound. Soon, his ears picked up a sound coming from the river, like a pitcher being filled in the water—a sound that an elephant would make when sucking water into its trunk. Pulling out a sharp arrow from his quiver, he quickly attached it to the string of his bow and discharged it in the direction of the sound. The arrow hissed like a snake as it shot through the air, and then Dashratha heard a dull thwack, which told him that it had hit its mark. He waited to hear the trumpeting of a wounded elephant, but what he heard instead chilled his blood: a human wail and the sound of a small body falling into the shallow water.

Dropping his bow, and dismounting from his chariot, Dashratha ran to the spot. Dawn was just breaking and, in the dim light, he saw a youth writhing in pain at the edge of the water. An arrow was protruding from his chest, and a dark patch was spreading around him. There was a pitcher lying next to him.

'Forgive me,' Dashratha said to the boy, kneeling beside him, trying to think of how he could ease his pain.

'Why have you shot me?' The boy asked, his voice strained. 'I'm just a simple ascetic. What enmity do you have with me? I just came to the river to get water for my old parents.'

'I…I thought you were an elephant,' Dashratha replied. 'I was hunting and thought I heard an elephant.'

'I was just filling water to take to my old parents.'

'Forgive me, dear boy. I am Dashratha, king of Ayodhya.'

'It's not my forgiveness you must seek, O king. By shooting a single arrow, you have killed not just me but also my blind parents. They are waiting for me to bring them water. How long will they wait before their sightless eyes become stony, and their bodies expire from thirst and hunger? I was their only hope of subsistence. They'll not even know what happened to their son. If you have courage, go to them and tell them what you have done. If you tell them the truth, it's possible that my father will forgive you.'

'Tell me where they are.'

'Their hut is just beyond those trees. Go to them quickly and ask for their forgiveness. But before you go, do me a favour and pull out this arrow that is tormenting my body.'

The boy's request put Dashratha in an agonizing dilemma. If he extracted the arrow, the boy would quickly bleed to death, but if he left the arrow plugged in his heart, he would die a long and tortured death. Also, he wondered, if this was a Brahmin youth; had he just killed another human being, or had he also incurred the grievous sin of killing a Brahmin?

As if reading his mind, the dying boy said, 'I am an ascetic but not a Brahmin, don't worry, O king. My father is a Vaishya and my mother a Shudra. Can you help me die? I can't bear this pain.'

With trembling hands, Dashratha extracted the arrow, and all the life blood poured out of the boy's heart, turning the water of the Sarayu red.

Dashratha sat with the boy until he breathed his last. Then he picked up the pitcher, and, filling it with water, went quickly in the direction that the boy had told him to go. Soon, he came upon the hut and saw an old couple sitting outside, looking with sightless eyes towards the path. When Dashratha was a few feet away, the father spoke. 'Is that you Shravana? Come closer, dear boy. You sported in the water long enough today. Here, your mother is sitting waiting for you. She's been telling me that you may be angry with us for something we said. Dear son, children should never be angry with parents. Don't take anything we say to heart. We are your parents. You are our only support—our eyes. Come son, why do you not come to us? Have you brought water?'

Hearing the father mistake him for his son filled Dashratha with even more remorse. He almost lost his courage, but taking a deep breath, he stepped forward and fell at the feet of the old couple. 'I am Dashratha, the king of Ayodhya. I have killed your son by mistake. I thought what I heard in the water was an elephant and shot it, but it was your son filling a pitcher of water. I have come to beg your forgiveness. Please tell me what I can do.'

The couple sat numbly for moment, staring with their sightless eyes at Dashratha, and then they began sobbing. The father turned a tear-smeared face to Dashratha and said, 'If you had not confessed to this yourself, the curse of a virtuous father, whose son you have killed, would have split your head into a hundred pieces. Because you have committed this evil deed by accident and you have confessed to it, you are still alive. Take us to the place where our son lies dead.'

Dashratha led the old couple to the banks of the Sarayu and guided them to Shravana's body. The old parents fell on their lifeless son's body, sobbing and wailing. 'Why don't you greet me, son?' the father lamented. 'Why don't you embrace your mother? Come. Get up. See, dawn is breaking. Get up and offer your morning prayers.' Taking his son's shoulders, he tried to raise him, but he was so feeble that he fell into the water. 'Oh, dear boy, you have left us,' he wailed. 'Now who will gather fruits for us and who will feed us? How will I care for your old and blind mother, whose heart longs for her son? Wait, dear son. Don't go to Yama's house yet. Wait another day until your mother and I can accompany you. We'll go together.'

Finally, his grief spent, Shravana's father placed his hand on his dead son's head and blessed him. 'Go, if you must. I ask Yama to consider you a great warrior and give you a warrior's welcome. You are virtuous and sinless and you deserve to attain liberation.' Then he offered the final water libation to his son so that his soul could ascend to heaven in ethereal form.

The old parents lit a funeral pyre for their son, and they prepared themselves to join him in the flames. But before they climbed into the pyre, the old man turned towards Dashratha and said to him: 'I curse you that this agony that I am feeling at being separated from my son may be your agony too. May this agony kill you as it is killing me.'

Many years later, suffering in agony for Rama, whom he had sent into exile for fourteen years, Dashratha remembered this curse and, unable to bear the separation from his son, passed away.

Myth from the Ramayana

◆

121

THE WAY OF THE CROSS

'Crucify him!' the crowd shouted, and Pontius Pilate, the Roman prefect of Judea, pronounced the sentence, 'I condemn Jesus of Nazareth, the King of the Jews, to be crucified.'

The archers led Jesus into the centre of the court, and the slaves threw down the cross at his feet. They tied his two arms to the centrepiece, and, forcing him to kneel, placed the heavy cross on his right shoulder. Then they pulled him up with the rope they had tied around him, and the march began.[50]

The procession was headed by a trumpeter, who sounded his trumpet at every corner, proclaiming the sentence. Pilate's own cavalry of soldiers was at the head of the procession, followed by three hundred infantrymen. Many women and children also joined the procession, some wailing and some just curious. Among them was a little boy who had been given charge of the crown of thorns, which Jesus had been made to wear earlier. Jesus himself, his bare feet swollen and bleeding, his whole body covered with wounds and blood from the scourging he had received the day before, trudged on, his back bent, sinking under the weight of the wooden cross. He was weak from loss of blood, his throat was parched, and he was burning from pain and fever. Behind Jesus were two thieves, Dismas and Gesmas, arrested for killing a Jewish woman. They were carrying their own crosses; one of them bore his stoically, while the other cursed and swore.

Jesus was led through a narrow and dirty back street, so as not to disturb the good citizens of Jerusalem on their way to the temple. But many people who lived on this street had taken time off from their day to watch the procession. They stood on the roofs of their houses or at their windows and, as Jesus passed, they yelled out insults. The slaves working in the street threw filth and mud at him, and the children filled their pinafores with sharp stones, and emptied them out in Jesus's path.

When the procession entered a wider street, more people came to watch the condemned men. This street was full of puddles, as it always happened every time it rained. People filled the deeper potholes with large stones so as to make it easier to cross, but Jesus could not lift his weary feet high enough to step on the stones. At one particularly big puddle, he tripped and fell, and the cross he was carrying landed by his side. The soldiers struck him with their whips and jerked on his ropes to make him rise, cursing at him. One of them took the crown of thorns from the boy and, jeering at Jesus, placed it once again on his head. They then hauled him out of the mud and put the cross back on his shoulder.

Mary, mother of Jesus, stood at the entrance of a residence that was on the way to Calvary, where the execution was to take place. She was waiting for the procession to pass that way. When she saw her son, sinking under the weight of the cross, still crowned with thorns, she wept. When the son looked at his mother, his control shattered a little, and his knees buckled and he fell again, this time on his hands and knees. Mary rushed into the street, blind to the executioners, the soldiers, and the crowd. All she could see was her son, suffering. She threw herself on her knees by his side and embraced him, but the soldiers ordered her to leave. She staggered away with the help of John and the other women and went to stand against a stone wall. There was so much anguish in her that the hand that clutched the stone wall left an impression on it forever.

Under an archway in a wall, Jesus stumbled again, but this time when he fell, he couldn't rise, despite the prodding and pulling. The soldiers, afraid that he might die here before he reached the place of execution, seized a man passing by with his three young children, and ordered him to help Jesus carry the cross. This was Simon of Cyreme, a pagan. He raised Jesus and, lifting the cross, took some of its weight on his own shoulder. As he walked behind Jesus, a strange peace descended on him.

The next street was long and lined with beautiful houses. As the procession passed through it, the door of one palatial house opened and a majestic woman named Seraphia stepped out, holding a young girl by the hand. They made their way through the mob, and when they reached Jesus, the woman fell on her knees before him. 'Let me wipe the face of my Lord,' she said gently and offered a veil to him. He took it in his left hand and pressed it to his face, wiping the sweat and blood with it, and then returned it to her. She kissed the veil and put it under her cloak. Her little girl wanted to offer Jesus wine from a jug she was carrying, but the soldiers pushed the jug away and struck Jesus more harshly than before. Seraphia returned to her house, carrying the veil on which the bloody face of Jesus had become imprinted in a perfect likeness. Later, Seraphia came to be known as Veronica—true portrait.

At the beginning of the road to Calvary, a group of women, carrying their young in their arms, waited for Jesus under the gate. When they saw Jesus's condition, they wept and lamented. Jesus stopped and looked at them with sadness, and said, 'Daughters of Jerusalem, don't weep for me, but weep for yourselves and for your children, because those days shall come when people will say that the wombs that are barren are blessed. Then they will tell the mountains to fall on them and the hills to cover them, because if they can do these atrocious things in prosperous times, what will they do in times of want?' The women wailed at his words, and the soldiers struck Jesus again, and the procession moved on.

When the procession reached the mountainous top of Calvary, Jesus crumpled to the ground. Simon wanted to help him again, but the soldiers pushed him away and dragged Jesus to the spot where his cross would be erected. First, they untied him and placed him on the cross to measure him against the wood, marking the places for his feet and hands. Then they shoved him into a cave while they prepared for his crucifixion. They nailed a board at the bottom of the cross, where the feet would rest and cut a hollow in the wood, where the head would rest. Instead of hanging suspended, they wanted his body to rest against the cross so that his torture would be prolonged. After that, they dug a deep hole in the ground so that the wooden cross would fall easily into it. There were eighteen men on the execution platform, strangers, in the pay of the Jews and Romans—short, thick-set men with ferocious faces, like wild beasts, drinking and joking as they made the preparations for the execution.

When they dragged Jesus out of the cave, they tried to pull off the cloak which his mother had woven for him, but the garment caught in the thorns of the crown on his head. Underneath, he wore only a short woollen scapular and a linen loincloth. His body was covered with open wounds and his shoulders and back were torn to the bone. After they stripped him, they made him lie on the cross to nail him to it. One man opened Jesus's arms and attached his right hand to the cross with a cord, another man knelt on his chest to hold him down, yet another flattened his palm, and another took a long nail, as thick as a man's thumb, and hammered it in, driving it right through the sinews of Jesus's palm into the wood of the cross. A groan escaped Jesus's lips, and blood gushed from the wound and splattered the men. Then they began on the left hand, but when they tried to pull the arm to place the hand in the hollow they had made, it didn't reach, so they pulled harder, until it dislocated. They drove the nail into that palm as well, but all Jesus could muster at this point were some weak groans. Next, they placed his feet upon the board, and, tying his knees to the cross, pulled and stretched, until his feet reached the board. Fastening the left foot to the right, they bored a hole in the feet and drove a nail through them until it went through the wood.

After that, they nailed the board that Pilate had inscribed in Latin to the top of the cross: *Iēsūs Nazarēnus, Rex Iūdaeōrum* (INRI)—Jesus the Nazarene, King of the Jews.

Once Jesus was nailed to the cross, they raised it, using ropes to make it stand erect. When they dropped it into the hole, hammering in five stakes to keep it steady, the crowd that until this moment had been loud and noisy, suddenly grew quiet. It was as though the cosmos realized the reality of what was happening: the cross of the deliverer was planted on earth.

There he hung from the cross, the crown of thorns still on his head, his mouth open from exhaustion and thirst, his hair and beard clotted with blood, his chest torn, his joints extended, dislocated, his skin stretched taut so that each rib was visible, blood trickling down from the gaping wounds in his hands and feet. He looked on the verge of death, and yet there was dignity in his face.

The crosses of the two thieves, Dismas and Gesmas, were then also raised, one on each side of Jesus. Gesmas the older thief, noticing Jesus's face had become paler, shouted, 'The demon that possessed him is about to leave him.'

Fearing that he was going to die, one of the soldiers took a sponge soaked with vinegar and, raising it on a pole to press it to Jesus's lips, said, 'If you are truly the King of Jews, save yourself. Come down from the cross.'

Jesus raised his head a little and uttered, 'Father, forgive them, for they know not what they do.'

And Gesmas cried out, 'If you are the Christ, save yourself and us.'

Dismas, the younger thief, called in a loud and angry voice, 'How can you insult him, when he is praying for you?' When he was a youth, Jesus had cured him of leprosy. 'He is truly a Prophet,' he now said. 'He is our King—he is the Son of God.' But Gesmas kept insulting Jesus. 'How can you not fear God?' Dismas shouted at him. 'You are condemned and justly so. You and I—we receive our due reward for our deeds, but this man has done no evil. You are now at the point of death. Repent.' And Gesmas repented. He said to Jesus, 'If you condemn me, it will be with justice.' And Jesus replied, 'You will experience my mercy.'

That morning, when Pilate had passed the sentence, a little hail had fallen, but by noon, when Jesus was crucified, the sun had come out. Now a thick red fog covered the sky, and the moon covered the sun, and as the day grew darker, everyone, except Mary and the most faithful, left.

Dismas raised his head and said to Jesus, 'Lord, remember me when you shall come into your kingdom.'

'I say to you. This day, you shall be with me in Paradise,' Jesus replied.

Mary heard her son and begged him to let her die with him. He looked tenderly at her and said, 'Woman, behold your son.' Then to John, his disciple, he said, 'Behold your mother.' And from that day on John looked upon Mary as his own mother.

In the ninth hour—in the darkest, loneliest hour of the eclipse, words spilled from Jesus's mouth: 'Eloi, Eloi, lama sabacthani?' (My God, My God, why have you forsaken me?)

Slowly, light returned and, in the increasing brightness, the paleness of Jesus's body became more visible. He had lost a vast amount of blood. 'I thirst,' he whispered. The disciples who were standing around the cross, bribed the soldiers to give him a little water, but the soldiers refused. Then they dipped a sponge in vinegar and gall to press it on Jesus's lips, but Abenadar, a Roman soldier, squeezed out the gall and poured some fresh vinegar on it. Fastening it to a lance, he raised it to Jesus' lips.

At last the hour of his death came—about three in the afternoon—and a cold sweat broke out on his body. John was standing near the foot of the cross, Mary Magdalene was sitting on the ground behind the cross, and Mary was standing nearby, looking at her dying son. 'It is finished,'

Jesus whispered, and raising his head a little, said clearly, 'Father, into your hands, I commend my spirit.' Then he bowed his head and gave up the ghost.

But the soldiers thought that Jesus was only pretending to be dead, so they decided to break his arms and legs to hasten his death, as they had done with Dismas and Gesmas. But there was among them a subaltern officer, Cassius, who was filled with remorse and sorrow. He quickly took his lance and thrust it so completely into the right side of Jesus that the point went through his heart and appeared on the left side. When he drew his lance out, blood rushed out, pouring over Cassius's face, filling him with repentance.

When they knew he was no more, Nicodemus and Joseph placed ladders behind the cross and, fastening Jesus's body with three straps, slowly pushed out the nails from his hands and feet. Cassius received these and placed them before Mary. Slowly, lowering the body to the ground, they wrapped it in linen, from knees to waist, and placed it in the arms of Mary. She held her son, his head against her raised knee, and his body stretched out on a sheet that had been laid out on the ground. While Magdalene pressed her face to his feet, Mary, mother of Jesus, held her son. She removed the crown of thorns from his head, and, taking up the sponge, began washing his body with water and tears. Then the others helped her clean the rest of his body with water of myrrh and embalm it with herbs and spices and sweet, scented powder. Crossing his stiffened arms over his chest, they wrapped more linen around him, swaddling him like an infant. This linen sheet forever bore the imprint of his body.

Finally, by the light of torches, they carried Jesus's body to the dark grotto that had been newly excavated, and laid it out. Mary kissed her son's face and Mary Magdalene his feet, and then everyone left. The men closed the grotto with the metal folding door, on which were two sticks—one straight down and the other across to form a perfect cross, and, rolling a large rock in front of its entrance, closed it off.

Myth from the New Testament

◆

122

THE EXTREME SUFFERING OF RAJA HARISHCHANDRA

Raja Harishchandra, king of Ayodhya, was renowned for his truthfulness and charity. He was loved by his subjects and honoured by the gods; however, he himself had one constant sorrow: he didn't have any children. 'I understand that each man must live his fate,' he said to his family priest, the highly evolved Rishi Vasishtha. 'But a man needs a son for his salvation. Even the sparrows are happier than I am, because they have offspring to nurture. Help me alleviate this grief. You are a master of mantras. Surely you must know a mantra which can help me procure a son.'

'Being childless is certainly a grave cause of sorrow for men,' Vasishtha replied. 'My advice to you is to pray to Lord Varuna. He is benevolent and a bestower of sons. Worship him with wholehearted devotion. Desires are achieved not only through fate but also effort. Put in the effort and you'll surely be rewarded by Varuna.'

Raja Harishchandra gladly set his mind on Lord Varuna and did tapasya for many years, sitting on Ganga's bank. Finally, the Lord of the Waters, who holds the divine noose of punishment, appeared before the king and asked him what he desired.

Harishchandra prostrated himself and said, 'O Lord Varuna, a son will free me from the three debts I owe to the devas, the ancestors, and the rishis. I desire a son.'

'I'll give you a son,' Varuna stated. 'What will you give me in return?'

'Anything. Ask for anything, Lord.'

'Are you willing to sacrifice your son in my honour?'

Raja Harishchandra was dumbfounded. He didn't know what to say, but then he thought, surely the god will not ask me to immolate the very son he gifts to me. Surely, this is a test. Let me get the son first, and then when the time comes, I'll worry about this contrary deal. And so he said to Varuna, 'Free me from this sorrow of being without an heir, O giver of boons, and I'll perform a yajna in your honour and sacrifice my son.'

'Then you shall have a son,' Varuna promised. 'Go home with my assurance, but make sure that you fulfil your promise.'

Harishchandra returned home a happy man and told his queen,

Shaivya, about Varuna's promise. Soon the queen became pregnant and, nine months later, on an auspicious day, when the planets were most favourable, she delivered a baby boy so beautiful, he looked like he was the offspring of the gods. The king, his happiness knowing no bounds, completed all the boy's natal ceremonies, named him Rohit, and then invited the whole kingdom to celebrate. Amidst much music, food, and dancing, he gave away in charity huge quantities of jewels and gold in honour of his son.

While the palace was in the midst of these celebrations, a Brahmin came to the gates and requested to see the king. When he was taken inside, he said to Harishchandra, 'I am Varuna. I've come to remind you of the sacrifice you promised me.'

Harishchandra's heart stopped. Drawing in a deep breath, he gathered himself together and then began the welcome rituals that are reserved for the highest Brahmins, spending as long as possible on each activity, his mind devising strategies to circumvent the promise he had made. Finally, once Varuna had been appropriately honoured, Harishchandra said, 'I haven't forgotten my promise, O god of gods. But I'm in a dilemma. In a human sacrifice, when the victim is immolated, both the husband and wife are entitled to the benefits of the ceremony. But my wife and I are not in a position now to reap these benefits, because after the birth of a child, the father becomes purified only on the tenth day and the mother at the end of a month. So, you see, in order to allow my queen the benefit that is due to her, I'm unable to perform the sacrifice for a month. Do you see my moral dilemma? You are all-knowing and the keeper of dharma, please show me and my queen mercy and allow us one month.'

'Fine,' Varun replied. 'I'll return after a month.'

The celebrations in Ayodhya continued after Varuna left, but they were very subdued, and a month later, Varuna-deva once again arrived at the palace. 'Bring your son, O king,' he ordered. 'Let the altar be built.'

This time Harishchandra was more prepared: 'Welcome, O great god,' he said obsequiously. 'My house has been sanctified with the touch of your feet. I welcome you with honour and respect, and I assure you that I haven't forgotten my promise at all. In fact, I think about it day and night, and I'm fully prepared to perform the sacrifice. But I'm also concerned about your honour. The high Brahmins say that those who have no teeth are not fit for the sacrifice. My son has no teeth yet, and I would not dream of dishonouring you. Once my son's teeth have emerged, I'll sacrifice him with due rites and rituals. I beg you to allow this extension, which dharma makes unavoidable.'

'Fine,' said Varuna. 'Let the boy get his teeth, but then you must perform the sacrifice.'

'Of course, my Lord,' Harishchandra bowed low and thanked the god. Then, having received this long reprieve, he began to enjoy fatherhood. Months passed. The boy's milk teeth began to appear, and within three years, he had all his teeth. But after the initial rituals of the first milk teeth, Harishchandra kept his son's increasing number of teeth under wraps. Of course, nothing is hidden from Varuna, and as soon as the boy's last molars had grown, he appeared again in Harishchandra's palace. 'Now begin the sacrifice, King,' he called. 'I can't wait any more.'

But, once again, Harishchandra was ready with an excuse. 'Begging your pardon, O god of gods, O knower of all truth, O upholder of dharma,' he said with bowed head. 'I've heard from elders and Brahmins that until a child has been through his tonsure ceremony of Chudakaran, he's not fit to be sacrificed, because he still has the hair he was born with. As soon as his head is ritually shaved, I'll immediately prepare him for sacrifice. You've been so patient, God. I plead with you in the name of dharma to wait just a few more years.'

'Enough!' Varuna shouted. 'You've been deceiving me all this time, but I will not be deceived any more. This is your last excuse. When I return after the child's Chudakaran, if you don't fulfil your promise, I'll curse you for breaking your word.'

However, on the boy's tonsure ceremony, too, Harishchandra was able to stall Varuna by saying that the three upper castes—Brahmins, Kshatriyas and Vaishyas—are considered twice-born only after their Upanayana—the sacred thread ceremony. This time, too, Varuna ranted and fumed, but once again, he allowed the delay, and then when he came to the thread ceremony, Harishchandra was able to buy even more time, till after the boy's Samvartana, when he concluded his formal education at the guru's ashram and returned home.[51] 'I make you a solemn promise that after his Samvartana I definitely will perform the sacrifice, and with full pomp and show,' he said to Varuna.

Varuna grumbled and growled, and then warning Harishchandra, 'Fulfil your promise at the boy's Samvartana, or be prepared,' he left.

By the time Rohit concluded his education, he was a young man and was acquainted with his father's promise to Varuna. He was also aware that his father had run out of excuses and would no longer be able avert his death, so after he was released from his guru's ashram, he decided not to go home and went to the forest instead, without informing his parents. Harishchandra and his wife continued to prepare for his Samvartana ceremony, and when Varuna showed up in Ayodhya, Harishchandra fell at his feet. 'I had every intention of sacrificing the boy today,' he cried. 'Believe me, O merciful deva. I was fully prepared. But now the boy has disappeared. I have had people looking for him everywhere, but we just can't find him.'

'I curse you,' Varun thundered. 'I curse you for deceiving me for years. For breaking your promise, may you be afflicted with dropsy.'

Instantly, Harishchandra's body began swelling from edema, and he took to his bed, wracked with pain. When Rohit heard about his father's condition, he thought about returning home, but Indra visited him in the forest and advised him not to go: 'Not only does your father owe Varuna, but now he also wants to rid himself of the disease. If you go home now, your death is certain.' Hence, Rohit decided that it was best for him to stay away from home.

A few more years passed. Rohit received news about Harishchandra's condition quite regularly, and then, one day, he heard that his father was dying. Thinking it was time he fulfilled his filial duty, Rohit prepared to leave for Ayodhya, but Indra visited him once again and dissuaded him. 'Your father is on his deathbed, and if you go home now, he'll surely sacrifice you to save himself. But he's an old man now, and even if he is cured of his disease, he will die soon anyway. My advice to you is to stay here and let him pass. Along with him Varuna's threat will also pass. Then, return home and take your rightful place as king.'

By now Harishchandra's edema had reached his heart, and he suffered grievously. 'You must find a way to help me get rid of this disease,' he begged his priest, Vasishtha.

'This sickness has been given to you by Varuna, and the only way you can be rid of it is if you fulfil the promise you made to him.'

'I would if I could find Rohit.'

'The promise you made did not specify which son you will sacrifice to Varuna. Just that you will sacrifice your son. So sacrifice another son.'

'But, you know that I don't have another son.'

'The scriptures say that there are ten ways for a man to acquire a son, and one of them is to buy a son. Surely in your kingdom there's a Brahmin who'll be willing to sell you his son for the right price.'

Pleasantly surprised to learn at how easy this could have been, Harishchandra made enquiries in his kingdom and soon found a very poor Brahmin named Ajigarta who had three sons, whom he could barely feed. The king offered to pay him a hundred cows for one of his sons to be sacrificed to Varuna, and the Brahmin willingly sold this middle son, Sunasepha. Harishchandra first officially adopted the boy with rituals, and then he prepared him for the sacrifice to Varuna.

Tied to the sacrificial post, Sunasepha wept so piteously that the slaughterer who was hired to slaughter him for the sacrifice would not pick up his weapon. Harishchandra ordered many others to kill the boy, but no one was willing. Then Sunasepha's own father came forward: 'O king,' he said. 'If you double the price, I myself will kill this boy so that you can complete the sacrifice.' Harishchandra immediately agreed to pay him one hundred additional cows.

When the father picked up the axe and raised it to slay his son, everyone present at the sacrifice cried out in shock. Someone said, 'What nature of a father is this, who is ready to kill his own son for wealth?' Others asked, 'Is this a Brahmin or a Chandala in a Brahmin's body?' And some others shouted at the father, 'Have you forgotten all tenets of dharma? They say a son is born of one's own soul. What salvation will you seek after you slay your own soul?'

Such a hue and cry arose from the people gathered at the site that the rituals could not proceed. The great Rishi Vishwamitra was also at the sacrifice, and he was filled with pity for the crying boy. 'Spare this boy, King,' he called to Harishchandra. 'Human sacrifices are performed to gain material desires, like wealth. He who wants his own welfare and who wants to preserve his own body ought not to cut another's body. Mercy is the highest virtue. If you practice mercy, you will be rewarded, but if you kill this son to fulfil your own promise to Varuna, you will incur the high sin of injuring another.'

'I am already suffering,' the king stated. 'What more can happen to me?'

Then Rishi Vasishtha confronted Rishi Vishwamitra, who was his arch-rival. 'What are you doing here? This sacrifice is under my auspices.' 'Who are you to obstruct it?'

Vishwamitra had arrived here with the purpose of heckling his rival, but now he was genuinely distressed at the boy's plight, so he went to the boy and whispered to him the secret Varuna mantra. 'Keep repeating this,' he told the boy, 'and Varuna will protect you.'

Sunasepha repeated the mantra fervently, and within minutes, the Lord of Waters manifested in his full splendour at the site of the sacrifice. Seeing him, Harishchandra fell to his knees and begged his forgiveness. 'I have been deluded by my own desires—first for a son and then a cure for my disease,' he sobbed. 'In my delusion I almost killed this boy. I'm a sinner, but I beg you to have mercy on me.' Varuna was pleased with the king's repentance. He freed the boy and forgave Harishchandra and restored him back to health. Healthy in body and freed of his obligation to Varuna, Harishchandra declared, then and there, that he would perform the Rajasuya Yajna for the prosperity and well-being of his subjects.

When this news reached Rohit in the forest, he immediately set off for home. Finally, reuniting with his son, Harishchandra celebrated the yajna with him, under the auspices of their family priest, Rishi Vasishtha.

Many years passed. One day, Indra organized a ceremony in Indraloka to which he invited all the Brahmarishis, including Rishi Vasishtha and Rishi Vishwamitra. These two rishis were bitter enemies, and the Harishchandra incident had further fueled their animosity. When they saw each other in Indraloka, a face-off was inevitable: 'You don't belong here,' Vishwamitra told Vasishtha. 'Only the highest Brahmins are invited. What credentials do you have?'

'I'm the high priest of Raja Harishchandra and the whole Ikshvaku clan—those kings are legendary for their truthfulness, charity, and dharma.'

Vishwamitra laughed. 'Is this the same Harishchandra who deceived Varuna-deva for years, and then, for his own benefit, was ready to slaughter a poor Brahmin boy?'

'At least he does not breach the dharma of crashing another priest's sacrifice site. He's a virtuous king, but you wouldn't know what virtue is.'

'I'll prove to you that your Raja Harishchandra is nothing but a liar and cheat, and if I fail to prove this, may I lose all my knowledge,' Vishwamitra challenged Vasishtha. And so the two rishis set out to defeat each other, wagering Harishchandra.

One day, Harishchandra was riding in the forest when he came upon a beautiful woman, who was sitting by a river and weeping. Dismounting, the king approached her and asked, 'Can I be of help, fair maiden? Don't be afraid. I'm Raja Harishchandra. In my kingdom, anyone who makes another unhappy is severely punished. Tell me, who has hurt you?'

'I'm Siddharupini, the manifestation of Success. Rishi Vishwamitra is trying to bring me under his control so that he'll be successful in whatever endeavour he undertakes. He's performing very difficult tapasya for this, and it's affecting me; I'm in pain. Can you stop him?'

'Surely,' the king assured her and went immediately to Vishwamitra's ashram, where he saw the rishi sitting in deep meditation, his body frail and emaciated. The king stood before him with folded hands and called loudly, 'O Maharishi! Stop. For what purpose are you doing tapasya? Tell me and I'll fulfil your desires. There's no need for you to ail your body with this severe austerity. Your practice is also causing trouble to the people in my kingdom, and I can't allow this. I prohibit you from doing this tapasya.'

Vishwamitra looked at the king with wrath-filled eyes, ready to burn him to ashes. But then, for some reason, he changed his mind. 'Here. I have stopped my tapasya, at your request,' he said to Harishchandra. 'Now you should go back and take care of your kingdom.'

By the time Harishchandra reached Ayodhya, time had rolled back many years. Harishchandra was once again a young man and returning from a successful hunt. As he neared his palace, he saw people running around in panic. They informed him that a monstrous boar had come into the city, wreaking havoc, trampling crops, bringing down walls, and goring people with his great big tusks. The king quickly turned his horse around and, calling his soldiers, set off to hunt the animal down. When the boar saw Harishchandra, he fled into the forest. The king chased him for a while and then lost sight of him, but by this time, he had left his soldiers behind and had gone so deep into the forest, that he could not find his way back. He was also hungry and thirsty, so he began searching for water. Suddenly, he came upon a beautiful, clear river with blue waters and fruit trees on its banks. Harishchandra quenched his thirst and ate some fruit, and then sat down under a tree to figure out how to get home, but because he was thoroughly exhausted, he soon fell asleep.

When he opened his eyes, a rishi was standing before him. 'Greetings,

King,' the rishi said. 'What are you doing here so far away from town?'

Harishchandra greeted the rishi and told him how he had got lost while pursuing a wild beast. 'Can you help me find my way back?' he asked. 'I'll reward you with great wealth.'

'I'm Vishwamitra, and I'll show you the way, but I don't want great wealth. My son is getting married, and all I want is help with the ceremony.'

'It'll be my pleasure to cover the full cost of the ceremony,' the king offered.

'Then come with me to my hermitage and we'll collect my son and his bride to be, and then we'll all go to Ayodhya, where they can be married.'

Accompanied by the rishi and the young couple, Harishchandra returned to Ayodhya, where he organized an elaborate wedding ceremony. After the nuptials were completed, Vishwamitra turned to Harishchandra and said, 'Won't you give the bridegroom a marriage gift? I hear you're a very charitable king.'

'Certainly. What can I give your son? Ask me for anything. My generosity knows no bounds.'

'Then, O king, I ask you to give to this bridegroom, your entire kingdom, the royal umbrella, and all your elephants, horses, chariots, infantry, and all the gems and jewels in your treasury.'

'I give your son this vast kingdom,' Harishchandra said without a moment's hesitation.

'It's done,' Vishwamitra declared. 'But now you must give me my dakshina. My Brahmin's fee. A gift without a Brahmin's dakshina is fruitless; to get the benefit of your gift, you must give me my dakshina as fixed.'

The king was a bit taken aback. He wondered how he would come up with the dakshina, now that he had lost his kingdom and all his wealth. But his concern was momentary. He had no doubt that he would be able to, somehow, procure the small sum for the rishi's dakshina, so he asked: 'Kindly tell me what is your dakshina, O rishi?'

'Two and a half loads of gold.'

This time, the earth shifted from under Harishchandra's feet. Two and a half loads of gold was not a small amount, even when one had wealth; in his current penurious state, it was an impossible sum. Promising the rishi that he would pay him on the morrow, Harishchandra mounted his horse and rode to his palace, deeply worried about how he would procure the gold.

'Where have you been?' his queen asked him, as soon as he entered the palace. 'We've been so worried.'

Without responding to her, Harishchandra went straight to his bedchamber and fell asleep in his bed of silken sheets. When he awoke in the morning a guard was waiting to deliver a message. 'Rishi Vishwamitra is at the door, demanding to see you,' he informed the king. Harishchandra quickly dressed, thinking that he would request the rishi for an extension on the dakshina. However, as soon as he stepped into the assembly hall, Vishwamitra pounced on him: 'I did not give you permission to sleep in my bedchamber,' he castigated. 'If you needed a place to sleep for the night, you should have come to me and I would have allowed you to stay one night as my guest.'

Harishchandra looked at the rishi in confusion.

'Don't look so confused, O king,' Vishwamitra laughed derisively. 'Have you already forgotten that you gave away your kingdom, you palace, your wealth, your soldiers—your whole dominion—as a gift to my son. And because it is all my son's, it belongs to me. Now leave my palace and take your family with you.'

The full import of what he had done struck Harishchandra, and he finally realized that he was completely destitute. But he was a dharma king renowned for his charity and truthfulness, so he bowed to Vishwamitra. 'Please accept my apologies,' he said. 'I'll leave the kingdom immediately. Let me just go back and get my queen and son.'

The citizenry of Ayodhya was thunderstruck at the news that their king was leaving. Weeping piteously, they begged Vishwamitra to return the kingdom to their beloved Raja Harishchandra, but the rishi was not moved. Not only that, when the king and his family were on their way out, he accosted Harishchandra. 'And what about my dakshina?' he demanded. 'You still haven't paid that. Of course, if you can't pay that, or if you want your kingdom back, then just admit that you lied, and I'll give it all back.'

'I am the scion of the Ikshvaku dynasty,' Harishchandra replied indignantly. 'I never lie. I've promised to pay you a dakshina of two and a half loads of gold, and you shall have it. It's true that I don't have the gold at this moment, but I'll work for it and pay you your dakshina in a month. This is my word.'

Harishchandra took his wife, Shaivya, and his young son, Rohit and walked out of Ayodhya. They journeyed on foot for many weeks, having only the fruit from the trees in the forest to eat and the hard ground to sleep on. Their clothes became rags and their bodies thin like that of beggars, when finally, they arrived in Kashi, the city of Shiva. This city was not owned by any king or Brahmin but was Shiva's own. Harishchandra was sure that in this city of devotion to the ascetic god, he would be able to find work that would allow him to take care of his family and also pay his debt to Vishwamitra. However, after searching for weeks, he discovered that he was unemployable. The only work people could offer him was that of a low-caste servant, and he, a Kshatriya, was unwilling to do the work of a Shudra.

And then the month was up, and Vishwamitra was in Banaras, seeking out the king, who, at that time, was living with his family in a broken-down shack near a field. 'I've come for my dakshina,' the rishi announced. 'Give it to me.'

Harishchandra was distressed to see Vishwamitra, but he still had faith in himself. 'It's only the morning of the day, O rishi. Come back later today and I'll have the gold.'

Shaivya had watched her husband's growing frustration all month, and she knew that his faith in himself was more his bravado, which was actually disguising his sense of hopelessness. She herself was growing quite desperate, because even after searching for a month, her husband had no job, and they had no food left, not even to feed their son. After the rishi left, she said to Harishchandra, 'This city seems to have many wealthy Brahmins; why don't you beg a Brahmin to give you the money in charity?'

'I'm a Kshatriya. I can't beg,' Harishchandra declared. 'I'll find another way.'

Just then Rohit began crying from hunger pains, and Shaivya finally lost her sangfroid. 'Then sell me,' she cried. 'I'm able-bodied and I don't have any Kshatriya inhibitions about serving someone. From the money you make from my sale, pay the evil Vishwamitra and feed our boy.'

'What are you saying, Shaivya,' Harishchandra was outraged. 'I'll rot in hell for selling the wife I married with Vedic rituals and promised to protect and preserve all my life.'

'Will it be better that that evil Brahmin curse you for not paying his dakshina? Will that not be a greater adharma? Sell me, I'm telling you.'

Harishchandra shook his head and searched extra hard for work that day, but soon it was evening and there was Vishwamitra again, mocking him. 'Just a few hours remain,' he warned. 'If you can't pay my dakshina, just tell me, instead of lying to me.'

'I still have a few hours, O rishi,' the king declared, his eyes burning with anger, but his voice servile.

'Fine. Take the few more hours. I'll be back soon.'

'I don't think we have a choice anymore,' Shaivya began to weep. 'Sell me. You'll not incur any sin, because you won't be doing it for personal gain, it'll be to save us all from suffering the grave sin of not fulfiling our word to the Brahmin. Don't hesitate, dear husband. It's evening already, and if you don't hurry, all the merchants will will be gone.'

His heart breaking and his hands shaking, Harishchandra took his beautiful and delicate wife by the arm and stood her in the market square. Then, with a throat choking with tears, he began calling: 'Is anyone looking for a maidservant? Here is this woman, my wife, who I am selling to anyone who will buy her for a price.'

'What nature of man are you who is selling his wife?' a passerby said with disgust.

Just then an old Brahmin came on the scene and bid for Shaivya, 'How much are you asking for her?' he asked Harishchandra.

'For me her value surpasses all the wealth in the world, but you, sir, decide a price.'

'According to the dharma shastras, the price of a female servant who is clever, good, well-qualified, and in possession of thirty-two auspicious qualities is one koti gold mohurs, and that is what I'll pay you.'

That price did not cover the full dakshina, but Harishchandra had no choice and he handed over his wife for the gold. The old man put the money on the ground and grabbed Shaivya by the hair. When she cried out in pain, her son, Rohit, ran to the Brahmin and began pulling on his arm, crying loudly, 'Don't hurt my mother. Where are you taking her?' When the Brahmin pushed Rohit away, the boy began to cry harder. 'Don't leave me, Mother,' he sobbed, running after Shaivya and throwing his arms around her middle. The old man smacked the boy with his staff and shouted at Shaivya to come along. The queen fell at his feet. 'Please, I beg you to let our son come with me,' she begged. 'I won't be able to live without him. I promise I'll not let him hinder my work; instead, he'll help me. He too will be your servant. Please let me take my son with me.'

'Fine,' the old man grumbled and threw down a few more gold mohurs to buy the boy, as well. Then he tied a rope around the hands of the queen and the prince and dragged them to his house.

Watching his delicate-as-a-rose-petal queen and lotus-faced son driven away like cattle, Harishchandra wailed, 'Oh, what fate has wrought this day? What injustice I have brought down on your heads. I, who was supposed to protect you and keep you, am myself sending you off to serve and live a life of whipping. Surely there's not another man alive who has suffered as I am suffering.'

Even as the king sat on the ground with his head in his hands, bemoaning his fate, the rigid-faced Vishwamitra arrived. 'Do you have my money?' he demanded. 'Where is it? You said your word is your life.'

'If only I could give my life to get my wife and son back,' the king sobbed.

'Stop your whining and pay my dakshina.'

When Harishchandra handed him the gold mohurs, the rishi mocked. 'Is this how you keep your word? By paying me a fraction of what you owe me?'

In response, the king walked to the market square and put himself on sale. But the only buyer who came forth was a Chandala who needed someone to work for him in the cremation ground.

'I can't.' Harishchandra cried, looking imploringly at Vishwamitra. 'I'm a Kshatriya. How can I work for a Chandala? Why don't you buy me yourself?' he said to the rishi. 'I'll serve you; I'll do whatever you say.'

'Okay.' Vishwamitra said. 'I'll buy you. But you'll have to do exactly as I say.'

'You'll be my lord and master.'

'You're bought,' the rishi said, tying a rope around his hands. Then he turned to the Chandala and asked him, 'Do you still need a servant? Because I've just realized that I don't need one anymore.' The Chandala nodded, money was exchanged, and Harishchandra was led away on a rope.

In the Chandala's house, Harishchandra was kept tied for three days, with very little food. On the fourth day, the Chandala released him and sent him to work: 'You'll remove the clothes from dead bodies, and for food, you'll eat whatever the bereaved relatives leave for the afterlife of their dead. And from today, you'll live in the cremation ground.'[52] And so Harishchandra, the former king of Ayodhya, who used to have dominion over a hundred kings, and who used to give away a king's wealth to the poor, became a penurious menial worker in the cremation grounds in Kashi, living off the leavings of the dead. Soon, his skin began to smell of rotting flesh, his hands became blistered from the simmering ashes, and his feet became crusted with blood and calluses. All day he wandered amidst half-burnt bodies, and at night he sojourned with the ghouls and lost souls. Many times, he thought about killing himself; but he didn't want to return to this hellish place, because the soul of a person who commits suicide returns to the same world it leaves.

In the meantime, Queen Shaivya began to serve in the old Brahmin's house, cooking and cleaning all day. She hardly got any rest and received only a little bit of food, out of which she ate just a few morsels and saved the rest for her son, who also worked as a servant.

Then, one evening, as Rohit was roping a bundle of palash wood in the forest for the Brahmin's sacrificial altar, a poisonous snake slithered out of an anthill and bit him. Some children playing nearby saw this and ran to the Brahmin's house to inform Shaivya. She fell down in a faint. When she came to, the old man was standing over her, yelling insults. She sat up sobbing and begged him to let her go to her son.

'Stop crying and get back to work,' he ordered. 'You can go after you have finished all the work.'

Her heart bursting with grief, Shaivya, somehow, completed the day's work, and then rushed to the forest, where she saw her son lying dead. Falling to the ground, she pulled his dead body onto her lap and began wailing. The sound attracted the attention of the night watchman, who came to check what was going on. When he saw a woman with dishevelled hair and a grotesque face covered with filth, pressing long, dirt-filled fingernails on a boy's face, he thought she was a rakshasi who had killed a child and brought him to the forest to feast on him. He quickly called his fellow guardsman, and with his help, captured the demoness and carried her to the Chandala's house. 'We've caught a rakshasi who was just about to devour a child,' he explained. 'You must kill her immediately.' The Chandala summoned Harishchandra and handed him an axe. 'Kill her,' he ordered.

Harishchandra looked at the frail-looking female lying on her side and didn't recognize her. She was too thin and her hair and face were covered in dirt, and she hardly appeared to him like a rakshasi. 'I can't kill this woman,' he said to his master.

'How dare you disobey me,' the Chandala shouted. 'You are a Chandala's slave. Our business deals with death. That's your dharma now—to deal with death. I order you to kill her.'

His body shaking with repugnance at his occupation and his heart filled with self-loathing, Harishchandra lifted the axe to cut off the woman's head. 'Forgive me, lady, for this heinous act,' he whispered. 'If I could save your life, I would, but I'm caught in the trap of fate.'

'You can kill me,' the woman responded in a weary voice. 'I don't wish to live. But I ask for only one favour. My son is lying dead in the forest. Let me look on his lotus face one last time and perform his last rites.'

Harishchandra nodded and asked the woman to lead him there.

As soon as Harishchandra saw Rohit on the ground in the forest, he recognized him. Then he looked more closely at the woman and realized who she was, and husband and wife fell sobbing into each other's arms. Shaivya related to him all that had happened to her and their son, and Harishchandra told her how he had become the slave of a Chandala. 'I know it's a sin to commit suicide,' Harishchandra told his wife. 'But I can't bear this life anymore and now that our son is gone, I have no use for this life. I've decided to immolate myself on my son's pyre.'

'Oh, my dear husband, I'll join you,' Shavaiya wept.

Harishchandra cut down a tree, and together, he and his wife prepared a cremation pyre and then laid Rohit's body on it. But, just as he was about to light the flame, the dark forest suddenly became bright.

'Stop, O king,' a heavenly voice commanded, and from the light emerged Indra and all the devas, including Lord Dharma. Accompanying them was Vishwamitra.

'You have proved to be truthful and dutiful, O king,' Dharma said. Then Indra sprinkled water on Rohit's body and the prince came back to life, immediately gaining his health and beauty. Harishchandra and his wife Shaivya were also transformed to their former robustness.

'We have come to take you back to your kingdom,' Indra said.

'But I'm not a free man,' Harishchandra replied. 'I'm a slave of the Chandala. How can I go without his permission?'

'I am that Chandala,' Dharma said with a smile. 'I'm also the snake and the old Brahmin that bought your wife.'

'But I don't have a kingdom; it belongs to Rishi Vishwamitra. I gave it away to his son.'

'There was no son or bride—it was all my maya,' Vishwamitra revealed. 'Also, the boar and the river, where you met Siddharupini, were all part of the test. And you have passed it with the highest degree of success.'

'Ayodhya was always yours, O great king,' Indra said. 'Come. It awaits.'

Harishchandra then happily returned to Ayodhya with his wife and son and ruled for a long time, always practising dharma, truth, and charity.

Myth from the Puranas

◆

123

IN THE FACE OF FEAR

There was once a jackal called Gomaya. One day, desperately looking for food and water, he wandered into a field that, a long time ago, used to be a battleground of great warriors. Now the only remnants of that glory were some broken arrows and a rusted battle drum that lay wedged between shrubs that grew thick and tall.

As Gomaya cut through the overgrowth, searching for something to eat, he began to hear loud, terrifying booms. He stopped in his tracks. This was surely some huge animal in the weeds that was waiting to pounce on him, he thought. 'O, you powerful gods,' he looked up at the sky and said, 'Save me from this danger I have walked into, unintentionally.' Then, his body shaking with fear, the blood pounding in his heart, he began to back away as quickly as he could with his tail between his legs. But then he said to himself, 'How do I know this animal is bigger than I am? Maybe it's something I can eat. Let me at least take a look.' He stopped again, and cautiously advanced in the direction from which the sound was coming. There, in the weeds, he saw a large object, and as the wind blew, branches from a shrub beat upon one side of it, and this is what appeared to be making the loud, rolling, booming sound. Seeing the helplessness of this creature, Gomaya laughed at his own fear. Going closer, he sniffed at it and smelled animal hide. When he struck it with his paw, the sound from it was loud and heavy, as though it was full inside—full of juicy flesh, maybe. 'How lucky I am,' Gomaya said, 'to have come upon this huge amount of food,' and then sinking his teeth into the hide, he tore it out. But after that, his teeth only encountered emptiness. Gomaya climbed inside the 'creature' thinking that perhaps there was something he was missing, but inside, too, there was nothing. For a moment, he stood confused and then said,

What a fearsome sound it made
I thought it was full of food
But when I checked inside it
I found nothing but wood and hide

Gomaya climbed out of the drum, laughing at himself, and then he continued his search for food.

Folktale from the Panchatantra

◆

124

TEES MAR KHAN

Once a weaver bought some jaggery to eat with his rotis. As he ate, some of it spilled on the floor, and soon flies began to settle on it. Their buzzing irritated the weaver, and he brought his hand down—thwack—to swat them. When he lifted his hand, he saw that he had killed most of the flies; he counted thirty. 'I'm a tees mar,' he said to himself proudly, 'a slayer of thirty. What am I doing weaving? I should be out there doing other brave things.' Hence, the weaver quit weaving and went to seek service with the king.

When the king asked him his name, he said: 'I'm Tees Mar Khan, the slayer of thirty.' The king was very impressed and employed him as a special soldier in his force.

One day a tiger, having lost its way, came into the town and created havoc. As people ran helter-skelter, the tiger got confused and began attacking, which made the townspeople panic even more. When the news reached the king, he sent for his special soldier, Tees Mar Khan. 'Kill the tiger,' he ordered.

Just the mere thought of the tiger made the weaver's heart pound in fear, but to the king he said bombastically, 'I have killed thirty. What is one tiger?' However, as soon as he left the palace, he ran towards the washerman's donkey shed. He thought he would hide there for a while and then borrow a donkey and quietly leave town. While he was on his way to the donkey shed, it began to rain quite heavily, and when he reached it and stepped inside, he saw that it was almost full. All the other people had also come there to hide from the tiger. 'I'm not afraid of the tiger,' he declared to them with bravado, 'it's the tapkua (the dripping), that I'm afraid of.'

Now, without anyone noticing, the tiger had also slipped into the donkey's shed to get away from the rain. When he heard Tees Mar Khan say that he was more afraid of tapkua than he was of the tiger, he wondered who was this tapkua creature that was so frightening? A little afraid himself, he nudged his way closer to where Tees Mar Khan was standing, feeling safer near this brave man.

Tees Mar Khan stayed in the shed all night and, at dawn, when it stopped raining, he took a rope and put it around the neck of the donkey standing closest to him. It was dark in the shed, and he couldn't quite see, but, finally he was able to lead the donkey out of the shed. As he walked towards his home to gather his belongings and leave town, he noticed people acting very strangely. They stopped what they were doing and stared at him. Some pointed at the donkey, and some at him, but Tees Mar Khan was in too much of a hurry to stop and ask them anything. At his house, he tied the rope of the donkey to the post and rushed inside. When he came out with an armload of his belongings, he saw that a crowd had gathered. The king was also there. 'Ah, my brave man,' the king stated, stepping forward. 'You're even braver than I thought. How did you manage to do this?' He pointed to the post, where tied up with a rope around his neck was the tiger.

'I...donkey...' Tees Mar Khan tried to speak, but the truth was that he was quaking at the thought that he had not only spent the night with a tiger but he had also walked home with him.

Taking Tees Mar Khan's lack of words as his modesty, the king handsomely rewarded him, and Tees Mar Khan cancelled his plan to leave town.

Soon after, the kingdom was invaded by a neighbouring monarch. The king appointed Tees Maar Khan as the commander-in-chief and sent him to the battlefield to lead his forces. Tees Maar Khan panicked. He had never ridden a horse or held a sword and, when he went into the field, just the din of battle frightened him half to death. At first he remained at the rear of the forces, but when the soldiers shouted, 'Khan Sahib, come on!' he unintentionally spurred his horse, and the animal, trained for war, charged. The sword flew out of the weaver's hand, and his body, too, would have followed suit, had he not tied himself to the horse. Instinctively, he grabbed on to a tree as he passed it, and so with the horse still charging, and his arms holding on to the trunk tightly, he pulled the tree right out of the ground. When the enemy saw the advancing commander-in-chief, who had the strength to uproot a tree on his way into battle, they panicked and fled.

Tees Mar Khan was hailed as the bravest man in the kingdom, and the king rewarded him by marrying his daughter to him.

Folktale from North India

◆

125

YUDHISHTHIRA'S DILEMMA

On the fifteenth day of battle in the Mahabharata war, the Kaurava general, Dronacharya overpowered the Pandava army. Reeling from the slaughter and destruction he was causing, the Pandavas were certain that on this day they would lose the war. 'He's consuming us like fire consumes hay,' they said to each other frantically. 'No one can stop him today. Not even Arjuna.'

Krishna, who was serving as Arjuna's charioteer in this great war, also became worried. 'As long as Drona has his weapons, he's like Indra—unbeatable,' he told Arjuna. 'Somehow, he must be made to lay down his weapons; only then he can be killed.'

'How is that possible?' Arjuna asked. 'Guru Drona will never give up his weapons as long as he's fighting, and he'll not stop fighting as long as he's alive.'

'It's obvious that a fair battle won't work. We'll have to use other means,' Krishna advised. 'I know that he has sworn to give up his weapons if Ashvatthama, his son, dies. Someone should tell him that Ashvatthama is dead.'

'But Ashvatthama is not dead.' Arjuna said, confused. 'In fact, the guru's son is invincible.' Ashvatthaman was, indeed, unconquerable, because not only was he a partial incarnation of Shiva, he was also born with a gem in his forehead that protected him like a shield from anything that could cause him harm.

'It doesn't matter whether Ashvatthama is dead or alive,' Krishna said to the Pandavas. 'We just need to convince Drona that he is dead.'

Arjuna realized the deception that Krishna was proposing, and he wasn't comfortable with it, but Bhima and the twins, Nakula and Sahadeva, immediately agreed with Krishna. 'Which one of us should tell him?' they asked Krishna.

'Drona knows very well that his son is unconquerable, so he won't believe any of you. The only person he will believe is Yudhishthira, because he knows Yudhishthira will never lie. Yudhishthira must go and tell him that Ashvatthama is dead.'

Everyone turned to look at Yudhishthira. He was Dharmaraja himself and had sworn to always tell the truth. 'How can you ask me to do this?' Yudhishthira asked, with a pained expression on his face. 'You know I can't lie.'

Krishna was a charioteer in the true sense of the word, guiding the Pandava brothers' chariot of life. At this moment, realizing the moral dilemma Yudhishthira was facing, he said to him: 'This is the moment, O king, when you must decide whether your personal dharma is more important than your dharma towards your brothers, your army, and your people. If Drona is not destroyed, he'll slaughter the rest of your army and then each one of you. Let alone victory, you may not even be alive to see Duryodhana become victorious. This is the moment of truth. It is up to you to seize it. Being Dharmaraja, you know that the choice is rarely between dharma and adharma; it is more often between one dharma and another. You must choose the most appropriate dharma at any given time. Have the courage to follow the dharma that the circumstance requires.'

But Yudhishthira, being the righteous man that he was, was still very reluctant to lie. Then, Krishna suggested a way out. 'What if you don't really have to lie?' he said to Yudhishthira.

'What do you mean?' the Pandavas asked, and Krishna whispered to them a secret strategy.

There was a war elephant in the Pandava army that was named Ashvatthama. He was a mighty beast—proud, valiant, and well-trained. For fifteen days, guided by his mahout, he had charged fearlessly through enemy ranks, striking terror into the hearts of Kaurava soldiers. At Krishna's behest, Bhima sought out this elephant and, aiming between his eyes, struck him a deathblow with his mace. The beast crashed to the ground, dead. Bhima then ran towards Drona, exclaiming loudly, 'Ashvatthama is slain.'

When Drona heard Bhima say this, the ground shifted under his feet. But he steadied himself, thinking, how can my son die? He's unassailable. Bhima is spreading rumours to shake my resolve and weaken me. It's a strategy. And so Drona held his bow more firmly and continued to relentlessly assail his enemies, shooting arrows that fell like torrential rain, piercing hearts and limbs and eyes. Within a short period, he had slain twenty thousand men. But, as he stood amidst the carnage like a divine conqueror, a shadow crossed his vision—Dhrishtadyumna—his nemesis, King Drupada's son, whom Drupada had received as a boon with the sole purpose of destroying his sworn enemy, Drona. Dhrishtadyumna had been in Drona's peripheral vision throughout the war, but now his presence in such close proximity seemed to Drona like a portent of death. At that instance, he remembered Bhima's words again—'Ashvatthama is slain!'—and a sharp pain shot through him. Was it possible that his son, who was destined to be chiranjiva—immortal—had been killed in this war; this war in which so many rules had been broken? Perhaps, the promise of his son's immortality was another casualty of this war. With these thoughts, Drona was filled with doubt, and he knew that there was only one way to make certain. Yudhishthira! Drona knew Yudhishthira would never lie, not even for the sake of getting this earth or the three worlds; not only because he was reputed in the world as Dharmaraja, but also because his swadharma, his own adherence to truth, would not allow him to lie. And so, Drona sought out Yudhisthira.

When Krishna saw Drona approaching the Pandavas, he urgently reminded Yudhishthira: 'If Drona fights for even half a day more, I can guarantee you that your troops will be totally obliterated. Save your brothers and your forces from Drona. O, Dharmaraja, know this that if a lie can save lives, it's not a sin.'

By this time, Drona had reached the group, fear for his son writ large on his face. 'Is it true?' he asked Yudhishthira. 'I know you'll never lie. Tell me the truth. Is my son slain?'

Yudhishthira paused for a brief second, and then drawing in a determined breath, said clearly, 'He is slain—Ashvatthama,' but then he lost some of his courage and added under his breath, 'the elephant.'

Drona only heard the words that were clearly uttered. He staggered and almost fell, his limbs melting like sand in water. Just then Dhrishtadyumna mounted a lethal arrow on his bow and aimed it at Drona's breast to finish him. Instinctively, because he was a warrior so trained, Drona's arm rose to counter the arrow. For a few brief minutes, he fought, but without thinking, and all the while lamenting, 'Ashvatthama. Ashvatthama.' Finally, grief overpowered him, and his bow and sword slipped away from his hands, clattering on the floor of the chariot. Then he sat down and closed his eyes in yogic meditation, and soon his soul left his body. When Dhrishtadyumna, who was born solely for the purpose of killing Drona, saw the life leave the body of his father's enemy, he was filled with rage for having been deprived of killing him with his own hands. He dragged Drona's lifeless body down from the chariot on to the bloody battlefield and chopped off the head, and then uttering a loud war cry, he held the head aloft by its grey locks, so that all could see.

In the midst of all this, no one noticed that as soon as Yudhishthira had uttered the lie, half-truth though it was, his chariot and horses, that used to be elevated four inches above the surface of the earth, had descended to the earth like those of the others around him.

Myth from the Mahabharata

◆

126

THOMAS'S JOURNEY TO INDIA

All the apostles of Jesus met in Jerusalem, and they divided the regions of the world among themselves so that each one would go to a specific land and preach the word of God. India fell into the lot of Judas Thomas,[53] but he didn't want to go. 'I am a Hebrew man,' he tried to reason with Jesus. 'How can I go amongst the Indians?' Then, one night, Jesus came to him in a dream and said to him, 'Fear not, Thomas. Go to India and preach the word there. My grace is with you.' But still Thomas did not obey. 'Wherever else you want to send me, I'll go, but I will not go to India,' he said to Jesus.

At that time, a merchant from India, called Abbanes, was in Jerusalem for business. He had been sent by King Gundaphorus[54] to buy a carpenter.

The Lord saw him walking in the marketplace at noon one day and asked him, 'Do you want to buy a carpenter?'

'Yes,' said Abbanes.

'I have a slave who is a carpenter, and I want to sell him,' and he pointed to Thomas, who was standing at a distance. The slave price was agreed upon: three litrae of unstamped silver. Then Jesus wrote up a deed of sale, which said, 'I, Jesus, the son of Joseph the carpenter, acknowledge that I have sold my slave, Judas by name, to Abbanes, a merchant of Gundaphorus, King of the Indians.' When the deal was signed and sealed, Jesus brought Judas Thomas to Abbanes, the merchant.

'Is this your master?' Abbanes asked Judas Thomas.

'Yes. He is my Lord,' Thomas replied.

'Then I have bought you from him,' Abbanes stated.

And Thomas kept silent.

On the following day, Thomas woke up early and prayed to the Lord for courage, saying, 'I will go wherever you send me, Lord Jesus. Thy will be done.' And he departed with Abbanes, taking nothing with him, except his price, which Jesus had given to him with the words, 'Let your price be with you, together with my grace, wherever you go.' Thomas met Abbanes at the ship, and helped him carry his baggage on board. When the ship sailed, Abbanes asked Thomas, 'What craftsmanship do you know?'

'In wood I can make ploughs and yokes and ox-goads, and oars and masts and pulleys for boats. In stone, I can make pillars and temples and court-houses for kings.'

'Yes, this is exactly the workmanship we need.'

And so they sailed towards India, and the wind was favourable.

Myth from the Gospel of Thomas

◆

127

DADHICHI'S BONES

In Treta Yuga, which is the second yuga in the cycle of Great Time, the Kalkeya danavas had become extremely powerful. Their chief was Vrta and, under his command, they constantly terrorized the devas. Vrta was born from his father Tvashtri's desire for revenge, because the gods had killed Tvashtri's ascetic son through treachery, and he had created Vrta with his energy, solely to destroy the devas. Vrta was a terrible danava. Every day he increased in size, extending in all directions, as far as an arrow can be shot. His face was dark, like a mass of clouds, the hair on his head and in his beard was red, like heated copper, and his eyes were fierce, like the mid-day sun. He held a trident, which seemed to pierce the sky, and with every step he took, the earth shook. He was so tall that it seemed he drank moisture from the surface of the sky and licked the stars with his tongue. His mouth was so deep, it could swallow the three worlds, and when he yawned, his massive tusks seemed capable of goring hundreds of people all at once. The army of the gods, with Indra at its head, fought many battles with him, but Vrta simply swallowed all the missiles and arrows that were hurled at him. Losing every battle, and terrified that he would devour the three world, the gods, feeling powerless and helpless, went to Vishnu and Brahma for help.

'You have to find a way of destroying Vrta,' they implored. 'He reduces our weapons to useless toys. It seems that we have no means to kill him, but he, on the other hand, can finish us all in one strike. If you don't destroy him, he'll destroy the world.'

'I know what you desire,' Brahma said, 'and actually there is someone who can help you. He is the great Rishi Dadhichi, who lives on the other side of Saraswati river. He's the son of Rishi Atharvana, who taught Tvashtri the skill of Narayana Kavacham—creating impregnable body armour. Atharvana taught this science to his son. Besides, Dadhichi is a great Shiva devotee and has received many boons from that great god, including a boon that has made his bones unbreakable.'

The gods asked Brahma how that had come about, and Brahma told them Dadhichi's story:

Dadhichi had a friend—King Kshuva. One day the two quarrelled about whose penance was greater. Dadhichi said he was a Brahmin; hence, the highest of the varnas, but Kshuva considered the king to be the highest, because he sustained the devas. Dadhichi got angry and struck Kshuva with his fist, and Kshuva retaliated by striking Dadhichi with his thunderbolt that broke all the rishi's limbs. Lying there, broken-boned, Dadhichi concentrated on his ancestor, the great Rishi Shukra, who knew the Mrtunjaya mantra, which gave one victory over death. Shukra then arrived and put together Dadhichi's broken limbs and also taught him the mantra. Then he advised Dadhichi to pray to Shiva by repeating the mantra, because Shiva himself is the Conqueror of Death. Dadhichi went to the forest and repeated the mantra enough times to please Shiva, and when the god manifested, he gave Dadhichi three boons: unbreakable bones, immortality, and absence of distress.

'All of you should go to Dadhichi and ask him for a boon—his bones,' Brahma advised the gods. 'Then create a weapon from his bones; it will be the most deadly and powerful of weapons, and with that, you'll be able to destroy Vrta.'

Indra was sceptical, because in the past he had once cut off Rishi Dadhichi's head, and he felt that the rishi would hold that against him. Indra had tried to prevent the rishi from teaching the science of resurrection to the Ashwin Kumars, the twin gods who are healers, because according to him, they were only physicians, not gods; hence, not worthy of receiving this knowledge of Brahmavidya. 'If you dare to teach those low-caste twins this vidya,' Indra had warned the rishi, 'I'll cut off your head.'

But the Ashwin twins had devised a plan: they themselves had sliced off Dadhichi's head and replaced it with a horse's head. The rishi had then taught the vidya through the horse's mouth, and when Indra beheaded him, it was the horse's head that he had cut off. Then, with their newly acquired knowledge of Brahmavidya, the twins had resurrected the rishi and replaced his original head.

Now when the gods, headed by Indra and accompanied by Narada, came to Dadhichi's ashram, the rishi welcomed them cordially, without any rancour towards the king of gods. The devas told Dadhichi about Vrta and how he was threatening the world with his dark powers. 'We need your bones,' they told him. 'We've heard of your courage and your generosity. Will you sacrifice yourself for the cause of saving the world?'

'This body is transient,' the sage replied. 'If it can serve the world by dispelling the darkness that the danava is spreading, then I'm at your service.' And right then and there, he sat down in yoga and controlled his senses, breath, mind, and intellect. Then, severing all bonds, he united his individual soul with the transcendental Brahman, and gave up his earthly life.

The gods then extracted the bones from his dead body and took them to Vishvakarma, the divine architect, who fashioned them into an indestructible weapon that had six sides and a spherical head. The weapon roared like a thunderbolt when it was hurled, and it destroyed every enemy in its path. This was the diamond weapon—the Vajra.[55]

Armed with this Vajra, Indra faced Vrta in battle again, and when he hurled it at the terrible danava, he crumbled, as though the celestial mountain Mandar had shattered and fallen to pieces. When the Kalkeyas saw their leader destroyed, they plunged into the fathomless ocean, and order was restored in the three worlds.

Myth from the Puranas

◆

128

DAVID AND GOLIATH

The Philistines and the Israelites faced each other on opposite hills over the Valley of Elah. A champion came out of the camp of the Philistines—a man from Gath, named Goliath, who was over nine feet tall. His helmet was of bronze, as was his armour, that weighed five thousand shekels. His greaves were also of bronze, and he carried a bronze dagger. He had a spear that was as long as a weaver's beam, and it had an iron head that weighed six hundred shekels. His shield bearer marched in front of him, shouting to the Israelites: 'You slaves of Saul, do you have any man who'll come and meet me one-on-one? If he can kill me in a fair fight, we'll become your slaves. But if I prove too strong for him and kill him, you shall be our slaves and serve us.'

When King Saul and the Israelites heard the Philistine, they were filled with dread, because no one in their ranks was capable of facing this giant. Goliath issued his challenge for forty days, but the Israelites had no one to send, so the armies of the Philistines and Israelites fought on.

Among the Israelites was an old man, Jesse, who had eight sons; three of his eldest sons were fighting with Saul. His youngest son was David, and he used to mind his father's flocks. One day, Jesse said to David, 'Run to camp and take your brothers this parched grain and loaves of bread, and give these cream cheeses to the commanding officer. See if your brothers are well and bring back some token from them.'

Early the next morning, David left a friend in charge of the sheep and set out on his errand. He reached the battle lines just as the Israelite armies were going out to take up positions and raise the war-cry. Leaving his things with the quartermaster, David ran to the line and went up to his brothers to greet them. While he was talking to them, the Philistine champion came out from the Philistine ranks and issued his challenge again. When the Israelites saw the man, they ran from him in fear. David, who had also heard the challenge, asked a man standing near him, 'Who is this Philistine that defies the army of the living god?'

'That is Goliath, the Philistine. The king will give a rich reward to the man who kills him. He'll also give him his daughter in marriage and will exempt him and his family from service.'

David's elder brother, Eliab, overheard David talking with the man and grew angry. 'What are you doing here, you rascal? And who is taking care of the sheep in the wilderness, while you are here watching the battle?'

'I only asked a question,' David replied. Then he turned to another man and asked, 'What if there is someone who can kill this Philistine and wipe out our disgrace?'

David's words were reported to Saul, and he summoned David to ask him what he meant. 'Do you know such a man?' he asked the young boy.

'I'll go and fight this Philistine myself,' David said to Saul.

'You can't fight him,' Saul replied, shaking his head. 'You're only a young boy, and he is a man who has been fighting all his life.'

'I am my father's shepherd—I protect his flock. When a lion or a bear carries off a sheep, it is I who go after it and fight the beast and snatch the victim from its very jaws. And if it attacks me, I grab its mane and smash it to death. I have killed lions and bears with my bare hands; what chance does this uncircumcised Philistine have? He has dared to defy the army of the living god. He who has saved me from the lion and the bear will surely save me from this Philistine.'

When Saul heard these words from the lad, he began to believe him. 'Go,' he said. 'May the Lord be with you.' Then he took his own tunic and put it on David. He also made him put on a coat of mail and a bronze helmet. Then he slung his own sword over the tunic and fastened it. But David was reluctant to go into battle with this gear. He said to Saul: 'How can I win a fight with weapons I've never tried before?' And he took everything off. Then he picked up his own stick, chose five smooth stones from the brook, which he put in his shepherd's bag, and, swinging his sling, went to meet the Philistine.

Seeing that his challenge had finally been accepted, the Philistine came towards David, with his shield-bearer marching ahead. But when he saw his rosy-cheeked challenger, he laughed contemptuously, and called out to him, 'Do you think I'm a dog that you have come to chase me away with a stick and a sling?'

David replied: 'Your dagger and sword and spear will all become useless in the face of the weapon that I carry—the name of the god whom you have defied. The Lord of the army of Israel will make you powerless. Then I'll kill you and cut off your head and leave your dead body and the bodies of all the Philistines for the wild animals. Everyone here will see that the Lord doesn't need a sword or a spear to save someone. This is the Lord's battle, and, through me, he will win it.'

Goliath swore in the name of his god and challenged David: 'Come on then. It's time I fed your flesh to the birds and beasts.' He then rushed towards David in a rage, and David ran to meet him, reaching for a stone from his bag. He slung it with such force that it struck the Philistine on the forehead and killed him instantly. The giant fell flat on his face on the ground, the stone buried in his forehead. Standing over him, David pulled the giant's sword out of its scabbard, and cut off his head.

When the Philistines saw their champion lying dead on the ground, they turned and fled. The men of Israel and Judah then shouted their victory and chased them all the way to the gates of Ekron, strewing the road with their bodies. David then picked up Goliath's head and brought it to Jerusalem.

Myth from the Old Testament

◆

129

THE HAUNTED MOSQUE

Once upon a time in a village in Kashmir, there was a very old mosque that had fallen into disrepair. The situation was so bad that one winter, after a heavy snowfall, one side of the roof collapsed. Now the mosque became quite unsafe, and the villagers stopped praying there. In fact, they were so afraid that the mosque would come tumbling down on them that no one ventured in, not even to light a lamp. Then the holy month of Ramzan came, and the villagers began to feel bad about abandoning their mosque. A village meeting was called, and it was decided that in this holy month, the men would undertake repairs of the mosque. Everyone offered thanks to Allah for giving them this wisdom. On the designated day, two repairmen volunteered to go into the mosque and survey the damage, while the rest of the village folk stood outside, waiting for them to return and give their report. They waited the whole day and half the night, but the repairmen didn't return. The following morning, the villagers found two dead bodies lying outside the mosque, with legs and arms broken, and the heads twisted right around. This did not seem the misdeed of a thief or a wild beast. This could only have been done by a jinn. Terror spread in the village. 'The mosque is haunted! The mosque is haunted!' everyone whispered fearfully around the village.

Another village meeting was called. The headman had no idea what to do next. If the danger was human, he would know how to deal with it, but this situation seemed beyond his control; so when the village elders looked at him with hope in their eyes, he shook his head in defeat. 'Forgive me,' he said. 'I don't know how to rid our mosque of this jinn. In fact, I'm afraid that if he gets it into his mind, he might begin to spread his terror beyond the mosque, in the village. In that case, only Allah can help us.'

The villagers, in panic, began to utter prayers. Then, at the back of the crowd, a young man stood up. 'I'm Ali, and I can rid the mosque of the jinn,' he declared. A sudden hush fell upon the crowd. Everyone turned around to look at the brave man who proposed to get rid of the biggest danger the village had ever faced. His body was slender, and he hardly looked strong enough to tackle a human adversary, let alone a monstrous jinn, but his eyes were bright with intelligence and his manner was confident.

'All I need is a hammer, a piece of wood with long nails driven into it, and a jug of kanji.'

'Young man,' the village headman said. 'This is a mighty jinn we're talking about. How can you get rid of him with just a hammer, a piece of wood and a jug of kanji?'

'Leave that to me,' Ali said.

Seeing that there was no other choice, the village elders and the headman decided to allow the young man to carry out whatever plan he had in mind. That night, equipped with a hammer, a plank of wood with sharp protruding nails, and a jug of tart, salted kanji, Ali entered the mosque. From the light of the moon, he could see the jinn lying on his back in the centre of the prayer hall. He was a huge jinn with thick, hairy arms and a chest as wide as the trunk of a grandfather oak. Ali stood at the entrance and called out, 'Hello, Uncle. How are you today?'

The jinn sat up in surprise. When he saw the bold young man at the entrance, he wondered why he was not afraid of him. But he was a smart jinn, and he didn't want to reveal his astonishment, so he replied in a friendly voice, 'Welcome, Nephew. I'm well.'

'You look tired, uncle,' the young man said. 'Shall I massage your back for you?'

The jinn was even more perplexed, but he didn't show it. In fact, he thought, getting a massage from the young man was the perfect way to teach him a lesson in fear. 'You're very kind, Nephew,' he said, lying down and turning on his stomach. 'A massage is exactly what I need. And, after the massage, please be kind enough to scratch my back. I have a terrible itch.'

Now everyone knows that the jinn's muscles are tougher than knotted wood. No human can massage his pain away. Also, his skin is thicker than leather, and no human has hard enough fingernails to offer him relief from an itch. That is why the cunning jinn had accepted Ali's offer, because he was sure the young man wouldn't be able to massage his back or scratch his skin; to punish him, he would kill him.

Ali came and sat beside the jinn. First, he took out his hammer and began hammering on his back, releasing the knots in his huge muscles, and when the jinn sighed in relief, Ali took the plank of wood and began scratching his back with the sharp nails. The jinn felt so relaxed, he began to doze off. Noticing this, Ali pressed the nails harder into his back, until they pierced his skin. Disturbed by the pricking, the jinn shifted his position and complained drowsily, 'Not so hard, Nephew. Your nails have begun to hurt a little.'

'Oh, I'm sorry, Uncle. I didn't mean to hurt you. Here, let me sooth the pain with some oil,' he said, and, picking up the jug of kanji, poured all of it onto the jinn's back. When the salty, tart kanji stung the jinn's pierced skin, he jumped up and, yelling in pain, ran out of the mosque and disappeared into the forest. Ali gathered his things and headed back to the village to inform the villagers that the jinn had left the mosque. The villagers were very grateful to Ali, and the village headman not only awarded him a large sum of money but also promised him his daughter in marriage.

For a while, everything went well in the village. The men began to repair their jinn-free mosque and the women began to prepare for the forthcoming wedding between Ali and the headman's daughter.

Meanwhile, in the forest, the jinn of the mosque met a community of jinns. When he told his fellow jinns about the young man who had tortured him, the other jinns were outraged. How dare a puny mortal outsmart one of their kind? The leader of these jinns was a fearsome, one-eyed jinn who was the smartest and strongest of them all. 'We must catch the young man and punish him,' he said. 'We need to set an example so that no human dares to mess with us again.' All the other jinns agreed and, together, they began to walk towards the village.

When the jinns were having their meeting in the forest, a poor woodcutter was cutting wood nearby, and he heard everything. Trembling with fright, he almost dropped his axe. When the jinns left, he ran to the village to tell everyone that the jinns were coming to get Ali. As soon as the villagers heard this, they moved as far from Ali as possible; they didn't want to be anywhere near him when the jinns came. Only one person in the village stayed by his side—the headman's daughter, who had come to love the man she was to marry. 'What are we going to do now?' she asked him, fearfully. 'The jinns will surely kill you.'

'Don't worry,' Ali replied. 'Go and get me a tin drum and a bag full of ashes from the stove.'

As soon as the headman's daughter returned with these items in a satchel, Ali sent her away to her house and told her to stay there. Then he went into the forest and looked for the tallest tree. When he found a poplar that was so tall it seemed to touch the sky, he put the satchel over his shoulder and climbed to the very top of the tree.

Everyone knows that no matter how smart, or strong, or cunning the jinns are, they can't climb trees, and this is what Ali was counting on.

Soon the large group of jinns, looking for Ali, came to the forest and found the young man they were seeking sitting up in a tree.

'Let's chop down the tree,' one jinn suggested. 'That way he'll crash to the ground and die.'

'I say,' said another jinn, 'let's burn the tree. That way he'll burn to death.'

'No,' said the one-eyed jinn. 'We must catch him alive, so that we can see the fear in his eyes when we punish him. I have a plan. Let's make a jinn-ladder. I'll stand at the bottom, since I'm the strongest. One of you can climb on my shoulders. Then another on his, and so on, until the last one reaches the human. And then we grab him.'

The other jinns agreed that this was a great plan, and they all began to form a jinn-ladder, with the one-eyed jinn at the bottom. Ali watched as the jinns drew nearer and nearer to him. Finally, when the last jinn climbed onto the shoulders of the one beneath him, Ali took out the tin drum from his satchel and began to beat on it. Rub-a-dub, rub-a dub, rub-a-dub.

The sudden sound startled the jinns so much that the jinn-ladder began to totter. Right away, Ali opened the bag of ashes and emptied it on the jinns. Blinded from the ashes, the jinns began to stumble and topple off. Now Ali started his chant.

'Rub-a-dub, rub-a-dub, goes the drum, and the ashes fall from the tree
The one-eyed jinn on the lower-most rung, I've dealt with all but thee.'

The one-eyed jinn's ears were ringing from the sound of the drum, his eyes were stinging from the ashes, and when he heard this threat, his heart burst with fear, and he fell to the ground, dead. The rest of the jinn ladder came crashing down, and most of the jinns also died instantly. Others who lived, took to their heels, never to return to Ali's village.

The whole village applauded Ali and celebrated his marriage with the headman's daughter in the mosque that they had repaired.

Folktale from Kashmir

◆

130

RUSTAM AND SOHRAB

Once, Rustam, the legendary Persian knight of Sistan was riding along the border of Turan, when he came upon a field that was filled with wild assess. Exhilarated at the prospect of the hunt, he urged his trusted horse, Rakhsh forward and began chasing the herd, stringing a sharp arrow on his bow. After he had brought down his prey, he set up a campfire and roasted the animal on a spit. Then, after enjoying a delicious meal, he lay down contentedly and soon fell asleep. As Rustam slept, Rakhsh, who was grazing nearby, wandered off, and some Turkish horsemen spotted him. They recognized the bridle-less fine horse as Rustam's and stole him.

When Rustam woke up, he whistled for Rakhsh, but it soon became clear to him that Rakhsh was lost. Inspecting the tracks around the spot, Rustam saw on the path that led to the town of Samagan, a trail of five horses; among them, one set of hoof prints was that of Rakhsh.

When the king of Samagan was informed by his guards that the great Rustam was coming into his town on foot, he was surprised, but was also excited. Who would not be honoured to host a hero whose legend was told both in battle campsites and in children's bedrooms? The king gathered his senior nobles and went to welcome Rustam. 'Our town is your town,' he said in greeting to Rustam. 'How can we serve you?'

'Someone stole Rakhsh while I slept,' Rustam informed the king. 'He was bridle-less. I've been following his tracks and they lead to the outskirts of Samagan.'

'If the horse is here, he'll be found,' the king assured Rustam. 'I'll also declare a prize for anyone who has information about him. In the meantime, allow me to welcome you to my palace. Stay with me as my guest tonight.'

Rustam accepted the invitation, and the king of Samagan arranged a great feast in his honour. The evening was filled with food, wine, music, and rosy-cheeked women, and at night, Rustam was taken to a suite reserved for the most honoured guests. He slept soundly, but in the middle of the night, he suddenly woke up. Someone was opening his bedroom door. Pretending to be asleep, he waited with his senses alert and his hand on the dagger under his pillow. Soon, he heard a shuffling

and the strike of a match, and then he saw candlelight approaching his
bed. The smell of roses wafted to his nose, and he opened his eyes to see
the most beautiful woman he had ever seen, looking down at him. Her
face was like a full moon, her eyes were onyx black under finely arched
eyebrows, and her hair was a cloud of dark curls.

'Who are you, dear lady?' Rustam asked softly. 'What are you doing
here in my room in the middle of the night?'

'I am Tahmineh,' she said in voice that sounded like gently flowing
water. 'I am the king's daughter. I've heard so much about you—how
you have conquered dragons and men alike. How warriors quake in their
shoes at the mere mention of your mighty mace, how you're so handsome
that women fall in a faint when you pass by them. You are here in my
father's palace. How could I let this opportunity go by? I needed to see
you for myself—to see if what they say is true.'

'And, do I live up to my reputation?' Rustam asked, his voice amused.

'Oh, yes,' Tahmineh replied.

'I'm glad not to disappoint you. How can I serve you, my lady?'

'I'm filled with desire for you. If you want me, I'm yours.'

Rustam was astonished at her boldness, but he also found it very
arousing; however, he was the king's guest, and this was the king's daughter.

'No one will know,' she said. 'It'll be our secret, but hopefully not
for long. I wish to bear your child. Don't worry, you won't violate any
honour. I'm an adult and it's my will. But if you still feel that you will
betray my father's trust, then tomorrow, I'll ask my father to marry us.'

Rustam took Tahmineh's hand and pulled her into his bed, and they
spent a passionate night together. The next morning, at Rustam's urging,
Tahmineh told her father that she had chosen Rustam as her husband,
and that he, too, wished to make her his wife. The king, who was already
exuberant with the news that his men had found Rakhsh, could hardly
contain his happiness at the news that the greatest of all warriors would
be his son-in law. Rustam and Tahmineh were married right away, and
Rustam spent many happy days in Samagan with his wife. But, finally,
it was time for him to go.

On the morning that he was to leave, as Rustam lay with Tahmineh
in his arms, savouring their last few minutes, yet sad at the thought that
he might never see her again, he removed a clasp from his arm and gave
it to his wife. 'If we have a daughter, braid her hair with this clasp; it'll

bring her good luck. And if we have a son, have him wear this on his upper arm as a token from his father.'

Tahmineh gave birth to a son. He had fierce dark eyes like his father, and a luminous face like his mother. Tahmineh named him Sohrab—the radiant-faced. Sohrab grew and learned everything that he was taught faster than any other boy had ever done. By the time he was three, he could ride a horse saddle and play polo; by the time he was five, he was an accomplished archer and javelin thrower; and by the time he turned ten, he was already a feared competitor in the field. He was also taller than any other boy and smarter than young men double his age. When he was born, Tahmineh had written to Rustam to tell him that he had a son, and since then, they exchanged occasional letters. Rustam would enquire how his son was doing and Tahmineh would write back with stories about Sohrab that made him sound like any ordinary child, who still needed his mother's care. She also never revealed his name. Sohrab, too, didn't find out about his father's identity till he was ten, even though he persistently asked Tahmineh. One day, when Sohrab came home upset because his friends had called him a freak who did not have a father, she finally told him, 'You do have a father. In fact, he's the most noble of knights. Your father is Rustam.' She then showed him a letter and three rubies cast in gold that Rustam had sent her, as well as the clasp. 'But you must not let your father know your name or how grown up you are, otherwise, he'll take you, and it'll break my heart. You must also promise that that you'll never let Afrasiab know this secret, or he will use it against Kay Kavus and your father.'

Afrasiab, the Turk, was the king of Turan and arch-enemy of Kay Kavus, who was Shah of Sistan. Rustam was a knight in the army of Kavus.

Sohrab was overjoyed to know who his father was. 'How can you ask me to keep this secret?' he demanded of his mother. 'Every boy knows about Rustam and dreams of meeting him one day, and I'm his son. I don't want to keep this a secret. I want to shout to the world that I'm the son of the greatest of all knights. He's so great that he deserves to be ruling Sistan not simply commanding an army.' And then he announced to his mother. 'I'll get my father the throne. I'll gather a force and fight Kay Kavus and dethrone him and give my father the royal crown and mace of Sistan. Then I'll march on Turan and also defeat Afrasiab and give his throne to my father, as well. I'll prove to the world that I'm my father's son.'

Tahmineh tried to dissuade her son. She was a mother and wanted to keep him protected as long as she could, but she also knew that his warrior spirit could not be caged. She knew that the time had come when he needed to make his place in the world.

The fact that Sohrab was Rustam's son did not remain secret from Afrasiab, whose spies were everywhere, and they discovered his identity when the boy began preparing to fight Kay Kavus. When Afrasiab was informed about this, he rubbed his hands in glee and called his two most trusted chieftains, Barman and Human, 'Make sure not a whisper reaches Rustam's ears that the boy is his son,' he commanded. 'When Rustam sees the young warrior mounting an attack on Kay Kavus, he'll fight to protect his monarch. I hear the boy is unbeatable. He'll kill the old knight, not knowing who it is. Then you can dispose of the young brat. Right now, take twelve thousand warriors and this letter from me to the boy. Tell him he has full Turkish support in his battle against Kavus.'

Sohrab accepted Turkish support and prepared to fight the Persians. When Kay Kavus received the news that the Turks were planning to attack Sistan and that leading them was a young powerful warrior who appeared like a second Sam, Rustam's celebrated grandfather, he sent an urgent missive to Rustam, who was in Zabulistan, his native land. 'Tell him to come with the haste of smoke,' he instructed Giv, the messenger, and Giv rode day and night, without rest, to reach Zabulistan to convey Kavus's message.

'A second Sam, you say,' Rustam said to Giv. 'I would believe it if you told me the young warrior is Persian. But a Turk? That's hard to believe.'

'That's what we've heard,' Giv said. 'And Kavus is in a panic. He has commanded you to come.'

'I'm not his to command,' Rustam said stated resentfully. 'I'm a free man. I don't fight for him—I fight for Iran.'

'Then come with me, my friend, because this young Turk threatens Iran.'

'I'll come, if only to see whether this daring youth is really like Sam.'

Before Rustam and Giv set off, they decided to have a drink together, but one drink became many, and, one day became three, and as they drank, the two fearsome warriors became quite sentimental. 'You know I also have a son,' Rustam told Giv. 'But he's only a little boy. His breath is still fragrant with his mother's milk. In a few years he'll become a mighty soldier, but for the moment, he needs his mother.'

'A child needs his mother,' Giv agreed, and then he was reminded about his mission. 'Kavus needs you. Will you come now?'

The next morning, Rustam gathered his knights and, mounting Rakhsh, headed towards Sistan. When Rustam and Giv presented themselves to Kavus, the king was filled with three days of anger at being kept waiting. 'Who are you?' he demanded of Rustam.

'I'm Rustam.'

'I don't know any Rustam,' Kavus spat.

Rustam turned around and was ready to walk out, when the other chieftains stopped him.

'I have no use for Kavus. He is not my king,' Rustam told them. 'I am my own king. My throne is Rakhsh's back, my crown is my helmet, my armour is my royal robe, and in my heart, I'm ready to die. I'm not afraid of Kavus.'

The chieftains then requested the king to relent. 'Without Rustam, the Turks will destroy us,' they warned him, and Kavus realized that he needed Rustam more than Rustam needed him. 'Come, old friend,' he said, cajoling the warrior. 'You know my anger. It boils over, but then it evaporates.'

The next day, under Rustam's command, a hundred thousand warriors of the Persian army set out towards the White Fortress, a Persian outpost that Sohrab had already seized. After marching for many days to the beat of drums tied to the backs of dozens of elephants, Rustam's force arrived at the fortress. When Sohrab received news of the Persian army's march, he climbed to the top of the fortress to survey the enemy ranks and saw that the armies were so vast that not a speck of earth was visible between their lines. 'That's a lot of men and a lot of weapons,' he said to Human, the Turkish chieftain. 'And soon I'll make it all a sea of blood.'

The Persian army pitched its tents outside the fort, and that night, Rustam, disguised as a Turk, slipped into the fortress to get a glimpse of the young Sohrab. Standing at a distance from the festivities, he saw him on a throne in the midst of revelry. He was as tall as a cypress, his chest was massive with muscle, and his limbs were loose and limber. He was laughing and joking with the men who surrounded him, as though he didn't have a care in the world. Rustam could see now how closely he resembled his grandfather, Sam. As he stood there marveling at this, a hand landed on his shoulder. 'Who are you?' a warrior asked. 'Come into the light so that I can see your face.' Rustam killed the man with one lethal strike of his fist and quickly slipped out of the fortress before he was discovered. The man he killed was Zindeh-razam, Sohrab's maternal uncle, whom Tahmineh had sent to arrange a meeting between Sohrab and Rustam.

The following morning, as the sun's rays began to spread across the sky, Sohrab summoned Hejir, the Iranian keeper of the fort, and climbed the tower to survey the Iranian forces below. 'I want you to tell me about the chieftains that are leading the forces,' he said to Hejir. Pointing to a colourful pavilion in the centre that had tents covered in leapard skin and a banner of a sun topped by golden moon, he asked, 'Whose is that?'

'That is the king's pavilion.' Hejir replied.

'And that black one with black tents and the elephant banner. Whose is that?'

'That belongs to the brave chieftain Tus, son of Nozar.'

'And that red pavilion with the lion banner with a jewel in the centre?'

'That is Guraz from the clan Keshvad.'

Pointing at each of the pavilions, Sohrab heard the names each of the chieftains in Kuvas's army, but there was no mention of the name he was longing to hear—Rustam.

Then Sohrab saw to one side a green pavilion, outside of which sat a warrior on a throne. Even sitting down he appeared to be head and shoulders above the soldiers surrounding him. Next to him stood a magnificent horse of a colour that resembled scattered saffron petals of red and gold. It was saddled and bridled, ready for his lord to ride into battle. Fluttering above the pavilion was a flag with a fearsome dragon, and a staff that was topped with a golden lion. 'Who's that?' Sohrab enquired of Hejir. 'Is that Rustam?'

Hejir thought, if I point out Rustam to this young Turk and he somehow, kills our great hero, who will defend Iran? Without Rustam, Iran will fall to the Turks. It's better to die than to live in an Iran without Rustam. And, so he said to Sohrab, 'That's a new knight who has joined Kavus's army. I don't know his name.'

'Where's Rustam?' Sohrab finally asked. 'He's the greatest warrior in the world. Will he not fight in this war?'

'Rustam may have decided to remain in Zabulistan for the spring festival,' Hejir replied.

'How is that possible? Kavus himself is here, ready to fight along with his best chieftains. If Rustam were to stay at home, enjoying the festivities of spring, the world would laugh at him. If you're lying to me, Hejir, I'll cut off your head, but if you show me Rustam, I'll make you a rich man.'

'Thank your stars you don't know Rustam,' Hejir replied. 'You wouldn't stand a chance before him.'

Sohrab struck Hejir with his fist so hard that the man fell to the ground. Then he descended from the tower and, rushing to his tent, donned his armour and helmet and rode into the battlefield, still seething with anger. Seeing him like a maddened elephant, his massive frame crackling with energy, and his weapons shining and ready to cut down anyone who crossed his path, the Persian soldiers were struck with fear. 'He's like another Rustam,' they whispered in awe.

'Is there anyone in all of Persia that will fight me?' Sohrab called a challenge to the enemy. Then he began cutting the ropes of all the pavilions, till they came tumbling down, creating havoc in the Persian army. The Persian soldiers scattered, and the Turks began proclaiming an early victory.

'Call Rustam,' Kavus screamed at his men. 'Tell him to come and face this terror.' Rustam rode into the battlefield on Rakhsh's back, with his contingent of soldiers riding beside him. 'Come and fight me, man to man,' he called to Sohrab. 'But let's do it in the open—single combat—away from this chaos.'

'Single combat you say, old man? You'll not be able to withstand even one blow from my mace. You'll need your whole army to fight me,' Sohrab answered.

Rustam laughed. 'So young and so brave,' he said. 'Old age does not mean weakness, young one—it means experience. I may be old but I've seen many wars and have conquered mighty warriors. I've never known defeat, and I don't intend to begin now. The stars are witness to my prowess. I have no equal in the whole world.'

Rustam's words struck Sohrab as truth rather than as a boastful challenge. 'I want to ask you a question,' he said seriously. 'Please answer me honestly. I think you are Rustam—from the noble clan of Sam and Nariman. Are you Rustam?'

Rustam looked at the young man and wondered how he should respond. For some reason, it became very important for him that this young man, whom he had never met before and would probably kill in battle, not see Rustam as serving another man. 'I am not that Rustam,' he said. 'Rustam is a great warrior, a free man, a champion among men. People honour him as a prince among men. I'm not that man.'

For a moment Sohrab had believed that he had found Rustam and his breath had quickened with excitement. Now his shoulders slumped.

'What? Have you already decided on defeat?' Rustam challenged.

In response, Sohrab kicked his horse and rode towards a secluded spot. Rustam followed, and the two prepared for single combat. They both fought hard with javelins, Indian swords, and maces—iron clashing against iron. They fought long and began to tire, but neither could claim victory or even an advantage over the other. Soon, their horses, too, were panting, slathered with sweat, so they separated to stand at a distance from each other. Their throats were parched, their bodies were hurting, and they were soaked in blood and sweat. Once they had rested, they flew at each other again, but, again, they were equally matched, exchanging blow for blow and arrow for arrow. That night's battle ended, with each one still standing and each one filled with respect for the other.

The next morning, they returned to the battlefield. Rustam, sitting on Rakhsh, challenged Sohrab by brandishing his naked Indian sword, but Sohrab was loath to accept the challenge. All night he had thought about this warrior, feeling a strange love for him. Now, with his sword still in its scabbard and a gentle smile on his face, he asked: 'Did you sleep well? Are you rested? Why do you want to fight me? Come, let's put our swords and maces and arrows aside and sit down and enjoy a drink together. Let the others fight and be enemies. My heart feels affection for you. I want to know who you are. What is your clan?'

'I won't fall for your childish tricks,' Rustam called out. 'Come and fight like a warrior—with weapons.'

'I was hoping to spare you death,' Sohrab replied sadly. 'It seems that I'll have to kill you after all. Come on then, let's fight, old man. Let's see how long you last.'

Getting off their horses, they tethered them and then advanced towards each other on foot, their mail clattering. Then Sohrab, like a maddened elephant, rushed at Rustam and struck so hard with his fist that Rustam fell. Sohrab then leapt at him and, drawing his dagger, was ready to sever his head, when Rustam stopped him. 'You are indeed a great warrior, but this isn't the custom of great warriors. A hero doesn't deliver a fatal blow the first time that his opponent is felled. He's called a lion only if he's able to bring his opponent down a second time, and then he kills him.'

Sohrab suspected that this was a trick, but he released Rustam anyway and even helped him stand. Then they both went to their horses and rode to the stream to pour cold water on their heads and wash the blood and grime from their faces. When they returned again to combat, Sohrab mocked, 'I let you escape the first time, old man,' he said. 'But this time, there'll be no escape. Prepare to die.'

Suddenly, moving with the speed of lightning, Rustam seized Sohrab by the shoulders and forced him to the ground. Then he quickly drew his dagger and stabbed him in the heart. Life blood gushed out of Sohrab's chest and mouth. Sputtering blood, he said, 'I brought this on myself. It's fate—it's not you but my fate that has dealt me this death blow. My love for my father has led to my death. My mother gave me a talisman by which my father would know me. After I die, one of my chieftains will take that talisman to him and tell him the tale of my courage and your treachery. He'll seek you out. You may hide like a fish in the sea or a speck in pitch darkness, but he'll find you. Even if you're a star among other stars in the night's sky, or even if you vanish from the earth without a trace, my father will find you and avenge my death. My father, Rustam, will hold that talisman and know that I, Sohrab, his son, sought him day and night, and died seeking him.'

The ground slipped from under Rustam's feet and he fell in a faint, but his heart was filled with so much anguish that his own cries of pain pulled him back to consciousness. 'Show me the talisman,' he said, brokenly, lifting his son's head on his lap.

'Open the straps of my armour and look at the clasp on my arm,' Sohrab said.

When Rustam saw the clasp he had given to Tahmineh, his vision blurred, and in blind sorrow, he clasped Sohrab to his chest and wept, 'Oh my son, my son. I'm your father, Rustam. I killed you with my own hands. You tried to stop me. You talked of love, and I, my senses dimmed by the evil of my own nature, fought on like a mad man. Shame on me! Shame on my warrior pride! Shame on my warrior strength!' He tore at his clothes and threw dust on his head.

'Don't weep for me, father. What had to happen has happened. Now promise me that you'll stop the war. The Turks fought with the Persians at my instigation. Be merciful to them. Go, please, and stop the king of Iran from slaughtering them. Go now.'

Gently placing Sohrab's head on the ground, Rustam ran to Rakhsh, and mounting him on a run, rode into the battlefield. When the Persians saw him riding like a mad man with his clothes ripped, his body smeared with blood, his face covered with dust, they were shocked. 'What has happened to you?' they asked.

Rustam told them of the unholy deed he had committed. 'Stop the war,' he called. 'The evil I've committed today is enough.' And then, accompanied by his chieftains and comrades, he rode back to where his son lay. They all dismounted and gathered around Sohrab, whose head had fallen to one side. His breath was sounding shallow; even the flow of blood had become a trickle. 'He's dying,' they whispered. Rustam pulled out his dagger to slice his own throat, but his friends stopped him. 'What purpose will your death serve?' they said to him. 'It won't bring your son back. Stay with him for as long as he lives. Hold him. He came seeking you, you can't leave him in his dying hour.' Rustam sank to the ground beside his son.

Then someone said, 'He lives, yet. Perhaps noshdaru, the elixir that heals all wounds, that Kavus keeps wih him, will save him.'

'Go quickly,' Rustam said urgently to his comrade, Gudraz. 'Go to Kavus and tell him to send me that noshdaru. Remind him of all the service I have done for him and tell him that today I ask for my son's life in exchange.'

Gudraz rode at the speed of wind to bring Rustam's message to Kavus, but Kavus' response was: 'It's true that no warrior has served me like Rustam. But it's also true that there's no greater warrior than him, and if his son lives, he'll become stronger. Then what guarantee is there that he'll not turn on me. You heard him when he said. "I have no use for Kavus. He is not my king."'

Gudraz listened to the king's words with anger and returned to Rustam with sadness. 'The king's evil nature is like a tree that only bears bitter fruit,' he told his friend.

'I'll go myself,' Rustam cried. 'I'll beg him and plead with him. I'll be his slave for the rest of my life in exchange for my son's life.' He mounted Rakhsh again, but he had gone only a few yards, when a chieftain caught up with him and gave him the news that Sohrab had passed away. 'He opened his eyes and looked around for his father. Then an icy breath passed through his lips, and his eyes closed again, forever.'

Rustam covered his son's body in gold brocade and placed it gently on a bier. Then he burned his royal pavilion and set ablaze his throne and silken tents covered in leopard skin. He threw dust on his head and carried his son's body back home to Zabulistan, where he buried him in a golden coffin filled with black musk. 'Goodbye, sweet, courageous son, lion of my clan. Your search is over, for your father knows you deep in his heart and will mourn you for the rest of his days.'

Folktale from Ferdowsi's Shahnameh, The Persian Book of Kings

◆

131

DEFEAT OF MARA

As the Bodhisattva approached the asvattha tree for his final enlightenment, he thought of Mara, Lord of Desire, and wished him to witness his victory. Even as the thought arose in his mind, it penetrated Mara's abode and appeared to him like a portent. Mara assembled his army. It consisted of terrible beings—some with hundreds of mouths; others with misshapen limbs; some pot-bellied, and others multiple-eyed; some had fiery tongues; others appeared like devouring serpents. They all held bows and spears and other sharp weapons, and together they all marched towards the Bodhi tree.

The Bodhisattva was like a mountain of gold as he came to the tree; taking a seat on the east side, he vowed not to rise again till he had attained enlightenment. Then the earth quaked six times. A messenger appeared before the Bodhisattva. He was from Kapilavastu, and he informed the Bodhisattva that his cousin, Devadatta, had usurped the kingdom, and people were suffering under his tyranny. 'You must come to Kapilavastu right away,' the messenger said. 'I've come to fetch you.' But the Bodhisattva sat firm, even more determined to achieve that tranquil mental state which all people can bring about to free themselves from samsara. As soon as the Bodhisattva ignored the messenger, he vanished, for he had been Mara in disguise, come to trap the Bodhisattva in the entanglements of the world again.

The goddess of the asvattha tree was grateful for the Bodhisattva at her roots and honoured him by placing her blossoms at his feet. The spirits of the surrounding trees came to enquire of the bodhi about the person who sat in her shade, and when she told them it was the Bodhisattva, they bowed before him, showering him with flowers and urging him to persevere.

In the meantime, Mara asked his three daughters, Lust, Delight, and Thirst, to disguise themselves as beautiful maidens and entice the

Bodhisattva. They wooed him with dance and song, and also tried to draw him into their net with flirtations, but he sat as immobile as a lily of still waters, as firm as Mount Meru, as sturdy as iron walls that gird the world. When Mara's daughters failed, Mara himself approached the seer and presented him with logical arguments about the pleasures of life and his duty as a Kshatriya, but the Bodhisattva could not be persuaded. Finally, when everything failed, Mara called his army to attack. As the army of darkness advanced towards the Bodhisattva, the earth turned dark and unearthly sounds filled the air. They hurled spears and shot arrows and attacked him with all manner of sharp weapons which could have killed him instantly. But even as the weapons reached him, they became flowers and fell at his feet.

Mara then took out his terrible discus, which could cleave Mount Meru, and, mounted his elephant, from where he discharged the weapon. But instead of severing the seer's head, the discus fell around his neck as a flower garland. Enraged, Mara shouted, 'Enough! Vacate this seat this instant.'

The seer responded, 'For long ages, I have aspired to this seat and have gained enough merit to occupy it. I will not leave it now.'

'I have more merit than you. I run the world,' Mara boasted. 'My army will bear witness to that. And the roar of 'We witness!' arose from his army. 'See,' Mara said proudly. 'What witness do you have?'

'I have only one witness,' said the seer, and, stretching out his hand, he touched the earth with the tips of his fingers, calling on her to witness his merit.

The Earth Goddess arose before him and, with a voice like a hundred thousand cosmic voices, said, 'I witness.'

Then Mara's army fled like so many leaves swept by the wind. Mara himself fell to the ground in shame, knowing that he had been defeated. He knew that he could not deter the Shakyamuni from reaching enlightenment and preaching it to the world so that people could attain Nirvana.

Folk-myth from the Buddhacharita

◆

132

KALI: THE GODDESS, THE WARRIOR, THE MOTHER

When the asuras Sumbha and Nisumbha conquered the thirty-three thousand gods and robbed Indra of his sovereignty, the heaven-dwellers remembered the goddess who had given them a boon that she would always come to their rescue, any time they needed her. Hence, the gods went to Himavat, where the goddess lived, and prayed to her. Just then Parvati came to the spot to bathe in the Ganga and hearing the gods' hymn of adoration, she asked them who they were worshiping. 'We invoke the unconquerable Ambika,' they said. Then, from Parvati's body, which is like a propitious kosha—a treasure house—her auspicious form of Ambika emerged, and she promised the gods that when the time was right, she would take care of Sumbha and Nisumbha. Because the goddess's auspicious form emanated from her kosha, she is also called Kaushiki, and since this form was bright and fair, the goddess that remained in Parvati was black and became Kalika.

One day, Chanda and Munda, the servants of Sumbha and Nisumbha, saw the goddess Ambika in all her beauty in a flower-fragrant garden on Himavat, and they reported to the asuras the vision that they had seen. Then they said: 'You possess all the precious gems in the world—Indra's jewel among elephants, Airavata; Indrani's Parijata tree; the celestial horse, Ucchaishravas; Kubera's gold-inlaid chariot; Varuna's umbrella with gold streamers; the garland Vaijayanti of undying lotuses; Yama's power over death; and Agni's two garments purified by fire. How is it that you don't possess this gem among women that we saw on Himavat?'

Intrigued by this description of Ambika, Sumbha sent his messenger, Sugriva, to the goddess with this message:

'My brother and I are lords of the three worlds. It is to us that the gods and daityas, gandharvas and nagas—all creatures of the three world—bow. We possess all the riches of the world and all the choicest gems. You are the most beautiful of all gems. Come to us willingly and marry one of us, and you will reign over the three worlds as a supreme queen.'

Ambika smiled at the message Sugriva brought her and sent Sumbha and Nisumbha a message of her own:

'It is true that you are sovereigns of the three worlds and most powerful, and it is true that if I marry you, I'll be a supreme queen. However, there is the small matter of a vow I took a long time ago: I'll only marry him who vanquishes me in battle, who breaks my pride, and who is my match in strength. Come here, then, and defeat me, and I'll willingly marry you.'

When the great asuras heard this, they dispatched another message to the goddess:

'You're a proud woman. But you're able to talk back only because you don't know our strength. You, a woman, and alone, are challenging us, when even the gods themselves can't speak to us face-to-face from fear. Come of your own accord with your dignity intact, otherwise you'll be dragged here by your hair.'

'Go tell your strong Sumbha and your heroic Nisumbha that my vow stands, and they can do whatever they want,' was Ambika's response.

Seething in anger, Sumbha ordered his general, Dhumralochana, to go to Himavat and bring the woman to him, dragged by the hair if need be. 'And if anyone comes in the way to protect her—deva, yaksha, gandharva—kill them,' he ordered.

Dhumralochana took sixty thousand of his daityas and went to the snowy mountain, where he immediately saw Ambika riding a lion and looking menacing and majestic against the snowy crags.

'Come on now,' he said, bidding her as he would a meek creature. 'I don't want to use force. Come with me willingly, and I'll take you to my lord without hurting you, otherwise be prepared. I'll drag you by the hair if I need to.'

'You come to me with an army of sixty thousand and say you don't want to use force. How do you expect me to respond?' With these words, the goddess gave just one roar and Dhumralochana was reduced to ashes. His army of fierce daityas then fell upon Ambika and her lion, brandishing sharp weapons and uttering loud battle cries. But the goddess and her mount pulverized the daityas' army with ease.

When Sumbha and Nisumbha heard that Dhumralochana and sixty thousand of his best warriors had been destroyed by a single woman, they were beside themselves with rage. With lips quivering and teeth gnashing, Sumbha then ordered his servants Chanda and Munda, who were the fiercest of the daityas, to go to Himavat and capture the woman by binding her limbs and dragging her to them. 'And if she puts up a fight, kill her and her lion and bring her dead body to me,' he thundered.

Chanda and Munda gathered an army and, placing the warriors in a four-fold formation, marched to the mountain, fully equipped with the most terrible weapons. As soon as they saw the goddess on the mountain peak, they gave orders to their archers to fire thousands of arrows that fell on Ambika like torrential rain. Not one of the arrows pierced her, but the goddess was now done playing games. She creased her brow in a wrathful frown, and from between her eyebrows, a dark, terrible form emerged with a tremendous roar that shook the three worlds.

This was Kali. Her mouth was cavernous, and her tongue was hanging out. Her eyes were red and her hair was wild. She was armed with a sword and a noose, and she held a massive staff that was topped with a skull. She fell upon the asura army and began devouring elephants and horses, along with their chariots and warriors, grinding them between her teeth, chewing up their weapons. Seeing their armies reduced to nothing, Chanda and Munda rushed against her, but Kali mounted her lion, seized Chanda by the hair and sliced off his head with one stroke of her sword. Then she did the same to Munda. Then, holding the bleeding heads by the hair, one in each hand, she went to Ambika and held them out to her, laughing, as though she had just won them in a game. 'Here, I've brought you Chanda and Munda,' she said.

Accepting the gift, Ambika replied. 'From today you will be famous in the world as Chamunda, and I'll be known as Chandika.'

With both their most ferocious generals dead, Sumbha and Nisumbha now prepared to battle with the goddess themselves. They gathered a massive force of their remaining generals and ordered them to march into battle. Even their remaining armies were so vast that they seemed to spread all across the heavens. Seeing the enormity of the asuras, the gods sent forth from their bodies their own Shaktis, each one equipped with the attributes of their male counterpart, and these Shaktis joined the goddess.

Before Kali began her destruction, Ambika gave Sumbha and Nisumbha one last chance to surrender. She sent Shiva as her emissary with a message to them: 'Return Indraloka to Indra and go live in peace in Patala. But if you want battle, then my jackals are ready to devour your flesh.' The asuras refused to concede and charged into battle. Swords clashed, arrows and javelins rained down on the combatants, maces struck limbs and flesh. Heading the goddess's army of Shaktis was Kali, her skull staff smashing heads and her sword chopping off limbs, and whatever remained of the bodies was torn apart by her lion.

When the asura armies were routed and began to flee, Sumbha and Nisumbha called into battle their greatest weapon—an asura so formidable that he could single-handedly destroy the host of gods. He was Raktabija. Each drop of his blood that spilled on the ground, became another asura of equal strength, and from the blood of that asura, another one was born. Soon, the battlefield was filled with a thousand Raktabijas, and they multiplied rapidly as Ambika and Kali and the Shaktis fought them. It became impossible for the goddesses to control Raktabija's proliferation, and defeat seemed imminent.

Chandika and Chamunda stood for a moment and surveyed the battle scene. 'Let's clean the field first,' Chandika said to Chamunda. 'Eat up all the Raktabijas that are swarming the field and the ones that spring from fresh blood. I will then attack the asura himself with all my weapons, and when his blood spills, you lap up every single drop before it falls.'

And so, Chamunda with her dark, red cavernous mouth wide open began grabbing Raktabija asuras with her gleaming white teeth and devouring them—hundreds and thousands in each mouthful. When only Raktabija himself remained, Chandika struck him with all her weapons at once, and whatever blood spilled from his body, Chamunda lapped up with her tongue. When the asura's body became bloodless, he fell to the ground, dead.

With Raktabija and most of their generals dead and others in retreat, Sumbha and Nisumbha themselves descended on the field with their own personal armies. The goddesses watched them advance. Standing in their chariots, the asuras' bodies were so enormous that they stretched from earth to heaven, and when they uttered a battle cry, every creature in the three worlds became petrified with fear. In response, Ambika pulled the string of her bow, and the twang that arose reverberated through the three worlds, replacing people's fear with reverence. Ambika's lion stamped his paws, causing the mountain to shake, and Kali jumped high into the heavens and struck the sky, making the firmament tremble. Then Chandika blew on her conch, and the battle began. Sumbha and Nisumbha both rushed at her at once, but she threw a lance which pierced Sumbha, and he fell down in a faint. Then Nisumbha rushed at her and they fought fiercely. Finally, Chandika threw a spear that pierced his heart, but even as it went through his body, another asura emerged from his heart and faced the goddess. She cut off his head, with her sword and both Nisumbha and his duplicate fell down dead.

In the meantime Sumbha revived from his faint, and seeing his dear brother dead, was deeply distressed. Wiping the tears from his eyes he stood before the goddess and said in a rage, 'Your strength has gone to your head and you've become arrogant, but the strength is not even yours; it belongs to these Shaktis who are fighting for you.'

'I fight alone,' the goddess said haughtily. 'These Shaktis are my own. See, vile creature, how they merge into me.' Then she called into herself all the energies, including Kali. They entered Ambika's breast and she stood alone and proud.

Then ensued the greatest and most terrible of single combats ever witnessed by anyone in heaven or on earth. Sumbha and the goddess fought one-on-one, matching weapon to weapon and battle cry to battle cry. They fought with every weapon they had, and, when they ran out of weapons, they fought hand to hand, Sumbha striking the heart of the goddess with his massive fist, and the goddess striking the asura's heart with her open palm. Finally, she grabbed him and, lifting him high, flung him to the earth. Dazed, the asura arose and rushed at her with a loud roar, but the goddess quickly retrieved a spear and threw it at him. It pierced his heart, and he crashed to the ground, lifeless.

When he fell, the earth, with her seas and islands and mountains, shook for a long time. After the reverberations stopped, the earth regained its well-being, and the sky grew pure. All the gods then hailed Ambika as the Goddess—the Mother of the World.

Myth from the Puranas

◆

133

DON'T DRINK THE WATER: YAKSHA'S TEST

One day, travelling through Kamyaka forest during their exile from Hastinapur, the Pandava brothers became very thirsty, but there seemed to be no water in sight. 'Climb up that tree, dear Nakula, and see if you can spot a pond or lake,' Yudhishthira said to his younger brother. Nakula climbed the tree and looked around. All around, he saw many groves of trees laden with fruit, and then he heard the call of the sarasa bird which lives near water bodies. 'There is definitely water somewhere close,' he called down excitedly to his brothers. 'I see sarasa birds.'

'Then go and find this lake and fill the quivers with water,' Yudhishthira told him.

Quickly climbing down, Nakula went in the direction that he had seen the birds, and soon came upon a sparkling lake. The water looked so inviting that he fell to his knees on the bank, thinking he would quench his own thirst before filling the quivers to take to his brothers. However, as soon as he reached his hands into the water, a booming voice, that seemed to come from every direction around him, told him to stop: 'O son of Madri, I possess this lake. Before you drink this water, you must answer my questions.' But Nakula was so thirsty that he disregarded the voice, and cupping water in his hands, brought it to his mouth. As soon as the water touched his lips, he fell down dead.

When Nakula didn't return for a long time, Yudhishthira and the other Pandavas grew worried. Then Yudhishthira said to the other twin, Sahadeva, 'Can you go and see what has happened to your brother? Bring him back and also get water for the rest of us.'

Sahadeva, too, went in the direction that Nakula had pointed out and soon came upon his brother's dead body, lying beside a placid, clear blue lake. He fell down crying, but his grief was overpowered by his thirst. Deciding to first take a drink and then deal with his brother's death, he reached to gather water in his cupped hands. Once again the voice boomed, 'O son of Madri, I possess this lake. Before drinking this water, you must answer my questions.' Sahadeva looked around, but when he didn't see anyone, he went back to the water and took a sip, and died instantly.

When Sahadeva, too, failed to return, the remaining brothers became even more worried. Yudhishthira then turned to Arjuna and asked him to go and search for his brothers and bring water. Arjuna picked up his bow and arrow and sword and proceeded in the same direction that his brothers had gone. When he saw his younger brothers lying dead on the ground near a lake, he mounted an arrow to his bow and searched the surroundings. But he couldn't see anyone. Perplexed, he put down his bow and arrow and decided to quench his thirst and then carry his brothers' bodies back, along with a quiver full of water. But as he reached for the water, the loud voice thundered: 'O Arjuna, you will not be able to drink this water. I have possession of this lake, and you must answer my questions before you drink any water or even carry away a drop of it.'

'Who are you?' Arjuna called. 'Come before me. You'll not speak like this again with your body riddled with my arrows.' And saying this, he picked up his bow again and shot numerous arrows in the direction from which he thought he had heard the voice. He was skilled in shooting at an invisible target, just by sound, but no matter how many arrows he shot, they did not hit any mark and just kept falling to the ground.

'Your efforts will all be futile,' said the voice, now coming from a different direction. 'First answer my questions, then you may not only quench your thirst but also take water for your brothers. But if you drink before answering my questions, you'll die as soon as the water touches your lips—just like your brothers.'

Arjuna heard the words, but suddenly his thirst became so unbearable that he had to drink the water. As soon as it touched his lips, he died.

After waiting for some time, Yudhishthira finally sent Bhima in the same direction. Bhima, too, arrived on the spot, and seeing the lifeless bodies of his three brothers beside the lake, he cried out in sorrow. 'Surely this is the doing of some yaksha or rakshasa,' he said to himself. 'I'll fight him, but let me first drink some water.' And, as before, as soon as he got to the water, the voice said, 'Don't even think about touching the water. I possess this lake. Before drinking the water or taking it, you must answer my questions.' But Bhima, driven mad by thirst, drank the water anyway and died instantly.

Having waited for Bhima's return, Yudhishthira now entered the mighty forest himself. All around him he heard sounds of animals and birds and saw trees full of fruits. Soon he came upon a lake so beautiful that it could have been designed by Vishvakarma, the divine architect, himself. The lake was surrounded by cane trees covered with pippla and ketaki vines, and lotuses and sindhuvara flowers, as white as pearls, were floating in its water. Exhausted and oppressed by thirst, he rushed towards the translucent water that seemed to him like the elixir of life, but then he saw his four brothers lying dead on the bank, their weapons scattered around them. Yudhishthira fell to the ground, wailing in grief. He caught Nakula in his arms and then Sahadeva. 'How can I live without you?' he cried. 'I promised mother that I'd look after you and protect you. How will I show her my face?' Then he took Arjuna in his arms: 'You were going to defeat all of Duryodhana's armies,' he lamented. 'You were the pride and joy of the Pandavas.' Then he lamented over Bhima's body: 'Who will keep your promise of breaking Duryodhana's thigh? Who will now avenge Draupadi of the insult of being dragged into the assembly hall? What has happened to you all?' he cried, searching his brothers' bodies for wounds. 'Who has slain these mighty warriors?' he asked the forest. Perhaps, it is Duryodhana, he thought. Did he sneak into the forest? Or perhaps that wicked man sent a secret messenger to kill my brothers through treachery.

Yudhishthira got up to search for signs of the enemy, but the twinkling water was too enticing, so he thought he would quench his thirst and then search for his brothers' killer. As he approached the water, a thought crossed his mind that the water might be poisoned, but his brothers' faces were not discoloured, and there was no sign that they had been poisoned. As soon as he plunged his hands into the water, he heard someone say: 'It is I who has caused your brothers' deaths. I am a crane, and I possess this lake. If you drink even a drop of this water before answering my questions, you will be my fifth victim.'

'Who are you?' Yudhishthira asked. 'You must be a god or a demi-god. A simple bird could not have brought down four mountains of energy and strength. You have achieved a feat that not even the gods themselves or gandharvas or asuras or rakshasas could have achieved. What is your intention? Why have you done this?'

'I am a yaksha, not a bird, as you rightly guessed.' And, suddenly, right there before him, a huge-bodied yaksha materialized. His eyes were shining with unnatural light; he was as tall as a palm tree, and his body was blazing like the sun. 'I have killed your brothers, because despite my warning, they drank the water without my permission. I asked them to first answer my questions, but they disregarded what I said. I say the same to you: answer my questions and you may drink the water of this lake, but if you drink without answering, you, too, will join your brothers.'

'I'm not in the habit of taking that which belongs to someone else. But I'm thirsty, and I'll answer your questions to the best of my knowledge.'

And the questions and answers began:

Yaksha: What is that which makes the sun rise? Who remains near him? Who makes him set? And in what is he established?

Yudhishthira: It is Brahma that makes the sun rise. The celestials remain near him. Dharma makes him set, and he is established in truth.

Yaksha: What makes one learned? What exalts one's status? What is one's own second? And by what does one become wise?

Yudhishthira: The study of the Vedas makes one learned. Asceticism exalts one. Intelligence is one's own second. And care of the old makes one wise.

Yaksha: Is there any person, endowed with intelligence, worshipped by the world, respected by all creatures who, though enjoying sensual pleasures and breathing, is not alive?

Yudhishthira: That person who does not satisfy the gods, the guests, the servants, the ancestors, and his own self, though breathing, is not alive.

Yaksha: What thing is weightier than the earth? What is it that is higher than the sky? What is swifter than the wind? And what is more numerous than grass?

Yudhishthira: The mother is weightier than the earth; the father is higher than the sky; the mind is swifter than the wind; and thoughts are more numerous than grass.

Yaksha: What is that which does not close its eyes while sleeping? What is that which does not move after being born? What is that which has no heart? And what is that which swells with its own force?

Yudhishthira: Fish do not close their eyes while sleeping. Eggs do not move after being born. A stone has no heart. And a stream swells with its own force.

Yaksha: What is it that wanders alone? What is it that is born again after being born? What is the antidote to cold? And what is the largest field?

Yudhishthira: It is the sun that wanders alone. The moon is reborn. Fire is the antidote to cold, and the earth is the largest field.

Yaksha: What is the highest form of religion, renown, heaven, and happiness?

Yudhishthira: The highest form of religion is liberality; of renown, it is charity, of heaven, it is truth, and of happiness it is good conduct.

Yaksha: What is the best of actions and the best of wealth? What is the most important of all gains? And what is the best of all kinds of happiness?

Yudhishthira: Skilfulness is the best of all actions. Knowledge is the best of wealth. Of all gains, health is the most important. And contentment is the best of all happiness.

Yaksha: Renouncing what in oneself makes one endearing, wealthy and happy?

Yudhishthira: Abandoning a sense of pride makes one endearing; renouncing desire makes one wealthy, and giving up greed makes one happy.

Yaksha: What is knowledge? What is tranquility? What is simplicity?

Yudhishthira: A thorough grasp of divinity is knowledge; peacefulness of mind is tranquility; desire to do good to all is kindness, and equanimity of mind is simplicity.

Yaksha: What is the thing with which the world is enveloped? Because of what can a thing not discover itself? For what are friends forsaken?

Yudhishthira: The world is enveloped by ignorance. It is because of spiritual darkness that a thing cannot discover itself. It is through avarice that one forsakes a friend.

Yaksha: What is the invisible enemy of men? What is an incurable disease? What is grief? What is wickedness?

Yudhishthira: Anger is the invisible enemy; covetousness is an incurable disease; ignorance is grief; and slandering others is wickedness.

Yaksha: Who is doomed to eternal damnation?

Yudhishthira: He who has wealth, but never enjoys it nor gives it away, and always says he has none is doomed to eternal damnation.

Yaksha: Birth, good character, study of the Vedas, or learning—what makes a person a Brahmin?

Yudhishthira: Not birth, nor learning, nor study of the Vedas; a Brahmin is only he who has good character.

Yaksha: What is marvellous? What is the path? What is the news?

Yudhishthira: In this world creatures die every minute, yet those who are alive think they are immortal—isn't that marvellous? There is not a single path that is conclusive. Truth about religion is hidden in caves. Seeking that is the true path. In this great cauldron of the world with the sun as the fire and day and night as fuel, time is cooking all creatures; that is the news.

The Yaksha was satisfied with Yudhishthira's answers. 'O king,' he said. 'As a reward, I'll restore the life of one of your brothers. Choose one brother.'

'I choose Nakula. Please bring him back to life,' Yudhishthira replied.

'Your brother Bhima is very dear to you, and Arjuna is your chief support. Why did you choose Nakula, who is only a stepbrother?'

'I chose Nakula so that both my father's wives, Madri and Kunti, have surviving children. They both are my mothers, and I revere them equally. If I can restore only one brother to life, then let it be Nakula.'

'Well said, O king,' the yaksha replied. 'Your choice shows your virtue. That's why I'll allow all your brothers to be restored to life.' And, at the yaksha's words, the four Pandava brothers, who were lying prone on the forest floor, rose up, feeling restored and satiated, as though their hunger and thirst had been appeased.

Yudhishthira was very glad to see his brothers alive and embraced each one. Then he bowed to the yaksha, who had once again become a crane and was standing before him on one leg. 'I know you are not a yaksha,' he said. 'Please tell me which god you are. Are you Indra, or one of the storm gods? Each of my brothers is able to fight a thousand warriors. They are undefeatable, yet you were able to first incapacitate them and then restore them. They have awakened as though from refreshing sleep. Are you a friend, or, perhaps, you are our father, Pandu?'

The crane then turned into Lord Dharma. 'I am your father, Yudhishthira,' he said smiling. 'I am Dharma. I came here to test you, and I am pleased with your wisdom and virtue and your sense of kindness towards all creatures.'

Myth from the Mahabharata

♦

134

GANESHA WINS THE RACE

Once Kartikeya, the eldest son of Shiva and Parvati, challenged his brother, Ganesha to a race.

'I'm faster than you,' he said.

'How can you say that?' Ganesha asked.

'You want to test it? Let's race around the world and see who returns first. This place, where our parents are sitting, will be our starting point. What do you say? Do you have what it takes to accept this challenge?'

'Sure,' Ganesha said. 'Let's race.'

Kartikeya quickly mounted his peacock, Parvani, and set off, feeling a little bad for Ganesha, because this would be such an unfair competition. He would surely finish this race and get back long before his pot-bellied brother went a few paces, riding on Mushika, his tiny mouse.

Circling the earth in record time, Kartikeya returned to the starting point, wondering how long he would have to wait for Ganesha to show up. But when he got there, he was shocked to see that his brother was already back. In fact, it seemed that he had been back for a while, because there were two empty plates of ladoos sitting before him. Or, maybe he hadn't even left.

'Didn't you take the wager?' he asked jeeringly. 'You knew you would lose.'

'No. I circled the world,' Ganesha said.

'Then how did you get back so quickly?'

'I circled our parents. They're my world.'[56]

Folk-myth

◆

135

MUSHKIL AASAN: DUA-E-BEHRAM YAZAD

Long ago, there was a woodcutter called Mishkin who lived in Iran with his wife and young daughter. He made a meagre living by selling bundles of wood in the market. They were simple folk, living a simple life without luxuries. But they were devout people, who had faith in Ahur Mazda.

One day, while Mishkin was in the forest cutting wood, his neighbours cooked food that was especially delicious and its aroma wafted into Mishkin's house. Smelling the aroma, his daughter's mouth began to water, and she went to the neighbour's house on the pretext of asking for kindling, hoping that they would offer her some of the food. The neighbours gave her some kindling but did not even mention the food. The girl returned, but the smell of their food still tempted her, so, after a while, she went back to the neighbour's house. 'The kindling you gave me burnt, and I've come to ask you for some more,' she lied, sniffing the air appreciatively, hoping that the neighbours would take the hint and offer her some of the food. But this time, too, the neighbours just gave her more kindling, without any mention of food. The girl came home but returned to the neighbour's a third time, saying that the last kindling had also burnt out. By this time, the neighbours had sat down to eat, and they had figured out her real desire, but they still did not offer her food. Instead, they admonished her about the kindling, telling her that it was a sin to put out a fire. Then they slammed the door in her face. The girl returned home in tears.

When Mishkin came home that evening and greeted his daughter, she burst into tears and sobbed out the whole story about the aroma of the neighbours' food and her attempts to get a taste of it.

Mishkin hugged his daughter. 'Tomorrow, we, too, will eat delicious food,' he promised, thinking he would work extra hard and cut extra wood, which would help him earn extra money to buy a few expensive food items. The next morning, Mishkin left for the forest earlier than usual, full of resolve to cut the best wood to sell in the market for more money. However, when he reached the forest, he was sorely disappointed, because the forest was on fire. Mishkin waited all day for the fire to die out, but it didn't. Finally, in the evening, he returned home quite morose, telling himself that the following day he would surely be able to cut good quality wood. But the forest fire was still raging the next day. That evening, let alone expensive food, Mishkin's family did not even have enough to eat. When, on the third day, Mishkin was still unable to cut any wood, he couldn't bear to go home and see his daughter's defeated eyes and pinched face. So, he sat near the house, weeping in despair

At that time, five angels, Behram Yazad, Ardibehsht Yazad, Meher Yazad, Bahman Yazad and Sarosh Yazad, were passing by, and seeing Mishkin, they stopped. 'What's wrong?' Behram Yazad, the angel who solves problems, asked Mishkin. 'Tell us, and if we can, we'll help resolve the problem.'

Mishkin's grief poured out and he told the angels everything—about how his daughter had hoped that the neighbours would share with her some of the delicious food they had cooked, and how they hadn't. He then told the angels how he had promised to feed his daughter equally good food, but the forest fire had thwarted all his efforts. Behram Yazad then scooped three fistful of dirt from the ground and poured it in Mishkin's lap. 'Keep this safely,' he told Mishkin. 'And when your situation has improved, tell your story to others and remember us with offerings of nuts, flowers and sweets.'

Mishkin did not realize that the five men he had been talking to were angels, so he was sceptical about the dirt. How is this dirt going to help me, he thought to himself? I'll just wait till they are gone, and then I'll empty out my lap. And when the angels left, he was ready to do just that, but a heavenly voice stopped him. 'Don't throw away the dirt, Mishkin, or you'll regret it for the rest of your life. Keep this dirt as safe as your life. It will be the cause of your prosperity.'

Mishkin wondered whose voice this was, but he decided he would pay heed to it—just to be on the safe side. Instead of throwing the dirt by the wayside, he took it home and threw it in a corner of the hut, and then forgot about it. That night, as the family slept, bright rays began to emanate from their hut. The neighbours thought that the hut was on fire and raised an alarm. But it wasn't a fire at all. In the corner of the hut, where Mishkin had thrown the dirt, was a pile of jewels so bright and radiant, they glowed like flames. By this time, the family had woken up and were flabbergasted at the sight. Mishkin then told his wife and daughter about his meeting with the five beings who had put some dirt in his lap and told him to keep it safely. 'They were obviously divine beings,' he said to his family in a hushed voice. 'And this is their gift to us.' Mishkin then hid the jewels in a safe place, and he and his family went back to sleep. The next morning, he took one of the jewels and went to a jeweller to sell it so that he could buy food. But when the jeweller saw the jewel, he was perplexed. He had never seen anything as unique as this, and he didn't know what it was worth. 'Name your price,' he said to Mishkin. But Mishkin himself had no idea how much any jewel was worth. He only knew about wood and axes, rope and knots, and a little bit about dirt.

So Mishkin decided to have the jewel appraised, but the appraiser, too, was astounded at the uniqueness of the jewel and couldn't price it. To resolve the issue, he made three piles of money and said to Mishkin, 'Toss your jewel and take which ever pile it falls on.' Mishkin's throw landed the jewel on the pile that had the most money, and he happily gathered that up and went to the market, where he bought so much food that he had to hire someone to carry it to his house. While the food was being delivered to his house, Mishkin remembered what the angels had told him, so on his way home, he stopped to purchase fruits, flowers and sweets to honour the angels and also to distribute these among people.

Soon Mishkin was able to buy his family a house, and what a house it was. It was more palatial than the king's palace. In fact, one day, passing by Mishkin's house, the king was so awed by it that he asked his attendants if they knew to whom it belonged. One of his attendants told him about Mishkin and his rags to riches story. The king was very impressed and wondered if all this wealth had made Mishkin arrogant. One day, he sent a plateful of food—from his dinner table to Mishkin's house. Mishkin was humbled by the king's gesture, and he wondered what would be an appropriate return gesture. Finally, he returned the king's platter with a large diamond sitting in it.

The king had never seen a jewel like that in his life, and the fact that Mishkin had given it away convinced the king that the man had a generous heart. The king had the diamond studded in a necklace for his daughter, and then he invited Mishkin's daughter to meet the princess. The girls met at the lake, where the princess and her friends often went to play. The two became friends and began to visit each other.

Some time passed. Then, one day, Mishkin decided to go on a pilgrimage. Before leaving, he instructed his daughter to honour the angels with offerings of flowers, sweets and nuts every day, as he had been doing ever since the dirt in his hut had become wealth. 'Don't miss a single day,' he warned his daughter. The girl did as her father had instructed for a few days, but, being busy with her friends, she soon forgot.

One day, the princess called all her friends for a swim in the lake. Mishkin's daughter was also invited, although she did not know how to swim. So, while the girls jumped in the water one-by-one, she sat on the bank. When it was the princess's turn, she took off her expensive clothes and diamond necklace and gave them to Mishkin's daughter and told her to watch over them. After playing in the water for some time, all the girls came out and got dressed. When the princess began to put on her clothes, she noticed that the diamond from her necklace was missing. 'Did you take my diamond?' she accused Mishkin's daughter.

'Why would I do such a thing?' Mishkin's daughter asked.

'Because you are jealous of me,' the princess replied. Then she went home and told her father. The king confiscated Mishkin's wealth and house and put his daughter and wife in jail.

In the meantime, as Mishkin was returning from his travels, he was waylaid by robbers, who stole all his money and belongings. When he arrived home, he discovered that his wife and daughter were in prison. In utter dismay, he went to the king and begged him to free his wife and daughter and put him behind bars instead. 'How can I sit by and watch, while the women of my family suffer?' he told the king. The king agreed, and, releasing his wife and daughter, put Mishkin in prison. Sitting in his cell, Mishkin wondered why he had suffered such a reversal of fate. He wondered what he had done wrong and begged the angels to help him. That night an angel came in his dream and said to him, 'Behram Yazad gave you so much, and all you had to do was make a simple offering to him every day with nuts and flowers and sweets. You couldn't even do that.'

Mishkin then realized what had happened—that his daughter had forgotten to make the offering, as he had instructed her. He begged the angel for forgiveness and pleaded for another chance.

'You'll get another chance,' the angel replied. 'Tomorrow morning when you wake up, look under your pillow. You'll find a few coins there to buy nuts, flowers and sweets. You'll also be freed, but you must find someone who will buy the nuts and flowers and sweets from you and offer them in prayer to Behram Yazad.'

Sure enough, when Mishkin woke up the following morning, he found coins under his pillow and, soon after, he was set free. With the coins, he bought nuts, fruits, and flowers and then tried to find someone who would buy these from him to offer in prayer to Behram Yazad. The first man he met was on a horse and on his way to the market. 'I can't,' the man told him. 'I'm in a hurry. My son's getting married, and I'm on my way to buy clothes for the wedding.' A short distance away, that man's horse tripped and the man fell down, breaking his leg. Then Mishkin came upon a sad, old man. He stopped him and requested him to buy these items from him. 'Sure,' the old man said. 'My son is very sick and will probably die; I'm on my way to buy his shroud. But I can buy your items as well.' When the old man returned home, he offered the items he had bought from Mishkin in prayer and, soon after, his son began to recover. Filled with gratitude, the old man went searching for Mishkin, and when he found him, the two men prayed together to Behram Yazad with offerings of nuts, flowers, and sweets. From that day on Mishkin did not miss a single day of prayer. Although he and his family were once again reduced to penury, and there was a stain on their good name, they were at least free, and for that Mishkin was grateful.

Some days later, the king, queen and princess were walking in the garden when a big bird flying overhead suddenly dropped something from its beak—it was the diamond from the princess's necklace. The king recognized it immediately and realized that his daughter had wrongfully accused Mishkin's daughter, and he himself had wronged Mishkin. He sent for Mishkin and apologized profusely for the error. 'What can I do to make it up?' he asked.

'My family and I carry the shame of being called thieves. Who will marry their son to my daughter?' Mishkin said.

'I will,' the king replied, and offered his own son, and soon Mishkin's daughter was married to the prince.

Now the two families became very close, spending much time in each other's company. One day, watching Mishkin prepare to offer prayers to Behram Yazad, the queen noticed how he set aside a platter of flowers, sweets, and nuts.'

'What is this you do?' she asked Mishkin. 'What is the significance of this ritual?'

'This is the source of all my happiness,' Mishkin replied, and he narrated the whole story to her.

'I have brothers who have been lost for seven years,' the queen shared her own sorrow. 'If they return home to me, I'll make your story known throughout the kingdom. And together, the queen and Mishkin prayed and made offerings to Behram Yazad for the return of the queen's brothers. Three days later, the brothers returned to the kingdom safely. The queen rejoiced and thanked Behram Yazad, and then she began to spread the word, making sure that everyone in her kingdom heard this story. She also urged the people to have faith in Behram Yazad and pray to him to make their mushkil aasaan (troubles fade).

Parsi prayer and folk-myth

◆

136

KARVA CHAUTH

In the olden days, there was a royal couple who had seven handsome sons and one beautiful daughter, whose name was Veeravati. She was the youngest and the most pampered—not just by her parents but also by her brothers.

When Veeravati became pubescent, her parents married her to a neighbouring king. As she was leaving her parents' house, the elders told her that she must leave behind her dolls and give up childhood games, because she was now a married woman. But, ignoring these directives, Veeravati continued to play with her dolls in her husband's house. The king was indulgent, and let her be. 'She'll grow up soon enough,' he would say.

A year passed. In the month of Kartika, a few days before her first Karva Chauth, Veeravati's brothers came to take her home with them so that she could observe her fast there, under their caring and watchful eye. On the day of the fast, Veeravati woke up before daybreak and ate the customary sargi that her mother-in-law had sent, and then she began to fast for the rest of the day. Not being used to deprivation of any kind, she started feeling hungry in the middle of the day, and by late afternoon, she was starving. Her brothers couldn't bear to see her suffer; they begged her to eat, enticing her with all kinds of sweetmeats. Veeravati was tempted, but she reluctantly refused, knowing that she had to wait till moonrise.

All day, she sat and embroidered, trying to keep herself distracted, waiting impatiently for the sun to set and the moon to rise. However, when the sun went down, and still the moon was nowhere in sight, she couldn't bear her hunger any more and began to complain about how late the moon was in rising. She didn't know that because this Karva moon is on the fourth day of the full moon, it rises four times later than usual.

Her brothers grew distraught at Veeravati's condition, and finally, they went into the garden to the massive peepul tree at the far end, and lit a bonfire behind it. Then they came and told Veeravati that the moon had risen. Relieved, Veeravati ran outside to see, and sure enough there was a bright light in the distance, near the horizon. Quickly, she completed the worship of Goddess Gauri and her spouse, Lord Shiva, who are the objects of worship for the wives who pray to them for the longevity of their husbands' lives. Then she rushed inside to the lavish spread that her brothers had prepared.

Just as Veeravati put the first bite in her mouth, a messenger arrived with an urgent message: her husband, the king, had died. Leaving everything, Veeravati rushed back to her husband's house. On the way there she met Gauri and Shiva. Tearfully, she asked Gauri: 'Why did my husband die?'

'It's because you broke your fast before moonrise. What you saw was not the real moon. It was only a fire behind a peepul.'

'What am I to do now?' Veeravati wailed. 'I've killed my husband.'

Seeing Veeravati's distress, the goddess took pity on her. 'There is one way that you can revive him.'

'I'll do anything,' Veeravati said.

'Go home and take care of your husband's body for a year. Next year, in the month of Kartika, on this same fourth day of the waning full moon, fast all day without complaining, and then give Karva water to the moon, when it rises. Do it with full faith and strict ritual, and your husband will come back to life.'

When Veeravati arrived home, she saw her husband's body on the floor. It was pierced with hundreds of needles. These were all the needle points she had pierced into the fabric while embroidering to distract herself. Veeravati fell to the floor beside her husband's corpse and began picking out the needles, one by one.

That whole year, Veeravati plucked the needles from her husband's body. When the day of Karva Chauth arrived, only one needle remained. Realizing what day it was, she got up and went to the market to buy the items she would need for the fast and for the Karva, thinking that when she returned, she would remove the last needle from her husband's body.

Veeravati had a personal maid who had watched her mistress take out needles from the king's body. When Veeravati left for the market, the maid sat down beside the king and pulled out the last needle. The king woke up. When he saw the maid beside him, he mistook her for his wife. And so, when Veeravati returned, the maid had become the queen, and she had become the maid.

One day the king had to travel out of the kingdom on some business, and he asked his queen what she wanted. 'New clothes and jewellery,' she replied. Then the king asked his queen's maid what she wanted, and

Veeravati asked for two dolls. The king thought this was a strange request; it also reminded him of something, but he couldn't quite remember what it was. When he returned, he gave the queen her clothes and jewellery and the two dolls to Veeravati. After that whenever he saw the maid taking a break from work, she would be sitting and talking to the dolls, saying over and over, 'Roli became Goli, and Goli became Roli.'

On the day of Karva Chauth, Veeravati once again fasted, and, that day, when the king heard her talking to her dolls, he asked her why she repeated the words, Roli became Goli, and Goli became Roli. Veeravati told him the whole story of how she had mistaken the bonfire behind the peepul as the moon, how her embroidery needles had pricked his body, and how the maid had plucked out the last needle and become the queen, while she, the queen, had become the maid.

Realizing his mistake, the king banished the maid and lived a long and happy life with Veeravati.

Vratakatha / folk-myth

◆

137

THE TALE OF SMALL FEET

The yogi said to King Vikram, 'I need a brave man to help me complete a mantra. Will you help me?'

'Yes,' said Vikram.

'Then go down that road in a southerly direction until you come to an asoka tree. A corpse is hanging from its branches; bring it to me.'

Vikram began walking in the direction that the yogi had pointed. It was a very dark night, but the glowing embers in funeral pyres gave him enough light. When he arrived at the tree, he noticed that there was a cloud of smoke around it, which seemed to be coming out of the tree itself. When he looked up, he saw that a corpse was, indeed, hanging from its upper branches. Vikram climbed the tree and cut through the rope from which the corpse was hanging. As the dead body crashed to the ground, it screamed.

The king was surprised but not afraid. He thought that, perhaps, the man was not dead after all. So, he quickly climbed down the tree and laying a hand on the man's chest, checked for a heartbeat. Suddenly a chilling laugh came from the corpse, and Vikram realized that it had been possessed by a vetala (spirit). 'Why do you laugh?' Vikram asked. In response, the corpse just flew back into the top branches of the tree and hung from there again. Undeterred, Vikram once again climbed the tree and, grabbing the corpse, threw it on his shoulder. Then, climbing down, he began walking towards the banyan tree in the cremation ground, where the yogi was waiting for him.

As Vikram trudged along with the corpse on his shoulder, he felt it stir. Then it spoke to him. 'O king, I'll tell you a story to pass the time. The story has a question at the end of it. If you know the correct answer, you must tell it to me. But if you know the right answer and withhold it, your head will split into a thousand pieces.'[57]

'In a city lived a king by the name of Mandlika. His wife was the daughter of the king of Malwa, and her name was Chandravati. The two had a daughter, whom they had named Lavanyavati. When the daughter was of marriageable age, the king's relatives cheated him out of his kingdom and all his wealth. Afraid for the safety of his family, the king fled with his wife and daughter to Malwa, carrying with him as many jewels as he could. The first night that they were travelling, they found themselves in the Vindhya forest, a territory that was known to be infested by Bhils. As they neared a Bhil village, the king told his wife and daughter to hide in the forest. 'If I have to worry about your safety, I'll not be able to fight,' he told them. So the queen and the princess went into a grove of trees and carefully concealed themselves. When the Bhils saw the king, they fell upon him with swords and knives. The king fought valiantly, but, ultimately, the chief of the Bhils killed him, and the others stole all the jewels he was carrying.

When the queen and the princess saw the king killed, they were grief-stricken, and also afraid that the Bhils would find them and kill them as well. Hoping to escape the murderous robbers, they crept out of their hiding spot and began to walk deeper into the forest. Soon they came upon a lotus lake near a large asoka tree. By now they were totally exhausted, so they sat down under the tree to rest, and as they sat, it hit them how alone and helpless they were, and this made them weep.

At that time, a local chieftain, Chandasimha, and his son,

Simhaparkarma, were hunting in the forest. When they saw two sets of footprints leading from the trees to the lake, they wondered to whom they belonged. The footprints appeared to be of women; one set was obviously of a woman whose feet were smaller than the other's. 'Let's follow these footprints,' Chandasimha said to his son. 'If we find these women, you can choose one of them for a wife.'

'I'd like to marry the lady who has the smaller feet, because she's obviously younger and will suit my age. But you must marry the older one with the bigger feet.'

'What are you saying, son? Your mother passed away only recently. She was a virtuous woman and the best wife a man could have. I have no wish to marry again.'

'Father, a householder's house is not complete without a wife. You know what they say—a house without a wife is like a prison without chains. If you don't marry this woman, I won't marry either.'

Chandasimha agreed to do as his son suggested, and, following the footsteps, the men found the two women sitting beside the lotus lake. Queen Chandravati was a dark beauty, and she wore shining pearls around her neck. And the princess, Lavanyavati, was fair and glowing, like moonlight.

When the women saw the two men on horses, they were fearful, thinking they were robbers, but Chandasimha quickly allayed their fears. 'Don't be afraid,' he said. 'I'm a chieftain of Vittpapuri and this is my son. We were hunting in this forest and saw your footprints. Please tell us what two beautiful, high-born women, such as yourselves, are doing in this forest, all alone and unprotected?'

Chandravati started weeping again and told the men the sad story about why they were fleeing to Malwa, and how her husband had lost his life fighting with the Bhils.

'We're at your service,' Chandasimha said. 'My son and I propose marriage to you and to your daughter.'

The two women accepted the proposals and went with the chieftain and his son to Vittpapuri, where the son married the queen, because she was the one with the smaller feet, and the father married the daughter, whose feet were bigger than her mother's. So the daughter became her mother's mother-in-law, and the mother became her daughter's daughter-in-law. They lived happily with their husbands in Vittpapuri and had many children.

When the vetala finished telling the story, he asked King Vikram, 'What was the relationship of the children that were born to the mother and daughter who were married to the son and father? If you don't give me the right answer, your head will split into a thousand pieces.'

Vikram thought for a while, but he couldn't come up with the right answer and remained silent. The vetala, inhabiting the dead body on Vikram's shoulder, laughed, 'O king, you have answered the question to each of my stories, but it seems that you don't know the answer to this one. Yet, you are unafraid. You walk on with steady steps, completing the mission that the yogi has set for you. I'm pleased with you and will give you some advice that will save your life. I'm leaving this body now, and you can take it to the yogi. He'll request me to enter it and then honour me. But the corpse is just a means to summon me. His real intention is to sacrifice you so that he can gain mastery over the magic of the Vidyadhars and be able to enjoy all the pleasures of the earth. If you want to live, do as I say: when he tells you to lie on the ground with all your limbs touching the earth, ask him to demonstrate how, and when he lies down to show you, cut off his head, and you'll become the master.'

Vikram thanked the vetala, to which he responded, 'Enjoy the pleasures of the earth, king.' Then, with a diabolic laugh, the vetala left the corpse.

Folktale from the Baital Pachisi

◆

138

HIRAMAN, THE PARROT

There was once a poor bird-catcher and his wife who never seemed to have enough to eat. One day the wife said to the husband, 'Stop selling every bird you catch. Today, whatever you catch, let's cook it and eat it.' The bird-catcher agreed, and they went out with their rods and nets. But that day, they didn't catch a single bird. Then, just as the sun was setting, a parrot, whose green feathers glistened like an emerald, flew into their net. It was a hiraman from the Molucca islands. The wife took the fluttering bird in her hands and poked and prodded it all over. 'It's such a tiny bird,' she said. 'It'll barely be a mouthful.'

Suddenly the bird spoke in a human voice, 'Don't kill me. Take me to the king and sell me to him. He'll give you a lot of money.'

At first the couple were quite astonished to hear the parrot speak, but then they became excited at the thought of the money they could make. 'What price should we ask from the king?' they wanted to know.

'Leave that to me,' the parrot replied. 'When the king asks you my price, just say that the parrot will tell you himself.'

The next morning the couple took the Hiraman to the palace. The king was delighted by the pure green colour of the bird and asked the bird-catcher how much he wanted for it. 'Maharaj,' said the bird-catcher. 'That's for the bird to decide. If it pleases the Maharaj, please ask the bird.'

'What? Does the bird speak?' the king said, amused. Then he turned to the parrot and said in jest, 'Well, Hiraman, how much are you asking for yourself?'

'Maharaj, my price is ten thousand rupees,' the bird replied.

The king was amazed, but he thought that even for a talking bird, the price was too much. He was about to refuse when the Hiraman spoke again, 'It may sound like a high price, but in time I'll prove my worth.'

The king laughed, 'What can a little bird like you do to be worth ten thousand rupees?'

'When the time comes, you'll see. I promise you, you will not be disappointed.'

More out of curiosity at the bird's promise than satisfaction with the deal, the king agreed to pay the full price to the bird-catcher, and he returned home with wife, thrilled by his good fortune.

The king kept the Hiraman in a golden cage in his own rooms, and within just a few days of acquiring him, he became completely enchanted with him. The bird was very intelligent—far more intelligent than many of his ministers. Not only did he reply astutely to every question the king asked, but also, whenever the king felt the need for some piety, the bird recited the names of gods. He knew all the names of the three hundred and thirty-three lakh Hindu gods.

The king spent so much time with the parrot that his six queens began to feel quite neglected. Together they decided that the only way to bring the king's attention back to them was to kill the bird, so they began to wait for an opportune moment when they could get their hands on him. One day, the king had to go out of town on business, and the queens decided to use this opportunity. But the question was: who, out of the six of them, would do the deed? When they couldn't come to a consensus, they decided that they would let the Hiraman pick his own killer: they would ask him who was the ugliest of all the queens, and whomever he named would be the one to strangle him.

When, at the appointed time, the six queens entered the king's chamber and advanced towards Hiraman, he guessed their intent and began to recite the three hundred and thirty-three lakh names of the gods and goddesses. The queens stopped, feeling ashamed for even thinking evil thoughts about the pious creature, and they left without harming him. However, the next day, their jealousy returned with full force and they resolved that they would not let pity or piety cloud their objective. So, entering the king's room, they marched right up to the cage and asked the parrot, 'O Hiraman, who amongst us is the prettiest and who the ugliest?'

'How can I tell?' the Hiraman replied. 'I can hardly see you from behind these bars. I can only answer those questions honestly after I have looked at each of you closely. Set me free so that I can take a look.'

But the queens were reluctant to open the cage. 'If you're worried that I'll fly away, you can close all the windows and doors of the room,' the parrot said. The queens did as he suggested and let him out. He flew around them for a few minutes, inspecting their faces, and then, flying to the corner of the room, said, 'None of you have the beauty of even the tiny toe of the princess who lives beyond the seven seas and the thirteen rivers.'

The queens lunged at the Hiraman, but, with a flapping of wings, he quickly escaped through a small water spout, that he had already scoped out. Once outside, he flew around for a bit till he found a woodcutter's hut and went in through an open window. When the king returned the following day and discovered the empty cage, he asked the queens if they knew Hiraman's whereabouts, but they pretended ignorance. The king had his men search the palace and the grounds, but when not even a feather of the Hiraman's could be found, he became depressed. He lost interest in everything and, day after day, just sat in his chamber, staring at the empty cage, lamenting, 'Oh my Hiraman, where are you?' The king's ministers were afraid that he would lose his mind, so they had a town crier announce to the citizenry that whoever found the king's pet parrot would be rewarded ten thousand rupees. The woodcutter, who had seen the parrot in his hut, was delighted. Armed with a net, he tried to catch the Hiraman, but he hardly had to put in any effort, because the parrot just flew into the net, as though he wanted to be caught. The woodcutter then put him in a cage and carried him to the palace, where he presented him to the king and returned home with ten thousand rupees.

'Where were you?' the king asked the Hiraman, and the parrot told him everything about how the queens had come into his chamber to kill him and how he had got away. The king had the six queens banished to the wilderness, where they were eaten by wild beasts. Then the king asked the Hiraman about the princess he had mentioned, who lived beyond the seven seas and thirteen rivers, and whose little toe had more beauty in it than the any of the six queens. 'Does she really exist?' he asked. 'Do you know how I can get to her?'

'I can actually take you to her. She's waiting for you, even though she doesn't know it yet.'

'Tell me what to do,' the king said. 'How do I reach her?'

'What you need is a pakshiraj, a winged horse, who can fly beyond the seven seas and the thirteen rivers.'

'I have many horse breeds in my stables,' the king replied. 'Maybe one of them is a pakshiraj. Shall we go and check?'

The king and the Hiraman examined every horse in the stable. There were many fine breeds, but the Hiraman could not find a pakshiraj among them. But then they came to a feeble pony, so thin that only a layer of skin seemed to cover his ribcage. 'That's the one,' the Hiraman said, excitedly. 'He's a true pakshiraj—a true breed one. But he needs to be nourished and fattened before he can make the long journey. I think he should be ready in six months.'

The king had the pony removed from the general stable and transferred to a luxurious stall. He also put his personal groom in charge of his care, making sure that he was fed with the finest grain. In six months' time the skinny, malnourished pony was transformed into a magnificent steed. The Hiraman inspected him and declared that he was fit to carry out his plan. Then he told the king to have his silversmith make a large quantity of khais (fried grains of rice wrapped in silver sheet), and, finally, the king and the Hiraman and pakshiraj were ready to leave.

Before starting on their journey, the parrot warned the king, 'When you start, just give pakshiraj one blow with the whip; if you give him more than one, he'll stop right there, no matter where we are. And on the way back, too, when we're ready to leave, just strike him once, and that's all, or we'll be stuck in the middle.'

The king then mounted pakshiraj and taking the Hiraman and the bag of silver khais, gently touched the steed with his whip, and off they went, like a leap of lightning, over vast regions and the seven seas and thirteen rivers. That very night they landed outside the palace of the princess, whose small toe had more beauty than all the king's former queens.

The Hiraman instructed the king to quickly tie the horse to the big banyan tree that was right near the gate, climb up the tree, and hide himself in the branches. Then the Hiraman took the bag of khais and, flying into the palace, began to lay the silver grain in a trail through the corridors to the princess's bedroom. After that, he flew to the tree where the king was hiding, and waited. Sometime after midnight, the princess's maid got up to use the bathroom and seeing the silver trail of khais, awakened the princess. The princess stepped out of her bedroom and began picking up the silver, grain by grain, till she came to the end of the last corridor. Then she opened the gate and found the last grain of khais right under the tree. As soon as she picked up that last grain, the Hiraman nudged the king off the tree, and he landed before her. As the parrot had instructed, he quickly mounted pakshiraj, grabbed the princess, and with the Hiraman perched on his shoulder, struck pakshiraj on the back with the whip so they could fly back to his kingdom.

Pakshiraj was flying like the wind, and the king with the princess in his arms was dreaming about getting home and marrying her, when instinctively, from habit, he struck pakshiraj's back again with the whip, as he would do with his other horses. Pakshiraj immediately began descending to the ground in the middle of a dense forest.

'Oh no. What have you done?' the Hiraman admonished the king. 'I told you that you mustn't strike pakshiraj more than once, or we'll stop in the middle of the journey, and now here we are, grounded in a forest.'

It was night, so they ate the fruits from the trees and went to sleep, huddled close together. There was nothing else to do, because Pakshiraj was reduced to a powerless pony.

The next morning, they woke up to the sounds of a hunting party. It was another king, who often hunted in this forest. When this king found them, he took one look at the princess and was instantly struck by her beauty. At his orders, his men grabbed the princess and placed her on his horse, and he sped away. But before he left, he shot arrows into the king's eyes and blinded him. His men also took away the pony, so that he would have no means of following them. Now the king who had crossed seven seas and thirteen rivers was left helpless and blind and alone, but he still had his Hiraman.

The other king took the princess to his palace, where he locked her in a room, and he had his men put the emaciated pony in the stable. But when this king tried to approach the princess, she told him she was observing a six-month fast for Shiva and that he must not touch her for six months, or Shiva would burn him with the fire from his third eye. To convince him, she performed a devotional service to Shiva every day. She gave herself six months, because she knew that is how long it would take for pakshiraj to regain his strength. The princess also got permission from the king to take care of her pony, and she began feeding him with the finest of grain that she managed to get from the kitchen. She hoped that when pakshiraj gained his strength, she would be able to escape on him and find her king. She desperately needed the Hiraman's help, but she had no idea how to look for him. Then she hit on a plan. She asked the servants to scatter heaps of rice and wheat and lentils on the roof of the palace for the birds, saying that this, too, was part of her vow to Shiva. And so, every day hundreds of birds flocked to the palace's roof to peck at grain. Every day she scrutinized the flocks, hoping to see the Hiraman among them.

The Hiraman stayed in the forest to take care of the blind king. Then, one day, he met some birds who told him that they had been feasting on grain scattered on the roof of a palace nearby. 'It's like an open feast,' they told him. 'Any bird from anywhere can come and eat. We've heard that a princess has made a vow to Shiva to feed us birds for six months.' The Hiraman knew, instantly, who was laying out this feast and why, and the very next day, he went there.

When the princess saw the parrot, she jumped for joy and ran to pick him up. She told him about her ruse of the six-month fast, and he told her how the blind king was faring. Then, they both consoled each other that the six months were almost over, and pakshiraj would soon be ready. 'But what about the king?' the princess asked, sadly. 'Will he ever see again?'

'Actually, I know of the cure,' Hiraman said. 'When Pakshiraj has regained his strength, escape on him and come to the forest. I'll make sure that the king is cured.' And that very day the Hiraman began to make preparations to get the antidote for blindness—an eye salve made with the excrement from chicks of the bihangama bird. But that bird lived on a tree outside the gate of the princess's own palace which was seven seas and thirteen rivers away. Before flying back to that location, the Hiraman gathered lots of fruit from the trees, and placing it before the king, told him to take care till he returned. He reached the princess's palace at night and then waited in the tree, underneath the nest of the bihangama birds, holding a leaf in his beak to receive the chicks' droppings. When he had gathered enough excrement to make a salve, he flew back over the seven seas and thirteen rivers, carrying the leaf carefully in his beak. On reaching the king, he placed the leaf on the ground and applied the excrement to his eyes. Instantly, the king's sight was restored.

In the meantime, in the other king's palace, pakshiraj gained strength every day, and, on the last day of the six months, when the princess came to tend to him, he neighed, declaring he was ready. The princess jumped on his back and off they went. When they reached the king, he quickly got on pakshiraj's back, and with the Hiraman perched on his shoulder, flew to his capital city.

The princess and the king were soon married amidst much celebration and jubilation, and from that day onwards, they lived happy and fruitful lives, having many sons and daughters and grandchildren. The Hiraman lived with them for a long time and often recited the names of the three hundred and thirty lakh gods and goddesses for the princes and princesses and their children.

Tota Maina qissa from Bengal

◆

139

THE SOWER

As Jesus sat by the lakeside, so many people gathered around him that he had to get into a boat in order to talk to all of them. Then Jesus spoke in parables to all the people standing on the shore.

He said: 'A sower went out to sow. As he sowed, some seed scattered along the path, and the birds came and pecked at it. Some seed fell on the rocky ground, where it sprouted quickly, because the soil there was shallow; but when the sun came up, the young plants withered away in no time, because the roots couldn't take hold. Some other seed fell among the thorns, which choked the plants. But some of the seed fell into good soil, where it yielded a crop a hundred, sixty or even thirty times more than what was sowed. Come and hear what I have to say about this parable:

'When a man hears about the Kingdom of God but fails to understand what he has heard, the evil one comes and takes away what has been sown in his heart. This was the seed that was sown along the path. The seed that was sown on the rocky ground is a man who hears the word and, at once, rejoices but does not internalize the meaning; because it does not take root in him. It has no lasting value, and if he has to face trouble or persecution because of the word, he denounces it. The seed that was sown in the thorns represents he who hears the word but is so caught up in worldly concerns and outward show that the word suffocates beneath the weight of these things and is lost. But the seed that fell into good soil is that man who hears the word and not only accepts it but also understands it. He is the one who produces a crop that is a hundred or sixty or thirty times more than he sows.

Parable from the New Testament

◆

140

THE MILLIONAIRE

Once, while travelling through Lahore, Guru Nanak was invited to dinner by Duni Chand, who was one of the richest men of the city. Arriving at his palatial home, Guru Nanak saw numerous flags planted in the courtyard. When the Guru asked Duni Chand the reason for the flags, the man proudly declared that each flag represented one lakh rupees that he had made. Guru Nanak congratulated him on his good fortune, and then, taking out a needle from his satchel, he gave it to Duni Chand. 'Can you keep this needle safe for me, please, and give it to me in the next life, when I ask for it?'

Duni Chand took the needle carefully and, bringing it to his wife, told her to keep it safely. 'Baba Nanak will ask for it in the next life. He's told me to keep it for him.'

'Have you gone crazy?' his wife said. 'You can't carry the needle into the next life. Go and give it back to him.'

When Duni Chand returned the needle to Guru Nanak with his wife's message, the Guru looked at Duni Chand sadly. 'If you can't carry a tiny needle with you to the next life, how will you carry these lakhs of rupees?'

Duni Chand fell at Guru Nanak's feet. 'Tell me what I should do to ensure that my wealth goes with me?' he begged.

'Share it with the poor in this life,' Guru Nanak advised.

And that is how Duni Chand learned charity.

Folk-myth from the Guru Nanak Janamsakhis

◆

141

THE WISDOM OF NOT BEATING A WIFE

A raja's son was of marriageable age. Before sending his envoys all over the kingdom to search for a suitable bride, the raja asked the prince, 'Son, tell me what qualities you are looking for in your bride?'

'I'm not particular about her qualities,' the son replied. 'My only condition is that she should let me beat her, whenever I'm in the mood to give her a good beating. And she should agree to this condition before the marriage.'

The king was shocked, but he sent his men out, anyway, to see if they could find a maiden who would consent to this condition. The envoys searched the whole kingdom; they even searched the neighbouring kingdoms, but they couldn't find a single girl who was willing to be beaten by her husband, even if he was a prince. Then, finally, a poor man's daughter agreed to wed the prince.

After the two were married, the prince and his bride spent many days of happy matrimony. Then, one evening, as they were sitting and enjoying each other's company, the prince suddenly got up and pulled out a stick from under the cot. 'I'm going to beat you now,' he said, rolling up his shirt sleeves. 'And don't try to escape. You agreed to this.'

The girl nodded. 'I did agree to it, but at that time, I didn't know what I know now.'

'What do you mean?' the prince asked impatiently.

'Well...you're not really you. Everything you are is because of your father. So, it won't really be you who'll be doing the beating; it'll be your father's son. I agreed to be beaten by someone who is his own person. When you've made something of yourself, then you'll have earned the right to beat me.'

The prince realized that what his bride said was true. Hence, he decided that he would go to a foreign land to do trading and then return home with his own wealth to show his bride that he was worthy. Gathering a band of attendants and piling merchandise on horses and elephants, he left his kingdom with great pomp and show, convinced that soon he would return with double the wealth and, perhaps, an expensive stick or two with which to beat his wife. His bride bid him farewell. She also secretly planted one of her own men with special instructions in the prince's entourage.

The prince journeyed for many days until he came to the country called Lutia. When he and his men rode into the city, Lutia Raja was on the roof of his palace, taking a stroll. When he saw the prince's cavalcade, he called his man and sent him to meet the travellers. It was Lutia's convention that whosoever wished to enter the country, first had to answer the king's question. So, halting the prince's party, the king's man posed the question: 'Do you believe that prosperity is forever, or do you believe prosperity lasts only a day?'

'Forever,' the prince replied, without a second thought.

Instantly, he and his men were surrounded by Lutia's soldiers, who seized all the merchandise and the horses and elephants. The prince's attendants fled—every single one of them, except the princess's man. For days, the prince and his man wandered the streets of Lutia, penniless and hungry; then the princess's man suggested to the prince that they had better find work, or they would die of starvation. They searched for employment everywhere, but the only work they could find was to be hired as servants in a rich merchant's house. He didn't pay them anything but gave them a place to sleep and two meals a day.

They lived in the merchant's house for many months. Labouring all day, the prince soon lost his princely airs, along with his good looks. His body became lean and his clothes bedraggled, until all that remained on his body was his loincloth. Soon, that too, became threadbare, and he had to plead with the merchant to give him a few coins so that he could at least buy a new loincloth.

That day, during his bath, when the prince discarded his old loincloth, he didn't notice that his man picked it up and quickly hid it in a bag.

Now when the princess heard what had happened to her husband, she gathered a troop of men and, disguising herself as a merchant, set out for Lutia. Before she left, she sent her spies into the country to find out as much as she could about the situation. The spies returned with information about the question that the Raja of Lutia asked all travellers and also about how he resolved issues of dispute. Knowing this, the princess carried with her nothing except a shawl and a mouse.

As soon as the princess's entourage reached Lutia, an armed soldier blocked their way. 'It is our Raja's command that you answer a question before you come into Lutia,' he declared.

'What is the question?' the princess asked in a disguised masculine voice.

'Do you believe that prosperity is forever, or do you believe prosperity lasts only a day?'

'Prosperity lasts only a day,' she answered.

'Then come with me,' the soldier said and led her and her men to the king's palace.

While the princess and her men waited, the king's men fetched the prince and his man from the merchant's house. It was the king's practice to let fate decide who would receive the confiscated wealth—the traveller who believed that prosperity lasted forever or the traveller who believed it lasted only for a day. This was the game that the king played with travellers who came to Lutia, and the decider of the game was his favourite cat: the person towards whom the cat jumped was the recipient of all the wealth.

As the prince and the disguised princess sat across from the raja and his cat, the princess threw a shawl around her body and hid the mouse in its folds. Every few minutes she would lift the fold and let the cat see the twitching mouse. When the cat was released, she jumped right into the princess's lap, making the princess the winner of all the wealth that used to belong to the prince. Loading everything on her horses and elephants, the princess returned home to the palace, while the prince went back to the merchant's house in Lutia.

However, by now the prince was tired of his life of servitude and drudgery, so, he quit his job and returned home. Somehow, he managed to have his men deliver him his princely clothes before he entered the palace, and then, adding an extra swagger to his gait, he went to meet his wife. 'I've been working all these months in a foreign land,' he told her, boastfully. 'I've been very successful and have made a lot of money, which I have hidden in a secret place. And now, I'm going to beat you.'

'Before you do, let me show you something,' the princess replied and took the prince into a room where she had stacked all the merchandise that she had brought back from Lutia.

'How...where...?' the prince floundered.

'And I have something else to show you, as well,' the princess said. 'Take a look at it and then tell me if you still want to beat me.' Saying this, she pulled out from her pocket the prince's tattered loincloth.

Seeing a reminder of his days when he was far from princely, the prince felt ashamed. After that he never thought about beating his wife.

Folktale from the Santhal tribe

◆

142

A MONKEY'S HEART

Once upon a time, the Bodhisattva was born as a monkey who lived in a Himalayan forest by a bend of the Ganga. At that time there was a crocodile dwelling in the Ganga. One day, the crocodile's mate saw the strong and well-built monkey, and she felt a craving to eat his heart, so she said to her husband, 'Can you bring me the heart of that king of monkeys? I have a great desire to eat it.'

'Dear wife,' said the crocodile, 'we live in the water, and he lives in the trees: how can we catch him?'

'I don't care how you catch him,' she replied, 'but if I don't get his heart, I'll die.'

'Don't get upset,' the crocodile consoled his wife. 'I'll think of some plan and will soon bring you his heart to eat.'

One day the monkey came to the bank of the Ganga to get a drink. This was the opportunity the crocodile was seeking. He drew near the water's edge, and said, 'Dear monkey, aren't you tired of eating the tasteless fruits that grow in this old forest. There's a forest on the other side of the river, in which mango and breadfruit trees grow in abundance. The fruit of those trees is as sweet as honey. Why don't you cross over to that forest and enjoy a feast of that delicious fruit?'

'I would like to,' the monkey replied. 'But the Ganga is too deep and wide. I can't cross it.'

'If you wish to go, I can take you. Just get on my back, and I'll carry you across. I have to go there anyway, so it'll be no trouble.'

Excited at the idea of eating mango and breadfruit, the monkey climbed up on the crocodile's back. However, when they had gone just a little way, the crocodile plunged into the water, taking the monkey with him.

'Dear friend, can you please stop doing that!' the monkey cried. 'Otherwise I'll drown.'

The crocodile laughed. 'That's exactly what I am hoping will happen. Do you think I'm carrying you on my back for no reason? My wife has a craving to eat your heart, and I want to bring it to her.'

The monkey did some quick thinking and then replied, 'Friend, I'm glad you told me, because my heart is not in my body. We monkeys never keep our heart inside our body, otherwise when we go jumping from tree to tree, it would be smashed to pieces.'

'Oh,' said the crocodile. 'Then, where do you keep it?'

The monkey pointed to the bank of the Ganga where there was a fig tree with clusters of ripe fruit hanging from the branches. 'See?' he said, 'All the monkeys' hearts hang from that fig tree.'

'It's a good thing you told me,' said the crocodile. 'If you show me which one is your heart, I'll just take that, and I won't have to kill you.'

'Okay. Take me to the tree then, and I'll point it out to you,' the monkey replied.

When the crocodile brought the monkey to the bank, he immediately leapt off his back and climbed up the fig tree. 'You fool!' he called to the crocodile. 'No creature keeps its heart hanging on a tree. You may have a great, big body, but you have no sense.' And then he broke into a mocking verse:

There is rose-apple treat and a mango treat
But these figs are all I wish to eat
Big is your body but small is your brain
Now go, crocodile, and to your wife explain.

The crocodile left, feeling miserable and stupid, wondering how he would explain what had transpired to his wife.

Folktale from the Jatakas

◆

143

ONE ALPHABET OF WISDOM

Upendra Bhanja was a renowned Odiya poet of the eighteenth century. He was not only a great poet, who is supposed to have composed fifty-two kavyas, but he was also very learned. However, Bhanja was not born with a brilliant mind. He was born a simpleton, although, in a royal family. All his life, people made fun of him and questioned how a bokka—a fool—like him could be the grandson of the great poet, Dhananjaya Bhanja. In fact, to be wise and creative like his grandfather was his greatest desire, and that is what he always prayed for at his family's Kali temple.

One evening, when Bhanja was returning from the temple, he was accosted by a wild woman. Her eyes were bright with a strange light and her hair was loose and tangled around her body. This was Chandi, Kali's most ferocious form. But Bhanja, in his simplicity, did not recognize her. 'What do you want?' he asked the woman.

'I want your blood,' she said.

Bhanja picked up a sharp stone and, cutting his finger with it, extended his hand to her.

Chandi put his finger in her mouth and began sucking his blood. Soon, Bhanja was on the point of losing consciousness and the words, 'Oh Ma' escaped his lips.

As soon that cry reached Chandi's ears, she became a mother. She immediately stopped drinking Bhanja's blood, and restored him to full health. 'My son,' she said. 'I asked you for your life blood, and you offered it to me without a moment's hesitation. Now I want to give you a boon. Ask me for anything.'

'Ma, give me wisdom,' he said. 'Give me imagination so that I can write great poetry like my grandfather.'

'Open your mouth, son,' Chandi said. And when he did, she wrote one alphabet on his tongue. From that day on, every word that Bhanja spoke was wise and every thought he expressed was poetic.

Folktale from Orissa

◆

144

BEWARE THE COMPANY OF EVIL PEOPLE

With evil people neither stay nor go;
The heron died for being with the crow

The high road to Oogein is long and shadeless. There are no trees, except for one large peepul. In that tree a crow and a heron lived together. One hot summer day, a weary traveller passed that way, and, seeing the shade under the peepul, decided to rest there. Putting down his bow and arrows, he lay on the ground and soon fell asleep. Before long, the shadow of the tree shifted, leaving the left side of the man's face exposed to the sun's glare. The heron saw this, and being the kindly bird that he was, he perched on the tree and spread out his wings so as to provide shade to the traveller's face. The poor fellow, exhausted from travel, unaware of the shifting shadows of the tree or of the heron's generosity, continued to sleep soundly, snoring away with his jaw hanging open. The sight of the man's restfulness was too much for the malevolent crow. He perched right over the man and made a large dropping in his open mouth, and then he flew off. The traveller woke up with a start, and tasting bird shit, spit it out with a curse. Then he looked up at the tree to see who was the culprit, and seeing the heron, he fitted an arrow on his bow and shot him dead.

Folktale from the Hitopadesha

♦

145

DAYDREAMERS

Gopal Bhar had neighbours who were daydreamers. One day, the man told his wife, 'When I make enough money, I'll buy a cow.'

'That's good,' said the wife. 'I'll feed it and take care of it and milk it every morning.'

'But where will we keep the milk? We don't have a large enough pot to hold all the milk that the cow will give.'

So, the following day, the wife went to the market and bought four clay pots of varying sizes. When she brought them home, the man wanted to know what each one was for.

'Well, this large one is for the milk, this medium one is for the buttermilk, this round one is for the butter, and this last one is for the milk I'll give to my sister.'

'What? Your sister? How dare you give our milk to your sister, and without my permission? I won't allow it.' The man picked up the pot his wife had bought for her sister and smashed it on the floor.

'I'm the one who cares for the cow day and night; you don't lift a finger,' the woman screamed at her husband. 'It's none of your business what I do with the milk.'

'You bitch. Why do I spill my sweat and blood all day? So that you can squander it on your relatives? I'll teach you how to give away our milk,' shouted the husband, picking up a stick to beat his wife.

'Then milk your own stupid cow and buy your own stupid pots,' the woman screamed, grabbing the other pots she had bought and hurling them at her husband's head.

Hearing all the shouting and smashing, Gopal came to investigate what was going on in his neighbour's house. When he saw the man beating his wife with a stick, he immediately intervened, 'Stop! Why are you beating her?' he asked the man.

'This bitch says she'll give away all the milk to her sister. I'll see how she does that.'

'What milk?' Gopal Bhar asked.

'The milk our cow will give.'

'What cow?'

'The cow I'll buy when I have enough money.'

Gopal Bhar then grabbed the stick from the man and began beating him with it.

'What're you doing?' the man shouted. 'Why are you beating me?'

'Your cow has been eating all the cucumbers and beans and gourds in my vegetable patch.'

'What cucumbers and beans and gourds?'

'The ones I've been planning to plant, and the ones that your cow will destroy.'

Realizing what they had been doing and seeing all the broken pieces of the smashed pots around them, Gopal Bhar's neighbours felt very embarrassed.

Gopal Bhar folktale

◆

146

DEATH OF A DONKEY

A miller and his son once went to the market. They took their donkey along to carry the grain they were planning to purchase from the market.

When they started from home, the miller's son rode on the donkey, while the father walked beside him. Along the way, they met some people. 'Look at the selfish boy,' they said. 'Riding the donkey while his old father has to walk.'

Embarrassed, the boy immediately got off and told his father to ride the donkey instead.

After a little, while they met another group of people. 'Look at that father,' they said. 'Making his young son walk while he sits on the donkey like a king.'

The father, too, became embarrassed and quickly dismounted, and both father and son decided that it was best to just walk along with the donkey. However, a little further, another group of people looked at them and laughed: 'Look at that father and son. Even though they have a donkey, they're walking. What a waste.'

The miller got back on the donkey and told his son to climb up behind him on the animal's back. But, just down the road was another group of people. They were shocked to see the sight: 'That's cruelty to animals,' they declared. 'The poor donkey—having to bear the weight of two grown men.'

Hearing this, father and son both got off the donkey and decided that they should carry the animal. They tied the donkey's forelegs together and then his hind legs, and slipping a pole between his legs, they lifted it on their shoulders. They trudged on like this for a while, with the donkey hanging on the pole between them. Slowly, the rope that held the donkey's legs together began to slip and, eventually, the knots just opened. The donkey crashed to the ground and died instantly and, the father and son could do nothing except sit by the dead donkey and weep.

That is why they say: listen to what everyone has to say, but do what you think is right for you.

Mullah Nasruddin folktale

◆

147

SUITABLE VOCATION

Once, Krishnadevaraya had his portrait painted by the famous artist Raja Verma. The king was so pleased with his likeness that he honoured the artist with the post of minister of administration. Raja Verma was a gifted artist, but he had no talent for administration. Soon the state's administrative machinery began to fall apart, and people began to suffer. The king's other ministers tried to warn him, but Krishnadevaraya didn't seem to understand the gravity of the situation. Finally, the ministers asked Tenali to help. 'Let me look into this,' Tenali promised. 'Obviously, advising the king has proved futile. I must find another way to show him his error.'

Soon after, Tenali invited Krishnadevaraya to his house for dinner, telling him that it was a special day of celebration for his family, and it would not be complete without his presence; therefore, the king couldn't refuse. On the day of the dinner, the king arrived in Tenali's house and was received with great honour and respect. Tenali had borrowed gold plates in which to serve the food, and he had rented a thick carpet and silk cushions to seat the king. Krishnadevaraya was quite pleased by the hospitality and eagerly awaited the meal. He was very fond of food and loved to have a variety of dishes at each meal. Seeing the elegance of the other arrangements, he was sure that the dinner would be a culinary delight. However, when Tenali's wife laid it out, Krishnadevarya was very disappointed to see that it consisted of only a couple of dishes. But by now, he was so hungry that he filled his plate with whatever there was and began eating, only to gag on his first mouthful. The food was not only undercooked but it also tasted like sawdust.

'Tenali,' Krishnadevarya said, swallowing a mouthful of food with water. 'Who's the chef?'

'A friend of mine,' Tenali said innocently. 'He's a carpenter.'

'What?' the king couldn't help laughing. 'No wonder the food tastes like sawdust. You can't expect a carpenter to cook good food.'

'Why not, Maharaj?' Tenali asked innocently.

'Because a carpenter is trained in carpentry, not in cuisine.'

'But Maharaj, if a painter can run an administration, why can't a carpenter cook a royal feast?'

Realization dawned on Krishnadevarya. 'I've been quite blind, haven't I?' he said. 'Thank you for helping me realize my error, but you've put me in quite a quandary. Giving Raja Verma the minister's post was my way of honouring him. How can I take back the honour? Raja Verma is a good man, and I don't want to insult him.'

'I agree with you, Maharaj. Raja Verma is, indeed, a very good man and an excellent painter. But he is a failure at administration, and he knows it. That's why, I'm certain that he'll help you resolve this situation without any dishonour to you.'

The following day, Tenali made sure that Raja Verma heard about the inedible food that Tenali's carpenter had cooked for the king. That very day, he resigned from his post as minister of administration and went back to being the talented painter that he was trained to be.

Tenali Raman folktale

◆

148

FIVE ARROWS OF DESIRE: KAMADEVA

Himavat, the king of mountains, and his wife, Mena, gave birth to a baby girl, whom they named Parvati. When Parvati turned eight, Himavat took her to Mount Kailash to ask Shiva if he could place her in his service. Shiva agreed, and young Parvati began to serve him, alongside his ganas. Years passed. Parvati blossomed into a beautiful, sensual, young lady. She still attended to Shiva, but now her motive was not just service. She was secretly in love with him. However, Shiva was completely oblivious to the external world; his inward contemplation was complete and unshakeable.

The gods knew something had to be done to discompose him so that he would begin to desire Parvati. They needed Shiva and Parvati to marry and to have a son so that the boy could destroy Tarakasura. Ever since that asura had received two boons from Brahma, of lifelong youth and victory, he had been causing great misery to the gods. If he had had his way, he would have also become immortal, because that had been his third request, but Brahma had refused to grant him immortality, and had, instead, offered him his choice of death's agent. And so, Tarakasura had chosen his killer: an infant—no more than seven days old. Brahma had granted the boon, and the asura had congratulated himself on his cunning, for he was pretty sure that his choice of a death agent rendered him almost immortal.

Made fearless by his boons, Tarakasura had defeated the gods and threatened to destroy the world. War-weary and disheartened, the gods had finally gone to Brahma for help.

'Is there any way we can defeat this asura?' they had asked him.

'Only an infant no more than seven days old can kill him.'

'In other words, Tarakasura is indestructible,' the gods had wailed. 'What child can be so powerful immediately after he is born?'

'Actually, such as child is very possible,' Brahma had replied. 'But you will have to facilitate his birth.'

'Whose child will it be?'

'Shiva's. A son borne by his new wife.'

'That's impossible,' they had shouted. 'You know better than us that after Sati's immolation, Shiva has lost all interest in worldly affairs. He's somewhere in the Himalayas, deep in meditation. And you know what that means—let alone sensual pleasure, wife, and child, he's not even conscious of the world. Think of another candidate, Brahmaji,' the gods had implored. 'Shiva isn't an option.'

'Actually, it can only be Shiva's son who can destroy Tarakasura,' Brahma had told the gods. 'Shiva's is the only seed fiery enough to create a child who will become a consummate warrior in the first seven days of his life.'

Brihaspati, the chief priest of the gods, had come up with a plan—to request King Himavat and Queen Mena to have a daughter, who would induce Shiva out of his meditation. The royal couple had agreed, and the result was Parvati. But now the question was—how to make Shiva notice Parvati? It was imperative that this happen soon, because Tarakasura's oppression was increasing by the day. The gods tried whatever they could to rattle Shiva, but the god sat on Kailash, unperturbed.

Finally, his patience exhausted, Indra summoned the god of love, Kamadeva, to Indraloka.

When Kamadeva came, accompanied by his wife, Rati, and his best friend, Vasant (Spring), Indra ordered him: 'Conquer Shiva. Pierce him with your arrows so that he feels such intense desire for Parvati that he is compelled to marry her.'

'Shiva is unconquerable,' Kama replied with trepidation. 'His senses are so controlled that my arrows will not even register. Besides, I'm fearful of what he'll do to me if he becomes angry at me for disturbing him, which he surely will be. Such schemes to conquer him ricochet back on the schemer.'

'Kamadeva,' Indra thundered, 'you have no choice. A blacksmith is of no use without his tongs...do you get my drift?'

Kamadeva bowed in obeisance, trembling at Indra's veiled threat. 'I'll try, O great Indra,' he said. 'But, may I please request assistance from your apsaras? Rambha, Urvashi, Tilottama and Sukeshi and the others are irresistible in their sensuality. If they help me, I may be able to accomplish this most difficult of tasks.'

Together with the peerless apsaras and Rati and Vasant, Kamadeva went to Kailash. Just by the arrival of this pheromone-inducing group in Kailash, the atmosphere became romantic—the sky became clear blue, with soft tendrils of clouds floating about on gentle breezes. The air filled with the tender songs of kokila lovebirds, asoka, champa, and chameli bushes suddenly burst into full bloom, and grapevines became heavy with sweet, intoxicating fruit.

Shiva was seated in total stillness on a tiger-skin in a small hamlet between tall trees covered with vines. Ganga flowed out of his locks, and the moon hung resplendent on his head. A necklace of rudraksh beads adorned his neck, ashes were smeared across his forehead, and snakes ranged around his neck and upper body. His ganas guarded his abode, and the bull, Nandi, grazed nearby, keeping a watchful eye out for intruders.

Kamadeva thought it prudent to conquer Shiva in stages. He decided that first he would move the god's other emotions, such as memory, jealousy, and anger, and then, finally, shoot the five arrows of love. With this plan in mind, Kama made himself miniscule and, evading his guards, entered Shiva's body through his ear and filled him with desire. Shiva was roused from his meditation, because he suddenly remembered Sati, his beloved who had died in Daksha's fire. Then he was overcome with new grief. But even as his mind began to think more actively about Sati, Shiva halted his thoughts. He realized that he had been assaulted by Kamadeva, the god who quickens all desire. Shiva then took a deep breath, deliberately filling his mind with anger, and when he released his breath, it emitted so much Yogamaya that it almost consumed Kamadeva. Burning up, the god of love flew out of Shiva and hid under a devadar tree. Then, taking a few moments to gather his wits and bring his fear under control, Kamadeva selected five arrows from his quiver and trained his eye to the exact spot where Shiva was seated.

Just when he closed his eyes and envisioned his five arrows piercing Shiva, Parvati appeared on the scene with her friends, carrying platters full of flower garlands. Parvati selected a garland of datura flowers, whose fragrance is an aphrodisiac, and tiptoeing up to Shiva, placed it around his neck. At that very moment, Kamadeva mounted an arrow with a mango blossom head called sammohan (bewitching) on his bow and shot it at Shiva's heart. As the arrow pierced him, Shiva opened his eyes and looked upon Parvati. He was bewitched. His eyes were transfixed on her face, his heartbeat increased, and his mind became agitated.

Unable to move his gaze away from Parvati, Shiva realized the change that had occurred in him. His eyes then darted in all directions and he saw Kamadeva hiding under the devadar tree, still holding the incriminating bow. The third eye on Shiva's forehead opened and the immense desire that had risen in his body erupted into flames around Kamadeva, burning him to ashes in mere seconds. When the flames began to spread in the grove, Shiva brought them under control by distributing fire among the mango trees, spring, the moon, flowers, black bees, and nightingales. But the flames, like desire-filled arrows, began to fall everywhere, tormenting people, so Shiva took a deep breath and drew them back into his body. However, the flames that had struck sensuous people remained within them, tormenting them forever.

When Rati saw her husband reduced to ashes, she was devastated. She smeared her body with the ashes of her smara—memory of her husband—Kama, who is also called Smara, and going to Shiva, fell at his feet. 'I beg you to bring him back to life,' she wailed. 'It wasn't his fault.'

At that moment, the gods, too, arrived on the scene. 'Calm your anger, O Great God,' they said. 'We are the ones who sent Kamadeva to break your samadhi. We need you. You must marry Parvati and have a son. The asura Taraka is destroying the world and needs to be dealt with, and Brahmaji says that only your son can accomplish this most difficult task.'

Ignoring the gods, Shiva turned to look at Rati with compassion in his eyes. 'Forgive me, Devi,' he said. 'I can't recreate Kama's body, but I will restore his life. He will be born again and will be famous in the world as Ananga (without limbs)—the invisible Kama—Desire that no one will be able to see but all mortals will feel.'

Making this promise to Rati, Shiva ignored the gods and went back into samadhi. The gods now turned to Parvati with their plea. 'It is up to you, devi,' they said. 'Awaken him and save the world.'

'It shall be done,' Parvati promised. Through all these travails, she had realized that the only way to reach the god was on his own level. Therefore, finding a suitable spot on Kailash, she began to do tapasya. It took her many years to reach Shiva through her subconscious, and when she did, she conveyed to him that she was the reincarnation of his Sati. When Shiva received this subliminal message, he immediately opened his eyes and gazed upon Parvati, and saw in her his own beloved Sati. The love and desire that Kamadeva had evoked in him was moved again, and he allowed it to fill his mind and body.

Soon after, Shiva married Parvati, and they had a son, Kumar, who, in the first six days of his life, learned the science of war, and on the seventh day, challenged Tarakasura and killed him.

Myth from the Puranas

◆

149

THE GIRL WHO BECAME A FLOWERING TREE

There were two sisters who lived with their poor mother. All their lives the girls had seen their mother work hard to take care of them by cleaning and cooking for other people, so, when they came of age, they began to think of ways to help their mother. One day, the younger sister said to the older one, 'I have a plan. I'll turn myself into a flowering tree, and you gather the flowers from the tree and sell them.'

The older sister was amazed. 'What are you saying? How can you become a flowering tree? And what'll I tell Amma when she asks where you are?'

'I'll show you. And Amma doesn't have to know. Now, do as I ask. Sweep the whole house, then take a bath, and bring two pitchers full of water to me. But make sure that your fingernails don't touch the water in the pitchers. I'll wait for you under the tree in our yard.'

The older sister did exactly as her sibling asked. She swept all the floors, took a bath, and then went to the well to draw water. Filling two pitchers, she brought them out to the yard, making sure her fingernails did not touch the water. In the meantime, the younger sister had also swept and washed the ground under the tree, and when her older sister came with the water, she sat down at the base of the tree and instructed her: 'I'll sit here and meditate, and when I'm deep in meditation, pour one pitcher of water all over my body. I'll then turn into a flowering tree. Then you pick as many flowers as you can. But make sure that you don't break a single sprout or tear a single leaf. When you're done picking the flowers, pour the second pitcher of water on me, and I'll become a person again.'

The older girl followed every instruction: she waited till her younger sister was deep in meditation; then she carefully poured water on her from one pitcher, making sure that she wet her whole body. At once, her sister turned into an enchanting flowering tree. Its branches spread over the whole yard and were filled with flowers whose beauty and fragrance surpassed anything the older sister had ever seen or smelled. She then tenderly picked the flowers, taking extra care not to break a single sprout and not to tear a single leaf. When she had enough flowers to fill a large basket, she poured the water from the second pitcher on the tree, and immediately, her sister came back into her human form and shook the water out of her hair.

The sisters then strung the flowers into garlands and arranged them in the basket. 'To whom shall I sell these?' the older sister asked.

'Take them to the king's palace,' the younger sister suggested. 'They will surely fetch a good price there.'

The town that the girls lived in was ruled by a king who had two daughters and a son. The elder princess was married to a prince of another kingdom, but the younger one and the prince still lived with the king and queen. The elder of the flower girls thought that the person most likely to buy her flowers at the palace would be the younger princess, so she stood below the princess's windows and began to call out, 'Flowers! Flowers! Beautiful, fresh flowers.' When the princess opened her window, such a heavenly fragrance wafted up to her nose that she immediately sent a maid to fetch the flower girl, and when she saw the world's most beautiful flowers, she begged her mother to buy them all.

'How much for the whole basket?' the queen enquired.

'I'm a poor girl and you're a queen. Pay me as you see fit,' the girl replied, and the queen paid her with a handful of coins and bought all the flowers.

When the girl returned home with the money, her younger sister told her to hide it.

'But I thought we were going to help Amma with the household expenses. If we hide the money, how can we use it to help?'

'We'll give her the money when we have more of it, because if we tell her now, she'll be angry and will stop us from doing it again.'

The next day, the sisters, once again, swept the floors of the house and under the tree, and the elder sister poured water on her younger sister to turn her into a flowering tree. Then, after picking the flowers, she changed her sister back into a person, and together they strung the flowers into garlands, which the elder sister took to the palace and sold to the princess. The queen gave her a handful of coins again, which she brought home and hid. This continued every day for many days. Then one day, at the palace, the prince came to see his sister in her room and smelled a fragrance that intoxicated him, and he saw the garlands of flowers. He had never seen flowers as beautiful and fresh as these. 'Where did these come from?' he asked his sister. 'On what kind of tree do these grow?' The princess waved her hand dismissively and said, 'It's a just a poor flower girl who brings them every day. I don't know where she gets them from.'

The prince was enraptured by the flowers and was curious to see the girl who sold them, so the following day, he hid behind a wall to watch the flower girl when she came to the palace. After she had sold her garlands, he followed her home. Seeing her go into a little hut with a yard that had a tree, he hid across the street to keep watch, and remained there all evening and all night. In the evening, he saw an old woman go into the hut, and, at first light, he saw her leave. Then he saw two girls emerge—one, whom he had already seen, and another, who he thought was unusually lovely. As the prince watched, the girls swept the hut and the yard, and then the beautiful one sat down under the tree, while the other one waited. Soon, she picked up a pitcher of water and poured it on her seated sister. At once, the girl became a tree, blooming with the flowers that had so captivated him.

After watching the whole ritual of the girl becoming a person again, the prince returned to the palace and went straight to his room, where he lay down in his bed, feeling despondent. All day he refused to eat or engage in any activity, and when his mother came to ask him what was wrong, he just turned his head and looked the other way. In the evening, his friend, the minister's son, came to see him, and the prince narrated the whole story to him. 'I'm in love,' he said to his friend. 'I want that girl who turns into a flowering tree. If I don't get her, I'll kill myself.' 'Take heart, my friend,' the minister's son said. 'I'll see what I can do.' He went directly to the king and told him the tale. 'If he doesn't get the girl, he'll surely die,' he finished. The king had only one son and didn't want to jeopardize his life, so he immediately sent his minister to make enquiries and bring him the parents of the girl. It took a little time, but, finally, the king's guards found the old mother of the two girls and brought her to the court. She was terrified, wondering what punishment awaited her and for what crime. All the way to the king's court, she wept and prayed, and, as soon as she was brought before the king, she fell to her knees, begging him to have mercy. 'I'm just a poor serving woman, Maharaj,' she cried piteously. 'If I've done something that is wrong in your esteemed eyes, please forgive me.'

'Don't cry, Amma,' the king said. 'You have not done anything wrong, and I haven't brought you here to punish you. I have summoned you to make a request. I hear you have two daughters. Will you give me one of them?'

The old woman stopped crying. How does the king know about my two daughters, she wondered, and began to worry—why does he want one of them? What will he do to her?

'What is your answer, Amma?' the king prompted.

'Wh...what a great ho...honour you confer on me and my dau... daughters, Maharaj,' she stammered.

'Splendid,' said the king and offered her a symbolic tambula from a silver platter to seal the deal.

Taking the betel leaf and nut, the old woman left the palace, worried sick about her daughters and also angry at them for bringing this worry upon her. As soon as she reached home, she took a switch and began beating them. 'Shameless girls. Where have you been? I told you not to go out of the house. Not to let any man see you. I'm only an old woman. How am I to protect your virtue? Now see what you've done by disobeying me.'

'What has happened, Amma?' the girls cried.

'The king has seen you,' she yelled. 'Tell me how he saw you?' The younger girl told her the whole story of how, desiring to help with the household expenses, she had been turning herself into a flowering tree, and how the older sister had been selling the flowers at the palace. The girls then brought out the money they had earned. Hearing this tale, the old woman beat her daughters even more. 'Liars,' she cried. 'O Murugan, now my daughters have become liars. Who has ever heard of a girl becoming a tree. Do you think I'm a fool?'

'Wait,' the sisters cried to their mother. 'Let us show you.' And the two girls carried out the whole water ritual again, with the younger girl first becoming a flowering tree and then changing back to herself again. The old woman was dismayed to see her daughter's transformation, and she finally understood that somehow the king had discovered her daughter's secret. The following day, when the king's men came to take her to court again, she went with a heavy heart, wishing that she could somehow protect her daughter from the fate that awaited her, but she knew that there wasn't anything she could do. With the endurance of one who has suffered long, she faced the king. However, her resignation turned to joy when the king said, 'Amma, I have called you to announce the date of the wedding between my son and your younger daughter.'

The marriage of the prince and the flowering-tree-girl was a grand affair to which every citizen of the kingdom was invited. After the nuptials, the new bride waited for her groom in their room that was decorated felicitously with jasmine flowers. However, the prince didn't come to her all night. Then, just before dawn, he came and sat on the bed, watching her. The girl was awake, but he didn't touch her or say a word, although she felt that he wanted to speak. For three more nights, the prince stayed away from the bridal room till dawn, and then when he did come into the room, he just sat and watched his bride. Finally, on the fourth morning, when the prince came and sat on the bed, the girl asked, 'Why have you married me? What do you want from me? I'm your wife, and you don't even come close to me.'

'If I tell you, promise me that you'll do as I ask.'

'I'm your wife. I'll obey you. Tell me what you want from me.'

'I know you can become a flowering tree. Show me. I want us to sleep on your flowers.'

'I...how...what do you mean? I'm an ordinary girl like any other. What do you mean I should become a flowering tree? I'm not a magician.'

'I've seen it with my own eyes. I want to see you do it here, in front of me. Show me. I'm your husband. You should not keep any secrets from me.'

When the girl hesitated, he said, 'If I promise to honour you and keep your secret, will you then show me?'

The girl nodded and asked him to bring two pitchers of water and instructed him about how to pour first one pitcher on her to turn her into a tree and then the other to return her to human form. 'But make sure that you pour the water carefully and soak me completely. And when you pick the flowers, make sure you don't break any sprouts or tear any leaf.'

The prince did as she instructed, and when she turned into the tree, he carefully plucked a handful of blooms and spread them on the sheet, and then he poured water on the tree from the other pitcher to turn her back into his bride again. That night the prince and the girl made love on a bed covered with the most beautiful and fragrant flowers ever used for a nuptial bed.

They were happy for many days. Every night, the girl became a flowering tree, and her husband plucked her flowers to his heart's content, then he turned the tree into his bride, and, in the morning, they threw the wilted flowers out of the window. Soon, a pile began to build outside the window, like a small fragrant hill of withered blooms.

In the meantime, the princess, who had no idea about the identity of the girl her brother had married, waited every day for the flower girl to come to the palace to sell her beautiful flowers, but it seemed that she had vanished. Then, one day, she saw the pile of flowers outside the window of her brother's bedroom. They looked and smelled exactly like the flowers she used to buy from the flower girl and she wondered how her brother and sister-in-law were getting the flowers, when she hadn't even seen the flower seller in weeks. So, one night, she spied on her brother and his wife and was amazed to see her sister-in-law's transformation. The next day the princess decided that she and her friends would visit the orchards of Surahonne for a picnic and play in the swings that were roped to the trees. She also decided to take her sister-in-law with her and sought her mother's permission for this. 'Ask your brother if you can take his wife,' the queen told her.

'Please let me take her with me,' she begged her brother. 'She'll have so much fun playing with us on the swings. Don't you think your wife is entitled to have some fun?'

'Of course she's entitled. I'll let her go, but you must promise to take good care of her. Don't let her come to any harm.'

And so the princess, the prince's bride, and a number of the princess's friends went to Surahonne. For a while the girls played on the swings, pushing each other, swinging high and low and twirling around, and singing songs—nostalgic songs of childhood, naughty songs of budding womanhood, and romantic songs of meeting their handsome princes.

Suddenly the princess halted all play and gathered her friends around. Then she accosted her sister-in-law. 'Give us some flowers,' she demanded. 'Look! None of my friends have any flowers in their hair. Come on. Turn yourself into the flowering tree and let us pluck some flowers.'

'What nonsense are you talking about?' the prince's bride replied.

'Oh, I know all about you and how you turn yourself into a flowering tree to entice your lovers.'

The prince's bride was shocked and hurt. She wondered how the princess had found out. Had her husband divulged her secret? Her heart hurt at this thought and tears filled her eyes. 'How do you know?' she asked brokenly.

'Never mind how I know,' the princess replied. 'I just know that you enticed my brother with this trick.'

'I swear to you I didn't,' the prince's bride pleaded. 'Please believe me.'

'Then prove it to me.'

'How?'

'Turn yourself into a tree right now, and I'll know that you don't do it just to attract lovers.'

Reluctantly, the flowering-tree-girl agreed and asked the princess and her friends to bring two pitchers of water and then instructed them on how to carefully pour the water from first one pitcher and then the other. 'But make sure that you soak me completely and also make sure that you don't break a single sprout or tear a single leaf.'

Then she sat down cross-legged and began to meditate. The girls, excited to see the trick, began to pour the water on her head, but they were silly and uncaring and didn't pay attention to her instructions, and they poured the water haphazardly. She turned into a tree, but only half a tree. Just then it began to rain, and the girls plucked the flowers hurriedly, breaking off the sprouts and tearing the leaves. In a hurry to get home, they then quickly poured the second pitcher on the tree, spilling some of the water on the ground and only some on her branches. She became a woman again, but with only half a body.

The princess and her friends ran quickly into their waiting carriages, forgetting all about the prince's bride. She lay there, half-bodied, on the muddy ground, while it rained and rained. Soon the water began to puddle and the mud shifted, carrying her with it into a gutter. All night, she lay in the gutter, unable to crawl out. In the early morning, as cotton wagons began to drive by, one of the wagon drivers heard an inhuman sort of groaning coming from the gutter. He stopped his wagon and went to look and saw a woman-like creature there. She had a beautiful face but only half a body, which was naked and grotesque. Taking pity on her, he pulled off his turban and covered her with it, and gathering her up, he gently laid her in his wagon. In the outskirts of a town, the wagon driver stopped at a public shelter, and left the half woman there. Laying her on the floor, he wished her well: 'I hope someone feeds you, and I hope you survive. You poor thing.'

In the meantime, the princess, who had returned to the palace without her sister-in-law, had to face her mother's questioning. 'Where is she?' her mother wanted to know.

'How do I know? Who knows where she went. It started raining and we all came home. She should've come home too. I don't know where she went.' And when her brother enquired about his wife, these were the very same answers she gave him.

The prince anxiously waited for his wife all evening and all night, and when she still hadn't returned by the morning, he sent out search parties, but his men returned empty-handed. As more days passed, his worry turned to grief. He was sure something had happened to her. He pressed his men to begin searching in hospitals, but when he received no news, day after day, the prince's grief slowly turned to despondency and then to depression. Soon, he left the palace to wander from place to place, searching for his wife. Then, after a while, he stopped searching and just began wandering, not caring where he went or what happened to him.

Meanwhile, in the shelter, the half-bodied princess began to draw attention. Servants and maids from the palace would see her on their way to fetch water and feel pity for her. This was the town in which the elder princess lived, and her maids thought that the face of this half-woman looked quite a bit like the queen's sister-in-law. When one of the queen's maids shared this information with the queen herself and asked her permission to bring the half-woman into the palace, the queen would not believe her. 'That's impossible,' she said indignantly. 'How can a half-bodied beggar woman look like my beautiful sister-in-law? Ask her who she is,' she ordered the maid.

'But she is very hurt and doesn't respond to anything we ask her.'

'Then let her be,' the queen replied.

Many more days passed and the maid once again petitioned the queen. 'Can we just bring her to the palace where she will receive better care? In the shelter, there's no one to feed her or put medicine on her wounds.'

'Fine,' said the queen. 'You can do that if you wish, but you have to take care of her yourself. Don't bother me about her again.'

The maid brought the half-woman to the palace and put her in one corner near the kitchen, so that someone would always be able to watch her. Every day, one or the other maids would bathe her with herbal water and apply soothing oils to her wounds, and, slowly, the half-woman began to heal.

Now the prince, wandering aimlessly through many lands, came to the town where his elder sister was queen, although he didn't realize where he had arrived. He looked like a sadhu, with his long, unkempt hair and beard and dusty robes, so no one paid him any heed. However, as he sat outside the palace gates along with other beggars, one of the queen's maids saw him and thought he resembled the queen's brother. She rushed into the palace to inform the queen.

'What rubbish,' the queen admonished the maid. 'How is that possible?'

'Come and look through the window and see for yourself.'

When the queen looked, she too was shocked to see the resemblance. 'Quickly,' she said to her maid. 'Bring him up. I'll know right away if he really is my brother.'

When they brought the beggar up to the queen, she took one look at him and knew that this dirty, dishevelled sadhu was indeed her brother. 'What has happened to you, dear brother?' she cried and wanted to embrace him, but he was stinking so much that she immediately ordered a bath for him and also had the maids warm up oil for his sunburned skin. After he was bathed, oiled, and fed, the queen took him to the royal guest room. 'What has happened to you?' she asked again, but the prince did not respond.

She hugged and kissed him and patted his hand, saying. 'I'm sure you'll tell me in your own time. Right now, just concentrate on getting better. We'll talk later.'

But no matter how many times his sister tried to talk to him, the prince refused to say anything. She tried to engage him in exciting activities, but he either refused to participate or performed them like an automaton.

She thought perhaps a witch had cursed him and called all sorts of witch doctors to cure him, but he refused their help. Finally, desperate to evoke some feeling in him, the queen resorted to sending beautiful maids to his bedroom every night. They caressed his body and tried to pull him out of his stupor, but to no avail. Then, one day, the maids dressed up the half-woman in beautiful clothes, took her up to the prince's bedroom, and left her on his bed.

The prince barely glanced at the form lying at the foot of his bed, and went to sleep, but at night he was woken up by a familiar touch on his feet that felt like his wife's caress. Sitting up hurriedly, he looked towards the end of the bed and saw a half woman caressing his feet with a stump of a hand, cooing softly like his wife used to do. The prince quickly lit a lamp and brought it close to the face of the half-woman. 'It really is you,' he said with bated breath, hardly believing his eyes. 'What has happened to you?'

And suddenly the half-woman, who had not spoken a word for months, broke into sobs. Then words began to pour out of her as she told him the whole tale of how his sister had taken her to Surahonne where she and her friends had accused her of enticing him into marriage with her flowers. She also told him how they had turned her into the half tree and then cruelly plucked her blooms and turned her back into this half-bodied person.

The prince embraced her half-body and wept with her. 'What should we do now?' he asked her.

'It's simple,' she said. 'Bring two pitchers of water, but make sure you don't touch the water with your fingernails.' When he brought the water, she instructed him: 'Pour the water from one pitcher on me. When I become a tree, wherever you see a broken branch, set it right; wherever you see a torn leaf, put it together. Then pour the water from the second pitcher on the tree.'

Very carefully, the prince followed her instructions. He poured the first pitcherful, making sure to soak her completely. When she became a tree, he put her broken branches back together and repaired the torn leaves. And when everything was set right, he gently poured the water from the second pitcher all over the tree. At once, his wife stood up, shaking the water from her hair. Then she fell into his arms.

That night the prince and his bride slept peacefully, holding each other close, and in the morning, they told the older sister what had happened. She embraced them and wept with them for all the sorrows they had suffered, and then she arranged for them to stay with her for as long as they wanted. Finally, she sent them back to her parents' house with a cartload full of gifts and a letter in which she explained to her father the cruel role his youngest daughter had played in the tragedy.

The king was overjoyed to see his long-lost son and daughter-in-law. He organized a grand tour of the city for his son, who sat atop an elephant in a decorated howdah so that all the citizens could see the prince and welcome him back. When the ceremonies were over, the king had his men dig a pit far away from the palace and had seven barrels of boiling lime juice poured into it. Then he had his youngest daughter thrown into the pit. Everyone who saw this said, 'Every wrong is justly rewarded.'

Folktale from Karnataka

◆

150

HER BEAUTY WAS HER CURSE: AHALYA

Brahma, the Creator, got tired of the monotony of creating people one after the other, as though in a mindless factory line. So one day, he decided to take some time off, and, in his leisure, he was inspired to create a woman who was different from any he had created before. He sculpted her with utmost care, making sure each facial feature, each curve of the body, each graceful limb, was the epitome of perfection. The result was a beauty so stunning that even Brahma himself was transfixed. He called her Ahalya, because she was a-hala (not-ugly). He called her Ahalya also because she was 'non-ploughed', and he could not bear the thought of any man 'ploughing' her for his pleasure. But then he became plagued with the question of who would marry her? Who would be worthy of her? It had to be someone who would not simply use her to fulfil his desire, but someone who would lie with her only for the noble purpose of producing offspring. After much deliberation about possible grooms, he decided on one of the Saptarishis—Gautama, who was highly evolved in his asceticism, and who had his senses and passion completely under control. Brahma knew that Gautama was a man of austere discipline and would not be affected by Ahalya's beauty. Of course, Gautama was also an old man.

So Brahma went to visit Gautama and proposed the match. Gautama accepted, and the woman was brought to his ashram, which was located on the outskirts of Mithila. Thus, Ahalya began living as the old rishi's wife, or as much of a wife as he wanted her to be. She took care of his material needs, tended to his students, and oversaw the running of the ashram. In other words, she was the ideal wife in all ways but one.

When Brahma created Ahalya, rumours of her beauty had leaked out and spread across heaven. Indra, the king of gods, had also heard these rumours and had become eager to see her for himself, but he knew that Brahma was keeping her hidden from covetous eyes. However, one day, before Brahma gave her to Gautama, Indra sneaked into Brahmaloka and, seeing Ahalya, immediately desired her. In fact, right then he began orchestrating a plan to acquire the woman, but when Brahma wed her to Gautama, Indra was left wanting. The king of gods, who is also called thousand-eyed, was not one to give up easily, so he began spying on Gautama, noting the time that he left the ashram and for what purpose, as well as the time he returned. He was especially interested in the rishi's absence from his ashram during the hours of darkness and noted that every morning before sunrise, he went to the river for his daily bath and was gone for a while. Indra also kept note of Ahalya and her activities and behaviours, especially keeping track of her menstrual cycle and the days when she was fertile.

On a day when Indra knew Ahalya was not ovulating, he waited for Gautama to leave for his bath, and, changing himself into Rishi Gautama, approached Ahalya. 'I've changed my mind about a bath today,' he said. 'I've decided to take it later. Right now, I want you to come to bed with me. I know you're not ovulating, but today I don't want to think about our progeny. I just want to enjoy your beauty. Will you come to bed with me?'

At first Ahalya was surprised.[58] She wondered what had happened to her husband. She knew him to be as controlled in his sexual habits as he was in other aspects of his life. He was not the kind of man who engaged in sexual activity simply for enjoyment, and he would never allow himself to be overcome by passion or lust. Surely this was not her husband, she thought. Then, she began to feel the splendour exuding from the man, like a celestial aura, and she could smell a divine fragrance, which was hardly the sickly-sweet odour of old age that surrounded her husband. Ahalya realized that this was the king of gods, Indra, who had disguised himself as her husband. As the realization hit her, her senses quickened, and, thinking about the proposition he had made, she began to desire him as well. All her married life, she had had to curb her own sexuality so as not to distract her husband from his asceticism; therefore, when she felt a jolt of lust, she welcomed it. Without revealing to Indra that she had recognized him, she gave him a coy smile and placed her sweetly sweating hand in his.

After her desire was satisfied, Ahalya confessed to Indira that she knew who he was. 'But now you must leave, O king of the gods,' she said. 'My husband will be returning any time, and he mustn't catch us together. You know his ascetic power. Who knows what he'll do?'

'There's still time,' Indra replied, changing into himself and drawing her back into his arms.

Ahalya sighed and rubbed her cheek against his chest, exulting in the strong, firm strength of his muscles. Indra laughed, his chest expanding at her appreciation of his virility. 'I'm not afraid of your husband, sweet lady,' he said, nonchalantly. 'I'll leave as I came—undetected. Have no fear.'

When Indra finally slipped out of Ahalya's bedroom, he changed into the form of Gautama again, in case someone was watching. But even then, he was quite fearful of getting caught, because Gautama was a formidable rishi, known for his anger.

Just as Indra stepped out of the hermitage, he saw Gautama returning from his bath. The rishi was blazing like a fire in his purity. He was drenched in holy water and was carrying firewood for the sacrificial altar and kusha grass to consecrate the first sacred rite of the day. They came face to face, the false Gautama and the real Gautama. And the real Gautama did not even have to employ his mental eye to know who this was, disguised as him. He knew that it was Indra, and he knew the misconduct in which Indra and his wife had engaged. He greeted the king of the gods with a curse: 'O king of the gods, that for which you pride yourself—your virility—will fall off, so that you never again proposition any rishi's wife.' At his words, Indra's testicles instantly fell to the ground. But Gautama was not yet done with his curse. He continued: 'And that for which you lust, will be all over your body—a thousand times.' And, right then, a thousand vaginas sprouted on Indra's body.

Indra fell at Gautama's feet. 'My virility is my honour and glory. Without it I am nothing. And how will I show my face in heaven looking like this? The other gods will laugh at me. How will I lead them? O great rishi, have pity on me,' he begged, but Gautama was relentless.

'If I can't lead the gods, there'll be chaos in heaven; it may even topple,' Indra pleaded.

That gave Gautama pause. He was a Saptarishi, born from Brahma's mind as one of the seven patriarchs of the human race. He could not be responsible for causing disorder in the world. Therefore turning contemptuous eyes on Indra, he pronounced an addendum: 'During the churning of the primordial ocean, Vishnu will create the beautiful Tilottama to entice the asuras. When the vaginas on your body look upon that promiscuous woman, they will become eyes—a thousand eyes.'[59]

'And what about my...manliness...?' Indra whined, but Gautama offered no recourse for this.

Indra fled to heaven, shame-faced, his body emblazoned with a thousand marks of his lust, devoid of his manhood. As he had expected, all the gods snickered as he took his place on heaven's throne.

'Joke all you want,' Indra said. 'But let me remind you that in this yuga, I am the god of rain clouds, and you know that the mortals equate my sexuality with fertility. Just think: no testicles—no fertility on earth; no fertility on earth, no sacrifices; no sacrifices, no sacrificial offerings... Need I say more?'

The gods, headed by Agni, immediately stopped laughing. This was a serious matter that needed an immediate solution. There was nothing they could do to revoke Indra's curse and his lopped off testicles, but the curse said nothing about replacements or grafting. 'What he needs are the testicles of a virile being,' Agni advised. So the gods took the testicles of a ram and grafted them to Indra's scrotum. They also declared that whosoever sacrificed a testicle-less ram would gain handsomeness and high rewards, because the sacrifice itself would sublimate the being that is sacrificed—in other words Indra.

After Indra left, Gautama turned wrathful eyes on his wife, who, on hearing her husband's angry voice, had come outside. 'What do you have to say for yourself?' the rishi asked Ahalya.

Unlike Indra, Ahalya faced Rishi Gautama defiantly. She didn't speak a word and stood ready to accept whatever punishment her husband was planning to mete out.

Gautama said to his wife, 'You were created by Brahma in his leisure and are peerless in your beauty. I curse you that from today your beauty will no longer be peerless. From today beauty like yours will be common among created beings.' He paused, waiting for Ahalya to plead, but she did not beg him for mercy or express regret.

Gautama was even more enraged. 'The beauty that enticed the gods and men alike, that beauty which is your pride, will become invisible to the eyes of gods and men so that no man or god will look at you and be distracted. You will become invisible to the world. Without food or water, lying on ashes, you will remain imprisoned in this hermitage, thinking about what you have done, till that time Vishnu reincarnates as the dharma-abiding, virtuous, ideal man, Rama, and release you. This will be your penance.'

Hence, while Indra's lust helped him gain the reputation of a thousand-eyed god with a ram's virility, Ahalya's one night of passion made her invisible to the world.

Myth from the Puranas and Ramayana

◆

151

THE VIRGIN MONK

Once upon a time, when Brahmadatta ruled in Banaras, the Bodhisattva was born in a wealthy Brahmin family in the north. After receiving training in all the arts, he adopted ascetic life and, gaining mental power from deep meditation, went to the Himalayas, where he began living with the animals. A doe conceived his son, and when he was born, they called him Isisinga. When the boy came of age, his father admitted him to holy orders, and with time and training, Isisinga became a sage of such severe austerity that the abode of Sakka wobbled. Rattled by the power of his virtue, Sakka knew that he had to find a way to corrupt him, and so he thought of a plan:

For three years, Sakka prevented the rain from falling in the kingdom of Kashi, and the land became parched. With no crops, there was a famine, and people gathered in the king's palace, demanding that he do something. The king decided to observe a fast to propitiate Sakka, but, despite his efforts, the land remained dry and barren.

One day, the king was woken up by a strange light in his royal chamber. As he peered at it, he saw that it was emanating from a celestial being suspended in mid-air. 'Who are you?' the king asked in awe.

'I am Sakka.'

'Why are you here?'

'Does rain fall in your realm, O king?'

'No, it hasn't rained for three years.'

'Do you know why it doesn't?'

'No. I don't know. I've tried everything.'

'I'll tell you the reason,' Sakka said. 'In the Himalayas, there is a powerful and virtuous ascetic named Isisiṅga. When it begins to rain, he looks up at the sky in rage, and the rain stops.'

'What is to be done?'

'If his virtue is broken, it'll rain.'

'But who can break his virtue?'

'Your daughter, Nalinka. Send her to this ascetic.'

The following morning, the king called his daughter and told her how Sakka had visited him in the night and advised him that she was the only one who could save Kashi from ruin. Nalinka agreed to do what her father asked, for the good of Kashi and its people.

Travelling in a sturdy, wooden chariot and accompanied by footmen and guardsmen and many elephants and horses, Nalinka made the arduous journey into the Himalayas. At the foothills, the party pitched tents and asked foresters the way to Isisinga's hermitage. Journeying some more, Nalinka finally saw a tiny hut amidst the green bhurja trees, just as the foresters had described. At that time the Bodhisattva was not at home; he had gone into the forest to gather wild fruits. But Nalinka's guardsmen noted that a watch had been set up around the hut.

To evade suspicion Nalinka disguised herself as an ascetic. But under the ascetic's bark, she had decked herself in ornaments. Then, carrying a painted ball tied to a string, she entered the hut, while the guardsmen stood outside.

Inside, Isisiṅga was seated on a bench near the door. When he saw Nalinka, he became afraid and hid in the shadows at the back of the hut. Coming into the hut, Nalinka shed her bark disguise and stood naked, dressed only in her ornaments. Then she started to play with the ball, throwing it in the air on the retracting string, and deftly catching it. The young man was fascinated by the ball. He slowly came out of hiding and asked: 'What fruit is this that you toss up, but it returns to you? What tree does it grow on?'

'It grows on Mount Gandhamadana. That's where my home is. There are many trees that bear similar fruits, which, even when you toss them, are not lost, but return into the hands of the thrower.'

Isisiṅga believed her and thought she was an ascetic like him—just of a different kind. 'Will you rest?' he offered. 'I can give you roots and berries to eat and water to drink and to wash your feet.'

'Thank you, I will,' Nalinka said. 'Do come and sit next to me. Let's play together with my fruit.'

Slowly and with care, Nalinka seduced the naive and virtuous Isisiṅga, till he lost all his virtue in consuming desire. Afterwards, they walked together to the tank and bathed. Isisiṅga, feeling strangely languorous, sat in the water, while his friend frolicked. When they returned to the hut, they spent many more hours, talking and playing. Isisiṅga, who still believed that his new friend was an ascetic, was fascinated by the world from which his friend came. He had never been outside his own hermitage and knew nothing about the world. He was now curious about it and was full of questions.

'Where do you live?' he asked her. 'How does one get there? What do you love about your home? Do you also eat roots and berries to satiate your hunger? How do you escape wild beasts? Please tell me everything.' Nalinka created an image of a scenic hermitage for him. 'In the north is the Khema river, which flows straight down from the Himalayas. On its bank is a charming spot where mango, tilak, and sal trees are full-grown. On that bank is a grove filled with the fragrance of cassia and trumpet-flowers and sounds of birds and other creatures. My home is in that grove. For food, I eat dates and roots, but all kinds of other fruits also grow there. It's a beautiful spot—very valuable to me. That's why I must go now, because I'm afraid that if I stay away too long, robbers will find it and destroy my hut.'

When Isisinga heard that the ascetic was getting ready to leave, he tried to dissuade her in any way he could. 'My father is out, foraging for fruit. But the sun is now setting and he will be here soon. When he comes, we'll all go together to your hermitage.'

The thought of the boy's father returning and discovering her in the hut with his son, motivated Nalinka to get out of there as soon as possible. Besides, she had already accomplished what her father had sent her to do. 'I'm sorry I have to leave now. You must come to visit me soon. My home is easy to find. Ask any holy man on the way to point you in the right direction.' And bidding him goodbye, she left the hut. Outside, her guardsmen quickly took her to the waiting carriage that was standing some distance away and, soon, she and her entourage were headed for Kashi.

Sakka was so delighted at Nalinka's success that that very day he caused rain to fall throughout the whole kingdom of Kashi.

Isisinga, on the other hand, was filled with overwhelming sadness and a strange longing. As soon as Nalinka left, a fever seized his body, and he lay in the hut, trembling and groaning. That is how his father found him when he returned.

'Oh my son. What's the matter? Are you sick? No wood has been cut, nor water drawn. The fire, too, hasn't been lit. Have you spent the whole day lying idle? I thought you enjoyed those chores. You didn't even get up to welcome me home. What's wrong?'

Isisinga told him what had happened that day: 'A young ascetic came to visit today. He was not too tall nor too short; his hair was long and black, and his cheeks were hairless. Around his neck there was a bright jewel and on his chest were two swellings that looked like burnished gold. He didn't wear a girdle of munja grass, but around his waist and wrists and ankles were ornaments of gold and precious stone. His mouth was petal-soft and pink, and when he smiled, I could see his pearly teeth. His voice was soft and smooth, yet firm and clear, and when it fell on my ears, it pierced my heart and made me yearn. He had smooth arms without any hair, and when he put them around me, I felt such delight. His hands were soft like cotton, and when he touched me, I felt a burning thrill. He's gone now. But see this rumpled seat of leaves and creepers, father? This is where we played our games, and then we went to the tank and bathed and played some more, and then we returned here and talked. Today, I can't recite any holy texts, nor can I light the fire, or chop the wood. In fact, I don't even feel like eating. I won't eat till I see my friend again. He's told me where he lives. Can we go there right away, Father? If I don't see him soon, I'll die.'

When the Bodhisattva heard his son, he knew at once that he had lost his virtue. 'My Son,' he said. 'She was not your friend, though she pretended to be. There are female demons who come to you disguised, to steal away your virtue merely by their touch, and they make you lose your true path. Beware of them.'

'She was a female Yakkha?' Isisiṅga exclaimed, and the thought that he had spent all day with her now horrified him. He resolved that he would put all thoughts of her out of his mind. 'Forgive me, dear Father,' he said. 'I'll not leave this spot, and I'll follow my true path.'

The Bodhisattva was relieved, 'Come, then,' he said. 'Let's continue our lessons in cultivating charity, pity, sympathy, and equanimity.'

Folktale from the Jatakas

◆

152

THE ANKLET

In a town called Salipura, there lived a merchant who had a son named Gunakara. The young man had a beautiful wife called Sridevya, who had a lover called Subuddhi. The whole town knew that Sridevya was having an extramarital affair, although they didn't know with whom. Many of Gunakara's friends tried to tell him about this. Even his own father, the merchant, warned his son not to be fooled, but Gunakara was so blindly in love with his beautiful wife, that he refused to believe anyone. 'Where's your proof?' he would say. So his father decided to bring him proof.

The old man began to watch Sridevya's comings and goings, and one night, when she slipped out of her husband's bed and went towards the cluster of asoka trees that grew near the house, he followed her and hid behind a tree. He saw her lie down on a bed of blossoms, and embrace a man. From where he was, he could not see the faces of the two lovers, but he could see their legs. In the moonlight, Sridevya's fair-complexioned, shapely, bare legs and silver anklets were clearly visible. The father-in-law waited till the couple finished their lovemaking, and when they fell asleep, he tiptoed up to them and carefully removed one of Sridevya's anklets. What he didn't know was that Sridevya had woken up when he touched her leg and had seen her father-in-law remove her anklet.

As soon as the old man returned to the house, Sridevya quickly woke up her lover and sent him on his way. Then, going back to her husband, she lay down in bed with him and shook him awake.

'What is it, dear?' her husband mumbled.

'Wake up. Just now your father came into our bedroom and removed my anklet. The pervert. I feel so...so violated,' she said, shuddering delicately.

Gunakara came fully awake and, jumping out of bed, barged into his father's room, fuming. 'Why did you take my wife's anklet?' he demanded. 'Why did you touch her at all? Don't you have any sense of decency—touching your daughter-in-law when she is sleeping with your son.'

'But she wasn't sleeping with you. She was sleeping with another man under the asoka trees. That's why I took her anklet—to prove to you that she's spending her nights with her lover—not you.'

Sridevya, who had also arrived on the scene, burst into tears. 'Why are you lying?' she asked her father-in-law, her tear-streaked face innocent and distressed. 'Why are you trying to turn my husband against me? Don't you want your son to be happy?' Then she turned to Gunakara and pleaded with him: 'Don't believe him, please. I'm faithful to you. I swear.'

'If she's so innocent, let her prove it,' the father declared. 'Let the yaksha decide.'

The village had a tutelary yaksha who judged truth and untruth. Whenever a person charged with a crime was brought before him, he seized the person. If the alleged criminal was innocent, he or she was able to easily slip out of his grip, but if not, the villagers knew that the person was guilty.

When Sridevya heard her father-in-law's challenge, she went pale, but then she quickly recovered and began to think of a plan. 'I'm not afraid of the yaksha's grip,' she stated righteously. 'In fact, I'll gladly go to him, because he'll prove my innocence, once and for all.'

'Yes. Let the yaksha decide,' Gunakara said. 'That way when my dearest Sridevya is proved innocent, everyone will stop maligning her.

Let's do it tomorrow morning.'

Later that night, Sridevya once again slipped out of her house and went to see her lover, but only to instruct him. 'Tomorrow, when I am being taken to the yaksha, I want you to act like a madman and come and grab me by the neck.'

'What? You want me to grab you in front of everyone? I thought the whole idea was to keep our liaison secret.'

'Don't ask questions. Just do it. And remember to act like a madman.'

By the following morning, word had spread about Sridevya's implicating anklet, and a crowd began gathering under the tree in which the yaksha lived. People were eager to see Sridevya publicly incriminated. In the crowd was Subuddhi, Sridevya's lover. He was standing near the front, already acting crazy, making faces, muttering to himself, and laughing and crying for no reason.

Soon Sridevya, flanked by her husband and her father-in law, began walking towards the yaksha tree. She was freshly bathed and was carrying flowers with which to worship the yaksha. As the trio drew near the crowd, Subuddhi dashed out of it and grabbed Sridevya by the neck. She screamed and tried to push him off, but he seemed to have her in a chokehold. Gunakara and some young men from the crowd had to beat him off.

Once the crowd settled down, Sridevya and her husband and father-in-law approached the tree, and, just as Sridevya placed the platter of flowers it its roots, an unseen force grabbed her, pinning her arms to her sides and gluing her feet to the ground. Then a loud voice boomed from the branches. 'Speak. woman. Has any man, other than your husband, touched you?'

Sridevya bowed her head and answered, 'O revered yaksha, no man, except for my husband and that crazy man who just grabbed me by the neck, has ever touched me.'

The crowd waited in anticipation for the yaksha to pronounce the woman a liar and punish her. But to everyone's surprise, Sridevya's body was released and she stepped away from the tree, freed. People could hardly believe the outcome, but they accepted the yaksha's verdict and dispersed.

'See, I told you I'm innocent,' Sridevya said to her father-in-law in righteous indignation.

The old man scratched his head in perplexity. Gunakara smiled fondly at his wife and took her home. As they left, a soft rumbling came from the tree that sounded very much like laughter. The yaksha had seen through Sridevya's act and was applauding her for her cleverness.

Folktale from the Shukasaptati

◆

153

TWELVE MOUSE CUBITS

In olden times, the penises of young men were twelve cubits long and they kept them coiled around the waist. Also, the vaginas of women were in their armpit.

A young woman was once frying mahua flowers in her fenced courtyard. At the same time, a young man was walking down the lane on the other side of the fence. As the woman stood over the fire, she began to sweat, and when she raised her arm to wipe the sweat from her forehead, her vagina became exposed. Just then, the young man happened to look her way. When he saw her vagina, a sensation began to spread in his penis and it began to grow and unwind. He took it in his hands and guided it over the fence towards the woman, and its tip touched her ear. She started and looked to see what it was. Then she picked up a spatula and gave it a good whack. The young man shrieked in pain and ran from the site, pulling urgently on his penis, trying to gather it back as quickly as possible, completely uncaring of what he stepped on in his haste. As it happened, he trampled on at least twelve mice.

The rodent community was very upset, and they went to Cando to complain. When they told him what had happened, Cando said, 'Oh, that is not good. We must do something about the penis.'

Cando gathered all the animals and birds and, together, they decided that the man's penis must be shortened considerably.

'It would not be fair to make it shorter than twelve cubits, because after all, that is what man has been promised,' said Cando.

'How about if we measure it according to mouse standards,' one wise old mouse said, and everyone agreed that was fair and appropriate. So, a smart young mouse measured out twelve arms' length worth of penis, and then the other mice gnawed off the rest of it.

As they were doing this, Cando also decided to move the vagina to a spot on a woman's body where it would not be so easily exposed, and he placed it in the fork of her legs.

Folktale from the Santhal tribe

◆

154

HOW SHIVA'S LINGA CAME TO BE WORSHIPPED

There was an excellent pine forest, where sages devoted to Shiva performed elaborate worship with loud eulogies three times a day. For the rest of the day, they meditated on him. These sages were so engrossed in their asceticism that even though they were married, they ignored their duties of marital life and also their wives, who passed the seasons waiting for their husbands' embrace. The sages grew arrogant in their abstinence, thinking they were votaries of Shiva—the Yogeshwara—who, through his yogic power, had harnessed all the sensual and sexual energies in his body.

One day, when the sages went into the forest to gather twigs for the sacrificial fire, Shiva decided to test them. He assumed an ugly male form, and, smearing his completely naked body with ashes, he went amongst the sages' wives. Holding his penis in his hand, he began to make lewd gestures at the women. Some of the women became frightened and ran away, but others, excited, went closer to him, and still others tried to embrace him.

Meanwhile, the sages returned and seeing a stranger entice their wives, they were infuriated. 'Who are you?' they demanded. 'How dare you behave like this with our wives? Don't you know that such perverted actions are against Vedic conventions?'

Shiva only laughed in response, which made the sages more furious. 'Stop this, at once,' they shouted. But, instead of stopping, Shiva shook his organ at them. So they proclaimed, 'Let your penis fall to the ground!' And immediately, Shiva's organ fell off.

As soon as the divine phallus touched the ground, it burnt everything around it. Then it began to move like a flame, burning whatever came in its path. It went to the netherworld; it went to heaven; and it came down to earth. Wherever it went, it blazed, never once coming to rest. All the worlds became distressed, and the terrified inhabitants tried to find shelter, but the phallus was relentless. Finally, everyone decided to seek refuge with Brahma. When Brahma heard what had happened, he realized that they had all been deluded by Shiva's maya.

'Oh, you wise seers! You fools,' Brahma said in contempt. 'Shiva came to test you and you didn't even recognize him. You saw his organ only as obscene and lascivious, when, in fact, it is the generative force of the world. You thought his phallus a wild, lusting organ, when, in reality, it is the symbol of divine ecstasy. Thinking his phallus unconventional and perverted, you cursed it to fall off, when, in truth, it is Shiva's own characteristic sign. Through your ignorance, you have invited chaos in the three worlds. I can tell you this, that until you stop that phallus from roaming the three worlds, there will be no prosperity anywhere. You need to pacify his symbol, and hold it in one place.'

'How are we to do that?' the sages wailed in distress. 'Please guide us.'

'Go to Goddess Parvati, the daughter of the mountain, and plead with her. She is the epitome of divine stability and the goddess of fertility. She is the only one to match Shiva's force. If she takes the form of a vulva—the yoni—and receives Shiva's phallus, it will become calm. Make an eight-petalled diagram of a lotus to establish the centre of the world, fill a pot with water from a sacred ford, and sprinkle it with sprouts of barley and durva grass to invite abundance. Then, anointing the phallus with the water, call upon the Goddess to take her place as the yoni and request her to accept the phallus within her. When the daughter of the mountain is satisfied, Shiva himself will be gratified, and the linga will rest. This will stop the world from decay, and felicity will prevail.'

The sages did as Brahma had advised, and Shiva became pleased. He said to the sages and to the other gods. 'When desire is uncontrolled, it can destroy the world; and asceticism is of no use unless it acknowledges desire. Desire needs to be controlled, not denied. That is dharma—the perfect balance. My phallus needs to be supported by Parvati's yoni— the true balance that sustains Creation. Only with this balance is there prosperity and happiness in the world.'

And so it is that Shiva's linga became famous in the three worlds as Shiva-Shiva—the auspicious one who brings happiness.

Myth from the Puranas

155

THAT ARE YOU

In times past, there was one called Shvetaketu Aruneya. His father, Uddalaka Aruni, said to him, 'Be a celibate student, Shvetaketu. Never in our line was born a man who did not study the Vedas—none who was a Brahmin merely by birth.' So Shvetaketu went to a teacher when he was twelve, and he studied the Vedas until he was twenty-four. By the time he returned home, he had acquired great learning, but he had also become opinionated and arrogant about this learning.

His father asked him, 'Dear child, now that you are opinionated and arrogant about your learning, did you ask for that information which makes the unheard heard, the unthought thought, the unknown known?'

'How, sir, is that instruction imparted?' Shvetaketu asked.

'Just as by knowing one lump of clay, all that is made of clay becomes know—the transformation being just a matter of words, the reality being only clay. Just as by knowing one lump of gold, all that is made of gold becomes known—the transformation being just a matter of words, the reality being only gold. Just as by knowing one pair of nail scissors all that is made of iron becomes known—the transformation being just a matter of words, the reality being only iron. This, my dear, is the instruction.'

Shvetaketu replied, 'Surely my revered teachers did not know this instruction. Because if they had known it, why would they not have revealed it to me? But you, my revered father, should reveal it to me.'

'That which is the finest essence—that essence is the self of *all this*. That is the real, that is the self, and that are you, O Shvetaketu.' Then Aruni asked his son to bring him a fruit from a banyan tree.'Here it is,' Shvetaketu said, handing over the fruit.

'Break it.'

'It is broken.'

'What do you see in it?'

'Atom-like seeds.'

'Break one of these, my son.'

'Here it is. I've broken one, Father.'

'Now, what do you see?'

'Nothing, Father.'

'This atomic fineness that you cannot perceive, from that very fineness this banyan tree sprang. That which is this finest essence, that very essence is in *all this*. That is the real, that is the self, and that are you, Son.'

Then Uddalaka gave his son some salt. 'Put this salt in the water and come to me in the morning,' he said.

Shvetaketu did as his father instructed. In the morning when he went to his father with the bowl of water, Aruni said, 'Find me the salt that you put in the water last evening.' Shvetaketu searched for the salt in the water, but he couldn't find it. Then Aruni told his son: 'You can't find it, because it has dissolved completely. Now take a sip from this end. How does it taste?'

'It's salty,' Shvetaketu replied.

'Now take a sip from the centre. How does it taste?'

'It's salty.'

'Now take a sip from that end. How does it taste?'

'It's salty.'

'Now throw this water out and come back to me.'

When Shvetaketu did as his father instructed and returned to him, Aruni said to him, 'You see, the salt was always there. It was everywhere. You just couldn't see it. In the same way, my son, you do not perceive Being; although, it is always present. That is your finest essence. That is the real, that is the self, that are you, Shvetaketu.

Myth from the Upanishads

◆

156

THERE'S MORE LIGHT HERE

A passerby saw the Sufi master Mullah Nasruddin[60] on his hands and knees outside his house, searching for something under a streetlamp.

'Have you lost something?' he asked.

'Yes. My key,' the Pir replied.

The man came to help and began looking around. After a while, when neither of them could find the key, the man asked the Pir, 'Are you sure you lost it here?'

'Oh, I didn't lose it here. I lost it in my house,' Nasruddin said.

'Then why are you looking for it here?' the man asked, surprised.

'Because my house is dark. There's more light here,' Nasruddin replied.

Mullah Nasruddin folktale

◆

157

THE MIRACLE OF THE PROPHET'S BIRTH

When Amina, the mother of the Prophet, was pregnant, a voice said to her, 'You are pregnant with the Prince of People. When he is born, you must say, 'I have put him under the protection of the only One, away from the evil of every envious person. And you must name him Muhammad.' During her pregnancy, she also had a vision—a light issued forth from her in which she could see the castles of Busra in Syria. Soon after, Abdullah, the Apostle's father, died; at that time, his son was still in his mother's womb.

The Prophet was born on a Monday, 12th Rabi'al-awwal in the year of the elephant. When he was born, his mother sent a message to his grandfather, and when he came to see the infant, she told him about what she had heard and seen. The grandfather took the Prophet to Kaaba and thanked Allah for the gift. Then he took him back to his mother and found a woman to nurse him.

Halima, the Prophet's foster-mother, relates that she left her country with her husband and little son, whom she was suckling. There was a famine that year and nothing was left. She rode on a piebald she-ass, and she and her husband brought along an old she-camel that did not give a drop of milk. They could not sleep all night because their infant child cried incessantly from hunger. There was no milk in her, and the she-camel couldn't provide any either. But they hoped to be delivered from this destitution, and so they pressed on

When they arrived in Mecca, Halima and the other women of the Banu Sad tribe looked for children to nurse. The Prophet was offered to each one of them, but they all refused to take him, because he was an orphan; he didn't have a father who could pay for their services. When every woman, except Halima, had found a child to nurse, and they were ready to depart, Halima said to her husband, 'I don't want to go back with my companions without a suckling child; I'll take that orphan.'

'Yes. Do that,' her husband replied. 'Perhaps Allah will bless us for it.' So Halima went and brought the Prophet, only because she could not find any other child.

As soon as Halima held the child close to her, her milk began to flow. He drank his fill, and Halima's child, too, drank all he could. Then they both slept peacefully. But that night, the she-camel became restless, and when her husband went to check on her, he saw that her udders were full. Halima milked her, and she and her husband drank the milk and had a restful night. In the morning, her husband said, 'I think, Halima, you have taken in a blessed soul.'

For two years Halima and her husband benefitted from the Prophet's blessings, then Halima weaned him. He was growing up faster and stronger than any other boy, and at two he was ready to be brought back to his mother, but the couple didn't want to part with him yet. So, Halima said to his mother, 'Leave your little boy with me and let him grow in my care. There is a plague in Mecca and the climate, too, is not conducive.' At first Amina was loath to leave her child, but when Halima persisted, she agreed.

One day, a month or so after Halima and her husband returned, the Prophet and his foster-brother were pasturing their lambs behind the tents. Suddenly, the brother came running to his parents and said to them 'Two men dressed in white garments have seized my brother and have thrown him down. They have ripped open his belly and are squeezing it.'

Halima and her husband ran to the spot and found the Prophet standing up, seemingly unharmed, but red in the face. When they asked him what had happened, he replied, 'Two men in white garments came and threw me down, opened up my belly, and were searching for something. I don't know what.' They carried him back to the tent, and the Prophet's foster-father advised Halima to take him to his family before something happened to him.

When they brought him to Amina, she asked them why they were returning him when they had been so eager to keep him. They tried to evade the issue, saying only that they didn't want him to come to any harm. But Amina knew something had happened and insisted that they tell her, and when they did, she asked them, 'Do you think that he is possessed by Satan?' 'Yes,' they replied. 'No,' she corrected them. 'It is Allah, not Satan who has him in his care.' And then she told them about the voice she had heard and vision she had seen when she was carrying him. 'When he was born, he placed his hands on the ground and raised his head to heaven,' she told them.

The Prophet himself, once, described to his companions what had occurred that day. 'While my brother and I were pasturing animals behind our tents, two men in white garments came to me with a gold platter full of snow. They grabbed me, opened up my belly, and extracting my heart, split it open. Then they took out of it a black drop of blood, which they threw away. After that they washed my heart and my belly clean with the snow. Then one of them said to the others, 'Weigh him against ten of his people.' They did so, but I proved heavier. They weighed me against a hundred people and then a thousand, but I proved heavier still. 'Let him be,' the man said. 'For if you were to weigh him against all the people, he would outweigh them.'

Myth from the Life of Muhammad

◆

158

A PALACE IN HEAVEN

Thomas the Apostle came to India with Abbanes, who was a naval merchant in the court of King Gundaphorus of Taxila. Abbanes had acquired Thomas in Jerusalem for his carpentry skills, so when he was presented to Gundaphoros, the king asked him, 'What crafts do you know?'

Thomas replied, 'The craft of carpenting and building. In wood, I can build ploughs and yokes and pulleys and boats, and in stone, I can build pillars and temples and court-houses for kings.'

'Can you build me a palace?' the king asked.

'Yes. That is what I do. I am a carpenter.'

Gundaphorus took Thomas to the site that he had in mind for the palace. It was a suitable place—woody, with plenty of water. 'So when can you begin?' the king asked.

'Not in this season,' Thomas replied. 'I'll begin in the month of October and finish in the month of March.'

The king was surprised, because summer was considered the most suitable month to build. 'Can you not have it ready by winter?' he asked.

Thomas assented, and the king was pleased. 'Can you draw me a plan to show me what the palace will look like?' he asked. Thomas took a stick and drew a plan on the ground: he set the doors towards the rising sun and the windows to the westward breezes. He also drew a bake house in the south and aqueduct to the north.

Satisfied with his skills, Gundaphoros gave Thomas a lot of money for the job and promised him that he would send additional funds on a regular basis and also provide food and shelter for the workers.

Taking the money that he received from the king, Thomas began touring the cities and villages and distributing all of it among the poor and afflicted. Some months later, he sent a message to the king that the palace was built, except for the roof. On receiving this message, the king sent gold and silver to complete the roof.

Then, one day, Gundaphoros came to visit the city, and he enquired from his friends what they thought about the palace that Thomas was building for him. 'What palace?' they asked. 'He's not building anything. All we see him do is work with the poor and sick. He goes among people, teaching them about a new god. He himself seems to be a simple man, because he fasts and prays and eats only bread with salt and water, and he wears only one garment in the heat or cold.'

Gundaphoros was livid. The man he had hired to build his palace had been lying to him about the amount of work he had accomplished. He had, in fact, not done a spot of work, and to make matters worse, he had squandered away all the money. Seething with anger, Gundaphoros went himself to see Thomas and asked him. 'Have you built me my palace?'

'Yes, I have.' Thomas replied.

'Then shall we go and see it?'

'You can't see it now,' Thomas said, 'but when you depart from this life, you'll see it.'

Gundaphoros ordered his guards to put Thomas in chains, along with the merchant who had brought him, and set a date for their execution.

Abbanes, the merchant, pleaded with the king, weeping and begging for forgiveness, but Thomas was joyful. He told the merchant not to fear. 'Only believe in God,' he said, 'and you'll be set free.'

With the date of execution drawing near, Gundaphoros debated in his mind what would be an appropriate means of delivering the punishment—flaying or fire? Then he received word that his beloved brother, Gad, had died. Grief-stricken, he rushed to his brother's place, where his men were preparing his body for burial. But as they put him in his royal robe, Gundaphoros saw the corpse stir, and soon Gad regained consciousness. Everyone in the room was amazed. Gundaphoros, too, could hardly believe what he was seeing, but he was overjoyed to see his brother alive again. He embraced Gad and kissed his face again and again.

'You have been a good brother to me,' Gad said to Gundaphorus 'Can you do me one more favour?'

'Of course.'

'Swear an oath that you'll grant it.'

'I swear,' Gundaphorus replied.

'Sell me the palace which you have in heaven.'

'What are you talking about? I don't have a palace in heaven.'

'Yes you do. The slave that you intend to put to death has built a palace for you in heaven.'

Gad then described what happened to him after the angels took his soul to heaven. 'They showed me around and asked me where I would like to live. I saw a beautiful palace and asked if I could live in one of the rooms of that palace. 'Sorry,' they said. 'That doesn't belong to you. That's the palace that the Christian has built for your brother.' And I said to the angels, 'Please let me go back to my brother so that I may buy that palace from him, because he has no idea about it and will sell it to me.' And so they put my soul back into my body. And here I am. Sell me that palace, brother.'

Gundaphorus realized then what Thomas had been doing all these months with the money he had given him. 'Brother,' he said to Gad. 'I can't sell you that palace, because it's not in my power, but I can give you a man who can help you build a palace of your own, even better than mine.' Then he released the merchant, Abbanes, and the Apostle, Thomas, and he himself became a Christian.

Myth from the Gospel of Thomas

◆

159

HANUMAN'S HEART

After completing fourteen years in exile, Rama and Sita returned to Ayodhya. On the day of Rama's coronation, the whole city celebrated, and the royal couple gave gifts to all their friends who had helped them in the war against Ravana. Sita gifted Hanuman a necklace of pearls that were so large and luminous that each pearl looked like a mini moon. She had received this very precious necklace from Vibhishana, Ravana's brother, who himself had obtained it from Varuna, the Lord of Waters.

All who had received a gift were pleased, except Hanuman. He sat in one corner in the assembly hall, putting each pearl in his mouth, biting down on it till it cracked, and splitting open the bead to look inside it. Then he shook his head and threw away the pieces in disgust. Everyone present in the assembly wondered about this strange behaviour; some even laughed at him. 'He's a monkey after all,' they said. 'What does he know about the value of pearls?'

'That's exactly what I'm doing,' Hanuman said to them. 'I'm looking for the value of each pearl, but I haven't yet found one that is valuable.'

'The value is in the whole pearl; it's in how it shines,' someone advised.

'You're mistaken,' Hanuman told him. 'That's from the outside. The real value of something is only if it has Rama inside it. None of these have Rama inside them. Mata Sita has given me a useless gift.'

'Not everything has to have Rama inside. Your body doesn't. It's made of flesh and blood and sinews and five elements,' a wise minister said.

In response, Hanuman got up and, digging his long nails into his chest, ripped it open, pulling apart the skin and flesh to reveal his heart. Instead of a flesh and blood pulsating muscle, people saw Rama and

Sita sitting there, exactly as they were on the throne, and on Hanuman's exposed ribcage, they saw the word 'Rama' etched on each bone.

Folk-myth

◆

160

THE HARE IN THE MOON

Once upon a time, when Brahmadatta was ruling in Banaras, the future Buddha was born as a hare, and he lived in a forest. On one side of this forest was a mountain, on another was a river, and on the third, a village. He had three comrades—a monkey, a jackal, and an otter. During the day, each one hunted for prey in his own area, and at night, all four came together. The wise hare would advise the other three and teach them the Doctrine, saying, 'Give alms, keep the precepts, and observe fast-days.' The three would listen to him and promise, before returning to their own lairs in the thicket.

One summer night, the future Buddha looked up at the sky, saw the moon, and perceived that the next day would be a day for fasting. 'Tomorrow is a fast,' he said to the others. 'You three should keep the fast and generously give alms; if anyone comes asking for food, give him your own food, if need be.'

'Very well,' they said, and retired for the night to their lairs.

The following day the otter started out early and went to the banks of the Ganga to hunt for prey. Earlier, a fisherman had caught seven red-fish and, stringing them on a vine, had buried them in the sand on the river bank. Then he had gone on downstream, catching more fish. The otter smelt the fish buried in the sand and dug them out. He then called out three times, 'Does anyone own these fish?' When no one claimed ownership, he put the vine between his teeth and dragged it into his lair. Then he remembered that it was a day of fasting. 'I'll eat these when it is the proper time,' he said to himself, lying down.

That morning, the jackal also went out to hunt for prey. In the hut of a field-watcher he saw two spits of meat, one iguana, and a jar of ghee with a cord handle. He called out three times, 'Does anyone own these?'

and when he saw no owner, he placed the cord of the ghee jar around his neck, took hold of the spits of meat and the iguana with his teeth, and brought them home to his lair. Then he lay down, remembering that he was keeping a fast, and he, too, said to himself, 'I'll eat these when it is the proper time.'

The monkey brought home from the forest a bunch of mangoes, but then he, too, remembered that he was keeping a fast. Deciding to eat when the time was right, he also lay down in his lair.

The future Buddha, however, remained in his thicket, thinking he would go out at the proper time and eat dabba-grass. But then he thought, if a supplicant comes asking for food, I'll only have grass to give, and he may not want grass. I have no sesame, rice, or other such food. So if any supplicant comes asking for food, I'll give him some of my own flesh.

When Sakka heard such fierceness and zeal, his marble throne grew hot. Looking carefully on earth, he discovered the cause and decided to test the hare. Disguised as a Brahmin, he went first to the lair of the otter.

'What do you want, Brahmin?' the otter asked.

'If I could get something to eat, I would be able to break my fast and perform the duties of a monk,' the Brahmin replied.

'I'll give you food,' said the otter and recited:

I found seven red-fish
Buried in the river bank
O Brahmin, these are my own;
Come eat them and live within this forest

'I'll return a little later,' said the Brahmin. Then he went to the jackal, and from him, too, he begged for food. The jackal also said he would give him food and recited:

A watchman who guards the field
His food I took—
Two spits of meat, one iguana,
And one jar of ghee.
These are my own, O Brahmin.
Come eat and live within this forest.

'I'll return a little later,' the Brahmin said again and went to the monkey.

The scenario played out again, and the monkey, offering the Brahmin food, recited:

> Ripe mangoes, clear and cold water.
> All these, oh Brahmin, are my own;
> Come eat and live within this forest.

'I'll return later,' said the Brahmin and went to see the hare.

'What do you want, Brahmin?' the hare, too, asked.

'If I could get something to eat, I would be able to break my fast and perform the duties of a monk,' replied the Brahmin.

The future Buddha was delighted. 'Brahmin,' said he, 'you have done well in coming to me for food. Today I'll give alms such as I've never given before; and you'll not have broken any precepts by destroying life. Go, my friend, and gather wood, and when you have made a bed of coals, come and tell me. I'll sacrifice my life by jumping into the bed of live coals. And as soon as my body is cooked, you can eat my flesh and perform the duties of a monk.' Then he recited:

> The hare has no sesame seed,
> nor beans, nor winnowed rice.
> But I am of flesh that the fire will roast.
> Come eat it and live within this forest.

Sakka then created a fire with his divine power. When he came and told the future Buddha that the fire was ready, the hare rose from his seat of dabba-grass and shook himself three times, saying, 'Whatever insects there may be in my fur should come out; I must not let them die.' Then he jumped into the bed of coals, as delighted in his mind as a royal flamingo which alights in a cluster of lotuses. However, the fire did not burn so much as a pore of the future Buddha's body. Instead, he felt as if he had entered a cool place, somewhere above the clouds. Calling to the Brahmin from within the burning coals, the hare said, 'The fire you have made feels cool on my body. What does it mean?'

'I am no Brahmin,' said Sakka. 'I am Sakka, and I came to test you.'

'Your efforts are useless, Sakka,' the hare thundered. 'Test or not, I am always willing to give.'

'Wise hare,' said Sakka, 'your virtue will be proclaimed till the end of this world-cycle.' Then, taking a mountain, Sakka squeezed it, and with the juice, he drew the outline of a hare on the disk of the moon. Thereupon in that forest, and in that thicket, he placed the future Buddha on some tender dabba-grass, and taking leave of him, departed to his own celestial abode.

And so these four wise creatures continued to live happily and harmoniously, keeping the precepts, and observing fast-days, till they passed away according to their deeds. In that existence, the otter was Ananda, the jackal was Moggallana, the monkey was Sariputta, while the wise hare was the Buddha.

Folktale from the Jatakas

◆

161

KNOWING WHEN TO CONCEAL THE TRUTH

In the city of Rajpur, there was a king called Hansa. He was a fair and just king, known for his devotion to truth and nonviolence. One day, he decided to visit the temple dedicated to the first Tirthankara, Rishabhdeva. During the month of Chaitra, when the full moon appeared, people came from faraway places to worship in the temple, which was located on top of Mount Ratnasringa.

Before he left, Hansa handed over control of his kingdom to his council of ministers and told them to safeguard it. However, a few days after King Hansa's departure, another king, called Arjuna, attacked Rajpur. King Hansa's army fought valiantly but was defeated, with many of the generals losing their lives on the battlefield. Gaining control of the palace and the treasury, Arjuna installed himself as king and began to enforce his authority over Hansa's entire kingdom.

King Hansa was on his way to the temple when he heard about the defeat of his army. The courtiers and members of the royal family who were travelling with him were devastated at the news and advised him to return to the city, but the king said, 'We're on a spiritual mission and that is what we should be thinking about. Let's continue on our journey to the temple.' His courtiers, however, were worried about the safety of their families at home, so, one by one, they all went back, till only one loyal umbrella-bearer remained.

On their climb to Ratnasringa, the king and his servant entered a dense forest and lost their way. Now Hansa became concerned about his servant's well-being, in case they became separated, so he took off his royal dress and jewellery and gave them to his servant, telling him to use them to fend for himself if the need arose. It so happened that they did get separated, and Hansa found himself all alone. Suddenly, a deer ran in front of him and then disappeared. Right after that a hunter ran up with a bow in his hand and asked the king if he had seen the deer. The king thought if he told the truth the deer would get killed, so he decided not to answer and tried to distract the hunter with small talk. Frustrated by his conversation with the king, the hunter finally left.

By now the king was tired, so he sat down under a tree to rest. Hiding nearby were some robbers, who were discussing how they would rob the monks who would soon pass this way. Hearing their conversation, Hansa began to think of a way to save the monks, but then some guards came riding up and asked him if he had seen the robbers. The king was once again in a dilemma—should he tell the truth or not? If he told the guards about the robbers, they would surely punish them, but if he didn't reveal their whereabouts, the monks would suffer. 'My friends,' he said to the guards. 'Why don't you protect the monks, instead of looking for the robbers?' The guards agreed to that prudent suggestion and left to go and guard the monks. The robbers heard King Hansa and were touched by the way the stranger had saved both them and the monks. They came out of hiding and thanked him. 'My dear friends,' King Hansa said to them. 'Why don't you give up this fugitive life and become good citizens?' The robbers promised that they would consider his advice and left.

Soon, a group of horsemen stopped by the tree under which Hansa was sitting and asked him if he had seen King Hansa. 'What do you want from him?' the king asked. They told him that they had been sent by King Arjuna to catch the former king and kill him. King Hansa remembered that his servant was wearing his clothes and jewels, and he worried that if they found him, they would mistake him to be Hansa and kill him, so he stood up and said, 'I am King Hansa. Do what you've been sent to do.' Then he closed his eyes and began reciting the Navkar Mantra, waiting, without fear, for the sword that would cut off his head.

In an instant the horsemen were gone and in their stead was an angel. 'O king, I am overwhelmed by your compassion and your truth. Through your wisdom, you know that if uttering the truth can hurt people, it is better not to tell it. My chariot is at your service. It will take you to the temple.'

Riding with the deva in his chariot, King Hansa reached the summit of Ratnasringa and offered worship. Then, escorted by the deva, he went back to his kingdom, where miraculously, Arjuna had been captured and put in prison. He pardoned Arjuna and released him and, once again, began to rule the city of Rajpur with truth and compassion.

Jain folk-myth

◆

162

IN WHICH DIRECTION IS KAABA?

One of the last travels that Guru Nanak undertook was to Mecca. With his faithful companion, Mardana, who was a Muslim, the Guru went on Haj, dressed as a Haji in blue robes, carrying a fakir's staff and a lota.

By the time he reached Mecca, the Guru was tired, and he lay down to rest near the Sacred Mosque, not realizing that his feet were pointed towards Kaaba. A kazi, passing by, saw the Guru's disrespect and yelled at him. 'Move your feet, you ignorant man,' he said. 'Are you an infidel that you are sleeping with your feet pointing in the direction of the Kaaba?'

'I'm sorry, my man,' Guru Nanak replied. 'I'm an old man, and I was too tired to notice the direction in which I slept. Would you be so kind as to move my feet in the direction away from Kaaba?'

The kazi lifted the fakir's feet and pulled them away, but when he looked up, he saw that the Kaaba was still in the same direction as the feet of the fakir. So the kazi pulled the feet in another direction, but again, when he looked up, the Kaaba was still there, right across from the old fakir's feet. The kazi moved Guru Nanak's feet in many different directions, but no matter in which direction the Guru's feet pointed, the

Kaaba, too, moved in that direction.

Finally, the kazi gave up and fell to his knees before the Guru with his head bowed. 'Forgive me,' he said. 'Please tell me who you are.'

'I'm only a simple man of God, and I tell you that He is in every direction.'

Folk-myth from the Janamsakhis

◆

163

KIRTIMUKHA

One day Shiva was sitting on Mount Kailash with his lotus-eyed, supple-waisted bride-to-be, Parvati, when Asura Rahu, that eclipser of the moon, arrived with a message from the Daitya king, Jalandhar: 'Hand over Parvati, the fairest of all maidens, to me, the new king of the three worlds. You are a beggar who has abandoned the world and who wanders in cremation grounds. You don't deserve the glorious Princess of the Mountains. I will make her my queen.'

Jalandhar had performed great austerities to gain supreme power, and with that he had unseated the gods from heaven and created his own new order for the three worlds. He now wished to subjugate Lord Shiva, the Destroyer of the World, by humiliating him.

At Rahu's insulting words, Shiva's Ajna Chakra, the third eye of command, began to glow between his eyebrows and a tremendous energy exploded from it, which took the physical shape of a massive lion-headed monster. He was lean and emaciated, as though a manifestation of insatiable hunger. He roared like thunder, his eyes burnt like fire, and his dishevelled mane spread to the farthest reaches of space. As soon as he was born, he pounced on Rahu to appease his hunger, but Rahu was adept at eluding his pursuers. He stepped out of the demon's reach, but he knew that he wouldn't be able to escape him for long, so he did the only thing he could to save himself. He fell at Shiva's feet, begging him to be his refuge. What could the benevolent Great Lord do but give him protection. 'Let him go,' he commanded the lion-headed demon.

But now the creature that had been created solely to devour, was left with nothing to eat. 'Whom shall I eat?' he asked Shiva. 'I'm hungry. Assign me someone on whom I can feast and appease my hunger.'

For a moment, Shiva was perplexed, wondering who to assign as victim of this monster, who was Shiva's own incarnate power of destruction. Even as he thought this, Shiva knew the answer. 'Devour your own hands and feet,' he said to him.

And so the demon began to voraciously eat himself. He started at the feet, and after he had finished those off, he ate his hands, and still kept going, eating his arms and his legs. Then he also ate his belly and his chest, but when he tried to eat beyond that, his teeth would not reach any further. Now only his face was left. Shiva was delighted at the sight of this being, this manifestation of his wrath, devouring himself, as if consuming his own base substance, till nothing but a radiant, pure, glorious face remained. 'Stop!' Shiva called. 'I am well-pleased with you, my beloved son. Henceforth, you will be known as Kritimukha, the Face of Glory, and you will be present forever at my door, gracing the entrance of my places of worship. Whoever seeks my grace must first honour you.'[61]

Myth from the Puranas

◆

164

ALL THAT IS LOST

There is an angel who always watches over people and records everything before it is forgotten. His name is Yode'a, which means the 'one who knows', and he is the angel of losses. He has a legion of angel servants who always carry shovels, because they constantly dig and search for all that is lost.

In life, a lot is lost.

Every Tzaddik—the righteous one—is a servant of Yode'a, digging and searching for losses, but sometimes the righteous one himself is lost. Then, it is necessary to search in the dark—the unknown—and the light that must be used in this pitch-darkness is that of the soul. It is a very small light—even smaller than a candle's—but it illuminates even the darkest of corners. In this light of the soul, Yode'a, the angel of losses, can see all that is lost.

Myth from Be'er Ha-Hasidut

◆

PART THREE

The Seeded Pod

165

CREATION OF DEATH

When Brahma created the universe, he was brimming with creational energy; as a result, he created an abundance of human beings. They multiplied rapidly, and none of them died, because Death had not yet been created, and soon, the universe was overcrowded. Watching the three worlds swell with living beings, Brahma wondered how to do away with the surplus population. But no matter how many solutions he considered, he couldn't come up with an efficient way to destroy life. Unable to devise a way to control this explosion of life, Brahma became frustrated; frustration led to anger, and anger built into such a fury that his pores began to emit fire, which spread to all quarters of the world. That fire began to burn heaven and earth and sky and all the mobile and immobile beings of the universe.

Seeing every creature burn in the flames, Shiva's heart filled with pity. He said to Brahma, 'These beings have been created by you. Don't be angry with them.'

Brahma replied, 'I'm not angry. Nor is it my desire that all created beings should be destroyed. But I need to lighten the load of the Earth; that is why destruction is necessary. Earth herself has requested me to do this, because she's sinking in the water under the immense weight of these creatures who continue to multiply. I didn't intentionally evoke my anger. My frustration at not finding a suitable means of destruction manifested itself as fire.'

'But your destruction has become mindless. If it continues at this rate, the universe will soon be empty. Control your energy with your energy and destroy with deliberation.'

The self-created Brahma then exerted energy to suppress the fire surging from his body. From that energy, a lady emerged. She was dressed in robes of black and red and had black eyes and black palms. She was wearing a pair of sparkling earrings and was decked in divine ornaments and a garland of lotuses. As soon as she appeared, she sat on Brahma's right side and asked him what she should do.

'You're Death. Kill these creatures of the universe,' Brahma said to her. 'Foolish or learned, weak or powerful—begin to destroy them all but with deliberation. That is why I've called you. Kill them without exception. That is my command."

Death began to cry profusely. But she did not let her tears fall to the ground, in case the sorrow in them brought harm to the earth; instead she caught the drops in her cupped hands. Filled with pity for the creatures of the earth, she said to Brahma most respectfully, 'O creator of the world, how can a lady who has sprung from you perform such a terrible act—an act that is sure to terrorize people. I can't do this. You must find me a task that is full of virtue. How will I be able to cut short the lives of infants, youths, the elderly, who have done me no injury? How can I kill dear sons and other loved ones—brothers and sisters and mothers and fathers? If I kill them, their surviving relatives will surely curse me, and the tears of the grief-struck survivors will burn me. Thinking of this, I'm filled with fear.'

'O Death, I have created you to destroy all creatures. Go and begin your task. Don't be afraid of performing this act. Go, now,' Brahma urged.

But Death, still holding her teardrops in her hands, did not move or say a word.

'Go. I command you,' Brahma said again. But Death just stood there, looking at him abjectly.

Brahma smiled compassionately at her mute appeal, and, even as he smiled, Death went away. Not having made any promises to Brahma, she went to a spot in the mountains called Dhenuka. There, for one thousand five hundred crore years, she stood on one foot, holding her tears in her hands, doing penance for disobeying Brahma. When her penance was complete, Brahma called her and again commanded her to begin killing living beings. But, once again, without a word and without making any promises, Death returned to Dhenuka with her tears, and, this time, she stood on the other foot for twenty thousand years. Then she stayed in the forest for one thousand more years, living only on air. Then for eight thousand years, she practised the vow of silence on the bank of River Kaushiki. Then going to Mount Meru, where the gods had performed their own initiation sacrifices, she took another vow and stood motionless for one lakh crore years, standing on the toes of her feet, holding her cupped hands steady so that not one teardrop would spill on the earth.

Finally, tired of waiting for her, Brahma went to where she was. 'What are you doing?' he questioned. 'I created you to kill people. Go and do what I have asked you to do.'

Death, still having misgivings, replied to Brahma with her head bowed deeply. 'I want to please you, but I'm unable to destroy living creatures.'

'Listen to me, dear girl. You will not incur any sin from destroying living creatures. In fact, eternal virtue will live in you. All the gods and I are concerned about your well-being and will not abandon you.'

When Death still hesitated, Brahma came up with an idea: 'The tears that you hold in your hands—let them go. They'll take the form of terrible diseases and possess living beings, and they are the ones that will destroy the living, when the time comes. That way no one will blame you. I will also have Anger and Desire help you. When living creatures arrive at their end, you will send Desire and Anger against them, and they are the ones that will kill. You yourself will not incur any sin. Now go and do as I ask.'

Afraid that if she demurred any more, Brahma would curse her, Death finally assented. She began sending Anger and Desire to living creatures in their last hours, and those worked as her agents. Also, the tears she had shed, invaded people's bodies as diseases, which, when their last hours came, snatched away life. But Death herself remained faultless.

Myth from the Mahabharata

◆

166

THE DEAD MAN

Appeal to Agni:

> O Agni, don't burn him or consume him. Don't let his body or skin be scattered. After you have ripened him with your fires, send him on his way to join the ancestors. That path is waiting for him and the gods will guide him down that path.

Farewell to the dead man:

> O being, may the sun receive your eye and the wind your spirit. Go
> to the sky, or to the waters; go, take root in the plants. Wherever
> your merits take you, that is your fate.

Appeal to Agni:

> O Agni, he who is sacrificed to you with oblations, send him on,
> wearing new life. Let him rejoin a body; let him have offspring. Let
> him live again.

Myth from the Rig Veda

◆

167

CROSSING THE CHINVAT BRIDGE OF SEPARATION

In the middle of the world is Daiti peak. It is as tall as a hundred men,
and it is the fulcrum for the scale of Rashnu, the divine spirit of truth
and justice. One end of it rests on Mount Alburz and the other leads to
the road to heaven. In the middle is the Chinvat Bridge—the bridge of
separation—which separates the good from the wicked. At the top of the
bridge is the spiritual dog.

When a man passes away, his soul sits near his head for three days,
heckled by the evil deva, Vizaresh, who fills it with fear. That is why a
fire must be lit near the head of the departed and be kept burning for
three nights. During those three nights, as the body decays, the man is
as distressed as though his house were being torn down by nasa, which
causes death and pollution. But for three nights, the soul, sitting near
the head of the body, hopes that maybe blood will flow again and wind
will enter the body and life will return. Then, on the dawn of the fourth
day, if it is the soul of the good, it will think that Ohrmazd will make
him sovereign, and if it is the soul of the wicked, he will think that the
body with which he had movement is gone: now where shall he go? Then
a breeze comes, and, for the righteous, it is fragrant and soft and full of
the sense of triumph, cheering the soul. But for the wicked, this breeze

is a stinking and putrid wind, filled with the sense of defeat, infusing the soul with fear and discomfort.

All souls begin their journey towards Chinvat Bridge. The soul of the ashvan person, the righteous, who lives by asha, is first met by a healthy cow full of milk, and meeting the cow, it feels content. Then it is met by a beautiful virgin, dressed in white, and she brings the soul joy. Next, the soul proceeds to the garden of plenty, full of fruits and flowers and grain, and here it feels nourished and replenished. This soul then meets Daena, the spirits of revelation, and asks, 'Who are you, radiating such happiness that my happiness and comfort seem to come from you?' And the spirits reply, 'We are here because of your own Daena—your own discernment and good deeds.'

If the soul is wicked, it is met by a feeble, dry cow, who makes the soul feel weak. Then a vile, ugly crone, whose very aura emits scorn, meets the soul and fills it with dread. This soul then comes to a barren garden without trees, without water, without comforts, and it feels pained. And when this soul meets Mithra Saroosh and Rashnu, the guardian angels of a person's core values of kindness, promise-keeping and justice, and asks them, 'Who are you who appear so harmful?' the spirits reply. 'Your own wicked character and wicked deeds have brought us here.'

Then the souls are brought to Mount Alburz and taken to the summit. Here, for the righteous, the victorious fire, Farnbag, dispels the darkness and helps the soul cross the bridge to where the Yazdas are. These divinities purify the soul and hand it over to the good wind, who leads it across the bridge with the three steps of good thoughts, good deeds, good utterances that it had practised. With the first step, the soul goes to the sphere of the stars, with the second, to the sphere of the moon, and with the third, to the sphere of the sun, up into the shining abode of total harmony—the heavenly abode of light and song—Garo-deman.

For the wicked, the floor of the bridge is a sharp-edged knife. The soul is asked to take three steps of wicked thoughts, wicked deeds, and wicked utterances that it practised, but the soul does not want to go. It is asked three times. The first time the soul replies, 'It would be better if you sever me with a sharp knife;' the second time it replies, 'It would be better if you shoot me with an arrow;' and the third time, it replies, 'It would be better if you take my life from my body.' And this behaviour becomes a fearful wild beast, who lunges at the soul, forcing it to walk on the knife-edged bridge, and when the soul crosses the bridge, it falls headlong into Druj-demana—the abyss of darkness, evil and deceit.

The soul whose meritorious deeds equal wicked deeds will be sent to Hamistagan— a middle place of neutrality where neither joys nor sorrows exist till Frashokereti, the Day of Judgement and Renewal.

Myth from the Bundahishn

◆

168

ONLY WHEN YOUR TIME HAS COME

There was a road, and anyone who travelled on it ended up dead. No one knew how the people died. Some said a snake bit them, some said a scorpion stung them, and some said an unknown force constricted their throats till they couldn't breathe. Whatever it was, that road was a death-trap.

One evening, a very old man, who was sick at heart and tired of living, decided to take the death road. As he was walking on that road, wondering how death would take him, a giant scorpion, as large as a hen, appeared before him. Taken by surprise, the old man drew back at first, but then he realized that this was the killer on the road. But, even as he stepped forward to accept the death-sting, the scorpion changed into a long snake, and, instead of biting the old man, it began to undulate towards the field adjoining the road. Disappointed yet wonder-struck at this magical creature, the old man began to follow the snake, hoping that it would realize his presence and deliver him death.

For a while the snake just meandered around the trees and bushes in the field, and then it slithered into an inn. The old man followed him and saw him bite many of the people there. Then it slithered out and headed towards the king's palace, where it went up a water spout into queen's bedroom. The old man stood below and soon heard a scream and then loud wails; the snake had bitten the young princess who had been sleeping beside her mother.

Back on the road, the snake glided a short distance. Then the road suddenly became a river, with people waiting on either side to cross, but there was no ferry in sight. The snake now changed into a water buffalo and ambled towards the water's edge, the brass bells around its neck, ringing merrily.

'Oh look, that buffalo is going to cross the river,' people said. 'Let's get on its back and go across.' And every one of them climbed onto the buffalo's back. It waded into the water and began crossing, but when it came to the deep middle, it shook the people off. They all tumbled into the water and drowned.

By this time the old man had found a boat and crossed the river, but the buffalo was already on the other side, only now it was no longer a buffalo; it was a tall, handsome brown bull with sturdy flanks and long curved horns, nonchalantly grazing on the river bank, flicking away flies with its tail. As the old man stood looking at it, wondering what it would do next, he saw a farmer come by. The man peered in every direction and then, cautiously approaching the bull, slipped a noose around its neck. The animal remained passive and amiably allowed itself to be driven by the farmer to his cowshed and tied up alongside the cattle. The old man, once again following like a shadow, stationed himself in a dark corner of the shed. In the darkest hour of the night, the bull changed into a snake again and bit all the other animals in the shed.

Leaving the farm, the snake, with the old man still behind him, arrived at the edge of another river. Here, he changed into a beautiful maiden dressed in bridal clothes, and sitting down on a boulder, began to weep copious tears. Soon, two soldiers wearing uniforms, and whistling merrily, came to the river. They were brothers. Seeing the enchanting woman, the elder of the two approached her and asked why she was crying.

'My newly married husband went to get me some water and slipped and fell into the river,' the maiden cried. 'I saw his body swept away. Now I'm alone and sacred. I'm an orphan with no one to go to. I don't know what to do.'

'You have nothing to worry about,' the soldier said. 'You and I will go to the next town and get married. Then you'll always have me and I'll protect you.'

The woman stopped crying, and, wiping away her tears, she said with a sweet smile, 'I'll marry you, but on two conditions: You'll never question what I do and you'll always do what I ask.'

'Your wish is my command,' the soldier replied, gallantly.

'Then please go and get me a cup of water. I'm dying of thirst.'

As soon as the elder brother turned away to get water, the woman grabbed the younger soldier's hand. 'It's you I love, not your brother. That's why I sent him away. While he's down by the river, let's run away.'

The younger brother pulled his hand back. 'I can't do that,' he said reproachfully. 'You are promised to my elder brother. You are like a sister to me now.'

The woman let out a loud wail, calling to the older brother. 'Your younger brother is an evil man,' she cried. 'Seeing you gone, he propositioned me.'

The older brother came running back and drew his sword. The two brothers began to fight, and, soon, both their bodies lay on the ground, hacked to pieces. The young woman then changed back into the snake and glided away, and the old man followed.

Just as the sun began to break at the horizon, the snake changed into a very old man with a long white beard. His back was bent and he leaned heavily on a thick staff. It was such an unthreatening form of the mysterious, death-dealing creature that the old man, who had been following him all night, finally gathered his courage and came out of the shadows. 'Who are you?' he asked the very old man with the white beard.

'People call me the Lord of Death,' he replied.

'All night I've seen you change many forms and bring death to people, even to young people who could have lived for many more years. I'm old and sick at heart and tired of life, and I want to die. I've been following you all night. Why don't you give me death?'

'It's not your time yet. I only give death to those whose time has come,' he said, and vanished.

Folktale from Punjab

◆

169

DEATH OF PUSHPAK

The gods were assembling in Indraloka, with Indra, resplendent on his golden throne, presiding over the meeting. He had with him his favourite parrot, Pushpak, who was perched on one of the posts of the throne.

As soon as each god arrived, he was announced and shown to his seat. When Yama, the Lord of Death, arrived, he happened to glance at Pushpak, and he smiled at the parrot in greeting. Seeing the Lord of Death glance at him and smile, Pushpak's heart quivered. Surely, Yama wouldn't cast a glance at him and smile without reason, Pushpak thought. It must mean that his end was near. Thinking this, the parrot began to shake in every feather. Noticing the parrot's extreme distress, the gods asked him what was wrong. 'Lord Yama has come to take my life,' Pushpak replied.

'Dear Yama, please spare Pushpak's life,' the gods requested. 'He's very dear to Indra.'

'I've no authority in such matters,' said the Lord of Death. 'Speak to Devi Destiny.'

So the gods referred the matter to Destiny.

'That's not my domain,' the devi replied. 'That's Mrityu's decision. Speak to him.'

Mrityu had not been invited to this assembly of gods, but now he was summoned. And as soon as Mrityu arrived and looked at Pushpak, he died.

'Why did you kill Indra's parrot?' the gods asked Mrityu. 'We only summoned you to question you about death.'

'You summoned me only because I had an appointment with Pushpak, here in Indra's assembly,' Mrityu responded. 'When the time comes, as it must for every living being—king or beggar, human, animal, or bird— destiny creates the cause, and the being is caught in the effect. There is no escape.'

Folktale from the Panchatantra

◆

170

THE MUSTARD SEED

Kisa Gotami was a young woman who was married to the only son of a wealthy man. Soon, she had a son of her own—a beautiful boy, who charmed everyone. But when the boy was just a toddler, he died. Gotami was stricken with grief, and in the madness of her sorrow, she clasped her dead child to her bosom and began going from house to house, asking everyone to give her medicine that would revive her son.

People looked at her with pity and shook their heads, but one Buddhist mendicant, thinking she did not understand what had happened to her child, said to her, 'My dear child, I myself don't have the medicine you seek, but I know of one who has it.'

'Please tell me who that is,' Gotami pleaded.

'The Buddha can give you medicine. Go to him,' the mendicant replied.

She went to Gautama, and, paying him homage, asked, 'Lord, do you know of any medicine that will cure my son?'

'Yes,' said the teacher. 'I do know of such a medicine.'

It was the custom that when doctors prepared medicine for the sick, the family and friends of the sick person provided the necessary herbs, so Gotami asked the Buddha what herbs he needed.

'I want some mustard seed,' Buddha replied. Gotami eagerly got up to get it, because this was a very common herb, and she knew that everyone would have it. But as she was leaving, the Buddha added, 'It must be only from that house in which no son, or husband, or sister or wife, or parent, or slave has died.'

'All right,' she said, and holding her dead child to her bosom, went into the neighbourhood to ask for a mustard seed from every house. Each house she went to had some seeds to give her, but when she asked, 'In this house has any son, or husband, or sister, or wife or parent or slave died?' the people replied, 'Lady, what are you saying? The living are few, but the dead are many.' In every house, she heard, 'I've lost a son,' or, 'We've lost our parents,' or, 'I've lost my slave.'

Finally, unable to find even a single house in which no one had died, Kisa Gotami began to realize the truth. Going into the forest, she separated her dead son from her bosom with great resolve and left his body there. Then she returned to the Buddha.

'Have you brought the mustard seed?' he asked.

'My Lord,' she replied, 'I don't have it. People tell me that the living are few, but the dead are many.'

Then the Buddha talked to her about the impermanence of all

things, till her doubts were cleared away and she understood that death is inevitable.

Buddhist parable

◆

171

RAMA IS TRAPPED IN LAKSHMANA'S DEATH

When Lakshmana died, his friends and relatives grieved for him, and then built a funeral pyre for his cremation. But when they asked Rama for Lakshmana's body, Rama grew crazed. He cursed them: 'May you yourself burn on that pyre,' he cried. 'May your fathers and mothers burn on it and also your grandfathers. You evil men. May your friends and relatives also die with you.' Then, embracing Lakshmana's body, he said to his brother, 'Come Lakshmana, let's go somewhere else—away from these heartless men.' He tried to lift his brother in his arms but almost fell under the dead weight. His friends tried to help by lending their shoulders, but he pushed them away, trying to hide Lakshmana from their eyes. Carrying the body to an inside room, he laid it down on a couch, crying plaintively, 'Wake up, Lakshmana. Why are you still sleeping, my brother? Wake up and come and take your bath.' Then he gathered his brother in his arms again and placed him on his own golden bath stool near the bath that his servants had prepared for him. He poured water on him from a golden pitcher and then, drying his body, smeared sandalwood paste on him and dressed him in silken garments and gold jewellery. After that, he ordered his servants to lay out a lavish meal of the most delicious foods and fine wines served in golden utensils. The obedient servants, never having disobeyed an order from Rama, hurried to do his bidding once again, even though their hearts were breaking at the emotional state of their lord.

When the food was laid out, Rama tried to feed Lakshmana, putting morsels into his mouth, but nothing would go in, just as the words of the Lord Jinendra don't enter the ears of someone not seeking salvation. 'Why don't you eat, dear one?' Rama said to his brother. 'You may be angry with me, but don't take that anger out on this innocent food.' And then, lifting a lotus-shaped cup of wine, he placed it against Lakshmana's lips. 'You always loved wine,' he said. 'This is the finest of wines. Why don't you drink it?' He tried to pour the wine into the mouth, but how could those lifeless lips sip the sweet liquid?

In this way, Rama, whose mind was deluded with love for his brother and who had not learned detachment from the binding relationships of worldly life, did everything for Lakshmana that one would do for a living person. He also sang for him, played him music, and then put him on his lap, affectionately kissing his head and his cheeks, cajoling him, begging him to wake up.

With Rama in this crazed state, his enemies cast their eyes on him, like dark clouds thundering and raging at the bright sun. They had been smarting from the defeat they had suffered in Lanka, and with revenge on their minds, they went to Charuratna, the son of Sunda, Ravana's nephew, and told him what they intended. Charuratna took them to Vajramali, Ravana's grandson through Indrajit and incited him by relating the events that occurred: 'Lakshmana killed my father and my uncle, and made Viradhita the king of Patala. When Rama was suffering from Sita's loss, he struck up a friendship with Sugriva and, with the help of his Vanar Sena, crossed the ocean in chariots to conquer Lanka. In the process, they destroyed many islands. Rama and Lakshmana learned the magic spells, Singhvahini and Garudavahini, and used them to capture Uncle Indrajit and other great warriors of our clan. And it was Lakshmana who obtained a Chakraratna and killed Ravana with that magic wheel. Now that same Lakshmana, who was responsible for destroying our line, is caught in the wheel of time and is dead. And that monkey army that fought us so boldly has been weakened and will be easy for us to conquer. Rama himself is stricken with a strange kind of love and grief—carrying around his brother's dead body like some crazy man. He, who once was renowned for his prowess with weapons, is now laid low because of his delusions. We should strike now. We have no one to fear.'

Vajramali, who was burning with fury at how Rama and Lakshmana had made his family suffer, summoned his ministers and commanded them to gather their armies. Joining forces with Charuratna, they marched towards Ayodhya. When the citizens of Ayodhya heard about the enemy approaching their kingdom, like a vast ocean let loose, they became fearful and tried to appeal to Rama. But Rama only clutched Lakshmana tighter in his arms, while his great bow, Vajravrata, curved like a fearsome frown on Yama's forehead, just lay there, idle.

At that moment, the thrones of two gods, Krtantavaktra and Jatayu, began to shake. Krtanta had been a leader of Rama's armies in his former birth, and Jatayu had been a vulture who had once helped Rama. Both of them had been reborn in heaven as gods. They both remembered that in their former birth they had promised Rama to come to his aid if ever he needed it. Now, using their divine vision, they saw the condition that Rama was in and the threat that the combined armies of Charuratna and Vajramali posed. 'We must help him,' they said and descended to Kosala. 'You go and confuse the enemy,' Krtanta said to Jatayu, 'while I protect Rama.'

Jatayu, who was a master shape-shifter, changed himself into a huge mountain and stood in the path of the armies. Being blocked by a mountain, the warriors turned around, only to discover that behind them was another mountain. Hedged in from both sides, they tried to retreat, but suddenly they saw before them, spreading from heaven to earth and in every direction, hundreds of Ayodhyas. The warriors were flummoxed. 'This is the doing of the gods,' they cried in fear. 'How can we fight the gods?' They desperately sought to flee, but they were trapped. Finally, Jatayu, taking pity on them, made an opening in the south, and through that the warriors fled as fast as they could.

When Vajramali, the son of Indrajit, saw how puny his forces appeared before the power of the gods, he was ashamed of his arrogance. 'How can I face my people after this defeat?' he said to Charuratna. 'What happiness can I hope for; what contentment?' At that moment, he gave up his anger and advised Vajramali to do the same, and together they renounced worldly life and became monks under the guidance of Muni Rativega.

As soon as Jatayu saw the enemy chiefs become naked ascetics, he quickly withdrew his weapons of maya and bowed before them in apology. Then he proceeded to Ayodhya to see how Krtanta had fared with Rama. Krtanta was trying to bring Rama to his senses by engaging in ludicrous activities, like watering a dead plant and churning a pot of water. Jatayu understood immediately what Krtanta was trying to do and joined him. They yoked dead oxen to ploughs; they planted seeds in a rock; they crushed sand in a crusher meant for seed and grains. Rama watched them perform these nonsensical acts for a long time; then he finally spoke,

'Foolish men. Why are you watering dead plants and planting seeds in stone and churning plain water to get butter? These will not yield what you desire. Why are you doing these useless things?'

'Why are you carrying around this body that has no life in it?' Jatayu asked him. 'What do you hope to gain? Don't you realize that your brother is gone and, by holding on to him, you yourself are doing something that is useless?'

Jatayu's words penetrated Rama's mind, like a light shining through rain clouds, and realization dawned on him; he was finally free of grief. Then he recollected the doctrine of the Jinas, and he was filled with peace. It was like he had been reborn. Human life is as fragile as a drop of water clinging to a blade of grass, he thought. I wandered from birth to birth, in hell, as an animal, as a god, and with great difficulty, I achieved this human birth, the only state in which it is possible to gain release. I was going to waste it in delusion. Wives, brothers, relatives, wealth—in the cycle of births, these come easily. True knowledge is difficult to find.

When Jatayu and Krtanta saw that Rama had awakened, they revealed themselves to him, and Rama, recognizing his companions from another birth, thanked them for coming to his aid. Then a gentle, fragrant wind blew from heaven, the sky was filled with heavenly chariots, and celestial voices sang about Rama's deeds, celebrating his past and present.

Released from the prison of his grief, Rama cremated Lakshmana's body on the banks of the Sarayu river. Then, turning to his younger brother, Shatrughana, he said, 'My brother, now you must rule over this mortal kingdom. I will retire to the forest to free my mind of earthly desires and strive for final liberation.'

Myth from the Padma Purana of Ravisena

◆

172

DEATH OF A MOSQUITO

Dressed in fashionable clothes, Mosquito went looking for a husband. Along the way, she met Bull. 'Where are you going, pretty lady?' Bull asked.

'I'm looking for a husband,' Mosquito replied.

'What do you think about me?' Bull said, puffing his masculine chest.

'What do you do?'

'I plough the field all day; I sleep in the shed all night. I eat straw and make dung and live a happy, carefree life.'

'You're not for me,' Mosquito said and went on her way. Then she met hoe, who gave her an appreciative whistle and called out. 'Hey beautiful. Where are you headed?'

'I'm out looking for a husband.'

'Will I do?' Hoe asked, pulling himself up to his full height.

'What do you do?'

'I break up soil and weed. At night I stand in one corner, and in the morning I dig into the soil and cut the weeds again. It's a pretty good life.'

'You're not for me,' said Mosquito, waving a dismissive hand. As she walked through the village, Rat darted out from one corner and would have crossed the street, but seeing her, he stopped. 'You look very beautiful today,' he said, twitching his whiskers. 'May I ask where you are going?'

'Out to find a husband.' Mosquito replied.

'Would you consider me?' Rat asked.

'What do you do?'

'I roam the world. I take what I want. I eat what I like. If you marry me, you can do the same.'

Mosquito clapped her hands in glee. 'You're the perfect man for me,' she said.

Soon Rat and Mosquito were married. They lived happily for some time. Then one summer day, on a particularly hot afternoon, Rat came home feeling very thirsty and asked Mosquito for water. Mosquito held out a cup of water for Rat, but she came a bit too close to his nose, and when Rat took one big sip of water, he accidently inhaled her. He sneezed right after, and his wife flew out of his nose. But sadly, she was dead.

Rat was devastated, but he had to do what was necessary. He built a pyre and cremated his wife, and then, as is customary, he scattered her ashes in the water tank. As a result, the water in that tank became muddy. That water tank was also used by an elephant, who came there every day to cool himself. When he saw the water, he asked the tank why it was muddy.

'Haven't you heard?' the tank asked. 'Rat's wife, Mosquito, died. He cremated her and then scattered her ashes in this water. That's why it's muddy.'

Elephant was so saddened to hear the news about Mosquito that he broke off one of his tusks and went and lay down under a palm tree.

Seeing his face all bloody, the tree asked Elephant, 'Why is your tusk broken?'

'Haven't you heard?' Elephant replied. 'Rat's wife, Mosquito, died, and Rat cremated her and sprinkled her ashes in the water tank and muddied it. I was so sad at this news that I broke my tusk.'

The tree was also very upset at the news and, as a result, it shed its leaves. A crow used sit in the branches of the tree, and when he found them bare, he asked the tree the reason. 'Haven't you heard?' the tree replied, 'Rat's wife, Mosquito, died, and Rat cremated her and sprinkled her ashes in the water tank, which muddied the water. Elephant was sad at this news and broke his tusk, and I too was so upset that I shed my leaves.'

On hearing this sad tale, the crow flew away and sat on a crumbling wall and plucked out an eye. 'Why have you plucked out your eye?' the wall asked the crow, and the crow replied: 'Haven't you heard? Rat's wife, Mosquito, died and he cremated her and sprinkled her ashes in the water tank, which muddied the water. On hearing about this misfortune, Elephant broke his tusk, and the tree shed its leaves in sympathy. When I heard about it, I plucked out my eye.' On hearing this news, the crumbling wall collapsed and was reduced to rubble.

A farmer's wife used to walk that way every day, carrying a bundle of food on her head for her husband. When she saw the wall was no more, she asked, 'You have stood here for so long. Why have you suddenly become rubble?' 'Haven't you heard?' the heap of the rubble said, 'Rat's wife, Mosquito, died. He cremated her and then sprinkled her ashes in the water tank, which muddied the water. When Elephant heard the sad news, he broke off his tusk, and when the palm tree heard, it shed its leaves. As soon as the crow heard about it, he plucked out his eyes. Then how could I remain standing? So, I fell down and became rubble.'

After hearing about this tragedy, the farmer's wife threw away her bundle of food and went home crying. When the farmer returned and asked his wife why she had not brought him his food that day, the wife began crying again and told him what had happened. 'Rat's wife,

Mosquito, died. After cremating her, he sprinkled her ashes in the water tank, making the water muddy, so Elephant asked the tank the reason, and when he learnt of the news, he was so sad that he broke off his tusk. Seeing his bloody face, the palm tree enquired what had happened, and when it found out, it shed all its leaves. Then the crow heard about it and plucked out his eye, and learning about the tragedy from the crow, the wall fell down. After all this, how can you think about food?'

'You're right,' said the husband. 'To show my sympathy, I will break my plough,' and he did. When the couple's son discovered that his father had broken his plough and was not going to work, he asked him why. The farmer then told his son the whole story about how Mosquito had died, and how Rat had muddied the water with her ashes. How Elephant had broken off his tusk in grief, and how the palm tree had shed its leaves in sympathy. How the crow had plucked out an eye, and how the wall had become rubble. 'Your mother was so sad that she threw away the food. Then how could I continue to plough my field? So I broke my plough.'

'If that is the case, Father,' said the son. 'Then how can I go to school? I, too, am in mourning.'

'What has happened is, indeed, very sad, Son,' said the farmer. 'But you still have to go school.'

Chain tale from Tamil Nadu

♦

173

AFTER THE LAST SOUL IS BORN

In seventh heaven is a luminous chamber called Guf. This is the Treasury of Souls. In this chamber are all the souls that God created in his six days of Creation, and they are all destined to be born. Here, in Guf, they are pure and immaculate—unsullied. Some souls are bright like a small sun and some flicker like a candle. When it is time for one of them to be born, the Angel Gabriel thrusts his hand into the chamber and draws out whichever soul he can catch. If it is a radiant soul, it will inhabit the body of a righteous person, and if it one whose light flickers, then the person who is born is not so fortunate.

When the soul begins to descend to earth, sparrows sing, because it is believed that they can see the soul in its descent. Angel Lailah guards this soul as it enters a human womb, and, stripped of its heavenly clothing, acquires garments of skin, flesh, and bones. When this soul completes its earthly life, the Angel of Death will come and remove its corporeal garb and restore its heavenly garments. The soul will then rejoice and fly up to God's Throne of Glory.

Some believe that the Guf contains an infinite number of souls, but others know that the number is finite, and when the last soul descends to earth, the Guf will be empty. Then an infant will be born on earth without a soul—born dead, and no sparrows will sing. The Messiah will then come, and it will be the beginning of the end of the world.

Myth from the Talmud

♦

174

CYCLES OF GREAT TIME

Prior to our Creation, there were thousands, and after our Creation, there will be thousands more. Each Creation ends with an apocalypse and then a new Creation begins again with the same gods, same events, and same worlds.

In the cycle of Great Time, there are four yugas supported by the cosmic cow. In each yuga, as virtue declines, the cow lifts one leg. In the first yuga—Krita—she stands on all four hooves. For seventeen lakh, twenty-eight thousand years men are born virtuous, they live virtuous lives, their minds naturally inclined to dharma order. Then a quarter of dharma decays, and Great Time shifts into Treta Yuga, in which men have to deliberately fix their minds on their dharmic duties. The cosmic cow now stands on three hooves for twelve lakh, ninety-six thousand years. The next yuga, Dwapara, is a precarious balance of dharma and adharma, and the dharma cow balances on two hooves for eight lakh, sixty-four thousand years. One half of virtue is irrevocably lost, and people pursue desires with passion, but they also recognize true virtue. And then, finally, Kali Yuga sets in. In this dark yuga full of ignorance, material wealth is the source of all virtue, passion dictates relationships, and falsehoods are the source of success. This yuga lasts only four lakh, thirty-two thousand years, because it is fast decaying, and the cosmic cow totters on only one hoof.

When dharma is completely depleted, the cycle of four yugas comes to an end. These four together are one Maha Yuga, which consists of forty-three lakh, and twenty-thousand human years. Then, creation returns to a state of non-differentiation and rests for one whole Maha Yuga. Brahma's day consists of one thousand Maha Yugas; this is called a kalpa, and it is four hundred, thirty-two crore years long. After being awake for one kalpa, Brahma sleeps for the next kalpa, and as he sleeps, all of Creation rests. Each year of Brahma has three hundred and sixty days and three hundred and sixty nights, and Brahma lives for one hundred years, which is three hundred and eleven lakh crore trillion human years.

When Brahma's lifetime ends, Vishnu, in the form of Rudra, permeates the seven rays of the sun. He drinks up all the water in all the worlds and ignites all that has become arid, burning everything mobile and immobile. This apocalyptic fire burns for one hundred Brahma years. Then, from his breath, Rudra produces variegated coloured clouds that fill up the sky and pour down rain, which roars through the flames and extinguishes the fires. It rains for one hundred Brahma years, and the worlds are flooded.

When the waters come to rest, a single ocean covers the three worlds for an equivalent amount of time. Then Vishnu, reclining on Shesha Naag in the primordial ocean, awakens. He blows out a breath from his mouth, which drives away the clouds. Then a lotus grows out of his navel, and in this thousand-petalled lotus, Brahma, the Creator, is born again, and he begins the act of another Creation.

Myth from the Puranas

◆

175

AL QIYAMAH

In the Name of Allah, the Compassionate, the Merciful

Does man think We shall never put his bones together again? Indeed, We can remould his very fingers.

Yet man denies what is to come. 'When will this be,' he asks, 'this Day of Resurrection?'

When the sight of mortals is confounded and the moon is eclipsed; when the sun and moon are brought together—on that day, man will ask: 'Where shall I flee?'

There will be no refuge. For, on that day, all will return to the Lord. On that day, man will be told of all his deeds, from first to last, and man will bear witness against himself, even though he will plead with excuses. Yet people love this fleeting life and are heedless of the hereafter. On that day, there will be joyous faces, looking towards their Lord. On that day, there will be mournful faces, dreading some great affliction.

When a man's soul is about to leave him and those around him cry,

'Who will save him?' When he knows it is the final parting and the pangs of death assail him—on that day he will be sent to the Lord. In this life, man neither believed nor prayed; he denied the truth and, turning his back, went to his kinsfolk, elated with pride. Thus, he has deserved this doom, he has deserved it well.

Does man think he will be left alone—not accountable? Was he not just a drop of ejaculated semen? Did Allah not make him a clot of blood and form and mould him, and give him male and female parts?

Do you doubt His power, then, to raise the dead to life?

Myth from the Holy Quran

◆

176

FRASHEGIRD: MAKING WONDERFUL

Zaratosht asked Ohrmazd, 'Will bodily creatures, who have passed away on earth, receive their bodies back at the final rehabilitation or will they become like shadows?'

Ohrmazd replied, 'They shall receive their bodies back and shall rise again.'

And Zaratosht asked, 'He who has passed away is torn apart by dog and bird and carried off by wolf and vulture. How will his body parts come together again?'

Ohrmazd's response to him was, 'If you had to make a wooden casket, would it be easier to make it if you had no wood and had to cut and fit it, or would it be easier if you had a casket whose parts were separated and you had to fit it together again?'

Zaratosht replied, 'If I had a branch of wood, it would be easier than if I had no wood; and if I had a casket with separate parts, it would be easier.'

Ohrmazd said, 'When those creations were non-existent, I had the power to fashion them; and now when they have existed and are scattered everywhere, it is easier to fit them together again. I have five storekeepers who receive the bodily substance of those who have passed away. One is the earth, which keeps the flesh and bone and sinews of men; one is the water, which keeps the blood; then there are the plants, which preserve the hair of head and body; there is also the light of the sky, which receives the fire; and the last is the wind, which holds and then returns the spirit of my creatures at the time of rehabilitation.

I call upon the earth and ask of it the bone and flesh and sinews of Gayomard, the first man, and the others that followed. The earth says to me, 'How shall I bring them, for I don't know which is the bone, flesh, and sinews of one, and which parts belong to another.'

Then I call upon the water and say, 'Bring forth the blood of those men who are dead.' And water responds, 'How shall I bring it, for I don't know which is the blood of one and which of the other?'

Then I call the plants and ask them for the hair of the dead. The plants say to me, 'How shall we bring it, for we don't know which is the hair of one and which of the other?'

Finally, I call upon the wind and ask him for the spirit of those men who are dead. Wind says, 'How shall I bring it, for I know not which is the spirit of one and which of the other?'

When I, who am Ohrmazd, look down upon the earth, water, plants, light, and wind, in my clear sight I know one from the other; for in my omniscience and clear thought, I can distinguish them as man can distinguish his thirty horses, who each have a unique caparison. I will send Airyaman, the Messenger, whose duty it is to fulfil the end. He will bring the bone and blood and hair and light and spirit, and I will put them together.

Myth from the Selections of Zadspram

◆

177

WE LIVE MANY LIVES

A Brahmin was very curious to know what happens to a person after he dies, and how he is reborn. To acquire this knowledge, he did years of tapasya and, finally, the gods agreed to provide him a glimpse into how we live many lives.

One morning when he went to the river to bathe, his spirit left him and entered the body of a cobbler's baby that was just being born. The child grew up, learned his family's trade, got married and had many children. Then, one day, he had a strange feeling that he was not of low caste but a Brahmin, and this disturbed him so much that he abandoned the life he was living and went away to another country.

In this country, the king had just died without an heir, and the ministers were following the customary practice to elect a successor: an elephant and a hawk were sent out into the kingdom, and whomever the two royal animals honoured, that person was crowned king. It so happened that when the elephant saw the Brahmin cobbler, he immediately lifted his trunk and trumpeted, and the hawk, too, came and perched on his right hand. And the people of the kingdom, who had gathered at the site, proclaimed him king.

He ruled for many years and lived a king's life of luxury. Then, one day, his cobbler wife, who had been searching for her husband all these years, discovered his whereabouts and his good fortune, and came to live with him. But her arrival revealed to the people of the kingdom the secret of his low caste. They were outraged. How could a cobbler of the lowest caste be their king? All those who were dvija—twice born through the thread ceremony—began to protest; some started elaborate cleansing rituals and, others, feeling polluted, jumped into the flames to purify themselves. And the king, unable to bear the public shame, threw himself into a fire.

As his cobbler's body burned, his spirit departed and re-entered his Brahmin's body, that was still lying on the river bank. Gaining consciousness, the Brahmin got up and went home. When his wife saw him, she was quite surprised. 'You finished your bath and your morning prayers very quickly today,' she said. 'You've been gone just a few minutes.'

'Only a few minutes?' the Brahmin repeated the words in his mind, incredulous. Is this what happens after death, he thought? Is this how a person is reborn? But then he wondered, did this really happen, or was it all a dream?

A week later, a man came to the Brahmin's house, begging for food. 'I haven't eaten in five days,' he said. 'I've fled my country, because without realizing it, we made a low-caste man our king, and now everyone is either fleeing the country or choosing death to escape the evil that might befall the kingdom.'

How can such things be? the Brahmin thought. I lived as a cobbler and raised a family for years, and then reigned as king for several years. Just when I was convinced that it was all a dream, this man arrives at my house and confirms the truth of these happenings. Yet my wife says, I haven't been absent from the house for long, and I believe her because she doesn't look a day older, nor is the place changed in any way. Maybe the soul passes through various stages of existence, according to a man's thoughts and words and acts, and in the great hereafter, time is measured differently: in that time, a day is equal to a yuga and a yuga is equal to a day.'

Folktale from Kashmir

◆

178

VISHNU IS CURSED TO BE REBORN ON EARTH

During a battle with the devas, the asuras were getting massacred. Terrified of being completely wiped out, they begged their guru, Shukracharya for help. But Shukra himself was powerless. 'My mantras are useless before Vishnu,' he told them. 'I need help. Let me go to Mahadeva and acquire the Shakti mantra. Wait for me,' he said to the asuras. 'I'll return as soon as possible. In the meantime, don't start any new battles. In fact, go to the devas and pretend that you want a reconciliation.'

The asuras, dressed in ascetic bark, went to the gods and told them that they had set aside their weapons and were taking up asceticism. 'We are seeking peace,' they said. The sceptical gods, not quite trusting the asuras, hesitantly agreed on peace. The asuras then went to Rishi Kashyapa's ashram and made a show of practising meditation. In reality, they needed a safe place to wait until Shukra returned.

In the meantime, Shukracharya went to Mount Kailash and petitioned Mahadeva.

'What can I do for you?' Shiva asked the guru of the asuras.

'Please give me the Shakti mantra so that I can help the asuras defeat the devas. Brihaspati, my opponent—the guru of the devas—doesn't have the knowledge of this weapon, so he won't be able to counter it when the asuras use it on the devas.'

The all-knowing Shiva was in a dilemma. He didn't want the devas to be defeated, but Shukra had come to him as a petitioner, and he couldn't refuse him. So he thought of a plan to deter Shukra. 'To acquire such a mantra, you'll need to do very difficult tapasya,' he said to Shukra. 'You need to stand on your head and inhale the smoke of burnt husk for one thousand years.' Mahadeva thought that Shukracharya, who was already an evolved rishi, would find this task beneath him and refuse, which would then be justification for him to deny him the mantra. But to his surprise, Shukracharya agreed to the penance and began a thousand years arduous tapasya of standing on his head and breathing in burnt husk.

When the devas heard that Shukra was engaged in austerities to empower the asuras, they picked up their weapons again and marched to Kashyapa's ashram. But the asuras faced them with humility. 'Why have you armed yourselves against us?' they asked. 'We told you that we've renounced fighting. You know the rules of war. When the enemy has given up weapons, you can't threaten them, as you're doing right now.'

'Liars!' the devas shouted. 'Don't pretend. We know what you're up to. We know you sent Shukracharya to Mahadeva to acquire the Shakti mantra. You can't deceive us. Get ready for war!' they challenged. But the asuras were in no position to take up the challenge. They fled the place and took refuge with Shukracharya's mother.

'I'll protect you,' she promised. 'You have nothing to fear in my hermitage.'

The devas followed the asuras to the hermitage and formed battle lines outside. The mother of Shukra warned the devas that the asuras were under her protection and they were not to shoot a single arrow, but the devas ignored her and began to slay the weaponless asuras. Shukra's mother was furious. 'Stop this instant,' she warned again. 'Or with the fire of my tapas, I'll put all of you to sleep.' And when the devas did not desist, she summoned Goddess Nidra (sleep) and sent her to overpower the minds of the gods, who instantly fell on the ground, senseless.

When Vishnu arrived on the scene and saw Indra and the other gods stupefied by sleep, he nudged Indra awake. 'Come into my body,' he whispered to him, and Indra, leaving his sleeping body on the ground, came awake in Vishnu's body. Shukra's mother, who was watching the sleeping gods with satisfaction, saw Indra's body suddenly become still, and beside it, Vishnu's dwarf form drawing himself tall to match Indra's height. She immediately knew what had happened and cast a spell that stupefied both Vishnu and Indra.

Shaking his head to throw off the daze, Indra implored Vishnu, 'Just kill the woman before she does any more harm to the devas. It appears that her tapas is so powerful, it surpasses even your strength.' And Vishnu, calling his trusted, last resort weapon, Sudarshana Chakra, hurled it at Shukra's mother, cutting off her head. As soon as the old woman's life left her body, the spell that had confounded the gods broke.

The devas revived, but on seeing the decapitated body of Shukra's mother, they became afraid. Bhrigu, Shukra's father, was famous for his wrath; he would undoubtedly seek revenge for the murder of his wife. And sure enough, when Bhrigu saw his wife's dead body and learned that Vishnu was responsible, his anger thundered in the three worlds, 'O Vishnu!' he shouted. 'You have done an extremely sinful thing. You murdered a woman who was not just a Brahmin's daughter but also a mother who was protecting those who came to her refuge. Being who you are, you should be ashamed of your actions. Because you have acted with tamas—the deep ignorance that pervades beings on earth—I curse you to become that being. Just like they are born and reborn in consequence to their tamasic actions, so will you be born and re-born on earth in different wombs, suffering the pain of rebirth.' Then, taking his wife's severed head and placing it on the body, Bhrigu sprinkled cold water on it and charged it with his mantras, making her whole again.

From that time on, Vishnu, trapped in samsara—the cycle of birth and re-birth—has been re-incarnating in this human world, like any other human being.

Myth from the Puranas

♦

179

DEATH AND REBIRTH OF GANESHA

Parvati created a boy from the dirt of her body. He was handsome in every way and full of strength and valour. When he was created, she said to him, 'You are my son.'

'Mother,' said the boy. 'What is your order? Command me.'

'Be my gatekeeper,' Parvati told him. 'Don't let anyone inside my rooms without my permission.' She also gave him a club to help him with his duty. Then, kissing him and embracing him, she left him at the door and went inside to take a bath.

Soon Shiva arrived and tried to go inside to his wife, but he found his way blocked by a boy. 'You can't go in without my mother's permission,' the boy declared. 'My mother is taking a bath.'

'Who is your mother?'

'Parvati.'

'Foolish boy. Parvati is my wife and she has no son. Who are you?'

'I'm her son, and I have been commanded by my mother to not let anyone inside.'

'You can't stop me from going inside. Don't you know who I am? I'm Shiva,' he said and tried to push the boy aside, but the boy took up his club and struck Shiva.

Shiva was infuriated. 'You obviously have no idea who I am. I'm Parvati's husband. Now stand aside and let me go to my wife.' But when he tried once again to enter forcibly, the boy beat him with the club again. Fuming with anger, Shiva called his attendant ganas and told them to deal with the boy at the door. Going up to the son of Parvati, the ganas mocked him and jeered at him. 'We are Shiva's ganas,' they said proudly. 'Who are you, you oversized boy?' 'I am my mother's gana,' the boy replied, 'And I'm guarding her door.' Then they fought with him, but he beat them all. Broken-boned and in pain, they returned to Shiva. 'He's too strong,' they said. 'We can't subdue him.'

'You are a useless bunch,' Shiva derided his ganas. 'What good are you if you can't even defeat a little boy.' Then Shiva decided to go to Brahma and let him figure out a solution. 'There's a boy at the door to my wife's rooms,' he complained to Brahma. 'He won't let me enter my own house. He's also brought down all my ganas. He needs to be brought under control and only you can do it.'

'I've tried already,' Brahma replied. 'Every being in that vicinity had been complaining about the boy, so I went to check. When I approached him to ask him who he was, he plucked my beard and then took up his club. I'm a Brahmin. I can't fight with him, so I came away, but even as I was leaving, he seized his club and destroyed my attendants. I had to run away to save my own life.'

'This is ridiculous,' Shiva declared. 'We can't manage a pesky little boy?' Then thinking that perhaps the other gods would know how to deal with this, Shiva went to Indra and Vishnu and apprised them of the situation. 'He has to be destroyed,' he said, and they agreed. 'Such opposition is dangerous for our existence.' Then they called all the gods and, joining forces, the gods advanced towards Mount Kailash, certain that the battle would be swift and painless.

When Parvati heard that the entire army of gods was headed towards her son, she became furious and called her two Shaktis, Kali and Durga, to assist her son. Kali assumed a terrible form, opening her mouth wide like a cavern inside a mountain, and Durga became lightning, and with their many arms, they began to fight the armies of the gods, alongside the boy, who repelled every weapon with his club. In no time at all, the gods lay helplessly on the ground, groaning in pain. Then Vishnu faced the boy, and the two Shaktis entered the boy's body, so that they could fight Narayana as one. Soon Vishnu, too, was defeated.

Finally, Shiva took up his trident and hurled it at his young foe. Infused with the Shaktis, the boy thought of his mother's lotus feet, and bowing before her in his mind, struck the hand that was holding the trident, and the weapon flew out of Shiva's hand. In the meantime, Vishnu once again engaged the enemy in combat, and, this time, when the boy threw his club at Vishnu, Garuda, Vishnu's loyal attendant, caught the club in his massive beak and shattered it. This was the opportunity Shiva was seeking. He grabbed his trident again and cut off the head of Parvati's son. And the boy fell to the ground like a great mountain.

On hearing that her son had been killed, Parvati first fell down lamenting, but then she thought of how all the gods and the hosts of her husband's ganas had banded together to fight with her son, who was just a boy, and her lamentation turned to fury. 'I'll destroy them all,' she roared, getting up, her eyes flashing with rage. In a moment, she created hundreds and thousands of Shaktis and commanded them to create a great fire, and that flaming deluge swept through the celestial forces, burning everything in its path.

'Is this dissolution?' the gods yelled in panic. 'Is this the end of time?' They all fled to Brahma. 'How can this deluge of fire be stopped?'

'This is the fury of the Goddess,' Brahma said. 'Only when she is appeased will this cease. Let me go to her in peace and beg her to show us a way.' Brahma then came to Parvati and, with great humility, propitiated her. 'You are Mother. You are the primordial Shakti. You are the cause of creation and of dissolution. Be at peace, Great Mother. Let your fury subside.' Then all the sages, who had also accompanied Brahma, bowed at her lotus feet and begged forgiveness. 'What can we do to appease your anger?'

'Restore my son's life,' she thundered. 'Only then will I be appeased.'

When the sages reported this to Shiva, he was penitent, but he could see no way to revive the boy. This may by the end, he thought. The Goddess will not be appeased, and her wrath will destroy everything. But then a thought came to his mind—a means to save the boy. It would birth a new god but perhaps that would be most beneficial for the three worlds. 'Go towards the north,' he told the gods. 'And bring back the head of the first being you see. I'll place it on the boy's body and restore his life.'

They laid out the boy's headless body on the ground and washed it with holy water. Then they went north. The first being they met was an elephant with a single tusk. Killing him, they brought his head back and gave it to Shiva, who fitted it above the boy's shoulders. All the sages then recited Vedic mantras and anointed his body with holy water, while Shiva meditated and restored the boy's consciousness. He woke up, as though from a long, refreshing sleep. Ruddy and handsome, with an elephant's head, he looked at everyone with peace.

A wave of jubilation spread though the gathering. Parvati, too, was delighted to see her son brought back to life. She took him in her arms, and, sitting down with him in her lap, smeared his forehead with auspicious vermilion. 'Be blessed,' she said. 'And be a blessing to everyone. You will be worshipped before all the other gods and will remove everyone's distress.' Shiva placed his hand on the boy's head and said, 'You are my son. From today, you will be the leader of my gana and everyone will call you Ganesha.'

Myth from the Puranas

◆

180

THE QUEEN WHO BECAME A DUNG BEETLE

Once upon a time, there was a king called Assaka who reigned in Potali, which is a city in the kingdom of Kasi. His queen consort, Ubbari, was very dear to him. She was charming and graceful and beautiful, though not as beautiful as a goddess. But she died, and the king plunged into a sea of grief. He had Ubbari's body embalmed with oil and ointment and laid out in a satin-lined coffin. Then he himself lay down on the floor beside the coffin and refused to leave its side. He also refused to eat or sleep and just lay there weeping and wailing. His parents and kinsfolk, friends and courtiers, priests and laymen begged him not to grieve so much. 'All things pass away,' they said to him. 'Even loved ones. You must accept that.' But the king was not willing to listen to anyone. Seven days passed, and yet he lay on the floor beside his dead wife.

At that time, the Bodhisattva was an ascetic, and he lived at the foot of the Himalayas. One day, as he looked around the region with his heavenly vision, he saw this sorrowful king and decided to help him. By his miraculous power, he rose in the air and, alighting in the king's park, sat down on the ceremonial stone, like a golden image. A young Brahmin, entering the park, greeted the ascetic and went and sat beside him. Soon, the Bodhisattva began to talk pleasantly with him. 'Is the king a just ruler?' he asked.

'Yes, the king is just,' replied the youth, 'but his queen has just died. He has laid her body in a coffin, and he himself has been lying beside her coffin for seven days, lamenting. Why do you not free the king from this great sorrow? Virtuous beings like you ought to help the king overcome his grief.'

'I don't know the king, young man,' said the Bodhisattva. 'But if he were to come and ask me, I would tell him the place where his former wife has become flesh again and get her speak to him.'

'Then, holy sir, wait here until I bring the king to you,' said the youth.

The Bodhisattva agreed, and the young Brahmin rushed to fetch the king, 'He has divine sight,' he said to the king, informing him about the ascetic. 'He says he'll show you where your queen has taken birth again and even make her speak to you.'

The king was overjoyed at the thought of seeing Ubbari again and, quickly getting into his chariot, drove to the park, where he greeted the ascetic and sat down beside him. 'Is it true that you know where my queen has been born again?' he asked.

'Yes, I do,' the Bodhisattva replied.

'Where is she?' the king asked excitedly.

'O king, she was intoxicated with her beauty and not virtuous—and now, as a consequence, she has become a dung beetle in this very park.'

'I don't believe you.' The king became angry. 'My Ubbari cannot have become a dung-beetle. How is that possible?'

'Then I'll show her to you and make her speak,' answered the Bodhisattva. And in a commanding voice, he said, 'Let the two that are busy rolling a lump of cow-dung, come forth before the king.'

By his power, two dung beetles crawled out from under a ball of dung and drew near to the stone seat where the king and ascetic were sitting. The Bodhisattva then pointed one out to the king. 'There is your queen, Ubbari, O king. She now lives with her husband, who is also a dung-beetle. Look!'

'I don't believe it,' cried the king.

'I'll make her speak!' Then the Bodhisattva gave the dung-beetle speech. 'Ubbari!' he called.

'What is it, holy sir?' she asked in a human voice.

'What was your name in your former birth?'

'My name was Ubbari,' she replied, 'I was the consort of King Assaka.'

'Tell me,' the Bodhisattva went on, 'who do you love best now—King Assaka or this dung-beetle?'

'Oh sir, that was my former birth,' she said. 'Then I lived with the king, enjoying shape and sound, scent, taste and touch; but now my memory is confused by rebirth. Now, if I had to, I would kill King Assaka, and with his blood, smear the feet of my husband the dung-beetle.' Then she uttered this verse in a human voice:

> Once with my beloved husband, Assaka, the great king
> I walked in this garden in summer and in spring.
> But now new sorrows and new joys have replaced the old,
> And it is the love of my dung-beetle I uphold.

When King Assaka heard this, he realized the truth. Returning to the palace, he had the queen's body removed and then took a purifying bath. He began ruling with righteousness and, some time later, married another queen.

The Bodhisattva, having instructed the king, and having set him free from sorrow, returned again to the Himalayas.

Folktale from the Jatakas

◆

181

JARATKARU WEDS JARATKARU

There was a celibate Brahmin named Jaratkaru. He was from a tribe of nomad Brahmins called Yayavara, who were bound by the tradition of their tribe to roam the world and sleep wherever night overtook them. Jaratkaru was an austere Brahmin, rigidly controlled in his habits and celibacy. All his life, he had practised innumerable vows of not sleeping, not eating, subsisting only on air, and yoking his sexual energy to empower his mind. He believed that by living in this way, he was guarding against the dictates of his name, which means 'great decay' (jara means decay, and karu means great). Then, one day, during his wanderings, Jaratkaru came upon a community of souls who were hanging by their feet from a viran rope. Their heads were in a hole and their feet were pointing up towards the sky. But the rope on which they were hanging was being gnawed by rats that lived near the hole.

'Who are you with you heads hanging down and your feet pointing up?' Jaratkaru asked the souls.

'We are Brahmins of the Yayavara clan,' they told Jaratkaru.

Jaratkaru was shocked to hear his clan's name and realized that these were his ancestors. He bowed in reverence before them and then asked urgently: 'Do you know that the viran rope on which you hang is being gnawed by rats?'

'Yes, we are aware that the viran rope from which we hang is being gnawed by rats. When the rope is chewed through, we will sink into the ground,' his ancestors stated.

'Then why do you hang here among these rats?' Jaratkaru asked.

'We have no choice,' they told him. 'We have no progeny. These rats are extinction, and this viran rope is time. We have a son called Jaratkaru, and he, wretch that he is, is causing the decay of our clan by choosing to become a celibate ascetic.'

Jaratkaru's throat went dry. 'But why are you hanging upside down?' he asked. 'What's the meaning of that?'

'We are sinners,' they replied. 'Jaratkaru makes us sinners, because even though we have the means to save our clan, it is as though we have no means. Only those who have offspring to carry on their name can be upright in the world. Because Jaratkaru is the last of our clan, our line will end with him. That is why we are sinking into the ground, head first. But who are you, young man?' they asked. 'Why has your face become pale on hearing our story?'

'I am that Jaratkaru. And you are my ancestors,' Jaratkaru told them. 'But I'm not a wretch. I've taken the vow of celibacy to gain merit in the world. I'm a Brahmin with rigorous control. Is that not insurance against decay? Is that not worthy of praise?'

'O son,' the ancestors said. 'The merit of penances and asceticism is no match to the excellent merit of being a father, of bearing offspring who will bear your name and carry on your line. Death is inevitable for everyone; the only insurance against it is offspring. The greatest merit in the world is to *be*.'

Jaratkaru hung his head in shame. 'O ancestors of my clan, it seems that I may have wronged you. Please advise me on what I should do so that I may right the wrong.'

'Take a wife,' they immediately responded. 'Bear children. Live in the world and live on through your offspring.'

'I'll do it,' Jaratkaru declared. 'But for you—my ancestors. Not for myself. For myself, I must live by the vows I've sworn to keep. That's why I'll marry only if my three conditions are met: I'll only marry a girl whose name is the same as mine, who is given to me willingly in alms by her relatives, and I will never be responsible for her food and shelter. If such a girl can be found, I'll marry her and have offspring to fulfil my obligation to you so that your souls can become upright and you can go to heaven. That'll be the only purpose of my taking a wife.'

Kadru, the mother of snakes, deeply desired a daughter, so, one day, in play, she sculpted a statue of a little snake girl. It so happened that

Shiva, in libidinous overabundance, sprayed Kadru's little snake girl statue with his semen, and she became a living, breathing snake girl.

And so, Kadru had a real daughter, and she named her Manasa, because she was the creation of her own mind.

One day, many years later, when Manasa had become a beautiful woman, Shiva saw her and was sexually attracted to her. But she informed him that she was his daughter; hence, he took her home to take care of her. Chandi, Shiva's wife, thought Shiva was having an affair with the girl and, in a fit of jealousy, she burnt one of Manasa's eyes to make her ugly. To appease Chandi's wrath and to ensure that the angry goddess would not harm Manasa anymore, Shiva abandoned the young snake woman. Kadru brought her daughter back home again, and her oldest son, the snake king, Vasuki, adopted her as his sister. He also changed her name from Manasa to Jaratkaru, because she had begun to decay from the eye downwards.

At this time, the snake clan was also threatened by extinction, because Kadru had cursed her sons that they would all burn in a sacrifice organized by King Parikshit of the Kuru clan. However, Brahma had lessened the curse by stating that the offspring of Vasuki's sister, Jaratkaru, would save the snakes. Now Vasuki was anxiously searching for a suitable groom for his sister so that she could birth the saviour of the snake clan.

Many more years passed. Jaratkaru, the Brahmin from the Yayavara tribe, unaware that there was a namesake bride being readied for him, became old and weary, roaming the world, begging for a bride to pay his debt to his ancestors. He had almost given up hope, when one day he arrived in Bhogavati, Vasuki's kingdom, and standing at the gates of the palace like a beggar, called, 'Does any creature have a maiden daughter to bestow on me as bride? She must bear my name, must be given to me as a gift, and must not expect me to provide her with food and shelter.'

Vasuki had been anxiously awaiting this moment. He quickly had his sister decked out in bridal silks and gold and rushed her out of the palace to the gates.

'O Brahmin, I give you my sister, Jaratkaru, as a gift,' Vasuki said to Jaratkaru, the Yayavara.

'Jaratkaru? Is her name really Jaratkaru? And do you give her to me in alms?'

'I do. I gift her to you,' Vasuki assured him.

'I'm poor and a Yayavara,' Jaratkaru warned. 'You are a king. Your sister is used to living in luxury. You have fulfiled two of my conditions, but you may not have heard my third condition: I will not provide her with with food and shelter.'

'I heard you,' Vasuki replied. 'Don't worry. I'll take care of that. You don't have to provide her a thing. I'll give her a house and fulfil her every need, except, of course, her wifely one, which you, as her husband, must fulfil.'

'Good. Good,' Jaratkaru responded. 'But I have one more condition, and this is for you,' he said to Jaratkaru, his soon-to-be-wife. 'I'm a Brahmin of strict vows. If you do anything displeasing to me, I'll leave you.'

Jaratkaru, the snake maiden, nodded.

'Wah! It is all settled then,' Vasuki said, rubbing his hands in relief. 'Let's prepare for the wedding ceremony.'

And so the Jaratkarus began to live, not quite happily, in the house that Vasuki gifted to his sister. Jaratkaru was an assiduous Brahmin, painstaking in his duties and vows. He repeatedly reminded his wife that if she did anything at all to displease him, he would leave her, and she, doubly honour-bound to her husband and to her brother, served her husband with the alertness of a dog, timidity of a deer, and instinct of a crow.

One evening, returning from a day of toil, Jaratkaru lay down with his head in his wife's lap and fell asleep. While he was snoring away, the sun began to climb into the western mountains. Now Jaratkaru was in a quandary: should she wake her husband up so that he could perform his evening prayers and light the evening fires, or should she let him sleep? She was afraid that if she woke him, he would be angry at being disturbed, but if she let him sleep, he would be angry that she hadn't woken him in time for his evening rituals. He was a man of rigid vows, after all. So Jaratkaru softly pressed her husband's shoulder and whispered as sweetly and lovingly as she could: 'O dear husband, O illustrious rishi of rigid vows and great penances, wake up, please. Suryadeva has reached the western sky. Wake up and touch water to your beauteous face, and perform your elevating prayers.' When her husband didn't stir, she pressed slightly harder on his shoulder. Jaratkaru woke up suddenly and looked at her with a disoriented gaze. 'O great one, I woke you only because the Lord of the evening has spread in the sky, and your prayers...' she began to say, but her husband interrupted her. 'What? You dare tell me what my duties are?' he hissed, his lips twitching in rage. 'I tell you that even the sun will not set if I remain sleeping. You have insulted me, O snake, and now I must leave you.'

'Oh, please, no!' Jaratkaru was distraught. 'Please believe me, Oh elevated one. I didn't intend to insult you. I bow to you in subjugation. Punish me if you will but don't leave me. What will I tell my brother? The continuance of our race depends on me...on you.'

'Leave you I must, for a Brahmin of my merit can't stay with someone who has insulted him.'

'No. No. Please. I did not...I honour you above all else. You can't leave me. I must...conceive...our child...' Jaratkaru was frantic, but her husband raised his hand to stop her and said: 'Is there!'

After her husband left, Jaratkaru rushed to her brother and fell into his arms. 'It wasn't my fault,' she wept. 'I didn't know what to do, and now he has left...I'm so sorry, dear brother.'

Vasuki's heart stopped. For a minute he couldn't think and just held his sister. Finally, he asked in a quaking voice, 'Are you...it's not my place to ask, I know...forgive me...it's not proper... but I must ask... have you...by any chance...are you...?'

'We were husband and wife in every way, and before he left, when I said to my husband, 'our child...,' he replied, 'Is there."

'Is there? Is there! That means...does it mean...? How does he know?' Vasuki glanced anxiously at his sister's middle and then averted his eyes in embarrassment. 'You show no signs.'

'My husband is a Brahmin of the highest virtue,' Jaratkaru said. 'He knows, and he never lies. Believe it, dear brother. My child is there!'

Hence, when Jaratkaru and Jaratkaru's son was born, that is what he was called—'Is there'—Astika—and so he rescued both the Yayavara Brahmins and the snake clan from extinction.[62]

Myth from the Mahabharata

◆

PART FOUR
———————————
The Lotus

182

ILLUSIONS OF BONDAGE: A CHILDREN'S STORY

A little boy asked his dhai-ma for a story and she told him the following tale of three non-existent princes:

Once upon a time in a city which did not exist, there were three brave princes, two of whom were unborn and the third had yet to be conceived. The princes, desiring to gain new experiences, left their city. The path was sandy and the sun was hot. Not able to bear the heat, they looked for shade and found three trees, two of which did not exist and the third had yet to be planted. They rested under the trees for a while, ate the fruit of the tree, and then moved on. Soon they reached the banks of three rivers, two of which were dry and the third had no water. They stripped their dusty clothes and plunged into the cool water in which they quenched their thirst and refreshed their bodies. Proceeding further, they came to a large, well-planned city, which was yet to be built. In the city they came upon three beautiful palaces, two of which had not been built and the third had no walls. Entering the palaces, they found three golden plates, two of which had been broken into two and the third had been completely smashed. In the plate that had been smashed, they placed ninety-nine minus one hundred grams of rice and cooked it. To sanctify this meal, they shared it with three guest Brahmins, two of whom had no body and the third had no mouth. After the holy men were fed, the princes ate the leftover rice and felt content and full of joy.

'My son,' dhai-ma said to the little boy, 'Always remember this story and you'll grow up to be a very learned man.'

The little boy liked the story very much.

Myth from the Yoga Vasishtha

◆

183

NACHIKETA: CONVERSATIONS WITH DEATH

There was a wealthy sage, Vajashravas, whose charity had earned him great fame. Once he held a Vishvajit sacrifice, in which one is required to give away all of one's possessions. He was in the process of distributing all his material possessions among Brahmins, when his young son, Nachiketa, asked him, 'To whom will you give me away, Father?' He was young, but he had the wisdom of sages. He felt that what his father was giving away was not true charity; genuine giving had to be of the self, so to help make his father's sacrifice truly successful, the boy was offering himself. But busy with the procedures of the sacrifice, Vajashravas ignored his son. Nachiketa asked the question again: 'To whom will you give me away, Father?' And when he still did not get a response, he shook his father's arm and repeated the words, 'Tell me, Father. To whom will you give me away?' Annoyed at being disturbed, Vajashravas snapped, 'I give you to Death.'

Instantly, Nachiketa was sent to Yama's abode. But the Lord of Death had not been expecting the boy and was away from Yamaloka. For three nights, Nachiketa remained unattended, without food or water. When Yama returned, his wife and ministers informed him about the boy who had arrived in Yamaloka three nights ago. 'He's still alive,' they told him. 'He says he has been given to you by his father.'

Yama welcomed Nachiketa as a guest and apologized for keeping him waiting. 'For three nights you have been in my house without food. Ask me for a boon for each of the three nights.'

'Let my father be free of anxiety,' Nachiketa requested. 'He's anxious, because I gave myself to Death. Let him not be angry at me, and when you release me, and I go back to him, may he recognize me. This is the first boon I ask,' Nachiketa said.

'When he recognizes you and sees you freed from the jaws of death, he'll be free of anger.' Yama promised. 'What would you like as your second boon?'

'In heaven there is no fear, because you don't hold sway there. Also age doesn't frighten anyone there. In heaven one is beyond hunger and thirst and sorrow; there's only happiness. In heaven people are immortal.

I have heard that you have knowledge of that Agni which people worship to get to heaven. Reveal that Agni to me.'

'I do know that Agni which leads people to heaven and to infinite worlds, and I'll reveal it to you. Know that this Agni lives in a secret place—in the intellect of the wise.' Then Yama revealed the secret of that Agni and of the sacrifice and taught Nachiketa about the accuracy of a fire altar. Nachiketa repeated that knowledge back to him, and Yama was so pleased with the disciple that he gave him a gift. 'This Agni that I have revealed to you will henceforth be called by your name—Nachiketa-Agni.' And to add to that, he gave Nachiketa a jewelled necklace of varied form and hue, which represented the various pious acts that one performs to go to heaven. He also told him that he who lays the Nachiketa fire three times and performs three acts of piety will go beyond death and sorrow, realize Brahman, and obtain limitless peace.

'And now that you have your second boon, ask for your third one,' Yama said to Nachiketa.

'I want to ask you about people who die. Some say they live after death, and others say they don't live. What's the truth? This knowledge is what I want for my third boon.'

'Even the gods have doubts about this, because its truth is difficult to understand. Choose another boon, dear boy. Leave this one be.'

'This is the boon I want.'

'Choose sons that will live a hundred years and grandsons that will also live just as long. Choose cattle and elephants and horses. Choose gold in large quantities, or vast regions of the earth. Or ask me for a boon to give you a life that will last as long as you want. I can even grant immeasurable pleasures, damsels, chariots, and music—all waiting for your enjoyment. Or ask me anything of your own choosing, and I'll grant it. But don't question me about death.'

'You are the End-maker. All these pleasures and riches that you mention will last only up to a certain time, and then they'll end—only till the glow of the senses lasts. Keep your vehicles and women and song and dance. How can man be satisfied with wealth, no matter how great it is? And we can live long, but it'll only be as long as you rule it to be. Now that I've met you, I have all the wealth and the long life I could have wished for. All I want now is the boon I asked. Tell me about death. Tell me about the Doubt—that which pertains to passing on.'

Yama had been testing Nachiketa to see if he would be deterred from his quest of self-knowledge, but Nachiketa's quest was true, so Yama imparted the knowledge he requested: 'There are two choices for man—to pursue that which is better or that which is pleasanter. The wise man chooses better and the foolish, pleasanter, because what is better comes from knowledge and pleasanter is born from ignorance. You, of course, have already rejected the pleasant, so you have already chosen better. The man who is caught up in satisfying his senses with wealth and food and enjoyments thinks that there is nothing beyond this world. He dies again and again—for him there is no deliverance from the sorrows and maladies of the world.

On the other hand, there are those who are knowers of Self—like you. There are many in the world who are not even aware that the Self exists. Then there are others of impure mind who are aware it exists, but they don't have the ability to know it. Then, every once in a while, there is a rare soul who speaks of it, and rarer still he who can find it. Know that the Self is beyond the reach of thought and reasoning.'

'Then tell me what is beyond cause and effect—beyond the past that was, and future that will be, and the present that is. What is that reality that is beyond reality?'

'The Self is never born nor does it die. It sprang from nothing, nor did it come out of itself to be something. It is unborn and eternal—everlasting and ancient. It survives unscathed when the body dies. The killer thinks the Self is for killing and the killed thinks of it as killed, but neither one knows the Self, for it neither kills nor is it killed. Smaller than the small, greater than the great, Self lies hidden in the heart of every being. A man who is free from desires sees the majesty of this Self. The bodiless in bodies, the stable in the unstable, the great and omnipresent Self—the wise man who knows this will have nothing left for which to grieve when the body dies.'

Having learned this wisdom, Nachiketa was freed from the cycle of birth and death.

Myth from the Upanishads

◆

184

RESURRECTION OF JESUS

Very early on Sunday, the morning after they had laid Jesus in the tomb, Mary, the mother of Jesus, Mary of Magdala, Joanna, and some of the other women brought spices that they had prepared for his body to keep it from emitting the smell of death. At the entrance to the tomb, they were surprised to see that the rock, which kept the tomb closed, had been rolled away. And when they went inside, they discovered that Jesus's body was gone. Utterly at a loss about what to do next, they stood staring at the empty spot, when two shining men suddenly appeared at their side. The women became afraid and started to back away, but the men spoke: 'Why are you searching among the dead for him who lives? Remember what he told you in Galilee—that he was the Son of Man? Remember he said he must be sacrificed for the sins of men and be crucified? But he will rise again on the third day.' The women remembered. They hurriedly left the tomb and went to tell the apostles what they had seen and heard, but the apostles didn't believe them.

That same day, two of the apostles, on their way to the village of Emmaus, which lay about seven miles from Jerusalem, were talking about all these strange happenings, when Jesus himself joined them and began walking alongside. But for some reason, they didn't recognize him. 'What are you talking about?' he asked them.

They stopped and looked bleakly at the man who had posed this question. Then Cleopas answered, 'You're probably the only person in Jerusalem who doesn't know what has happened in the last few days.'

'What do you mean?' Jesus asked.

'Did you not hear about Jesus of Nazareth?' they replied. 'He was a prophet whose speech and action empowered God and all the people. He was crucified. Our own priests gave him up, and they sentenced him to death. He was our hope for liberating Israel. This was three days ago, and then women we know gave us the astounding news that his body has disappeared from the tomb, but they saw two angels there who told them that he is alive. Some of us went to the tomb to check. Everything seemed to be exactly as it should be, but Jesus's body is definitely gone.'

'Why are you so reluctant to believe what the prophets said?' Jesus

asked. 'Is it not said that the Messiah will suffer before he attains glory?'
Then he explained to them passages from the scriptures that made reference
to Jesus.

When they reached the village, Jesus bid the men farewell and turned
to go on his way, but the two apostles stopped him. 'Why don't you stay
with us today? The sun has gone down, and it'll be dark soon.' Jesus agreed
and went with them to the house in which they were staying. Later that
night, when they sat at the table and Jesus broke bread with a blessing
and passed it to them, their eyes opened and they recognized him. But
at that moment, he vanished. The men became excited. 'We knew in our
hearts,' they exclaimed. 'The way he explained the scriptures, we felt him
in our hearts.'

Right away, they left for Jerusalem, where the apostles were assembling.
When they heard that the Lord had appeared to Simon, they described
their own meeting with him and how they did not recognize him until
he broke bread. Then, even as they were talking, Jesus was among them
again. Seeing him, the apostles drew back in fear, thinking he was a ghost,
and Jesus said to them, 'Don't look so disturbed. Believe what you see.
Why do you question this? Here! look at my hands and feet. Touch me
and see for yourself that I am no ghost. I am flesh and bone.'

When they still hesitated, he asked them if they had anything to eat.
They gave him a piece of fish and he ate it before their eyes, and said, 'I
told you about this when I was still with you, that whatever is written
about me in the scriptures will come true. It is written that the Messiah
will suffer for the sins of men and be put to death. But he will rise from
the dead on the third day to forgive them for their sins and liberate them.
That day has come. You are witnesses of this. Now go forth and proclaim
this message to all the people in all the nations.'

Myth from the New Testament

◆

185

SACHKHAND: THE REALM OF TRUTH

One day in Nanded, Guru Gobind Singh was testing out the string of a new bow that craftsmen from Hyderabad had brought for him, when an old wound on his left side re-opened. His physicians tried everything they could to heal it, but it became infected and the infection spread. When it began to debilitate his body, the Guru knew that his end was near. He decided then to build his own funeral pyre. He had his men construct a brick hut, and within the walls, he had them stack a pyre of sandalwood. Then he instructed his followers that after he entered the hut, the opening was to be sealed. 'No one should open the angeetha, no one should look inside, and no one should make a samadhi,' he instructed them.

Word about the Guru's intention spread fast and, from that day onwards, people began to arrive at Nanded for the Guru's last darshan, before he entered the angeetha. On the assigned day, everyone gathered around the angeetha, weeping and lamenting, but the Guru was calm—his face serene. He told his followers to take heart. 'All things born must perish,' he said. 'Love the shabad, not the body.'

The night before, he had already declared to the Khalsa that, henceforth, all Sikhs must accept the Granth as their Guru. 'Let anyone who wishes to see the Guru come and see the Guru. Anyone who wishes to hear the Guru's word should read the Granth, or hear the Granth being read.'

Now, sitting on his horse, Neela, dressed like a prince in a royal blue robe, wearing a turban with a golden kalgi, he called to the congregation: 'Waheguri ji ka Khalsa, Wahegurji ki fateh' (the Khalsa belongs to Waheguru and victory belongs to Waheguru). Then he rode into the hut. Soon people heard flames roaring inside and felt blazing heat seeping through the bricks.

Bhai Sangat Singh, a young follower who hadn't yet heard about the Guru's passing, was on his way to Nanded to visit the Guru and get his blessing. As he neared the camp,[63] he heard hoof beats and saw that riding through the trees towards him was the Guru himself. He was mounted on his favourite horse, Neela, and the Chitta Baaz (white falcon) was sitting on his shoulder. He was dressed in his blue robe and was wearing a turban with his signature golden kalgi. As he drew close to Sangat Singh, he greeted and blessed him as a true Sikh and then shared with him a little bit of the karah-parshad he was carrying. Then he rode away.

When Sangat Singh arrived in Nanded, he saw the hut aflame and was told by the weeping congregation that the Guru was no more. Young Sangat stood there, bewildered, and then he told everyone that he had just seen the Guru riding near the camp. The Sikhs did not disbelieve Sangat Singh, but they had also seen the Guru ride into the angeetha. Everyone was perplexed, and it was decided that the only way to verify the truth was to look inside the angeetha. So, when the flames died down, Bhai Daya Singh carefully opened the door of the angeetha and went inside. There was nothing there—no ashes, no remains of Guru Gobind Singh's physical body. The only object lying on the floor was a small gilded kirpan that the Guru used to carry in his waistband.

Folk-myth

◆

186

A GLIMPSE OF JANNAT

Once, riding through his capital, a king met an old fakir on the outskirts of his city. He was sitting on a rickety charpai outside his roughly constructed mud hut and reading the Quran. Dismounting, the king approached the fakir and asked him what he was reading.

'About Jannat,' the old man replied. 'I hope that Allah will find me worthy enough to accept me in Jannat one day.'

'Jannat and Jahannam are all here, baba,' the king stated.

'No son. This life is only a means for us to get there.'

'I can't believe something that I can't see. Do you know what this Jannat is like? Can you show me a glimpse?'

'What you ask for is dangerous, son, and your lack of faith puts you in grave jeopardy,' the fakir responded.

'If I can see Jannat, I'll become a believer,' the king declared adamantly.

'Then I promise you that one day I'll take you there,' the fakir promised.

'I'll wait for that day,' said the king, and bidding the fakir farewell, he continued on his tour of the capital. When he returned to his palace, he commanded his minister to make sure that the old fakir received food every day, for as long as he lived.

Years passed. Every once in a while, the king would send a message to the fakir, reminding him of his promise, and the fakir would respond with the message: 'It isn't time yet.' Then one day, the king received news that the old fakir was very sick. Quickly calling for his horse, he rode to the fakir's hut, and reached there just in time, because the old man was breathing his last. 'Baba, have you forgotten your promise?' the king asked.

'No, my son. In fact, the time has come to keep my promise. But, tell me, are you sure? Do you want to reconsider? It's really better to be patient and see Jannat only when Allah invites you.'

'Yes, I'm sure. I must see Jannat now,' the king replied.

'Then listen carefully. When they bury me and have erected my grave, give me your hand, and I'll take you there.'

'How can I give you my hand after you're buried?' the king asked, but the fakir had already passed.

After the fakir was buried, the king had a marble stone erected at the spot, and he came to visit it every day, often wondering what the fakir had meant. One day, sitting at the tomb, he put his hand on the marble and instantly the ground opened up. The astonished king looked into the gaping hole in the ground and saw a flight of rough steps, and, at the bottom of them, he saw the fakir sitting, just as he used to sit, on his rickety charpai, reading the Quran. The fakir beckoned to him to come down, and the king, mustering up his courage, stepped into the grave.

When he reached the bottom, the fakir rose, and gesturing to the king to follow him, began walking along a dark passage. Then he stopped and, looking solemnly at the king, moved his hand, as though to draw aside a heavy veil. No one knows what the king saw behind the veil or how long he looked, but when the fakir dropped the curtain, the king had had his glimpse of Jannat.

Trembling in every limb, the king stumbled out of the tomb, into the fresh air. The dawn of a new day was breaking, and, although, he had been gone just a few moments, he felt as though he had been gone a very long time. He tried to recall what he had seen behind the veil, but other than climbing down the steps, following the fakir, and seeing the veil lifted, he could not recall a thing. He also realized that all around him everything seemed quite different. In fact, he wasn't even sure if he was in his own city, yet somehow the road he walked upon led him to his own palace.

When he walked through the gates, he saw that the darbar was in session, and a man he had never seen before was sitting on his throne. Puzzled, he sat down in one of the ministerial seats and looked around. He could not recognize anyone; even his darbar looked different. Then the wazir, whom he did not know, came to him and asked how he had dared to sit without presenting himself to the king.

'But I am the king,' he said loudly. 'This is my kingdom.'

He heard exclamations all around and saw that everyone was looking at him strangely. Soon the room began to buzz with words like: 'mad', 'insane,' 'lost his mind'. The man on the throne then gestured to him to come forward. As the king approached the throne, he saw his reflection in a polished bronze shield that a bodyguard was holding and was horrified. What had happened to him? He was dressed in filthy rags. His long and dirty white hair was wild around his shoulders and a scraggly white beard lay on his chest. 'Tell me who I am,' he said in a trembling voice to the man on the throne. 'Who are you? Just yesterday I sat where you are sitting.'

The man on the throne looked at him compassionately, and the king could tell that he did not believe him. Suddenly, he remembered the signet ring he always wore on his little finger and was grateful to see that he still wore it. Pulling it off, he held it up as proof. The man on the throne took the ring and examined it with curiosity. Then he issued a command and dusty record books were brought in and also scholars who began to examine them. They found a faded image of the king's signet ring in a record of old coins and informed their monarch, who then informed the king: 'Old man,' he said. 'That signet ring belonged to a king who reigned seven hundred years ago. It is believed that he disappeared; no one knows where he went. How did you get the ring?'

The old king fell to the ground and lamented. He understood now that he had been judged. His lack of faith had made him impatient to see Jannat, which only belongs to the faithful. Getting up, he walked out of the palace without another word and went to the jungle to live out his remaining life in prayer and meditation. He lived twenty-five more years. Then the Angel of Death came and mercifully released him.

Folktale from North India

◆

187

KABULIWALLA AND BANKE BIHARI

Once, a Kabuliwalla came to Vrindavan to sell his wares of dry fruit and shawls. One evening, he stopped at a shop to buy some mithai when he saw a picture hanging on the wall—of a beautiful youth playing a flute. He was dressed in a yellow pitambar and was wearing a crown with a peacock feather in it.

'Who's that?' the Kabuliwalla asked the shopkeeper, pointing at the picture.

The shopkeeper looked at the Kabuliwalla in surprise, but then he realized that this man from Kabul probably had no idea about the god of Vrindavan. Jokingly, he replied, 'That's our prince, Shyam.'

'I want to see him in person,' the Kabuliwalla said. 'How can I see him? Where does he live?'

The shopkeeper, keeping up the ruse, pointed in the direction of the Banke Bihari temple and said, 'That's his palace. He lives there.'

The Kabuliwalla immediately went to the temple, but when he tried to enter through the gates, the temple guards, seeing his Kabuli salwar and shirt, knew that he was not a Hindu and refused to let him in.

'I just want to see the prince,' he implored. 'Can you get me an appointment?'

The guards shook their heads in confusion and pushed him away.

'Please. I just want to see him once.'

'You're a Musalmaan,' one of the guards explained. 'Only Hindus are allowed inside.'

'Then, can I wait here outside? That way, I can see him when he comes out.'

The guards thought the man was crazy and let him be. So the Kabuliwalla sat down by the temple gates to wait. He waited for days, not leaving the spot even for a minute. He didn't eat. He didn't sleep. All he did was watch the gate. Every day, he would see throngs of people go in three times a day—in the morning, afternoon and evening, and he would stand outside, listening to the sounds of singing and chanting and cymbals and drums. Then the people would leave and the doors would close, and he would settle down in his spot, waiting for Prince Shyam to come.

One morning, when the doors to the temple opened, he was able to sneak a glimpse of the inside. The curtain to the sanctum sanctorum was completely open and there he stood—Shyam—black like the night, resplendent in his pitambar, long flower garland down to his knees, and a peacock feather in his crooked gold crown. In that split second, the Kabuliwalla looked directly into the eyes of the idol of Banke Bihari. Then he was pushed away by the guards again, and he fell against the wall. He remained there all day in a trance, enraptured by the beauty he had seen.

Later that night, after the guards had locked up and left, the temple gates opened and Shyam walked out, seeking the Kabuliwalla. He saw him sitting against the wall, his gaze far way. Shyam touched him gently on the shoulder, and the Kabuliwalla's eyes focused to see his prince standing before him. 'You have come,' he said adoringly. 'Yes,' said Shyam, and sat down beside him. They spent the whole night together, talking and laughing like old friends. Once during the night, Shyam pointed at the Kabuliwalla's bundle and asked him what he was carrying. 'Is it a gift for me?' he asked.

'No...it's only my other set of clothes. They're old and worn out, but you can have them if you want.'

Shyam eagerly opened the bundle and, taking out the frayed Kabuli salwar and shirt, put them on, removing his gold and jewellery, which he placed in his friend's lap.

When the morning bells rang, Shyam got up. 'I'll see you soon,' he said and slipped back into the temple.

When the temple priests went to prepare the idol for the morning arti, they were flabbergasted. The idol of Banke Bihari stood in the sanctorum exactly as it always did, but instead of a pitambar, Banke Bihariji was wearing an old, worn-out Kabuli salwar kameez. And all his gold and jewels were gone. 'Thief!' 'Thief!' they shouted and rushed out. They saw the Kabuliwalla sitting by the gate as usual. His lap was full of Shyam's jewellery, but his life had left his body.[64]

Folktale from Uttar Pradesh

◆

188

IN SEARCH OF SELF

The Kasturi Mriga runs all his life, pursuing the fragrance that he always smells. Little does he know that the fragrance he seeks is coming from inside him.[65]

Folk wisdom

ACKNOWLEDGEMENTS

I am the kind of writer who gathers all her research before she sits down to write. This book taught me a new way of researching and writing—gradual discovery. Every story in this book was a different exploration, which was often triggered by something someone said or did. Hence, I want to thank those dear friends and loved ones—motivators—who, each in his or her own way, set me off in new directions.

Bridget Robin Pool taught me how to unlock folktales, and then I knew how to enter them. Rachna Rikhye told me a lovely story about the blue jay, a princess, and a lotus lake, and, trying to find its source, I discovered a treasure of origin tales. Vineeta Anand gifted me an embroidery of a tree of life, which sent me searching for stories about umbilicus trees—this was how I came upon folktales of the Khasi tribe. The inspiration behind the theme of empowerment in this book is Sudha Bakshi, whose courage awes me every day. The theme of friendship is inspired by Binny Rikhy, whose every act of friendship is a cementing. And then there is Babu, who suggested that I include a few stories about music; not only did I find tales about the magic of music but also included a tabla notation in one of them, which he composed. Finally, I want to thank my brilliant editor at Aleph, Simar Puneet, who affirmed for me that no matter the impulse or the direction, they all lead to my true north.

I want to also acknowledge a very young friend, Vikram East—a budding writer, a lover of stories. Watching him engage with the tale of the Trojan Horse, I was reminded of how, as a child, I, too, used to live within stories. Louise Glück says, 'We look at the world once, in childhood. The rest is memory.'

This brings me to my own memories. My father was the storyteller in our family. He passed away last year. I miss him terribly. While writing this book, I would talk to his photograph in my study, his face smiling red and yellow from the last Holi I played with him, and beg him to tell me again the stories of my childhood. I had forgotten bits and pieces and didn't know how to fill the gaps. Then I called my mother, who not only retold those stories to me but also narrated a few of her own that I had never heard before. I wonder now—was there always a story-teller in her?

NOTES

THE WORLD IS CREATED

1   Ahun Vairya: first of the four Gathic Avestan formulas; part of Gathic canon, attributed to Zoroaster himself. It is part of Kusti prayers; purifying and meditational declarations.

2   Heresy.

3   Demon/demonic—is the cause of heresy and blinds the righteous man from being able to discern between truth and falsehood.

4   According to *Bundahishn*, creation will last nine thousand years: three thousand years of spiritual creation when Ahura Mazda will prevail; three thousand years of physical creation and conflict between Ahura Mazda and Ahriman and rest followed by compromise.

5   The Minyong are a sub-group of the Adi, a tribal people of Arunachal Pradesh.

BEING HUMAN

6   The sacrifice is the ritual as well as the sacrificial offering (the victim). The two are identified.

7   Some scholars consider this hymn as the initiation of the caste system. If that is so, it is important to note that there is no indication in the hymn that the body parts of the Purusha are hierarchical. In fact, it is possible that the feet of the Purusha, from which the Shudras came, were considered the most auspicious, and the 'highest'. Especially significant is the fact that earth also comes from his feet.

8   See note 6.

9   Ten sons are mentioned but only the origins of eight are given. The other two, Pulaha and Kratu, are mentioned as sages marrying Daksha's daughters in other texts.

10   In the Gathas, the Zoroastrian canon, the daevas are 'false gods' (the Hindu deva, is possibly a reversal of this concept).

11   India's ancient name.

12   In the Hebrew Bible the term Shinar is used for the region of Mesopotamia.

13   Sophet Bneng is a small hill about 20 kilometres north of Shillong. It means Centre of Heaven.

14   An indigenous tribe of Meghalaya.

KINSHIP

15   A bonga is a supernatural power. It can control many natural phenomena, such as rain, tempests, cold, floods, epidemics and wild animals. More often than not, a bonga is a benevolent power.

16   Adivasis of Chhota Nagpur.

DESIRES

17   Sheikh Chilli, whose real name was Abd-ur-Rahim, also known as Abd-Ul-Karim, was a Qadiriyya Sufi master who lived during the reign of Mughal Prince Dara Shikoh (1650 CE). Sheikh Chilli's tomb is in Thanesar, Haryana.

GREED

18   Krishnadevaraya, the sixteenth-century iconic king of the Vijayanagar Empire, was not only a great general and administrator but also a connoisseur of art and literature. At his court were the famous Ashtadiggajas, eight celebrated poets of Telugu, and among them was Vikatakavi Tenali Ramakrishna, who was a great poet, famous for his wit and wisdom.

19   Weight unit measure: 1 pala=40 grams.

CONFLICTS

20   Mandar Parvat is a small hill in Banka District Bihar. It is 700 ft. high.

21   Yojana is a Vedic measure. 1 yojana=1.6 km, or 3280-84 ft. This means that Mt. Mandar is 57,745,600 ft. above sea level and extends 57,745,600 ft. below the earth.

22   Possibly the African baobab tree. According to legend, this tree is in the village of Kintoor in Barabanki district in Uttar Pradesh.

23   There are many speculations about the historicity of this wall. There are a few contenders: Great wall of Gorgan (called Red Snake), a Sasanian era defensive wall in northeastern Iran. It no longer exists (it was submerged in the sea in the eighteenth/nineteenth century); Alexander's Wall/Caspian Gates near Derbent, west of the Caspian Sea; the Great Wall of China; the Iron Gates mentioned in the travels of Xuanzang, seventh century (also no longer existing).

24   This is a cult battle between Vaishnavism and Shaivism, but, most interestingly, it gives insight into how the Shaivites wanted to create their own version of a Krishna. It also evokes the question of Krishna's origins; i.e. the questions scholars ask is how did Krishna assume Vishnu's persona?

25   According to legend, Lalu Jas Raj was the son of Raja Dipa Chand, who is considered the founder of Dipalpur.

26   The spot where he disappeared is a temple site—Baba Lalu Jas Rai. It is in Dipalpur, Pakistan.

27   This was a folk song that women sang in the villages of Punjab, especially in the Khanna caste families, to which Lalu belonged.

TREACHERY

28   Duryodhana died from a blow to his groin. Bhima struck this blow on Krishna's advice even though it was a violation of a rule of war.

29   In Jainism (and Buddhism), it means, 'one is worthy' of receiving knowledge.

30   This avatar of Vishnu was the Brahmin opposition to the Buddhist and Jain polemic that was undermining Brahmanism.

COMPASSION

31 Valmiki is considered the Adikavi, the first poet, because the shloka verse form he invented became the standard for classical Sanskrit poetry.

32 Prophet Muhammad's migration from Mecca to Medina.

33 640 grams in Vedic literature.

34 Ahoi Ashtami is in the month of Kartika on the eighth day of the new moon. It normally occurs a week before Diwali—two days after Karva Chauth. Mothers observe Ahoi Ashtami for the prosperity of their children by fasting all day and breaking their fast after sighting the first star.

PERSECUTION

35 In Valmiki's text only Surpanakha's ears and nose are cut off but in Kamban's *Ramayana*, her nipples are cut off as well.

36 Oghavati is a Vedic river, which may have been a tributary of the Saraswati that flowed near modern-day Ladawa in Haryana. It is believed to have dried up.

EMPOWERMENT

37 Mariamma and Yellamma are celebrated in Karnataka, but throughout South India they are worshipped in various forms. For example, in Tamil Nadu, they are Bavaniyamman and Matankiyamman; wherever there is a temple of the former, there is always a shrine for the latter nearby.

38 Modern day Sialkot in Pakistan.

39 Present day Tamluk in West Bengal, an important city in ancient India because of its trade.

40 Golden Isle, possibly the Indonesian archipelago.

41 Kingdom in Java.

42 This curse could be one of the reasons that Ravana does not approach Sita even though he has her captive in his Asoka Vatika.

43 In some myths Diti's buffalo son is called Durga; hence when the goddess kills him, she assumes his name.

SECRECY

44 A region in northern Afghanistan, possibly ancient Bactria.

45 Half-monkey half-man (like Hanuman).

ROMANCE

46 Alternate ends: In the *Rig Veda*, they do not meet. Urvashi gives a hint that Pururavas's sons may sacrifice and that he may come to heaven.

In the *Ramayana*: He takes three logs from each of the trees and goes back to his city. Making finger-length firesticks out of the wood, he produces fire with them, reciting Vedic mantras, and this is the special fire that the gandharvas mentioned. He sacrifices numerous times in this fire, and finally he becomes a gandharva—a part of Urvashi's world.

47   Weight unit used in British India. One maund was equal to approximately 25 lbs.

48   A traditional mode of Rajasthani welcome with opium water.

SUFFERING

49   According to some traditions, it is believed that an angry Shiva performed the fearsome and awe-inspiring Tandava dance with Sati's charred body on his shoulders. During this dance, Sati's body came apart and the pieces fell at different places on earth.

50   Stations of the Cross or the Way of the Cross, also known as Way of Sorrows or Via Cruces, refers to an imitation of the Via Dolorosa in Jerusalem, which is believed to be the actual path Jesus walked to Mount Calvary for his crucifixion. There are fourteen traditional Stations of the Cross.

51   A Samvartana ceremony is celebrated when a student completes his education and is declared ready to begin a life of grihasta—marriage, a family. This would normally be around the age of twenty-one. In the *Devi Bhagvatam* the two tales of Harishchandra's promise to Varuna and his debt to Vishwamitra appear in sequence. Additionally, in this text, the quarrel between Vasishtha and Vishwamitra is cited as the cause of the second tale, just as it is presented here. However, the Rohit of the first story is obviously about twenty-one and Harishchandra is an old man. However, it is clear from the events of the second tale that Rohit is a young boy and Harishchandra is able-bodied. The myth gives no explanation of this time discrepancy. Nor can this be considered mythical time. Therefore, I have the taken the liberty of adding a 'back to the future' element in this story—that Vishwamitra, creates an incident in Harishchandra's earlier life with his maya. I have also altered the end. In the myth he gives the kingdom to Rohit and he and Shaivya ascend to heaven with the gods. I have altered it to him returning to Ayodhya because Rohit is too young to take over (another problem with the myth). Also, for the other parallel story that encompasses all his life, he is obviously living on earth.

52   Harishchandra Ghat in Banaras got its name from this myth.

COURAGE

53   Thomas's name was Thomas Didymus; Thomas is Hebrew for twin, and Didymus is Greek for twin. Also, he is a carpenter like Jesus. The implication is that Thomas is Jesus's twin.

54   Gundaphorus IV was an Indo-Parthian king who ruled a kingdom in Northwest India (now Pakistan) in the middle of the first century CE. He is known from his coins that show the Greek god Zeus. His coins bear his name in Greek.

55   India's Param Vir Chakra is designed from Dadhichi's myth. The medal is a circular bronze, 3.49 cm in diameter. The state emblem appears in the centre, on a raised circle, and surrounding this are four replicas of Vajra. The motif symbolizes the sacrifice of Rishi Dadhichi.

CHALLENGES

56 In the *Skanda Purana*, Shiva sends his two sons to circle the world, and Ganesha circles Arunachala, to establish it as a holy site.

57 Vetala told Vikram twenty-four stories that had a riddle at the end which Vikram needed to answer. He knew the answers to all of them, and when he gave the correct answers to Vetala, the corpse flew off his shoulder back into the tree. The king then climbed back up and brought down the corpse, and, carrying it on his shoulder, began walking to the cremation ground. Then Vetala entered the body again and told the king another story. This was repeated twenty-three times. This is the twenty-fourth story.

SEXUALITY

58 In the *Padma Purana*, Ahalya is violated. She does not know that Indra is not Gautama. She pleads her innocence but is still cursed.

59 In the Valmiki *Ramayana*, Indra is cursed to lose his testicles. In the *Padma Purana* and Kamban's *Ramayana* his body is marked with a thousand vulvas.

SPIRITUALITY

60 Although Mullah Nasruddin is Turkish, this Sufi parable has been become part of the Indian ethos.

61 This emblem of Shiva appears in many temples as a finial on doorways. It has also acquired cultural and folkloric significance and has transformed into the nazar battu that people put on houses, businesses and vehicles to ward off the evil eye.

REBIRTH

62 The day on which Astika saves the snakes from the snake sacrifice is celebrated as Naag Panchami.

LIBERATION

63 That place today is a historical shrine called Takhat Sachkhand, Shri Hazur Sahib.

64 Since then, the darshan in the Banke Bihari temple is not continuous; the curtain of the sanctum sanctorum is never fully opened; it is flourished back and forth throughout the arti, because it is believed that if a devotee looks too long the Lord's eyes, he will either lose consciousness or the idol will walk away with him.

65 The musk deer has a gland in its body that produces musk. It is harvested by killing the animal. This Himalayan deer is an endangered species.

FURTHER READING

Abdullah, Yusuf Ali (trans.), *The Holy Quran*, Lahore: Sheikh Mohammad Ashraf Publishers, 1938.

Archer, W. G., *The Hill of Flutes: Life, Love and Poetry in Tribal India: A Portrait of the Santals*, Pittsburgh: University of Pittsburg Press, 1974.

Arnold, Sir Edwin (trans.), *Hitopadesha*, London, 1861, via www.columbia.edu

Avesta.org (Zoroastrian texts and prayers archive).

Beck, Brenda E.F., et al (eds.), *Folktales of India*, Chicago: University of Chicago, 1987.

Blackburn, Stuart, *Moral Fictions: Tamil Folktales from the Oral Tradition*, Helsinki, Finland: Suomalainen Tiedeakatemia, 2005.

Burton, Sir Richard F., *Vikram and the Vampire: Classic Tales of Adventure, Magic, and Romance,* London: Longmans, Green, and Co., 1870.

Cowell, E. B. (ed.), *The Jataka or Stories from Buddha's Former Births*, Vol. 11, New Delhi: Motilal Banarsidass Publishers, 1990.

Dey, Lal Behari, *Folk Tales of Bengal Folk Tales of Bengal*, London: Macmillan & Co, 1912.

Doniger, Wendy, (ed. & tr.), *The Rig Veda*, London: Penguin Books, 2005.

Dutt, M. N. (trans.), *A Prose English Translation of Mahabharata*, Calcutta: H. C. Dass, 1895.

———, *A Prose English Translation of Vishnu Puranam*, Calcutta: H. C. Dass, 1896.

Elwin, Verrier, *Myths of the North-East Frontier of India*, Shillong: North-East Frontier Agency, 1958.

Emmerich, Anne Catherine, *The Dolouros Passion of Our Lord Jesus Christ*, 1862, via www. sacred-texts.com.

Erndl, Kathleen M., *Victory to the Mother*, New York: Oxford University Press, 1993.

Ferdowsi, Abolqasem, *Shahnameh: The Persian Book of Kings*, Dick Davis (trans.), New York: Penguin Books, 2016.

Francis, H. T. and Thomas, E. J. (trans.), *Jataka Tales*, Cambridge: Cambridge University Press, 1916.

Granoff, Phyllis (trans.), *The Forest of Forty Thieves and the Magic Garden: An Anthology of Medieval Jain Stories*, London: Penguin Books, 2006.

Griffith, Ralph T. H. (trans.), *The Rig Veda*, 1896, via www.sacred-texts.com

———, *The Hymns of the Rig Veda*, Vol. 11, Benares: E. J. Lazarus and Co, 1889.

Gupta, Som Raj, *The World Speaks to the Faustian Man*, Vol IV, New Delhi: Motilal Banarsidass, 2001.

Heinrich Zimmer, *Myths and Symbolism in Indian Art and Civilization*, Princeton: Princeton University Press, 1946.

Internet Sacred Texts Archive at www.sacred-texts.com

Ishaq, Ibn, *The Life of Muhammad*, Alfred Guillame, (trans.), Karachi: Oxford University Press, 1955.

Knapp, Stephen, *The Secret Teachings of the Vedas*, New Delhi: Jaico Publishing House, 1993.

Knowles, James-Hinton (ed.), *Folk-tales of Kashmir*, London : Kegan Paul, Trench, Trübner, 1893.

Lutgendorf, Philip, *Hanuman Tales*, New York: Oxford University Press, 2007.

Nayak, Meena Arora, *Evil in the Mahabharata*, New Delhi: Oxford University Press, India, 2018.

————, *Endless Rain*, New Delhi: Penguin Books India, 2006.

————, *The Puffin Book of Legendary Lives*, New Delhi: Penguin Books India, New Delhi, 2000.

Parmar, Shyam (ed.), *Folktales of Madhya Pradesh*, New Delhi: Sterling Publishers, 1973.

Pintchman, Tracy (ed.), *Seeking Mahadevi: Constructing the Identities of the Hindu Goddess*, New York: SUNY Press, 2001.

Prasad, R. C. (trans.), *Tulsidas's Shriramcharitmanas*, New Delhi: Motilal Banarsidass, 1990.

Rafy, K. U., *Folktales of the Khasis*, London: Library of Alexandria, 1920.

Ramanujan, A. K. (ed.), *Folktales from India*, New York: Pantheon Books, 1991.

Sattar, Arshia (trans.), *Tales from the Kathasaritsagar*, New Delhi: Penguin Books India, 2000.

Schwartz, Howard, *Tree of Souls: the Mythology of Judaism*, New York: Oxford University Press, 2007.

Sharma, Vishnu and Rajan, Chandra (trans.), *The Panchatantra*, London: Penguin Books, 1993.

Sheorey, Indumati (ed.), *Folktales of Maharashtra*, New Delhi: Sterling Publishers, 1978.

Sister Nivedita and Ananda Coomaraswamy, *Myths of the Hindus & Buddhists*, New York: Dover Publications, 1967.

Srimad Valmiki Ramayana, Parts 1 and 11, Gorakhpur: Gita Press, 2006.

Steel, Flora Annie, *Tales of the Punjab*, London: Macmillan and Co., 1917.

Swynnerton, Charles, *Indian Nights' Entertainment: Or, Folk-tales from the Upper Indus*, London: E. Stock, 1892.

Tagare, G. V. (trans.), *The Bhagavata-Purana, Ancient Indian Tradition and Mythology*, Vol. 7, New Delhi: Motilal Banarsidass Publishers, 1999.

van Buitenen, J. A. B. (ed.), *Tales of Ancient India*, Chicago: University of Chicago Press, 1959.

Venkatesananda, Swami (trans.), *Vasishtha's Yoga*, New York: SUNY Press, 1993.

Wilson, H. H. (trans.), *Vishnu Purana*, Vols. 1 and 11, New Delhi: Nag Publishers, 2003.

Wilson, Martin (ed.), *In Praise of Tara: Songs to the Saviouress*, Boston: Wisdom Publications Inc, 1992.

Wortham, B. Hale (trans.), *The Enchanted Parrot: Being a Selection from the 'Suka Saptati', or, The Seventy Tales of a Parrot*, London: Luzac and Co., 1911.

Zaehner, R. C., *Zurvan: A Zoroastrian Dilemma*, Oxford: Clarendon Press, 1955.

Lightning Source UK Ltd.
Milton Keynes UK
UKHW011908030323
418024UK00013B/161/J